Philips'
Modern School Atlas

Seventy-eighth Edition

Edited by Harold Fullard M.Sc.

George Philip & Son Limited, London
© **1981**
ISBN 0 540 05384 8

Preface

To justify its title and to continue to merit the reputation it has gained over many years among teachers of geography, each new edition of PHILIPS' MODERN SCHOOL ATLAS receives most careful editing to ensure that every map is up to date and that its contents meet the changing needs of the geography syllabus.

Philips' Modern School Atlas was first published in 1906 and now, more than seventy years later, the atlas benefits from the improvements made over so many years and for this edition the wider use of the metric system has been reflected in conversion to, or inclusion of metric equivalents where they had not already been given in previous editions and particularly on thematic maps and in climate graphs. All maps and graphs have recently been reproduced afresh after extensive revision and a new colour scheme has been developed aimed at clear layer colouring on which the legibility of names is yet further improved and hill shading is added on the physical maps of the continents, to give a graphic impression of principal relief features.

The Modern School Atlas is designed to meet the requirements of those intending to take the examination in Geography for the General Certificate; and as the list of contents shows in detail the geology, structure, relief, climate, vegetation and human conditions of the whole world are illustrated, whilst for detailed regional study there are larger scale maps of more important political and highly developed regions.

Modern spellings have been adopted in accordance with the latest official lists, the rules of the Royal Geographical Society Permanent Committee on Geographical Names, the decision lists of the United States Board on Geographical Names and other sources. A selective index of names appearing on the maps have been included.

Where there are rival claims to territory the *de facto* boundaries have been shown. This does not denote international recognition of these boundaries but shows the states which are administering the areas on either side of the line.

HAROLD FULLARD

Contents

V-XII   Climate Graphs

a   Chart of the Stars

b-c   The Evolution of the Continents

d-e   The Unstable Earth

f-g   The Atmosphere and Clouds

h   Time Zones

1   General Reference

The World

1   Political and Communications, 1:153 250 000

2-3   Geology, 1:90 000 000
         Structure, 1:126 000 000

4-5   Physical, 1:100 000 000
         Astronomical Geography: Eclipses of the Sun and Moon,
         The Solar System, The Planets, The Earth's Orbit,
         The Phases of The Moon, Terrestrial Zones
         and Length of Day and Night

6   Temperature and Ocean Currents, 1:190 000 000

7   Pressure, Winds and
         Annual Precipitation, 1:190 000 000

8   Natural Vegetation, 1:148 000 000
         Climatic Regions, 1:148 000 000

9   Density of Population, 1:148 000 000
         Classification of Mankind, 1:148 000 000

10-11   Political and Communications, Hemispheres centred
         on London and its Antipodes, 1:100 000 000
         Air Routes shown on Hemispheres centred on
         San Francisco, Cape Town, Cairo and Shanghai
         1:300 000 000

Europe

12   Geology, 1:25 000 000
         Structure, 1:40 000 000

13   Physical, 1:20 000 000

14   Climate, 1:40 000 000

15   Natural Vegetation, 1:20 000 000

16   Political, 1:20 000 000

17   Annual Rainfall, Population,
         Languages and Religions, 1:40 000 000

18   British Isles: Physical, 1:5 000 000

19   British Isles: Solid Geology, 1:5 000 000

20   British Isles: Climate and Weather,
         Agriculture, 1:10 000 000

21   British Isles: Population, 1:5 000 000
         Industrial Regions of Midland
         and Northern England, 1:1 500 000

22-23   South and South-East England, 1:1 000 000

24   South-West England, 1:1 000 000

25   Wales, 1:1 000 000

26-27   Northern England, 1:1 000 000

28   England and Wales: Political, 1:2 500 000

29   Scotland and Ireland: Political, 1:2 500 000

30-31   Scotland: South, 1:1 000 000

32-33   Scotland: North, 1:1 000 000

34-35   Ireland: South, 1:1 000 000

36   Ireland: North, 1:1 000 000

37   Spain and Portugal, 1:5 000 000

38-39   Mediterranean Lands, 1:10 000 000

40-41   Italy and the Balkan States, 1:5 000 000

42-43   France, Belgium and Switzerland, 1:4 000 000
         France: Political, 1:8 000 000, Channel Is. 1:1 000 000

44   Low Countries and Lower Rhine, 1:2 000 000

45   Switzerland and Upper and Middle Rhine, 1:2 000 000

46-47   Central Europe, 1:5 000 000

48-49   Scandinavia and the Baltic Lands, 1:5 000 000

50-51   Russia and the Near East, 1:10 000 000

52   Central European Russia, 1:5 000 000

Asia

53   **Natural Vegetation,** 1:50 000 000

54-55   **Physical,** 1:40 000 000
Annual Rainfall, Population, 1:80 000 000

56-57   **Political,** 1:40 000 000
Languages, Religions, 1:80 000 000

58-59   **Climate,** 1:80 000 000
Evolution of the Monsoon, 1:100 000 000

60-61   **Union of Soviet Socialist Republics,** 1:20 000 000

62-63   **South-West Asia and the Nile Valley,** 1:15 000 000
Palestine, 1:1 500 000

64-65   **South Asia,** 1:10 000 000

66-67   **China and Japan,** 1:15 000 000
Japan, 1:7 500 000

68   **East Indies,** 1:15 000 000

Africa

69   **Climate,** 1:80 000 000

70   **Physical,** 1:40 000 000
Annual Rainfall, 1:80 000 000

71   **Political,** 1:40 000 000
Population, 1:80 000 000

72-73   **Northern Africa,** 1:15 000 000

74-75   **Central and Southern Africa,** 1:15 000 000

76   **South Africa,** 1:6 500 000
Cape Town, 1:1 000 000

77   **Natural Vegetation,** 1:40 000 000

Australia and New Zealand

78   **Climate,** 1:60 000 000

79   **Natural Vegetation,** 1:30 000 000
Annual Rainfall, 1:60 000 000
Density of Population, 1:50 000 000

80-81   **Australia,** 1:12 000 000
Australasia: Political, 1:80 000 000

82-83   **Eastern Australia,** 1:7 500 000
Papua New Guinea, 1:12 000 000

84   **New Zealand,** 1:6 000 000
New Zealand and Dependencies, 1:60 000 000
Samoa, 1:12 000 000
Fiji and Tonga Islands, 1:12 000 000

North America

85   **Natural Vegetation,** 1:32 000 000

86   **Physical,** 1:40 000 000
Temperature, 1:80 000 000

87   **Political,** 1:40 000 000
Rainfall, Pressure and Winds, 1:80 000 000

88-89   **Canada,** 1:15 000 000
Alaska, 1:30 000 000

90-91   **United States,** 1:12 000 000
Hawaiian Islands, 1:10 000 000

92-93   **Basin of the St. Lawrence and
North-East United States,** 1:6 000 000
North America: Population, 1:50 000 000

94-95   **Mexico, Central America and West Indies,**
1:15 000 000, Bermuda, 1:750 000, Jamaica,
Trinidad and Tobago, Leeward Is., Windward Is.,
1:5 000 000, Panama Canal, 1:1 000 000
North America: Annual Rainfall, 1:80 000 000

South America

96   **Physical,** 1:40 000 000
Political, 1:40 000 000

97   **Natural Vegetation,** 1:40 000 000
Climate, 1:80 000 000

98-99   **South America,** 1:20 000 000
Annual Rainfall, Population, 1:80 000 000

Polar Regions

100   **Arctic, Antarctic,** 1:50 000 000

Index

Climate station graphs (Temperature / Rainfall):

- ARKHANGELSK 7 — Temperature 30° — Rainfall 503 mm
- MOSCOW 154 — Temperature 28° — Rainfall 630 mm
- ASTRAKHAN 14 — Temperature 32° — Rainfall 163 mm
- LENINGRAD 5 — Temperature 26° — Rainfall 488 mm
- WARSAW 120 — Temperature 22° — Rainfall 559 mm
- BUCHAREST 82 — Temperature 26° — Rainfall 579 mm
- COPENHAGEN 13 — Temperature 18° — Rainfall 592 mm
- VIENNA 202 — Temperature 21° — Rainfall 650 mm
- ATHENS 107 — Temperature 18° — Rainfall 401 mm
- BERGEN 43 — Temperature 15° — Rainfall 2002 mm
- MUNICH 530 — Temperature 19° — Rainfall 866 mm
- PALERMO 108 — Temperature 15° — Rainfall 709 mm
- REYKJAVIK 28 — Temperature 12° — Rainfall 861 mm
- BORDEAUX 48 — Temperature 15° — Rainfall 831 mm
- MILAN 104 — Temperature 22° — Rainfall 803 mm
- LONDON 5 — Temperature 13° — Rainfall 610 mm
- MARSEILLES 75 — Temperature 15° — Rainfall 589 mm
- SCILLY 50 — Temperature 9° — Rainfall 826 mm
- MADRID 667 — Temperature 20° — Rainfall 419 mm
- FORT WILLIAM 52 — Temperature 11° — Rainfall 1999 mm
- LISBON 95 — Temperature 12° — Rainfall 686 mm

Map stations: Reykjavik, Arkhangelsk, Leningrad, Moscow, Astrakhan, Bergen, Fort William, Copenhagen, Warsaw, Bucharest, Scilly, London, Munich, Vienna, Milan, Athens, Bordeaux, Marseilles, Palermo, Lisbon, Madrid

The climate graphs should be used in conjunction with the maps illustrating the climate of the World, and also the more detailed maps of the Continents. The stations have been selected to show the various types of climate to be found throughout the World. On each graph the name of the station is followed by its height in metres above sea-level, so that comparisons between stations can be made after allowing for elevation. The line on the temperature graphs shows the mean monthly temperatures. The mean annual range of temperature (in degrees Celsius) is given above the temperature graphs. The rainfall graphs show the average monthly rainfall and above them is given the average total annual rainfall (in millimetres).

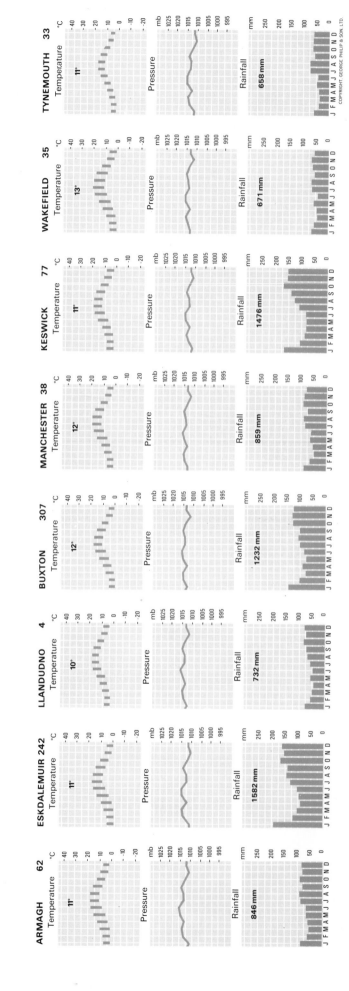

On these climate graphs of the British Isles, in addition to rainfall and temperature, mean monthly pressure is shown (in millibars and reduced to sea-level). Temperature is shown by a bar, the top of the bar representing the mean monthly maximum and the bottom of the bar the mean monthly minimum temperature. A mid point between these is the mean monthly temperature.

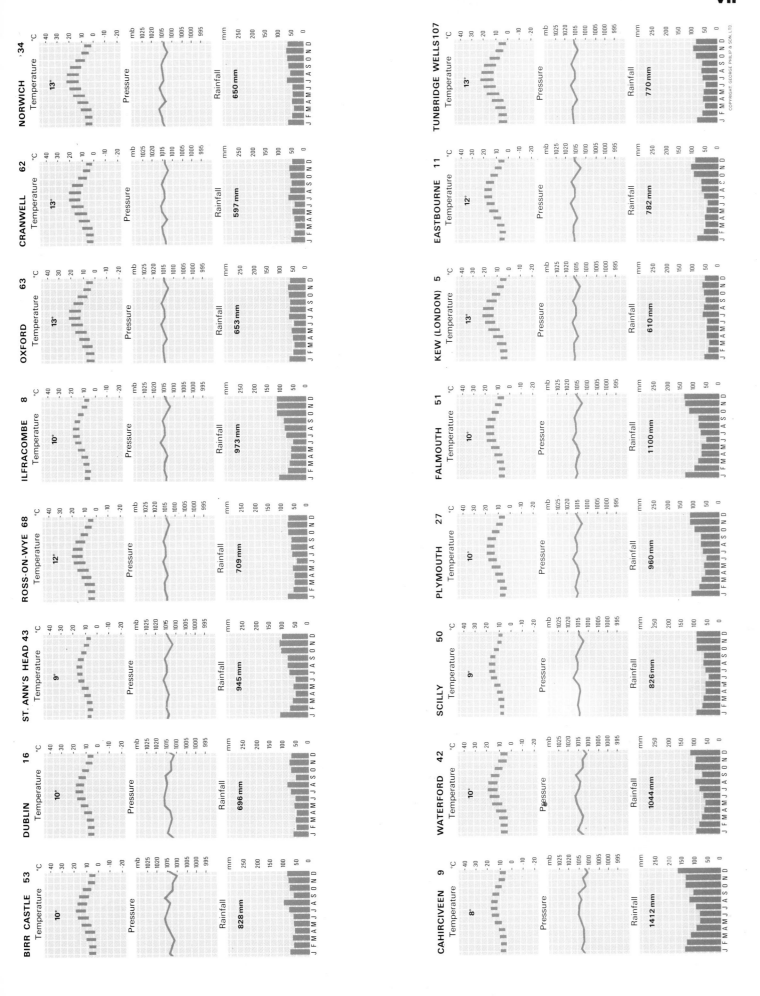

NORWICH 34 — Temperature °C — 13° — Pressure mb — Rainfall 650 mm

CRANWELL 62 — Temperature °C — 13° — Pressure mb — Rainfall 597 mm

OXFORD 63 — Temperature °C — 13° — Pressure mb — Rainfall 653 mm

ILFRACOMBE 8 — Temperature °C — 10° — Pressure mb — Rainfall 973 mm

ROSS-ON-WYE 68 — Temperature °C — 12° — Pressure mb — Rainfall 709 mm

ST. ANN'S HEAD 43 — Temperature °C — 9° — Pressure mb — Rainfall 945 mm

DUBLIN 16 — Temperature °C — 10° — Pressure mb — Rainfall 696 mm

BIRR CASTLE 53 — Temperature °C — 10° — Pressure mb — Rainfall 828 mm

TUNBRIDGE WELLS 107 — Temperature °C — 13° — Pressure mb — Rainfall 770 mm

EASTBOURNE 11 — Temperature °C — 12° — Pressure mb — Rainfall 782 mm

KEW (LONDON) 5 — Temperature °C — 13° — Pressure mb — Rainfall 610 mm

FALMOUTH 51 — Temperature °C — 10° — Pressure mb — Rainfall 1100 mm

PLYMOUTH 27 — Temperature °C — 10° — Pressure mb — Rainfall 960 mm

SCILLY 50 — Temperature °C — 9° — Pressure mb — Rainfall 826 mm

WATERFORD 42 — Temperature °C — 10° — Pressure mb — Rainfall 1044 mm

CAHIRCIVEEN 9 — Temperature °C — 8° — Pressure mb — Rainfall 1412 mm

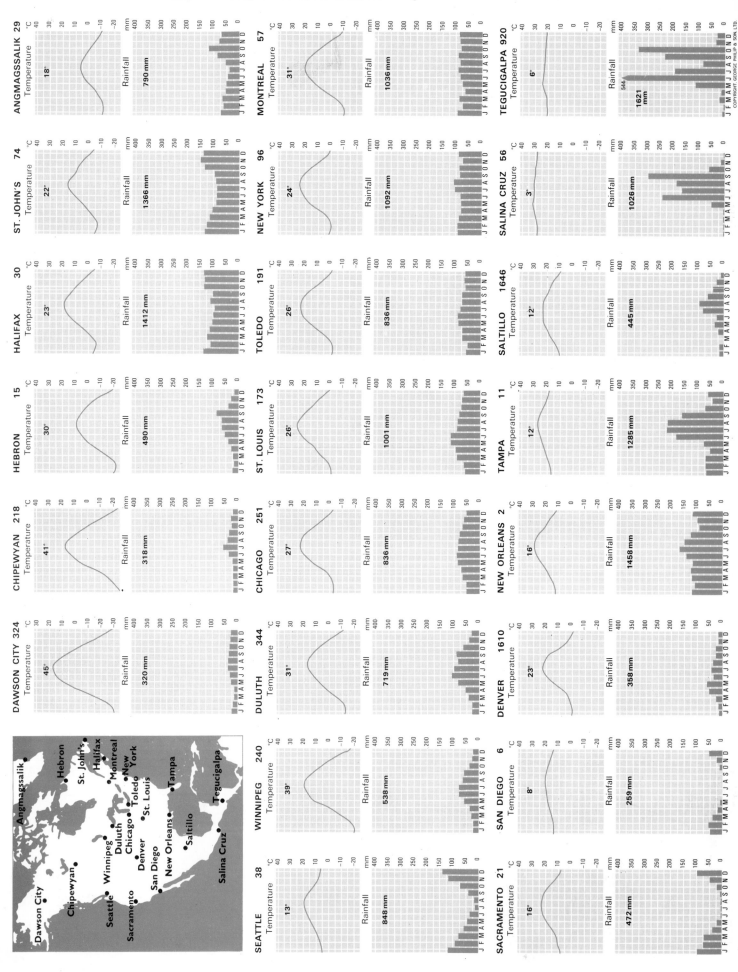

ANGMAGSSALIK 29 — Temperature 18° — Rainfall 790 mm

MONTREAL 57 — Temperature 31° — Rainfall 1036 mm

TEGUCIGALPA 920 — Temperature 6° — Rainfall 1621 mm / 544

ST. JOHN'S 74 — Temperature 22° — Rainfall 1366 mm

NEW YORK 96 — Temperature 24° — Rainfall 1092 mm

SALINA CRUZ 56 — Temperature 3° — Rainfall 1026 mm

HALIFAX 30 — Temperature 23° — Rainfall 1412 mm

TOLEDO 191 — Temperature 26° — Rainfall 836 mm

SALTILLO 1646 — Temperature 12° — Rainfall 445 mm

HEBRON 15 — Temperature 30° — Rainfall 490 mm

ST. LOUIS 173 — Temperature 26° — Rainfall 1001 mm

TAMPA 11 — Temperature 12° — Rainfall 1285 mm

CHIPEWYAN 218 — Temperature 41° — Rainfall 318 mm

CHICAGO 251 — Temperature 27° — Rainfall 836 mm

NEW ORLEANS 2 — Temperature 16° — Rainfall 1458 mm

DAWSON CITY 324 — Temperature 45° — Rainfall 320 mm

DULUTH 344 — Temperature 31° — Rainfall 719 mm

DENVER 1610 — Temperature 23° — Rainfall 358 mm

WINNIPEG 240 — Temperature 39° — Rainfall 538 mm

SAN DIEGO 6 — Temperature 8° — Rainfall 259 mm

SEATTLE 38 — Temperature 13° — Rainfall 848 mm

SACRAMENTO 21 — Temperature 16° — Rainfall 472 mm

Dawson City · Chipewyan · Seattle · Winnipeg · Sacramento · San Diego · Denver · Duluth · Chicago · St. Louis · Toledo · New Orleans · New York · Montreal · Halifax · St. John's · Hebron · Angmagssalik · Tampa · Saltillo · Salina Cruz · Tegucigalpa

Chart of the Stars

Northern Stars

Stars of the Middle Heavens

Southern Stars

a
KIL

The Evolution of the Continents

The origin of the earth is still open to much conjecture although the most widely accepted theory is that it was formed from a solar cloud consisting mainly of hydrogen. Under gravitation the cloud condensed and shrank to form our planets orbiting around the sun. Gravitation forced the lighter elements to the surface of the earth where they cooled to form a crust while the inner material remained hot and molten. Earth's first rocks formed over 3500 million years ago but since then the surface has been constantly altered.

Until comparatively recently the view that the primary units of the earth had remained essentially fixed throughout geological time was regarded as common sense, although the concept of moving continents has been traced back to references in the Bible of a break up of the land after Noah's floods. The continental drift theory was first developed by Antonio Snider in 1858 but probably the most important single advocate was Alfred Wegener who, in 1915, published evidence from geology, climatology and biology. His conclusions are very similar to those reached by current research although he was wrong about the speed of break-up.

The measurement of fossil magnetism found in rocks has probably proved the most influential evidence. While originally these drift theories were openly mocked, now they are considered standard doctrine.

The jigsaw
As knowledge of the shape and structure of the earth's surface grew, several of the early geographers noticed the great similarity in shape of the coasts bordering the Atlantic. It was this remarkable similarity which led to the first detailed geological and structural comparisons. Even more accurate fits can be made by placing the edges of the continental shelves in juxtaposition.

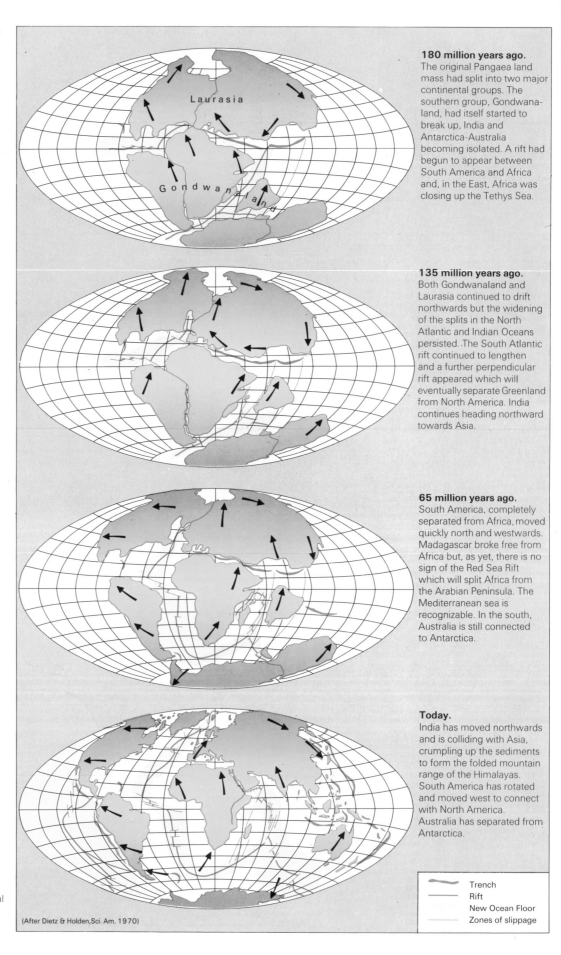

180 million years ago.
The original Pangaea land mass had split into two major continental groups. The southern group, Gondwanaland, had itself started to break up, India and Antarctica-Australia becoming isolated. A rift had begun to appear between South America and Africa and, in the East, Africa was closing up the Tethys Sea.

135 million years ago.
Both Gondwanaland and Laurasia continued to drift northwards but the widening of the splits in the North Atlantic and Indian Oceans persisted. The South Atlantic rift continued to lengthen and a further perpendicular rift appeared which will eventually separate Greenland from North America. India continues heading northward towards Asia.

65 million years ago.
South America, completely separated from Africa, moved quickly north and westwards. Madagascar broke free from Africa but, as yet, there is no sign of the Red Sea Rift which will split Africa from the Arabian Peninsula. The Mediterranean sea is recognizable. In the south, Australia is still connected to Antarctica.

Today.
India has moved northwards and is colliding with Asia, crumpling up the sediments to form the folded mountain range of the Himalayas. South America has rotated and moved west to connect with North America. Australia has separated from Antarctica.

Laurasia

Gondwanaland

	Trench
	Rift
	New Ocean Floor
	Zones of slippage

(After Dietz & Holden, Sci. Am. 1970)

b

Plate tectonics

The original debate about continental drift was only a prelude to a more radical idea; plate tectonics. The basic theory is that the earth's crust is made up of a series of rigid plates which float on a soft layer of the mantle and are moved about by convection currents in the earth's interior. These plates converge and diverge along margins marked by earthquakes, volcanoes and other seismic activity. Plates diverge from mid-ocean ridges where molten lava pushes upwards and forces the plates apart at a rate of up to 30 mm a year. Converging plates form either a trench, where the oceanic plate sinks below the lighter continental rock, or mountain ranges where two continents collide. This explains the paradox that while there have always been oceans none of the present oceans contain sediments more than 150 million years old.

IRANIAN Major plates
- - - - - Plate boundaries
→ Direction of plate movements

Trench boundary

The present explanation for the comparative youth of the ocean floors is that where an ocean and a continent meet the ocean plate dips under the less dense continental plate at an angle of approximately 45°. All previous crust is then ingested by downward convection currents. In the Japanese trench this occurs at a rate of about 120 mm a year.

Transform fault

The recent identification of the transform, or transverse, fault proved to be one of the crucial preliminaries to the investigation of plate tectonics. They occur when two plates slip alongside each other without parting or approaching to any great extent. They complete the outline of the plates delineated by the ridges and trenches and demonstrate large scale movements of parts of the earth's surface

Ridge boundary

Ocean rises or crests are basically made up from basaltic lavas for although no gap can exist between plates, one plate can ease itself away from another. In that case hot, molten rock instantly rises from below to fill in the incipient rift and forms a ridge. These ridges trace a line almost exactly through the centre of the major oceans.

Destruction of ocean plates.

As the ocean plate sinks below the continental plate some of the sediment on its surface is scraped off and piled up on the landward side. This sediment is later incorporated in a folded mountain range which usually appears on the edge of the continent, such as the Andes. Similarly if two continents collide the sediments are squeezed up into new mountains.

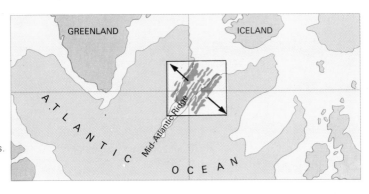

Sea floor spreading

Reversals in the earth's magnetic field have occured throughout history. As new rock emerges at the ocean ridges it cools and is magnetised in the direction of the prevailing magnetic field. By mapping the magnetic patterns either side of the ridge a symmetrical stripey pattern of alternating fields can be observed (see inset area in diagram). As the dates of the last few reversals are known the rate of spreading can be calculated.

The Unstable Earth

The earth's surface is slowly but continually being rearranged. Some changes such as erosion and deposition are extremely slow but they upset the balance which causes other more abrupt changes often originating deep within the earth's interior. The constant movements vary in intensity, often with stresses building up to a climax such as a particularly violent volcanic eruption or earthquake.

The crust *(below and right)*
The outer layer or crust of the earth consists of a comparatively low density, brittle material varying from 5 km to 50 km deep beneath the continents. Under this is a layer of rock consisting predominately of silica and aluminium; hence it is called sial Extending under the ocean floors and below the sial is a basaltic layer known as 'sima', consisting mainly of silica and magnesium.

Crust
Mantle
Outer core
Inner core

Continental crust   Ocean crust

Sediment
Granite rock (sial)
Basaltic layer (sima)
Mantle

Volcanoes *(right, below and far right)*
Volcanoes occur when hot liquefied rock beneath the crust reaches the surface as lava. An accumulation of ash and cinders around a vent forms a cone. Successive layers of thin lava flows form an acid lava volcano while thick lava flows form a basic lava volcano. A caldera forms when a particularly violent eruption blows off the top of an already existing cone.

The mantle *(above)*
Immediately below the crust, at the mohorovícic discontinuity line, there is a distinct change in density and chemical properties. This is the mantle - made up of iron and magnesium silicates - with temperatures reaching 1 600 °C. The rigid upper mantle extends down to a depth of about 1 000 km below which is the more viscous lower mantle which is about 1 900 km thick.

The core *(above)*
The outer core, approximately 2 100 km thick, consists of molten iron and nickel at 2 000 °C to 5 000 °C possibly separated from the less dense mantle by an oxidised shell. About 5 000 km below the surface is the liquid transition zone, below which is the solid inner core, a sphere of 2 740 km diameter where rock is three times as dense as in the crust.

Shield volcano   Cinder cone   Hornit cone   Caldera

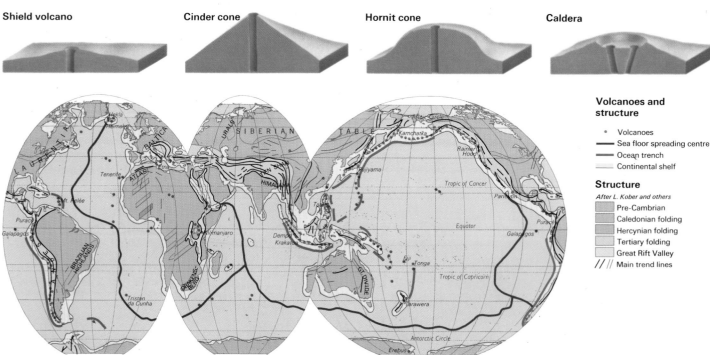

Volcanoes and structure

• Volcanoes
— Sea floor spreading centre
— Ocean trench
— Continental shelf

Structure
After L. Kober and others

Pre-Cambrian
Caledonian folding
Hercynian folding
Tertiary folding
Great Rift Valley
/// Main trend lines

Projection: *Interrupted Mollweide's Homolographic*

d

Major earthquakes in the last 100 years and numbers killed

Year	Location	Killed
1896	Japan (tsunami)	22 000
1906	San Francisco	destroyed
1906	Chile, Valparaiso	22 000
1908	Italy, Messina	77 000
1920	China, Kansu	180 000
1923	Japan, Tokyo	143 000
1930	Italy, Naples	2 100
1931	New Zealand, Napier	destroyed
1931	Nicaragua, Managua	destroyed
1932	China, Kansu	70 000
1935	India, Quetta	60 000
1939	Chile, Chillan	20 000
1939/40	Turkey, Erzincan	30 000
1948	Japan, Fukui	5 100
1956	N. Afghanistan	2 000
1957	W. Iran	10 000
1960	Morocco, Agadir	12 000
1962	N.W. Iran	10 000
1963	Yugoslavia, Skopje	1 000
1966	U.S.S.R., Tashkent	destroyed
1970	N. Peru	66 800
1972	Nicaragua, Managua	7 000
1974	N. Pakistan	10 000
1975	Turkey, Lice	2 300
1976	China, Tangshan	650 000
1976	Turkey, Van	3 800

World distribution of earthquakes

- Major earthquake zones
- Areas experiencing frequent earthquakes

Projection: *Interrupted Mollweide's Homolographic*

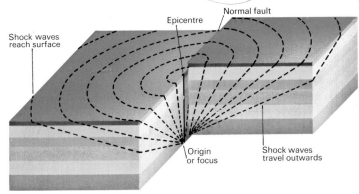

Earthquakes *(right and above)*

Earthquakes are a series of rapid vibrations originating from the slipping or faulting of parts of the earth's crust when stresses within build up to breaking point. They usually happen at depths varying from 8 km to 30 km. Severe earthquakes cause extensive damage when they take place in populated areas destroying structures and severing communications. Most loss of life occurs due to secondary causes i.e. falling masonry, fires or tsunami waves.

Alaskan earthquake, 1964

Seismic Waves *(right)*

The shock waves sent out from the focus of an earthquake are of three main kinds each with distinct properties. Primary (P) waves are compressional waves which can be transmitted through both solids and liquids and therefore pass through the earth's liquid core. Secondary (S) waves are shear waves and can only pass through solids. They cannot pass through the core and are reflected at the core-mantle boundary taking a concave course back to the surface. The core also refracts the P waves causing them to alter course, and the net effect of this reflection and refraction is the production of a shadow zone at a certain distance from the epicentre, free from P and S waves. Due to their different properties P waves travel about 1,7 times faster than S waves. The third main kind of wave is a long (L) wave, a slow wave which travels along the earth's surface, its motion being either horizontal or vertical.

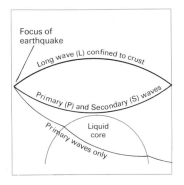

Tsunami waves *(left)*

A sudden slump in the ocean bed during an earthquake forms a trough in the water surface subsequently followed by a crest and smaller waves. A more marked change of level in the sea bed can form a crest, the start of a Tsunami which travels up to 60 km/h with waves up to 60 m high. Seismographic detectors continuously record earthquake shocks and warn of the Tsunami which may follow it.

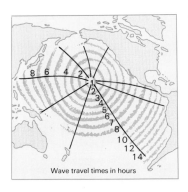

Wave travel times in hours

Principles of seismographs (left)

M = Mass
D = Drum
P = Pivot
S = Spring

Seismographs

are delicate instruments capable of detecting and recording vibrations due to earthquakes thousands of kilometres away. P waves cause the first tremors. S the second, and L the main shock.

The Atmosphere and Clouds

Earth's thin coating *(right)*
The atmosphere is a blanket of protective gases around the earth providing insulation against otherwise extreme alternations in temperature. The gravitational pull increases the density nearer the earth's surface so that 5/6ths of the atmospheric mass is in the first 15 kms. It is a very thin layer in comparison with the earth's diameter of 12 680 kms., like the cellulose coating on a globe.

Exosphere *(1)*
The exosphere merges with the interplanetary medium and although there is no definite boundary with the ionosphere it starts at a height of about 600 kms. The rarified air mainly consists of a small amount of atomic oxygen up to 600 kms. and equal proportions of hydrogen and helium with hydrogen predominating above 2 400 kms.

Ionosphere *(2)*
Air particles of the ionosphere are electrically charged by the sun's radiation and congregate in four main layers, D, E, F1 and F2, which can reflect radio waves. Aurorae, caused by charged particles deflected by the earth's magnetic field towards the poles, occur between 65 and 965 kms. above the earth. It is mainly in the lower ionosphere that meteors from outer space burn up as they meet increased air resistance.

Stratosphere *(3)*
A thin layer of ozone contained within the stratosphere absorbs ultra-violet light and in the process gives off heat. The temperature ranges from about -55°C at the tropopause to about -60°C in the upper part, known as the mesosphere, with a rise to about 2°C just above the ozone layer. This portion of the atmosphere is separated from the lower layer by the tropopause.

Troposphere *(4)*
The earth's weather conditions are limited to this layer which is relatively thin, extending upwards to about 8 kms. at the poles and 15 kms. at the equator. It contains about 85% of the total atmospheric mass and almost all the water vapour. Air temperature falls steadily with increased height at about 1°C for every 100 metres above sea level.

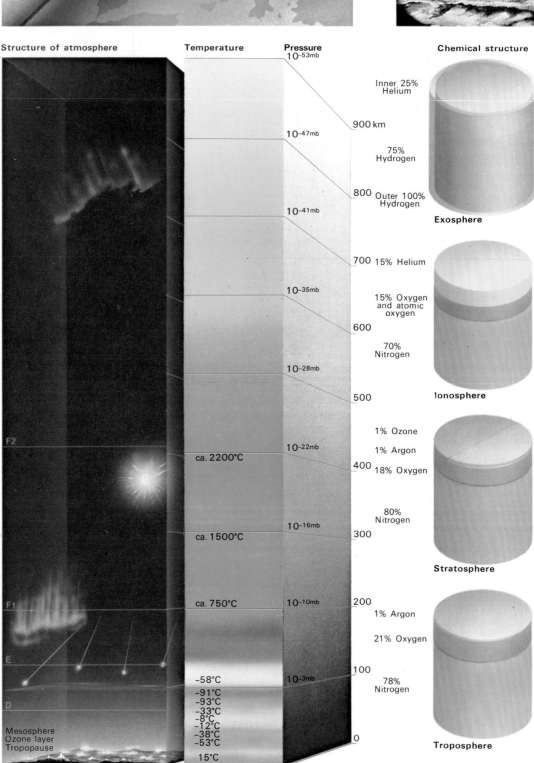

Structure of atmosphere | Temperature | Pressure | Chemical structure

600 km
15 km

Pressure
10^{-53}mb
10^{-47}mb
10^{-41}mb
10^{-35}mb
10^{-28}mb
10^{-22}mb
10^{-16}mb
10^{-10}mb
10^{-3}mb
10^{3}mb

900 km
800 km
700 km
600
500
400
300
200
100
0

Temperature
ca. 2200°C
ca. 1500°C
ca. 750°C
-58°C
-91°C
-93°C
-33°C
-8°C
-12°C
-38°C
-53°C
15°C

Mesosphere
Ozone layer
Tropopause

F2
F1
E
D

Chemical structure

Inner 25% Helium
75% Hydrogen
Outer 100% Hydrogen
Exosphere

15% Helium
15% Oxygen and atomic oxygen
70% Nitrogen
Ionosphere

1% Ozone
1% Argon
18% Oxygen
80% Nitrogen
Stratosphere

1% Argon
21% Oxygen
78% Nitrogen
Troposphere

1
2
3
4

f

Pacific Ocean
Cloud patterns over the Pacific show the paths of prevailing winds.

Circulation of the air

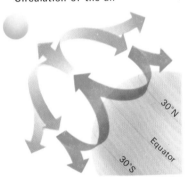

Circulation of the air
Owing to high temperatures in equatorial regions the air near the ground is heated, expands and rises producing a low pressure belt. It cools, causing rain, spreads out then sinks again about latitudes 30° north and south forming high pressure belts.

High and low pressure belts are areas of comparative calm but between them, blowing from high to low pressure, are the prevailing winds. These are deflected to the right in the northern hemisphere and to the left in the southern hemisphere (Corolis effect). The circulations appear in three distinct belts with a seasonal movement north and south following the overhead sun.

Cloud types

Clouds form when damp air is cooled, usually by rising. This may happen in three ways: when a wind rises to cross hills or mountains; when a mass of air rises over, or is pushed up by another mass of denser air; when local heating of the ground causes convection currents.

Cirrus *(1)* are detached clouds composed of microscopic ice crystals which gleam white in the sun resembling hair or feathers. They are found at heights of 6 000 to 12 000 metres.

Cirrostratus *(2)* are a whitish veil of cloud made up of ice crystals through which the sun can be seen often producing a halo of bright light.

Cirrocumulus *(3)* is another high altitude cloud formed by turbulence between layers moving in different directions.

Altostratus *(4)* is a grey or bluish striated, fibrous or uniform sheet of cloud producing light drizzle.

Altocumulus *(5)* is a thicker and fluffier version of cirro cumulus, it is a white and grey patchy sheet of cloud.

Nimbostratus *(6)* is a dark grey layer of cloud obscuring the sun and causing almost continuous rain or snow.

Cumulus *(7)* are detached heaped up, dense low clouds. The sunlit parts are brilliant white while the base is relatively dark and flat.

Stratus *(8)* forms dull overcast skies associated with depressions and occurs at low altitudes up to 1500 metres.

Cumulonimbus *(9)* are heavy and dense clouds associated with storms and rain. They have flat bases and a fluffy outline extending up to great altitudes.

High clouds

Middle clouds

Low clouds

Thousands of metres

1 Cirrus

2 Cirrostratus

3 Cirrocumulus

4 Altostratus

5 Altocumulus

6 Nimbostratus

7 Cumulus

8 Stratus

9 Cumulonimbus

g

Time Zones

WORLD TIMES AT 12.00 G.M.T.

Time zones

The world is divided into 24 time zones, each centred on meridians at 15° intervals which is the longitudinal distance the sun appears to travel every hour. The meridian running through Greenwich passes through the middle of the first zone. Successive zones to the east of Greenwich zone are ahead of Greenwich time by one hour for every 15° of longitude, while zones to the west are behind by one hour.

The International Date Line

When it is 12 noon at the Greenwich meridian, 180° east it is midnight of the same day while 180° west the day is only just beginning. To overcome this the International Date Line was established, approximately following the 180° meridian. Thus, for example, if one travelled eastwards from Japan (140° East) to Samoa (170° West) one would pass from Sunday night into Sunday morning.

International date line

Watch must be put back 24 hrs.

Watch must be put forward 24 hrs.

Time difference when travelling by air

London–Los Angeles (8780 km) (5456 miles)																		
In flight London routine	Take off	Take off Refreshments	Afternoon tea	Meal Dinner		Refreshments	Supper time	Bed	Motion picture				Sleep			Refreshments		Landing
G.M.T.	1600	1700	1800	1900	2000	2100	2200	2300	2400	0100	0200	0300	0400	0500	1600	1700	1800	1900	2000
American time	0800	0900	1000	1100	1200	1300	1400	1500	1600	1700	1800	1900	2000						
Los Angeles routine	Break-fast		Morning coffee		Lunch		Afternoon tea		Dinner										

London–Johannesburg (9055 km) (5627 miles)																		
In flight London routine	Take off	Meal	Dinner		Motion picture	Supper time	Bed		Rest period				Sleep			Break-fast	Landing	
G.M.T.	1800	1900	2000	2100	2200	2300	2400	0100	0200	0300	0400	0500	0600	0700	0800	0900		
Jo'burg time	2000	2100	2200	2300	2400	0100	0200	0300	0400	0500	0600	0700	0800	0900					
Jo'burg routine	Supper time	Bed				Sleep							Break-fast						

Zone 1
Zone 2
½ hour zones

h

GENERAL REFERENCE

Town sites in order of importance

Permanent Ice

▲ 8848   Height above sea-level
▼ 11,022   Depth below sea-level   } in metres
  1134   Height of lake-level

Principal Roads	Shipping Routes *(Distances in Nautical Miles)*
Principal Railways	*(The width of Route denotes relative volume of Sea-borne trade)*
Canals	Principal Air Routes
Shipping Routes *(Distances in Nautical Miles)*	*(All the above on page 1 only)*

Perennial Streams
Seasonal Streams
Seasonal Lakes
Marshes

Wells in Desert
Principal Oil Pipelines
International Boundaries
Internal Boundaries

Equatorial Scale 1:153 250 000

Scale for the degrees of Latitude

Projection : Mercator

COPYRIGHT GEORGE PHILIP & SON LTD

GEOLOGY
after
Beyschlag, Nalivkin and others

1:90 000 000

Ⓐ

GEOLOGICAL
CYCLES Ⓒ

Quaternary	Recent	
	Pliocene	
Tertiary (Cainozoic)	Miocene	Alpine Folding
	Oligocene	
	Eocene	
Secondary (Mesozoic)	Cretaceous	Laramide Folding
	Jurassic	
	Triassic	
	Permian	
Primary Upper (Palæozoic)	Carboniferous	Hercynian Folding
	Devonian	
Primary Lower (Palæozoic)	Silurian	Caledonian Folding
	Ordovician	
	Cambrian	
Archæan	Pre-Cambrian	

An Interpretation of
STRUCTURE
showing
the distribution of rigid masses and folded regions
after L. Kober and others

Ⓑ

Pre-Cambrian tables composite in structure, rigid since the Cambrian period and forming stable elements separating the geo-synclines of later times.
Regions of Caledonian folding; Siluro-Devonian earth movements.
Regions of Hercynian folding; Carbo-Permian earth movements.
Regions of Tertiary folding; Cretaceo-Tertiary earth movements.
The Great Rift Valley
Main Trend lines

Projections: Interrupted Mollweide's Homolographic

Sedimentary Rocks
Quaternary
Cainozoic
Mesozoic
Upper Palæozoic
Lower Palæozoic
Pre-Cambrian and
Metamorphic

Igneous Rocks
Volcanic
Intrusive

Ice caps
Unexplored regions

Arctic Circle

60

Tropic of Cancer

20

60

80

140

160

Equator

180

0

20

Tropic of Capricorn

40

60

Sea Depths

m   ft
4000   12 000
6000   18 000
8000   24 000

1:126 000 000

BALTICA

SIBERIAN TABLE
(ANGARALAND)

CHINESE
TABLE

G   O   N   D   W   A   N   A   L   A   N   D

O   N   D   W   A   N

?

?

COPYRIGHT·GEORGE PHILIP & SON LTD.

THE WOR

1:1

ECLIPSE OF THE SUN

The Sun   The Moon   The Earth

Moon's Shadow   Earth's Shadow   Moon's Orbit   Earth's Shadow

THE SOLAR SYSTEM

Path of a Comet

Mercury
Venus
Earth
Mars
Minor Planets

Jupiter   Saturn   Neptune

Uranus   Pluto

Scale of Distances

0   200   400   600   800   1000 Million Miles
0   400   800   1200   1600 Million Km

THE PLANETS
on a uniform Scale

Pluto
Neptune
Uranus
Saturn
Jupiter
Minor Planets
Mars
Earth
Venus
Mercury

Diameter of the Sun on same scale

LENGTH OF DAY & NIGHT ON THE EARTH
on 21st June

Tropic of Cancer
Equator
Tropic of Capricorn

6 Months Day
6 Months Night

PHYSICAL

0 000

POINTS OF THE COMPASS

N NNE NE ENE
NNW NE
NW ENE
WNW E
W E
WSW ESE
SW SE
SSW S SSE

ECLIPSE OF THE MOON

Earth's
Shadow
The
Moon
The Earth
The
Sun

TERRESTRIAL ZONES

North Pole
Arctic — NORTH FRIGID ZONE — Circle
NORTH TEMPERATE ZONE
Tropic of Cancer — Cancer
Equator — TORRID ZONE — Equator
Tropic of Capricorn — Capricorn
SOUTH TEMPERATE ZONE
Antarctic — SOUTH FRIGID ZONE — Circle
South Pole

THE EARTH'S ORBIT (THE SEASONS)
(NORTHERN HEMISPHERE)

Spring   Winter

March 21st
(Vernal Equinox)

June 21st
(Midsummer)   Aphelion   Perihelion   December 21st
(Midwinter)

The Sun

September 23rd
(Autumnal Equinox)

Summer   Autumn

THE PHASES OF THE MOON

New Moon

First Quarter   Noon   Last Quarter

Evening   Morning

Midnight

Full Moon

The yellow lines represent the rays of the Sun

1:190 000 000

January Temperature and Ocean Currents
(Northern Hemisphere— Winter)

ACTUAL SURFACE TEMPERATURE

°C	°F
30	86
20	68
10	50
0	32
−10	14
−20	−4
−30	−22
−40	−40

→ Warm Current
→ Cold Current

N. Pacific Current
Californian Current
Labrador
North Atlantic Drift
Oya-Siwo
Kuro Siwo
Gulf Stream
Northern Equatorial Current
N. Equatorial Current
Counter Current
Counter Current
Southern Equatorial Current
Guinea C.
N. E. Monsoon Drift
Benguela Current
Peruvian Current
Brazil Current
Agulhas C.
South Equatorial Current
Antarctic Drift

July Temperature and Ocean Currents
(Northern Hemisphere— Summer)

ACTUAL SURFACE TEMPERATURE

°C	°F
30	86
20	68
10	50
0	32
−10	14

← Warm Current
← Cold Current

N. Pacific Current
Labrador
North Atlantic Drift
Oya-Siwo
Kuro Siwo
Gulf Stream
Northern Equatorial Current
N. Equatorial Current
N. Equatorial Current
Counter Current
Counter Current
Southern Equatorial Current
South Equatorial Current
Guinea C.
S.W. Monsoon Drift
Benguela Current
Peruvian Current
Brazil Current
Agulhas C.
South Equatorial Current
Antarctic Drift

Annual Range of Temperature

°C

| 60 |
| 50 |
| 40 |
| 30 |
| 20 |
| 10 |
| 5 |
| 0 |

The annual range of temperature is the difference in degrees Celsius between the warmest and coldest months of the year.

Projection: *Hammer Equal Area*

January
Pressure and Winds

July
Pressure and Winds

Annual
Precipitation

NATURAL
VEGETATION

CLIMATIC REGIONS
after Köppen and others

Tropic of Cancer · Equator · Tropic of Capricorn · Arctic Circle

Gobi or Shamo
Steppes
Syrian Desert
Arabian Desert
Sahara
Sudan
Kalahari
Selvas
Llanos
Prairies

Natural Vegetation legend:

- Coniferous Forest
- Broad-leaved Forest and Meadow
- Evergreen Trees and Shrubs
- Temperate Rain Forest
- Monsoon Forest
- Tropical Rain Forest
- Thorn Forest
- Grassland
- Scrub, Steppe and Semi-desert
- Desert
- Alpine Tundra and Ice Desert

Climatic Regions legend:

TROPICAL RAIN CLIMATES
1   Equatorial Rain-Forest Climate: Rain at all Seasons.
2   Tropical Rain Savanna Climate with dry season.
DRY CLIMATES
3   Desert Climate with no rain.
4   Steppe Climate with little rain.
WARM TEMPERATE RAIN CLIMATES
5   with dry summer season
6   with dry winter season
7a 7b   with rain at all seasons.
      7a with hot summers
      7b with short summers
COOL TEMPERATE RAIN CLIMATES
8   Rain all year round & severe winter.
9   with severe dry winter.
10   POLAR CLIMATES – no warm season.

Projection: Mollweide's Interrupted Homolographic

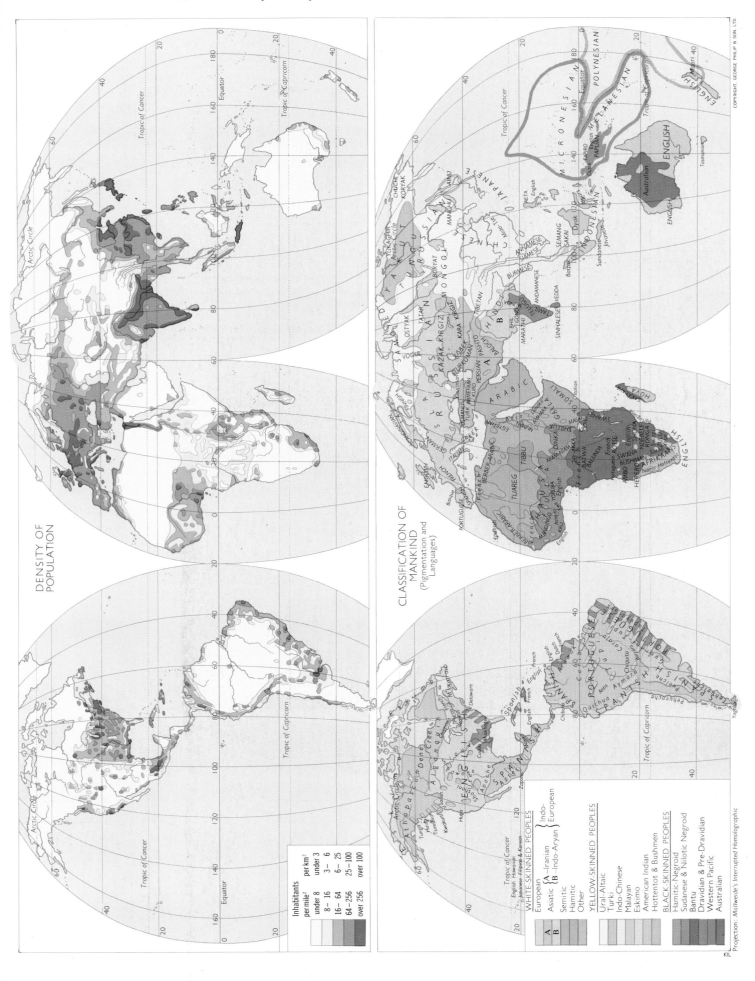

DENSITY OF
POPULATION

CLASSIFICATION OF
MANKIND
(Pigmentation and
Languages)

Projection: Mollweide's Interrupted Homolographic

COPYRIGHT GEORGE PHILIP & SON LTD

Inhabitants

per mile²	per km²
under 8	under 3
8 – 16	3 – 6
16 – 64	6 – 25
64 – 256	25 – 100
over 256	over 100

WHITE-SKINNED PEOPLES

European
Asiatic {A–Iranian {Indo- } European
        {B–Indo-Aryan}
Semitic
Hamitic
Other

YELLOW-SKINNED PEOPLES

Ural-Altaic
Turki
Indo-Chinese
Malayan
Eskimo
American Indian
Hottentot & Bushmen

BLACK-SKINNED PEOPLES

Hamitic-Negroid
Sudanese & Nilotic Negroid
Bantu
Dravidian & Pre-Dravidian
Western Pacific
Australian

KIL

1 : 300 000 000

2000 1000 0   2000   4000   6000 miles

2000   0   2000   4000   6000   8000 km

3091   Principal Shipping Routes

(Distances in Nautical Miles)

Projection : *Oblique Azimuthal Equidistant*

1:100 000 000

1000   500   0   1000   2000 miles
1500 1000 500 0   1000 2000 3000 km

CENTRED ON THE ANTIPODES OF LONDON

East from Greenwich   180   West from Greenwich

Midway I.   Yokohama 3419
Tropic of Cancer   Vancouver 2419
20   San Francisco 2098
Wake I.   Honolulu   Hawaiian Is.
3312
Bonin Is.
Mariana Is.   Marshall Is.
Guam   San Francisco 3658
Caroline Is.   1497   120
PHILIPPINES   Canton I.   Christmas I.
Manila   KIRIBATI   0   2783   Phoenix Is.   Equator
New Ireland New Britain   Society Is.   Marquesas Is.
Halmahera Solomon   TUVALU   SAMOA   Tahiti   Tuamotu
New Guinea Is. Honiara (Ellice Is.)   Rarotonga   Tropic of Capricorn
PAPUA NEW GUINEA FIJI   20   Cook Is.
Port Moresby   VANUATU Suva   International Date Line   Pitcairn I.   Easter I.   Panama 3410
Coral Sea New Caledonia Noumea   TONGA   3200   Galapagos Is.
Townsville   Cairns   40   4614
AUSTRALIA   Auckland
Sydney Canberra Wellington
Melbourne NEW ZEALAND Dunedin
Tasmania Hobart   Auckland I. Antipodes I.
SOUTHERN OCEAN   60
Macquarie I.
ANTARCTICA   SOUTH POLE
INDIAN OCEAN
Cocos Is.   Jombo 3120
Perth Fremantle

PACIFIC OCEAN

SOUTH AMERICA
Callao
Lima PERU
Arequipa
Valparaiso Antofagasta
Santiago CHILE
ARGENTINA BOLIVIA
Tierra del Fuego PARAGUAY
Rio de Janeiro URUGUAY BRAZIL
Buenos Aires Montevideo Porto Alegre
Bahia Blanca

Ross Dependency
S. Magnetic Pole Adelie Ld. Oates Coast
Wilkes Land Victoria Land Ross Sea
Qn. Mary Coast Byrd Land Ellsworth Land
Australian Dependency Kemp Ld. Marie Byrd Land
Enderby Ld. Queen Maud Land (Norwegian)
Weddell Sea Antarctic Peninsula
British Antarctic Territory Falkland Is.
Antarctic Circle   60
Bouvet I. S. Sandwich Is. S. Georgia Dependencies

Heard I.
Kerguelen
Crozet Is.   Pr. Edward Is. (S.A.)

ATLANTIC OCEAN

1:300 000 000

2000 1000 0   2000   4000   6000 miles
2000 0   2000 4000 6000 8000 km

—2743— Principal Shipping Routes
(Distances in Nautical Miles)

CENTRED ON CAIRO

CENTRED ON SHANGHAI

COPYRIGHT. GEORGE PHILIP & SON. LTD

1:25 000 000

EUROPE: GEOLOGY
after Franz Beyschlag and others

SEDIMENTARY ROCKS
Quaternary
Tertiary (Cainozoic)
Cretaceous
Jurassic — Secondary (Mesozoic)
Triassic
Primary (Palaeozoic)
Ancient (Pre-Cambrian)

IGNEOUS ROCKS
Volcanic
Intrusive

Exposed Coal Measures (Productive)
Terminal Moraines of the Great Ice Sheet

EUROPE: STRUCTURE
after E. Suess, Marcel Bertrand,
J. J. Sederholm, E. Haug, L. de Launay and L. Kober

a
b
The Pre-Cambrian Shield; primitive masses rigid since the Cambrian
period and forming the sub-structure of the continent.
a. Fenno-Scandian table.
b. Russian platform; covered by more recent deposits.

Caledonian folding; Siluro-Devonian earth movements.

Hercynian folding; Carbo-Permian earth movements.
a
b
a. showing present-day exposures in horsts and chains.
b. showing intervening subsidence.

Alpine folding; Cretaceo-Tertiary earth movements.

Ancient massifs within the Alpine system.

Trend lines

Tertiary volcanic regions.

1:40 000 000

Projection: *Bonne*

1:20 000 000

100   0   100   200   300   400   500 miles
100   0   200   400   600   800 km

Ural Mountains
Ob
Obskaya G.
Tundra
Nurobo 1894
1617
Pechora
Kanin Peninsula
Mezen
Kola Peninsula
White Sea
N. Dvina
Onega
L. Onega
L. Ladoga
Finland
Plain
Volga Uplands
Volga
Yana
Don
Central Russian Uplands
Ukraine
Dnepr (Dnieper)
Bug
Danube
Sea of Azov
Str. of Kerch
Kuban
Crimea
CASPIAN SEA −28
Caucasus 5633
Elbrus 5165
Rion
Kura
Araks
Terek
Armenia
Kurdistan
Euphrates
Kizil Irmak 3770
Ararat 5165
Anatolia
Taurus
BLACK SEA 2211
Bosporus
Rhodope Peninsula
Balkans
Morava
Danube
Wallachia
Transylvanian Alps
Mures
Tisza
Plain of Hungary
Carpathians
Tatra 2655
Pripyat Marshes
Pripyat
Dnestr (Dniester)
Prut
North
European
Plain
Niemen
Wisła (Vistula)
Odra (Oder)
Sudetes
Bohemian For.
Erz Geb.
Gt. of Finland
Neva
L. Chudskoye
G. of Riga
Gotland
W. Dvina
BALTIC SEA
Scandinavia
Kjolen
Lapland
Mts.
2123
North Cape
Nordkinn
Lofoten
Vesterålen
Tromsö
Indals
Dal
Klar
Vänern
Vättern
Öland
Bornholm
Skagerrak
Kattegat
Jutland
Sjælland
Weser
Elbe
Harz 1142
Black Forest
Vosges
Jura
Rhine
Taunus
Ardennes
Netherland
FISHER
GERMAN BIGHT
Heligoland
NORTH SEA
Dogger Bank
FORTIES
VIKING
Lindesnes
2469
3734
NORWEGIAN SEA
Arctic Circle
Iceland
Hekla 1491
Vatna Jökull
2119
SOUTH EAST ICELAND
Faröe Bank
FAEROES
Faröe Is.
Shetland Is.
Fair Isle
Orkney Is.
Hebrides
Great Britain
British Isles
Ireland
Fisher Bank
BAILEY
HEBRIDES
Rockall
ROCKALL
FASTNET
SHANNON
Valentia I.
C. Clear
Land's End
Irish Sea
1085
Snowdon
FINISTERRE
SOLE
PLYMOUTH
English Channel
DOVER
WIGHT
PORTLAND
THAMES
HUMBER
TYNE
DOGGER
CROMARTY
FORTH
FAIR ISLE
FORTH
TYNE
Seine
Somme
Brittany
C. Finisterre
B. of Biscay
BISCAY
Bay of Biscay
4061
Loire
Garonne
Gironde
Dordogne
Central Massif 1886
Cévennes
Rhône
Saône
Jura
Alps
Mt. Blanc 4807
G. of Lions
Pyrenees 3404
Ebro
Cantabrian Mts.
Duero
Douro
Old Castile
New Castile
Iberian Peninsula
Tagus
Guadiana
Sierra Morena
Guadalquivir
Andalusia
Sierra Nevada 3478
C. St. Vincent
C. Trafalgar
C. Spartel
Str. of Gibraltar
Maritime Atlas
Plateau of the Shotts
ATLANTIC OCEAN
Corsica
Sardinia
Ligurian Sea
Apennines
Tyrrhenian Sea
Tiber
Str. of Bonifacio
Gran Sasso 2914
Vesuvius 1277
Etna 3263
Sicily
Str. of Messina
Calabria
C. Bon
Malta
MEDITERRANEAN SEA
ADRIATIC SEA
Dinaric Alps
Po
Drava
Sava
Bakony For.
Bohemian For.
Pindus
Balkan Peninsula
Morea
Ionian Is.
Ionian Sea
Str. of Otranto
C. Matapan 5121
Aegean Sea
Crete
Cyprus 1951
Balearic Is.
C. Blanco

ft   m
12 000   4000
6000   2000
3000   1000
1200   600
600   200
0   0
200   −200
2000   600
4000   2000
6000   4000
12 000   m
ft

Projection Bonne   West from Greenwich 0 East from Greenwich   Sea areas named in ROCKALL weather forecasts

1 : 40 000 000

1 : 20 000 000

100   0   100   200   300   400   500 miles
100   0   100   200   300   400   600   800 km

FOREST VEGETATION

Northern Coniferous Forest—
 a. Fenno-Scandian Forest (pine, spruce, birch)
 b. Taiga (Siberian larch, fir, spruce)

Mountain Forest, mainly Coniferous (fir, pine, spruce), sometimes with lower belt of Broad-leaved Forest (oak, beech, chestnut)

Mixed Broad-leaved and Coniferous Forest } (oak, beech, fir, etc.)
Mixed Broad-leaved and Coniferous Woodland and Meadow

Mediterranean Evergreen Forest (evergreen oak, stone pine, cork—in S.W. Europe)

Mediterranean Evergreen Maquis and Meadow (myrtle and other aromatic shrubs, olive)

Tundra (moss, lichen, heather bog, dwarf willow, birch and alder)

GRASS VEGETATION

Grassland

Steppe

Salt Steppe and
Semi-Desert

Heath, Moor and
Sandy Coastal Wastes

Swamp Vegetation
(liable to inundation)

DESERT VEGETATION

Desert

Alpine (above
Timber line)

a   b

North limit of Oak (quercus robur)
Limits of Beech (fagus silvatica)
North limit of Olive (olea europaea)
East limit of Evergreen Oak (quercus ilex)
Seas and Lakes frozen in Winter

COPYRIGHT. GEORGE PHILIP & SON. LTD.

Projection: Bonne.

East from Greenwich

*Map labels:*

Ural Mountains
CASPIAN SEA
Obchais
Caucasus
BLACK SEA
Pontine Mts.
Taurus
CASPIAN SEA
Finland Lake Plateau
BALTIC SEA
Carpathians
Balkans
Sudetes
Pindus
AEGEAN SEA
NORTH SEA
Ore Mts.
Bohemian For.
Black F.
Vosges
ADRIATIC SEA
Apennines
A L P S
Cevennes
Pyrenees
Atlas Mts.
M E D I T E R R A N E A N   S E A
ATLANTIC OCEAN
Kjolen Mountains
Arctic Circle

1:5 000 000

20　0　20　40　60　80　100　miles
20　0　20　40　60　80　100　120　140　160　km

Shetland Is.

Foula

Sumburgh Hd.

Fair I.

Orkney Islands

C. Wrath
Dunnet Hd.　Duncansby Hd.
Pentland Firth

60

58

Rona

Butt of Lewis

Flannan Is.

Lewis
789

St. Kilda

Ben More Assynt
998　Shin

Ben Wyvis
1046
Moray Firth

Buchan Ness

O C E A N

Outer Hebrides

North Minch

North West Highlands
Carn Eige
1182

L. Maree

Glen Mor

Spey

L. Ness

Dee

Ben Macdhui
1311

Skye
1009

Ardnamurchan Pt.

Ben Nevis
1347

Grampians

Strathmore

Sidlaw Hills

F. of Tay
Fife Ness

Inner Hebrides

Mull

Firth of Lorn

Rockall Deep

L. Lomond
974

Forth Ochil Hills

Firth of Forth
Bass Rock

Islay

Arran

Clyde
Pentland Hills

Lammermuir Hills

Rockall Deep

A T L A N T I C

Firth of Clyde

Southern Uplands
Broad Law
840

Tweed
The Cheviot
816

N O R T H

238

Giant's Causeway
Fair Hd.
Malin Hd.

Tory I.

Mull of Kintyre

Merrick
843

Cheviot Hills

Erriga 752
Derryveagh Mts.

Antrim Mts.

Bann

North Channel

Nith

S E A

Dogger Bank

Donegal Bay
Erne

L. Erne

Neagh

Mull of Galloway

Solway Firth

Eden

Cross Fell
893

Tyne

30

Errisl Hd.

Achill I.

Mourne Mts. 852

St. Bee's Hd.
Sca Fell 978

Cumbrian Mts.

Tees

Vale of York
York Moors
454

Flamborough Hd.

54

Mweelrea 819

L. Mask
Corrib

I. of Man
Snaefell
620

737

Swale
Wharfe

Yorkshire Wolds

Spurn Hd.
Humber

Central Plain

Boyne

Morecambe Bay

Ure
Ouse

Holderness

Connemara

Liffey

I R I S H　S E A

Formby Pt.
Liverpool Bay

Aire

Don

Lincolnshire Wolds

Galway Bay

Shannon

Bog of Allen

Gt. Ormes Hd.

Mersey
The Peak 636

Trent

Lincoln Heath
Witham

The Wash

St. Bloom Mts.

Anglesey
Holy I.

Cheshire Plain

Derwent

Breckland

Yare
Lowestoftness

Derg
Barrow

Wicklow Mts.
926

Menai Strait

Snowdon
1085

Wreekin
407

Welland

The Fens

Loop Hd.
Shannon

Cardigan Bay

Cambrian Mts.

Nene

Gt. Ouse

52

Golden Vale

Suir

892
Plynlimon
752

Severn

Gt. Ouse

Stour
The Naze

Dunmore Hd.

Galty Mts.
920

Blackwater

Carnsore Pt.

Wye

Cotswolds

Cher well

Chiltern Hills

Thames

Macgillycuddy's Reeks 1041

Lee

Cork Harbour

St. David's Hd.

Tywi

Brecon Beacons

Avon

Marlboro' Downs
Kennet

Berks Downs

Thames

North Foreland

C. Clear

St. George's Channel

Milford Haven

Teifi

North Downs

Lundy

Bristol Channel
R. Severn

Mendip Hills

Avon

Salisbury Plain

Hampshire Downs

The Weald

Strait of Dover

Hartland Point

Exmoor
520

Parret

N. Dorset Downs

South Downs

Beachy Hd.

Dungeness

Bodmin Moor

Yes Tor
618

Dartmoor

Exe

Tamar

Needles
I. of Wight

Portland Bill

F R A N C E

Land's End

Isles of Scilly

Lizard

Start Pt.

E N G L I S H　C h a n n e l

50

West from Greenwich　0　East from Greenwich　

ft　m

3000　1000
1200　400
600　200
300
0　0
100　300
200　600
400　1200
600　1800
m　ft

1 : 5 000 000

50   0   50   100 miles

50   0   50   100   150 km

SEDIMENTARY ROCKS

| RECENT | | Alluvium |

TERTIARY
(Cainozoic) — Sands and Clays

SECONDARY
(Mesozoic)
Cretaceous—Chalk
Jurassic and Cretaceous { Clays / Sands
Jurassic—Oolitic Limestones
Liassic (Jur.) Triassic and Permian } Sandstones and Clays

PRIMARY
(Palaeozoic)
Carboniferous { Coal Measures / Limestone and Millstone Grit
Old Red Sandstone and Devonian
Ordovician, Silurian and Cambrian

ANCIENT
(Pre-Cambrian)
Torridonian, Longmyndian etc.
Metamorphic

IGNEOUS ROCKS

Various Ages
Volcanic (e.g. Basalt)
Intrusive (e.g. Granite)

OIL AND GAS FIELDS

● Oil field   ○ Gas field
– – – Oil Search Sector Boundary

Shetland Is.

Orkney Is.

Outer Hebrides

Skye

Ben Macdhui

Ben Nevis

Grampians

Beatrice

Derryveagh Mts.

Antrim Mts.

Cheviot Hills

Pennines

Connemara

Mourne Mts.

Cumbrian Mts.
Sca Fell

N. York Moors

Slieve Bloom Mts.

Wicklow Mts.

I. of Man

Morecambe

Lincolnshire Wolds

Galty Mts.

Anglesey

Snowdon

The Peak

Macgillycuddy's Reeks
Mts. of Kerry

Cambrian Mts.

Cotswolds

Chiltern Hills

North Downs

The Weald
South Downs

IRISH SECTOR
○ Kinsale Head

UNITED KINGDOM SECTOR

SOUTHWARD LIMIT OF GLACIATION

Exmoor

I. of Wight

Dartmoor

UNITED KINGDOM SECTOR

Tern   Thistle   Murchison
Cormorant   Dunlin   Statfjord
Hutton   Brent
Heather   Ninian
Alwyn

Odin
Frigg

Bruce
(Gas condensate)
Beryl
Heimdal
(Gas condensate)

Crawford   Balder

Gudrun   NORWEGIAN SECTOR
Brae   Sleipner
Thelma
Claymore   Piper   Maureen
Tartan
Renee   Andrew
Buchan
Forties   Montrose

Lomond
(Gas condensate)   Cod
(Gas condensate)

Albuskjell   N.W. Tor
Josephine   W.   Torfeld
Flyndre   Ekofisk   Ekofisk
Edda   Eldfisk
Auk
Hod
Argyll   DANISH SECTOR

W. GERMAN SECTOR

DUTCH SECTOR

Rough   West Sole   Ann
Audrey
Amethyst   Viking
Indefatigable
Nam   Pennzoil
Broken Bank
Dottie   Deborah   Sean   Leman
Hewett   Scram

West from Greenwich   East from Greenwich

Projection: Conical with two standard parallels

COPYRIGHT. GEORGE PHILIP & SON LTD.

WINTER CLIMATE ⒶA

Actual Temperature
January
°C   °F 46(78°C)
7   44
6   42
5   40
4   38
3   36
2   34
1   32
0

—— January Isotherms
reduced to Sea-level
°Celsius
→ Prevailing Winds

SUMMER CLIMATE ⒷB

Actual Temperature
July
°C   °F 64(77°C)
17   62
16   60
15   58
14   56
13   54
12   52
11   50
10

—— July Isotherms
reduced to Sea-level
°Celsius
→ Prevailing Winds

ANNUAL RAINFALL AND ISOBARS ⒸC

inches   mm
100   2500
80   2000
60   1500
40   1000
30   750
25   625

BAROMETER
millibars   inches
1036   30.6
1032   30.5
1028   30.4
1024   30.2
1020   30.1
1016   30.0
1012   29.9
1008   29.8
1004   29.7
1000   29.5
996   29.4
992   29.3
988   29.2
984   29.1
980   29.0
976   28.9
972   28.8
  28.7

—— January Isobars
—— July Isobars

AGRICULTURE ⒹD

Arable Land
Permanent Pasture
Upland Pasture
Moorland, Heath and Bog

W Wheat   B Barley
O Oats   P Potatoes
Fr Fruit   F Flax
      H Hops

Projection: Conical with two standard parallels

TYPICAL DEPRESSION ⒺE
3rd May 1964

Based upon the Meteorological Office Weather Charts, with the sanction of the Controller of H.M. Stationery Office.

HOUR OF OBSERVATION
0600h GREENWICH MEAN TIME

BAROMETER
Isobars are drawn for intervals of 4 mb.

WIND
Arrows fly with the wind. A full length feather represents 10 knots and a short feather 5 knots. A solid pennant ◣ represents 50 knots. Calm is indicated by a circle outside the weather symbol. ◯

TEMPERATURE
is given in °C and is shown on the charts by a figure alongside the station circle.

CLOUD SYMBOLS
◯ Clear Sky
◔ Sky ¼ covered
◑ Sky ½ covered
◕ Sky ¾ covered
● Sky covered
⊗ Sky obscured

WEATHER SYMBOLS
● Rain   △ Hail
, Drizzle   ▽ Shower
✶ Snow   ⚡ Thunderstorm
✷ Rain and Snow   ≡ Fog
     ≡ Mist

FRONTS
Warm front on the surface
Cold front on the surface
Occluded Front

TYPICAL ANTICYCLONE ⒻF
5th January 1965

1:45 000 000

COPYRIGHT. GEORGE PHILIP & SON, LTD.

1:5 000 000

20 0 20 40 60 80 miles
20 0 20 40 60 80 100 120 km

MINERALS
- Worked Coalfields
- □ Iron Ore
- ▽ Lead
- + Salt

INDUSTRIAL REGIONS OF LANCASHIRE, YORKSHIRE AND THE MIDLANDS

Leeds
Sheffield
Blackburn
Manchester
Liverpool
Stoke
Derby
Nottingham
Leicester
Birmingham
Coventry
Wolverhampton
Worcester
Northampton

INDUSTRIAL REGIONS

- Iron and Steel, Engineering, etc.
- Cottons, etc.
- Woollens, etc.
- Silk and Rayon
- Chemicals and Glass Products
- Earthenware and Porcelain
- Leather Goods
- Shipbuilding
- Other Unclassified Industries
- ● Centres of Basic Industry
- ○ Other Centres

- Rural Areas
- Moorland
- Principal Railways
- Ship Canal

INDUSTRIAL REGIONS OF THE NORTH-EAST COALFIELD

Scale of Insets
1:1 500 000

0 25 km
0 25 miles

The colours show the chief industries and the districts where they occur. Other industries are found in these districts, including new light industries, but in some areas coal mining still predominates.

Newcastle

COPYRIGHT GEORGE PHILIP & SON LTD.

Extension Northwards on same scale

The metropolitan counties of England and their populations are:—

1. Greater London 6 970 100
2. Greater Manchester 2 674 800
3. Merseyside 1 561 800
4. South Yorkshire 1 304 000
5. Tyne and Wear 1 174 000
6. West Midlands 2 729 900
7. West Yorkshire 2 072 500

In Scotland:—
Central Clydeside Conurbation 1 807 017

DENSITY OF POPULATION

per mile²	per km²
under 16	under 6
16– 32	6–12
32– 64	12–25
64–128	25–50
128–256	50–100
256–512	100–200
over 512	over 200

■ ● Towns with over 500 000 inhabitants
■ ● Towns with 100–500 000 inhabitants

GREATER LONDON, shown by boundary, ------ has a population of over 7 million

West from Greenwich 0 East from Greenwich

Projection: Conical with two standard parallels.

1:1 000 000

Motorways
Motorways under construction

West from Greenwich   East from Greenwich

1:1 000 000

SCILLY ISLES
on same scale

Isles of Scilly

Projection: Conical with two standard parallels

West from Greenwich

COPYRIGHT GEORGE PHILIP & SON, LTD

1:1 000 000

10 0 10 20 miles
10 0 10 20 30 km

Cardigan

Bay

BRISTOL CHANNEL

The Skerries
Carmel Head
Wylfa Head
Amlwch
Cemaes Bay
Llanfechell
128
Parys Mt.
Moelfre
Dulas B.
Red Wharf B.
Holyhead
Holyhead B.
Holy I.
Valley
Bodedern
Pentraeth
Gwalchmai
Llangefni
Anglesey
Beaumaris
Llanfaelog
Aberffraw
Gaerwen
Menai Bridge
Bangor
Newborough
Port Dinorwic
Malltraeth B.
Caernarfon
Menai Str.
Waenfawr
Caernarfon Bay
Pen-y-groes
Clynnog fawr
Snowdon
1085
Llanllyfni
Llanaelhaiarn
564
Nefyn
Tudweiliog
Llŷn Peninsula
Llanystumdwy
Porthmadog
Criccieth
Pwllheli
Llanbedrog
Aber-soch
St. Tudwal's Is.
Rhiw
Porth Neigwl
Tremadog Bay
Llanbedr
Llanddwyn
Bardsey Sd.
Braich-y-pwll
Trwyn Cilan
Bardsey I.

Puffin I.
Gt. Ormes Hd.
Lt. Ormes Hd.
Llandudno
Deganwy
Conwy
Penmaenmawr
Llanfairfechan
Conway B.
Rhos on Sea
Colwyn Bay
Colwyn
Abergele
Rhyl
Prestatyn
Rhuddlan
Mostyn
Holywell
St. Asaph
Henllan
Denbigh
Llansannan
Bylchau
Ruthin
Llanarmon
Minera
Cerrigydrudion
Gwyddelwern
CLWYD
Corwen
Glyn Ceiriog
Llangollen
Berwyn Mts.
Llanrhaeadr-ym-
Llangynog
827
L. Vyrnwy
Llanfyllin
Vyrnwy
Guilsfield
Welshpool
Oswestry
Whittington
Ellesmere
Chirk
Overton
Chirbury
Market Drayton
Wem
Shrewsbury
SHROPSHIRE
Westbury
407
The Wrekin
Wellington
Coalbrookdale
Ironbridge
Much Wenlock
The Long Mynd
Wenlock Edge
Clee Hills

LIVERPOOL
Bootle
St. Helens
Newton le Willows
New Brighton
Wallasey
Huyton
Warrington
Hoylake
Birkenhead
MERSEYSIDE
Garston
Widnes
Runcorn
West Kirby
Port Sunlight
Bebington
Neston
Ellesmere Port
Frodsham
Northwich
Chester
CHESHIRE
Tarporley
Winsford
Nantwich
Whitchurch
Audlem

GWYNEDD
Ffestiniog
Blaenau Ffestiniog
Trawsfynydd
853
Bala
Dolgellau
Cader Idris
893
Barmouth
Fairbourne
Llwyngwril
Tywyn
Aberdovey
Dovey
Machynlleth
Corris
Carno
Llanidloes
762
Plynlimon
Aberystwyth
Rheidol
Devil's Bridge
Ystwyth
POWYS
Rhayader
Elan Village
Llandrindod Wells
Builth Wells
Brecon
Black Mountains
886
Brecon Beacons
Merthyr Tydfil
Aberdare
Rhondda
MID GLAMORGAN
Pontypridd
Caerphilly
CARDIFF
Barry
Penarth
Newport
GWENT
Pontypool
Abergavenny
Monmouth
Chepstow
Ross on Wye
Hereford
HEREFORD AND WORCESTER
Ludlow
Leominster
Knighton

Fishguard
Strumble Hd.
Goodwick
St. David's Hd.
Ramsey I.
St. Brides Bay
Skomer I.
Skokholm I.
Milford Haven
Pembroke
Haverfordwest
Narberth
Carmarthen
DYFED
Cardigan
New Quay
Aberaeron
Llandovery
Lampeter
Tregaron
Llandeilo
Llanelli
Swansea
Neath
WEST GLAMORGAN
Port Talbot
Gower
Mumbles
Porthcawl
Bridgend
SOUTH GLAMORGAN
Cowbridge
Barry
BRISTOL
AVON
Weston-super-Mare
Mendip Hills
Bridgwater Bay

Motorways
Motorways under construction

Projection: Conical with two standard parallels
West from Greenwich
COPYRIGHT GEORGE PHILIP & SON LTD.
Based upon the Ordnance Survey Map with the permission of the Controller of Her Majesty's Stationery Office. Crown Copyright Reserved.

ft m
3000 1000
2400 800
1800 600
1200 400
600 200
300 100
0 0
50 150
100 300
m ft

DUMFRIES AND GALLOWAY

G a l l o w a y

New Luce
Sandhead
Luce
Bay
Port Logan
Drummore
Mull of
Galloway

Newton
Stewart
Minnigaff
Creetown
Gatehouse
of Fleet
Wigtown
Kirkinner
Whauphill
Sorbie
Garlieston
The
Machars
Port William
Whithorn
Isle of Whithorn
Burrow Hd.

Ken
710

Laurieston
Ringford
Kirkcudbright
Dundrennan

Corsock
Crocketford
Haugh of
Urr
Castle
Douglas
Dalbeattie
Kirkcudbright B.

Maxwelltown
Collin
Bankend
Ruthwell
New
Abbey
Caulkerbush
Criffell
569
Kirkbean

Dumfries
Dalton
Eaglesfield
Gretna
Gretna
Green

Kirk
Kirkfield

Kirkcudbright

S o l w a y   F i r t h

Silloth
Kirkbride
Newton
Arlosh
Abbey
Town
Beckfoot
Allonby
Crosby
Aspatria
Maryport
Fothergill
Flimby
Seaton
Workington
Harrington
Distington
Parton
Whitehaven
St. Bees Head
St. Bees

Ellen
Dearham
Cockermouth
Bassenthwaite
L.

Canonbie
Roadhead

HADRIAN'S WALL

Longtown
Smithfield
Gilsland
Greenhead
Brampton
Carlisle
Cumwhinton
Wigton
Red Dial
Thursby
Caldew
High Hesket
Croglin
Mealsgate
Bothel
High Pike
658
Coldbeck
Greystoke
Skiddaw
931
Threlkeld
Keswick
Greta

I R I S H

S E A

The
Skerries
Carmel Head
Holyhead
Holyhead B.
Holy I.

ft   m
3000   1000
2400   800
1800   600
1200   400
600   200
300   100
50   150
0   0
m   ft

Motorways
Motorways under construction

1:1 000 000

10   0   10   20 miles
10   0   10   20   30 km

Continuation Northwards on same scale

NORTH SEA

TYNE AND WEAR
Whitley Bay
Tynemouth
South Shields
Jarrow
Gateshead
Sunderland
Washington
Houghton le Spring
Seaham
Murton
Easington Colliery
Horden
Peterlee
Hartlepool

Darlington
Billingham
Stockton on Tees
Middlesbrough
Redcar
Marske by the Sea
Saltburn by the Sea
Staithes
Kettle Ness
Hinderwell
Lythe
Whitby
Robin Hood's Bay

CLEVELAND
Guisborough
Eston
Loftus
Howsker

Cleveland Hills
454

North York Moors
Fylingdales Moor
Eller Beck Bridge
Rosedale Abbey
Saltergate
Hayburn Wyke
Cloughton
Scalby Ness
Scarborough

YORKSHIRE
Northallerton
Hambleton Hills
Helmsley
Pickering
Vale of Pickering
Malton
Filey Bay
Flamborough
Flamborough Head

Ripon
Harrogate
Knaresborough
York
Stamford Bridge
Driffield
Bridlington
Bridlington Bay

Skipsea
Beeford
Hornsea

HUMBERSIDE
Beverley
Leven
Aldbrough
Hornsea
Holderness
Withernsea

LEEDS
Pudsey
WEST YORKSHIRE
Castleford
Pontefract
Wakefield
Goole
HULL
Hessle
Hedon
Paull
Burstwick
Keyingham
Patrington
Easington
Spurn Hd.

Barnsley
SOUTH YORKSHIRE
Rotherham
SHEFFIELD
Doncaster
Mexborough
Conisbrough
Scunthorpe
Barton upon Humber
New Holland
Barrow upon Humber
Immingham
Keelby
Stallingborough
Great Grimsby
Cleethorpes
Mouth of the Humber
Donna Nook

DERBYSHIRE
Chesterfield
Bolsover
Clay Cross
Matlock
Sutton in Ashfield
Mansfield
Worksop
East Retford
Gainsborough

LINCOLNSHIRE
Caistor
Market Rasen
Louth
Mablethorpe
Sutton-on-Sea
Alford
Lincoln
Horncastle
Skegness
Ingoldmells Pt.
Spilsby
Boston

NOTTINGHAM
Newark on-Trent
Southwell
Arnold
Carlton
Grantham
Sleaford

The Wash

NORFOLK
Hunstanton
Brancaster
Burnham Market
Wells
Holt
Cley

Continuation Map (Northwards)

Berwick on Tweed
Tweedmouth
Holy I.
Budle Bay
Farne Is.
Bamburgh
Seahouses
Beadnell
Embleton

BORDERS
Coldstream
Kelso
Jedburgh
The Cheviot
816

NORTHUMBERLAND
Wooler
Alnwick
Alnmouth
Rothbury
Morpeth
Ashington
Newbiggin
Bedlington
Blyth
Cramlington
Bellingham
Otterburn

Peel Fell
602

Sighty Crag
519

HADRIAN'S WALL
Hexham
Prudhoe
NEWCASTLE UPON TYNE
Tynemouth
South Shields
Wallsend
Jarrow
TYNE AND WEAR
Gateshead
Sunderland
Washington
Houghton le Spring
Stanley
Consett
Chester le Street
Hetton le Hole
Durham
516

West from Greenwich   East from Greenwich

1:2 500 000

SCOTLAND

NORTHUMBERLAND

CUMBRIA

TYNE & WEAR

DURHAM

CLEVELAND

NORTH YORKSHIRE

ISLE OF MAN

IRISH SEA

NORTH SEA

LANCASHIRE

WEST YORKSHIRE

HUMBERSIDE

MERSEYSIDE

GREATER MANCHESTER

SOUTH YORKSHIRE

CHESHIRE

DERBY

NOTTS

LINCOLNSHIRE

GWYNEDD

CLWYD

STAFFORDSHIRE

LEICESTER

NORFOLK

POWYS

SHROPSHIRE

WEST MIDLANDS

WARWICK

NORTHAMPTON

CAMBRIDGESHIRE

SUFFOLK

DYFED

HEREFORD & WORCESTER

BEDFORD

ESSEX

WALES

GWENT

GLOUCESTER

OXFORD

BUCKS

HERTFORD

MID GLAMORGAN

W. GLAMORGAN

S. GLAMORGAN

AVON

BERKS

SURREY

KENT

WILTSHIRE

HAMPSHIRE

WEST SUSSEX

EAST SUSSEX

SOMERSET

DORSET

DEVON

I. OF WIGHT

CORNWALL

ENGLISH CHANNEL

Projection: Conical with two standard parallels

West from Greenwich 0 East from Greenwich

COPYRIGHT.
GEORGE PHILIP & SON. LTD

1 : 2 500 000

Towns underlined in Northern Ireland give their names to the Districts in which they stand

The remaining Districts are:-
1 Fermanagh   5 Castlereagh
2 Moyle   6 Ards
3 Newtownabbey 7 Newry & Mourne
4 North Down   8 Down

SHETLAND IS.
On same scale

NORTHERN IRELAND

IRELAND

DONEGAL

MONAGHAN

CAVAN

LEITRIM

SLIGO

MAYO

ROSCOMMON

LONGFORD

WESTMEATH

MEATH

DUBLIN

CONNACHT

GALWAY

CLARE

OFFALY

LAOIS

KILDARE

WICKLOW

CARLOW

KILKENNY

TIPPERARY

LIMERICK

KERRY

CORK

WATERFORD

WEXFORD

LEINSTER

MUNSTER

ATLANTIC OCEAN

NORTH SEA

ENGLAND

SCOTLAND

HIGHLAND

GRAMPIAN

TAYSIDE

FIFE

LOTHIAN

STRATHCLYDE

BORDERS

DUMFRIES AND GALLOWAY

ORKNEY

WESTERN ISLES

Inner Hebrides

Outer Hebrides

North Channel

West from Greenwich

Projection: Conical with two standard parallels.

COPYRIGHT GEORGE PHILIP & SON. LTD.

1:1 000 000

10   0   10   20 miles
10   0   10   20   30 km

NORTH

SEA

Motorways.
Motorways under construction

SHETLAND ISLANDS
on same scale

SHETLAND

Projection : Conical with two standard parallels

1:1 000 000

10   0   10   20 mjles
10   0   10   20   30 km

IRISH SEA

WESTMEATH
L. Iron
L. Owel
Mullingar
Royal Canal
L. Ennell
The Downs
Delvin
Athboy
Trim
Killucan
Dunshaughlin
Summerhill
Rathmolyon
Dunboyne
Clonee
Ward
Finglas
Glasnevin
Clontarf
Howth
Howth Hd.
Irelands Eye
DUBLIN
DUBLIN (Baile Atha Cliath)
Malahide
Portmarnock
Baldoyle
Donabate
Swords
Cloghran
Balbriggan
Skerries
Lusk
Rush
Lambay I.
Naul
Ardcath

Clara
Tullamore
Daingean (Philipstown)
OFFALY
Bog of Allen
Grand Canal
Portarlington
Barrow
KILDARE
Kildare
Monasterevan
Droichead Nua (Newbridge)
Naas
Clane
Celbridge
Lucan
Clondalkin
Liffey
Dundrum
Blackrock
Dún Laoghaire (Dunleary)
Dalkey
Killiney
Bray
Bray Head
Greystones
Gt. Sugar Loaf
504
Newtownmountkennedy
Newcastle

LEINSTER
LAOIS
Port Laoise
Mountrath
Castletown
Stradbally
Athy
Kilkea
Moone
Timolin
Ballitore
Dunlavin
Hollywood
Donard
Poulaphouca Res.
Kilcullen
Ballymore Eustace
Sally Gap
Roundwood
Laragh
Annamoe
Glendalough
Wicklow Mountains
Lugnaquilla 926
WICKLOW
Vartry Res.
Ballinaclash
Rathnew
Wicklow
Wicklow Hd.
Glenealy
Kilbride
Rathdrum
Avoca
Mizen Hd.
Wooden Br.
Glenart Castle
Arklow
Arklow Hd.
Kilmichael Pt.
607

Abbeyleix
Ballylynan
Castledermot
Arless
Ballickmoyler
Rathvilly
Hacketstown
Knockananna
Aughrim
Tinahely
Shillelagh
Coolgreany
Wicklow Gap
Coolattin

CARLOW
Carlow
Tullow
Clonmore
Ballon
Kildavin
Craanford
Carnew
Gorey
Courtown
Riverchapel
Camolin
Ballycanew
Ballygarrett
Cahore Pt.

KILKENNY
Kilkenny
Kilmanagh
Callan
Kells
Windygap
Kilmaganny
Bennettsbridge
Gowran
Graiguenamanagh
Thomastown
Inistioge
Muine Bheag (Bagenalstown)
Borris
Goresbridge
Mt. Leinster 796
Ballymurphy
Kiltealy
734
Bunclody (Newtownbarry)
Ballycarney
Ballindaggin
Enniscorthy
519 Blackstairs Mt.
Vinegar Hill
Rathnure
Glynn
Ballywilliam
Clonroche
WEXFORD
Blackwater
Ford
Oilgate
Castlebridge

New Ross
Ballynabola
Foulksmills
Taghmon
Wellington Bridge
Killurin
Wexford Harbour
Wexford
Rosslare
Rosslare Harbour
Greenore Pt.
Broadway
Tuskar Rock
Churchtown
Carnsore Pt.
Lady's I. Lake
Tacumshin L.
Saltee Is.
Bridgetown
Killinick

Comeragh Mts. 755
Clonmel
Carrick-on-Suir
Carrickbeg
Portlaw
Kilmeaden
Waterford
Passage East
Cheekpoint
Arthurstown
Duncormick
Kilmore Quay
Bannow Bay
Baginbun Hd.
Fethard
Tintern Abbey
Dunmore East
Tramore
Tramore Bay
Brownstown Hd.
Hook Hd.
Waterford Harbour

Monavullagh Mts. 792
WATERFORD
Kilmacthomas
Annestown
Bunmahon
Knockmahon
Stradbally
Abbeyside
Dungarvan Harbour
Helvick Hd.
Ringville
Ardmore
Ardmore Head
Mine Hd.

Continuation North-West on same scale

Broad Haven
Benwee Hd.
Portacloy
Belderg
Downpatrick Hd.
Lenadoon Pt.
Erris Hd.
Annagh Hd.
An Geata Mór (Binghamstown)
Belmullet
Mullet Pen.
Glenamoy
380
Killala B.
Ross
Killala
Inniscrone
Crockets Town
Ballina
Bunnyconnellan
Ox Mts.
Foxford
Callow

Inishkea North
Inishkea South
Fallmore
Blacksod Pt.
Blacksod Bay
Saddle Hd.
Ballycroy
Carrowmore L.
Bellacorick
Crossmolina
Belville
Deel
L. Conn
L. Cullin
Lahardaun
Nephin 806
Beltra
Strade
Bellavary
Bohola

Achill Hd.
Dooagh
Keel
Slievemore 672
Castlehill
714
Nephin Beg Range
L. Feeagh
L. Beltra
Mulranny
Newport B.
Newport
Castlebar
Kiltamagh
Manulla
Balla
Dooega
Achill I.
Corraun Pen.
Achill Sd.
Achillbeg I.
Clare I.
Clew Bay
Westport B.
Westport
Croaghpatrick 765
MAYO
Killavally
Ballyglass
L. Carra
Ballyhmount
Louisburgh
Caher I.
Inishturk
Killadoon
Cregganbaun
Sheefry Hills
Partry Mts.
Lough Mask
Ballinrobe
Kilmaine
Inishbofin
Killary Har.
Mweelrea 819
Aasleagh
Glennagevlagh
Joyce's Country
CONNACHT
Carra
Inishshark
Tully Cross
Leenaun
Maam
Lough Corrib
Clonbur
Shrule
Aughrus More
Cleggan
Letterfrack
Maumturk Mts.
730
Benbaun
Clifden
Clifden B.

COPYRIGHT. GEORGE PHILIP & SON. LTD.

1:1 000 000

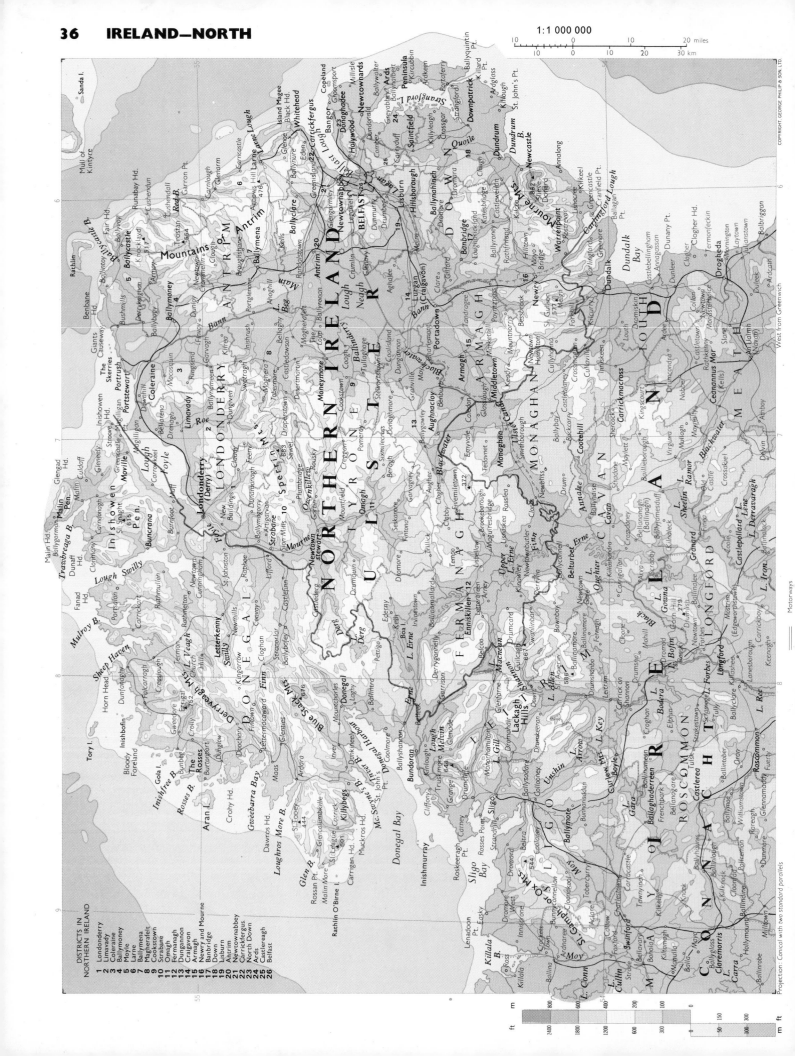

DISTRICTS IN
NORTHERN IRELAND

1 Londonderry
2 Limavady
3 Coleraine
4 Ballymoney
5 Moyle
6 Larne
7 Ballymena
8 Magherafelt
9 Cookstown
10 Strabane
11 Omagh
12 Fermanagh
13 Dungannon
14 Craigavon
15 Armagh
16 Newry and Mourne
17 Banbridge
18 Down
19 Lisburn
20 Antrim
21 Newtownabbey
22 Carrickfergus
23 North Down
24 Ards
25 Castlereagh
26 Belfast

Projection: Conical with two standard parallels

West from Greenwich

Motorways

1:5 000 000

50   0   50   100 miles
50   0   50   100   150 km

FRANCE

Montpellier · Béziers · Narbonne · Toulouse · Bayonne · Biarritz · Pau · Lourdes · Perpignan · Port Vendres · Port Bou

ANDORRA 3004 · 3356

Gulf of Lions · Gulf of Biscay

PYRENEES · Pamplona · NAVARRA · BASQUE PROVINCES · San Sebastián · Bilbao · Vitoria · Logroño

Barcelona · Badalona · Sabadell · Hospitalet · Gerona · 2224 · Tarragona · Lérida · Huesca · Zaragoza 2316

CATALONIA · **ARAGON** · Calatayud · Teruel 2019

Balearic Islands · Menorca (Minorca) · Mallorca (Majorca) · Palma · Ibiza (Iviza) · Formentera · Cabrera · 1445

Castellón · **Valencia** · Albufera de Valencia · Alicante · Elche · Murcia 2850 · Cartagena · Mar Menor · C. de Palos

SPAIN

OLD CASTILE · Burgos · Valladolid · Palencia · León · Zamora · Salamanca · Ávila · Segovia · Sierra de Gredos 2592 · 2262 · Sierra de la Demanda

NEW CASTILE · **MADRID** · Guadalajara · Cuenca · Serranía de Cuenca · Toledo · Montes de Toledo · Ciudad Real · La Mancha · Albacete

MURCIA · Lorca · Almería 2481 · 1790

ANDALUSIA · Granada · Sierra Nevada 3478 Mulhacén · Guadix · Jaén · Linares · Córdoba · Seville · Jerez · Cádiz · Huelva · Badajoz · Málaga · Marbella · Gibraltar (Br.) · La Línea · Algeciras · Ceuta · Tarifa

EXTREMADURA · Cáceres · Mérida · Don Benito

Sierra Morena · **Guadalquivir**

PORTUGAL

Oporto (Porto) · Coimbra · Lisbon · Setúbal · Évora · Santarém · Braga · Vigo · Viana do Castelo

GALICIA · La Coruña · Santiago de Compostela · Pontevedra · Lugo · Orense · Ferrol · Gijón · Oviedo · Mieres · C. Ortegal · C. Finisterre

ASTURIAS · **Cantabrian Mts.** · Santander · Picos de Europa 2648

BEIRA-ALTA · **BEIRA-BAIXA** · **BEIRA LITORAL** · **ALTO DOURO** · **TRAZ OS MONTES** · **MINHO** · **ALTO ALENTEJO** · **BAIXO ALENTEJO** · **ALGARVE** · **RIBATEJO** · **ESTREMADURA**

Serra da Estrela 1991 · Serra de Monchique 902 · C. de S. Vincent · C. da Roca

ATLANTIC OCEAN

MEDITERRANEAN SEA

Gulf of Cádiz · Strait of Gibraltar

MOROCCO · Tangier (Tanger) · Tetuán

ALGERIA · Algiers · Oran · Mostaganem · Boufarik · Koléa · Blida · El Asnam (Orléansville) 1985 · Bou Ismaïl · Ténès · C. Falcon · Sig

West from Greenwich · East from Greenwich

Projection: Conical with two standard parallels

m ft
5000 / 9000 / 3000 / 6000 / 2000 / 4500 / 1500 / 3000 / 1000 / 1200 / 600 / 400 / 200 / 0 / 200–600
ft m

CHANNEL ISLANDS

1:1 000 000

miles 0 5 10 20
km 0 10 20 30

Over 300 ft. Over 100 m
0–300 ft 0–100 m

The Casquets · Burhou
St. Anné
Alderney

Cap de la Hague
Auderville · St. Germain
Jobourg
Anse de Vauville
Beaumont
Cherbourg
Virandeville 178
Breuville
Diélette
les Pieux
Bricquebec
St. Jacques
Carteret
Barneville
Portbail
Baudreville
Bretteville
St. Germain
Pirau
Gouville

GUERNSEY
Vale · St. Sampson
Herm
St. Martin **St. Peter Port**
Sark
Forest Jerbourg Pt.
Torteval

Ecréhou Rocks

Grosnez Pt.
JERSEY
St. Peter · Trinity · St. Martin
Corbière Pt.
St. Brelade's
Gorey
la Rocque Pt
St. Helier

The Minquiers

Blainville
Coutainville

2 30' West from Greenwich

FRANCE

DEPARTMENTS

1:8 000 000

miles 50 0 50 100
km 50 0 50 100 150

ft m
12 000 · 4000
9000 · 3000
6000 · 2000
4500 · 1500
3000 · 1000
1200 · 400
600 · 200
0 · 0
200 · 600
m · ft

1. VAL d'OISE
2. YVELINES
3. ESSONNE
4. HAUTS-DE-SEINE
5. SEINE-ST. DENIS
6. VAL-DE-MARNE
7. VILLE DE PARIS

ENGLAND
ENGLISH CHANNEL
BELGIUM
PAS DE CALAIS
NORD
LUXEMBOURG
GERMANY
SOMME
SEINE MARITIME
AISNE
ARDENNES
MANCHE
CALVADOS
EURE
OISE
MARNE
MEUSE
MOSELLE
MEURTHE ET MOSELLE
BAS RHIN
CÔTES DU NORD
ORNE
EURE ET LOIR
SEINE ET MARNE
AUBE
HAUTE MARNE
VOSGES
FINISTÈRE
ILLE ET VILAINE
MAYENNE
SARTHE
LOIRET
YONNE
HAUTE SAÔNE
HAUT RHIN
MORBIHAN
MAINE ET LOIRE
INDRE ET LOIRE
LOIRE ET CHER
CÔTE D'OR
BELFORT
LOIRE ATLANTIQUE
CHER
NIÈVRE
DOUBS
VENDÉE
DEUX-SÈVRES
INDRE
SAÔNE ET LOIRE
JURA
SWITZERLAND
VIENNE
ALLIER
AIN
CHARENTE MARITIME
CHARENTE
HAUTE VIENNE
CREUSE
PUY DE DÔME
LOIRE
RHÔNE
HAUTE SAVOIE
BAY OF BISCAY
CORRÈZE
ISÈRE
SAVOIE
DORDOGNE
CANTAL
HAUTE LOIRE
ARDECHE
DRÔME
HAUTES ALPES
ITALY
GIRONDE
LOT
LOZÈRE
ALPES-DE-HAUTE-PROVENCE
ALPES MARITIMES
LOT ET GARONNE
AVEYRON
GARD
VAUCLUSE
MONACO
LANDES
TARN ET GARONNE
TARN
HÉRAULT
BOUCHES DU RHÔNE
VAR
GERS
PYRÉNÉES-ATLANTIQUES
HAUTE GARONNE
AUDE
HAUTES PYRÉNÉES
ARIÈGE
SPAIN
ANDORRA
PYRÉNÉES ORIENTALES
MEDITERRANEAN SEA
HAUTE CORSE
CORSE-DU-SUD

Projection: Conical with two standard parallels
East from Greenwich
West from Greenwich

1 : 2 000 000

10   0   10   20   30   40 miles
10   0 10 20 30 40 50 60 km

NORTH SEA

WESTFRIESCHE EILANDEN

NETHERLANDS

BELGIUM

LUXEMBOURG

GERMANY

FRANCE

Amsterdam · Haarlem · The Hague ('s Gravenhage) · ROTTERDAM · Utrecht · Leiden · Delft · Dordrecht · Arnhem · Nijmegen · Groningen · Leeuwarden · Zwolle · Deventer · Apeldoorn · Enschede · 's Hertogenbosch · Breda · Tilburg · Eindhoven · Venlo · Roermond · Maastricht · Middelburg · Vlissingen (Flushing) · Breda

Antwerp · Ghent · Brussels (Bruxelles) · Mechelen · Leuven · Hasselt · Genk · Liège · Namur · Charleroi · Mons · Tournai · Bruges (Brugge) · Ostend (Ostende) · Roubaix · Lille · Reims

Essen · DORTMUND · Duisburg · Düsseldorf · COLOGNE (Köln) · Bonn · Aachen · Mönchen-Gladbach · Krefeld · Wuppertal · Remscheid · Solingen · Münster · Osnabrück · Oldenburg · Emden · Koblenz · Wiesbaden · Mainz · Saarbrücken · Trier

MOSELLE · RHEINLAND · PFALZ · HUNSRÜCK · WESTERWALD · ARDENNES · PICARDIE · PAS-DE-CALAIS · SOMME · MEUSE · NORD

Projection: Conical with two standard parallels

East from Greenwich

ft   m
1200 400
600   200
0   0

1:2 000 000

Projection: Conical with two standard parallels 7

East from Greenwich

COPYRIGHT. GEORGE PHILIP & SON. LTD.

East from Greenwich

ICELAND
on the same scale
as general map

Seas and Gulfs

GULF OF BOTHNIA
BALTIC SEA
G. of Riga
G. of Gdansk
Skagerrak
Kattegat
The Sound
Store Bælt
Lille Bælt
Sogne Fjord
Hardanger Fjord
Oslo Fjord

Countries and Regions

FINLAND
ESTONIA
L A T V I A
LITHUANIA
R.S.F.S.R.
P O L A N D
G E R M A N Y
NETHERLANDS
D E N M A R K
NORWAY
HÄME
POHJANMAA
SATAKUNTA
UUSIMAA
PORI
TURKU
KOPPARBERG
GÄVLEBORG
VÄRMLAND
ÖREBRO
VÄSTMANLAND
UPPLAND
SÖDERMANLAND
ÖSTERGÖTLAND
JÖNKÖPING
KRONOBERG
KALMAR
BLEKINGE
HALLAND
GOTLAND
GÖTEBORG & BOHUS
ÄLVSBORG
SKARABORG
OPPLAND
BUSKERUD
TELEMARK
AUST-AGDER
VEST-AGDER
ROGALAND
HORDALAND
SOGN & FJORDANE

Cities and Towns

Helsinki (Helsingfors)
Tampere
Turku (Åbo)
Pori
Rauma
Uusikaupunki
Hanko (Hangö)
Tammisaari (Ekenäs)
Kotka
Lovisa
Lahti
Hämeenlinna
Porvoo
Heinola
Tallinn
Rakvere
Haapsalu
Pärnu
Viljandi
Valga
Valmiera
Cēsis
Riga
Jelgava (Mitau)
Tukums
Ventspils
Liepaja
Klaipeda
Kaliningrad
Chernyakhovsk
Sovetsk
Kaunas
Vilnius
Grodno
Białystok
Łomża
Ostrołęka
Gdynia
Gdansk
Elbląg
Grudziadz
Toruń
Bydgoszcz
Szczecin
Koszalin
Słupsk
Kołobrzeg
Stockholm
Uppsala
Västerås
Eskilstuna
Södertälje
Nyköping
Oxelösund
Norrköping
Linköping
Motala
Mjölby
Skövde
Falköping
Örebro
Kumla
Katrineholm
Karlstad
Arvika
Kristinehamn
Filipstad
Hagfors
Falun
Borlänge
Ludvika
Hedemora
Fagersta
Avesta
Sandviken
Gävle
Söderhamn
Hudiksvall
Bollnäs
Ljusdal
Mora
Lidköping
Vänersborg
Trollhättan
Åmål
Mariestad
Alingsås
Borås
Mölndal
Göteborg
Uddevalla
Strömstad
Varberg
Falkenberg
Halmstad
Ängelholm
Helsingborg
Landskrona
Lund
Malmö
Trelleborg
Ystad
Kristianstad
Karlshamn
Karlskrona
Växjö
Ljungby
Värnamo
Nässjö
Tranås
Jönköping
Huskvarna
Vetlanda
Oskarshamn
Västervik
Ulricehamn
Kalmar
Nybro
Visby
Oslo
Drammen
Kongsberg
Hønefoss
Hamar
Lillehammer
Gjøvik
Kongsvinger
Halden
Sarpsborg
Fredrikstad
Moss
Tønsberg
Sandefjord
Larvik
Skien
Porsgrunn
Kragerø
Risør
Arendal
Grimstad
Lillesand
Kristiansand
Mandal
Farsund
Flekkefjord
Egersund
Sandnes
Stavanger
Haugesund
Kopervik
Odda
Bergen
Flåm
Copenhagen
Roskilde
Helsingør
Køge
Næstved
Slagelse
Korsør
Svendborg
Nykøbing
Nakskov
Odense
Nyborg
Kolding
Vejle
Fredericia
Horsens
Aarhus
Randers
Silkeborg
Herning
Viborg
Skive
Aalborg
Hjørring
Frederikshavn
Thisted
Esbjerg
Ribe
Aabenraa
Sønderborg
Flensburg
Kiel
Lübeck
Hamburg
Bremen
Bremerhaven
Cuxhaven
Wilhelmshaven
Oldenburg
Emden
Groningen
Rostock
Wismar
Schwerin
Greifswald
Stralsund
Rønne
Bornholm
Öland
Gotland

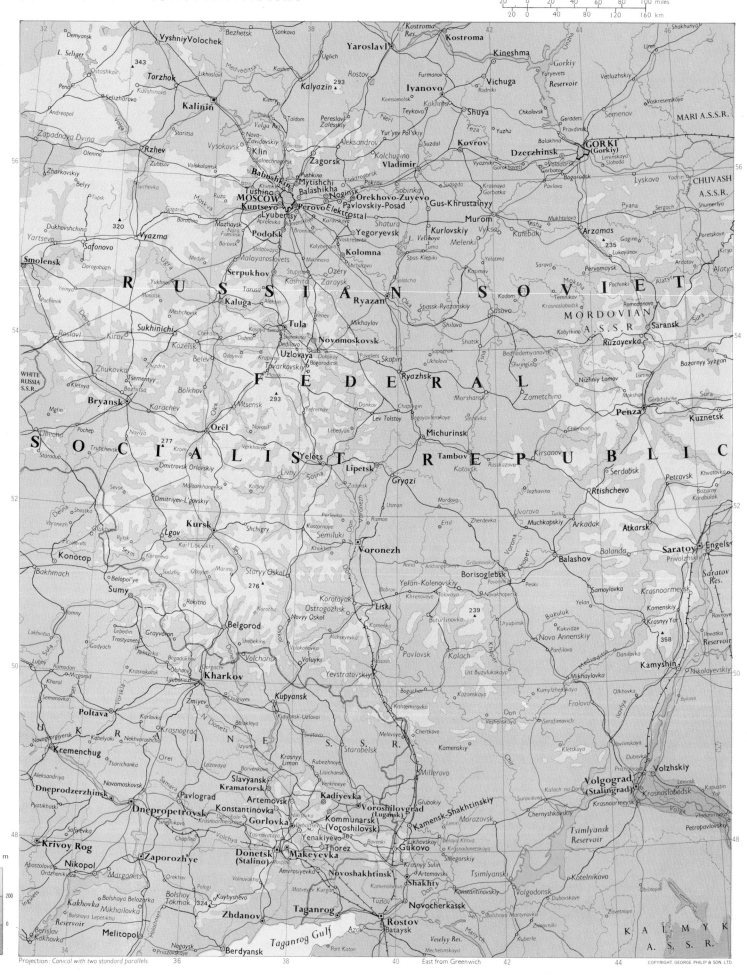

1:5 000 000

1:50 000 000

250   200   0   250   500   750   1000 miles
200   0   200   400   600   800 1000 1200 1400 1600 km

ARCTIC OCEAN

PACIFIC OCEAN

INDIAN OCEAN

Tropic of Cancer

Equator

East from Greenwich

Arctic Circle

Siberia

Japan

Mongolia

Gobi

Tibet

Himalaya

Takla Makan

Kirgiz Steppe

Kyzyl Kum

Kara Kum

Iran

Thal

Deccan

Great Arabian Desert

Rub' al Khali

Ural Mountains

Philippine Is.

East Indies Archipelago

Wallace Line

Projection Bonne

FOREST VEGETATION

Tropical Rain Forest (dipterocarpus, palms, arborescent and climbing ferns, lianas, bamboos, orchids, epiphytes, mangrove swamp forest on coast).

Monsoon Tropophilous Woodland and Open Jungle (eng forest, pyinkado (ironwood), teak, sal, banyan, sandalwood, lianas, bamboos, orchids, jungle, epiphytes; in eastern parts of East Indies, casuarina and eucalyptus).

Sub-tropical and Temperate Rain Forest (evergreen oaks, lauraceae, camellia, tea, magnolia, rhododendrons, crystomeria, arborescent ferns, palms, wistaria, lianas, bamboos, orchids, epiphytes).

Broad-leaved Deciduous Forest and Meadow (oaks, beech, maple, walnut, chestnut, paper mulberry, syringa, ferns, dwarf bamboos).

Temperate Mountain Forest (mainly coniferous, fir, pine, spruce, larch; sometimes at lower altitudes mixed with oak, chestnut, maple, birch; in North-West India, deodar)

Taiga or Northern Coniferous Forest—
(A) West Siberian Forest (Siberian fir, stone pine, spruce, silver fir, Siberian larch).
(B) East Siberian Forest (Siberian fir, eastern larch, stone pine).
(C) South-East Siberian Transitional Forest (eastern larch, Siberian fir, ayan pitch-pine, Manchu pine, with oak, elm, maple, walnut, wild apple).

Mediterranean Evergreen Forest (evergreen oak, plane, walnut, hornbeam).

Mediterranean Evergreen Maquis and Meadow (myrtle, box, olive).

Open Jungle and Xerophilous Scrub (teak, babul, acacia, tamarisk, tamarind, euphorbia).

Oases and Euphrates and Tigris Valleys.

GRASS VEGETATION

Transitional Zone of Wooded Steppe.

Temperate Grasslands and Steppe (stipa grass)

Savanna.

High Steppe (South-West Asia)

Steppe

Marsh Vegetation

DRY STEPPE & DESERT

Salt Steppe and Semi-desert (artemisia, saxaul, acacia, tamarisk).

Gobi and Central Asiatic Deserts (artemisia).

High Plateau Steppe and Desert (palaeoarctic vegetation).

Desert

Tundra (moss, lichen, heather bog, dwarf willow, birch and alder).

Alpine (ice desert).

Northern Limits of Siberian Larch (larix sibirica).

Limits of Date Palm (phœnix dactylifera).

Limits of Teak (tectona grandis).

Northern Limits of Palms.

Seas and Lakes frozen in Winter.

ANNUAL RAINFALL
1:80 000 000

mm		inches
3000		120
2000		80
1000		40
500		20
250		10

DENSITY OF POPULATION
1:80 000 000

Inhabitants	per mile²	per km²
	under 2	under 1
	2– 16	1– 6
	16– 32	6– 12
	32– 64	12– 25
	64–128	25– 50
	128–256	50–100
	256–512	100–200
	over 512	over 200

■ Towns of over
500 000 inhabitants

Projection: Bonne   East from Greenwich

ft	m
18 000	6000
12 000	4000
6000	2000
3000	1000
1200	400
600	200
0	0
200	600
2000	6000
4000	12 000
6000	18 000
m	ft

1:40 000 000

200   0   200   400   600   800   1000 miles
200   0   200   400   600   800 1200   1600 km

ARCTIC OCEAN

Svalbard
Fr. Josef Land
Severnaya
Zemlya
C. Dezhneva
(East C.)
Bering Str.

Bear I.
Novaya Zemlya
Kara Sea
C. Chelyuskin
Taimyr Peninsula
Byrrang Mts.
Laptev Sea
Foddeyev
New Siberian
Is.
Lyakhov Is.
Kotelny
Bear Is.
Wrangel I.
Chukot Ra.
Kamchatka
Peninsula
Komandorskiye
Is.

Barents Sea
Kolguyev
Kola Pen.
White Sea
Yamal Pen.
Gydan Pen.
G. of Ob
Putoran Mts.
Central
Siberian
Plateau
Lower Tunguska
Stony Tunguska
Olenek
Kolyma
Plain
Kolyma (Kolyma)
Indigirka
Cherskiy Ra.
3147
Verkhoyansk Ra.
Koryak Ra.
2562
Sredinny Ra.
4750
7999
Sea of
Okhotsk

N. Dvina
Pechora
West
Siberian
Plain
Narodnaya
1894
Ob
Ob
Yenisey
Angara
Lena
Aldan
Stanovoy Ra.
2482
Shantar Is.
Dzhugdzhur Ra.
Sakhalin
10.542
Hokkaido

Ural Mountains
Kama
Ural
Tobol
Irtysh
Eastern Sayan
Western Sayan
L. Baikal
496
Yablonovyy Ra.
2999
Amur
Hsiao Khingan Shan
Ta Khingan Shan
Manchurian
Plain
Khanka
Sungari
Reservoir
2744
2290
Tartary Str.
La Pérouse Str.
Sikhote Alin Ra.
Kuril Islands
Tsugaru Str.
Japan
Honshu
Fuji Yama
3776
Sea of
Japan

Yaman Tau
1640
Kirgiz Steppe
Belukha
4506
Altai
3957
Plateau of
Mongolia
Gobi
Selenga
Hsi-liao
G. of
Chihli
Shantung Pen.
Korea
Korea Str.
Shikoku
Kyushu
10.554

Aral Sea
Ust-Urt
Plateau
Muyun Kum
Syr Darya
I. Balkhash
342
Ili
Chu
L. Issyk-Kul
Tien Shan
7439
Turfan
Basin
154
Lop
Nor
Tarim
Tarim Basin
Takla Makan
Altyn Tagh
7723
Tsaidam
Nan Shan
6346
Koko
Nor
Ala Shan
Ordos
Plateau
3015
2894
Hwang-Ho
Great Plain of China
Yellow
Sea
East
China
Sea
Ryukyu Islands
7507
Tropic of Cancer

Turanian Plain
Kyzyl Kum
Amu-Darya
Kara Kum
Communism Pk.
7495
Pamirs
Hindu Kush
7789
8611
Karakoram Ra.
8126
Kunlun Shan
Plateau of
Tibet
Nam Tso
7756
Bayan Kara Shan
Minya
Konka
7590
Chinling Shan
4107
Red
Basin
Tung-Ting L.
Poyang
L.
Nan Shan
Wu-i Shan
2710
Formosa
3897
Formosa Str.
7559
Bashi Chan.
Bobuyan Is.

Helmand
5143
8126
Himalaya
8221
Everest
8848
Kanchenjunga
8598
Brahmaputra
Tsangpo
Asam
Hills
Khasi Hills
3143
Yangtze-kiang
Si-kiang
Ta Liang Shan
Luzon
2828
Philippine
Islands
Samar

Sulaiman Ra.
Chenab
Sutlej
Indus
Indo-Gangetic
Plain
Ganga
Yamuna
Chambal
Aravalli Ra.
Mt. Victoria
3053
Arakan Yoma
Salween
Irrawaddy
Mekong
3280
G. of
Tonkin
Hainan
South
China
Sea
5245
Mindoro
Panay
Negros
Cape Johnson Deep
10.497
8054
Mindanao

Saihan Ra.
Thar
India
Vindhya Mts.
Narmada
Satpura Ra.
Godavari
Ganges
Delta
Ganges
Arakan Yoma
G. of
Martaban
Andaman
Sea
Phanom Dong
Rak Tonle
Sap
G. of
Siam
Ca Mau Pt.
Mt. Apo
2954
Sulu Sea
5576
5842
Morotai
Halmahera

Oman
Ras al Hadd
Krishna
Deccan
Western Ghats
Eastern Ghats
Coromandel
Coast
Bay of
Bengal
Andaman Is.
Isthmus of
Kra
Malay
Peninsula
Natuna
Kinabalu
4101
Celebes
Celebes Sea
New
Guinea

Arabian
Sea
Laccadive
Is.
Malabar Coast
Anai
Mudi
2698
Palk Str.
G. of Mannar
Ceylon
Pidurutalagala
2524
Dondra Head
Nicobar Is.
Tenasserim
Ca Mau Pt.
Borneo
5123
Makasar Str.
Buru
7440
Ceram
Banda
Sea
Arafura
Sea

5875
C. Comorin
Maldive
Is.
Str. of Malacca
3466
Sumatra
3800
Sunda Islands
6073
Java
Sumatra
Java Sea
Semeru
3676
Bali
Lombok
3726
Sumbawa
5123
Flores
Sumba
Timor

DIAN OCEAN
Chagos Arch.
Equator
East Indies
Celebes
Australia

East from 80 Greenwich

COPYRIGHT. GEORGE PHILIP & SON. LTD.

RAINFALL
November to April

mm	inches
2000	80
1500	60
1000	40
750	30
500	20
250	10
125	5

1016 January Isobars
in millibars
→ Prevailing Winds

RAINFALL
May to October

mm	inches
2000	80
1500	60
1000	40
750	30
500	20
250	10
125	5

1016 July Isobars
in millibars
→ Prevailing Winds

Projection: Bonne   East from Greenwich

EVOLUTION OF

1:100 000 000

	mm	inches
MONTHLY	400	16
	200	8
RAINFALL	100	4
	50	2
	25	1

DECEMBER

JANUARY

FEBRUARY

MARCH

APRIL

MAY

1:80 000 000

| 400 | 0 | 400 | 800 | 1200 | 1600 miles |
| 400 | 0 | 400 | 800 1200 1600 | 2000 | 2400 km |

HE MONSOON

| 0 | 500 | 1000 | 1500 | 2000 miles |
| 600 | 0 | 500 1000 1500 | 2500 | 3000 km |

—— Isotherms
reduced to Sea-level °Celsius

1016 Isobars in millibars

→ Winds

JUNE

JULY

AUGUST

SEPTEMBER

OCTOBER

NOVEMBER

ACTUAL SURFACE TEMPERATURE

°C	°F
30	86
20	68
10	50
0	32
-10	14
-20	4
-30	-22
-40	-40

JANUARY TEMPERATURE

—— Isotherms
reduced to Sea-level
°Celsius

ACTUAL SURFACE TEMPERATURE

°C	°F
30	86
20	68
10	50
0	32
-10	14

JULY TEMPERATURE

—— Isotherms
reduced to Sea-level
°Celsius

East from 80 Greenwich

COPYRIGHT GEORGE PHILIP & SON. LTD

Ural Mts. Caucasus Elburz Hindu Kush Tien Shan Pamirs Kunlun Himalaya Yablonovyj Ra. Khingan Deccan Arctic Circle Tropic of Cancer Equator

R.S.F.S.R.
1. Daghestan A.S.S.R.
2. Kabardino–Balkar A.S.S.R.
3. Mari A.S.S.R.
4. Mordovian A.S.S.R.
5. North Ossetian A.S.S.R.
6. Tatar A.S.S.R.
7. Udmurt A.S.S.R.
8. Chuvash A.S.S.R.
9. Checheno–Ingush A.S.S.R.
AZERBAIJAN
10. Nakhichevan A.S.S.R.
GEORGIA
11. Abkhaz A.S.S.R.
12. Adzhar A.S.S.R.

1:20 000 000

100   0   100   200   300   400   500 miles
100   0   200   400   600   800 km

80   90   100   110   120   130   140   150   170

OCEAN

Laptev Sea

East Siberian Sea

Chukchi Sea

C. Dezhneva (East C.)

Gulf of Anadyr

St. Lawrence I. (U.S.A.)

Wrangel I.

De Long Is.

Henrietta I.

Bennett I.

New Siberian Is.

Faddeyev I.

New Siberia

Medvezhi Is.

Shmidt I.

C. Molotov

Komsomolets I.

Pioner I.

October Revolution I.

965

Bolshevik I.

Severnaya Zemlya

Boris Vilkitski Str.

3800

Chukot Range

Koryak Range

Bering Sea

Komandorskye Is.

Kamchatka Pen.

Petropavlovsk-Kamchatskiy

3621

4750

3456

3147

Sea of Okhotsk

1780

Sakhalin

1609

Yuzhno-Sakhalinsk

Sovetskaya Gavan (Soviet Harbour)

Khabarovsk

2078

Komsomolsk

Birobidzhan

Blagoveshchensk

Stanovoy Ra.

2482

2246

Yakutsk

A.S.S.R.

Verkhoyansk

2389

2682

2969

REPUBLIC

Irkutsk

3491

Ulan Ude

B U R Y A T
A.S.S.R.

Chita

1530

Krasnoyarsk

Nizhneudinsk

MONGOLIA

Ulan Bator
(Ulaanbaatar)

2800

3957

1949

4925

G   O   B   I

Peking

Kalgan

2400

Paotow

Shenyang Fushan
(Mukden)

Anshan

Antung

Manchuria

Harbin

Changchun

Szeping

Kirin

Tsitsihar

Vladivostok

Nakhodka

Ussuriysk

NORTH KOREA

Pyongyang

Wonsan

SOUTH KOREA

Soul (Seoul)

Taejon

Pusan

Sea of JAPAN

Hokkaidō

Sapporo

Hakodate

Honshū

Niigata

Kanazawa

Toyama

2290

3669

Lüta (Dairen)

Ingkow

	Boundaries of U.S.S.R.
	Boundaries of S.S.R.
	Boundaries of A.S.S.R.

COPYRIGHT. GEORGE PHILIP & SON. LTD.

1:15 000 000

100 0 100 200 300 miles

100 0 100 200 300 400 500 km

PALESTINE

- - - - - Armistice boundaries between Arab States and Israel, 1949-1967

1:1 500 000

10 0 10 20 30 miles

10 0 10 20 30 40 km

East from Greenwich

COPYRIGHT. GEORGE PHILIP & SON. LTD.

U.S.S.R.

FARYAB BALKH SAMANGAN TAKHAR BADAKHSHAN

BADGHIS HERAT GHOR BAMIAN WARDAK KABUL LOGAR NANGARHAR PESHAWAR KASHMIR

A F G H A N I S T A N

Kabul Peshawar Rawalpindi Islamabad Srinagar

URUZGAN GHAZNI PAKTYA KATTAWAZ-URGUN KHAN DERA ISMAIL KHAN

FARAH HELMAND KANDAHAR ZABUL

Herat Kandahar Quetta

CHAKHANSUR Dasht-i-Margo Registan

Khash Desert

P E R S I A (IRAN)

B A L U C H I S T A N

Makran Coast Range Central Makran Range Siahan Range Kirthar Range

Toba Kakar Hills Chagai Hills Sandy Desert

KHAIRPUR

A R A B I A N S E A

KARACHI Karachi Hyderabad HYDERABAD

PAKISTAN

SARGODHA Lahore LAHORE Amritsar Jullundur Ludhiana HIMACHAL PRADESH

Sialkot Gujranwala Multan BAHAWALPUR PUNJAB Chandigarh Ambala Dehra Dun

RAJASTHAN Bikaner HARYANA DELHI Moradabad Rampur

Great Indian Desert (Thar Desert)

Jodhpur Jaipur Ajmer Agra Gwalior Kanpur Jhansi

Mouths of the Indus Rann of Kutch GUJARAT Little Rann Udaipur

I N D I A (B H A R A T)

Ahmadabad Jamnagar Rajkot Vadodara Ujjain Indore MADHYA PRADESH Bhopal Nagpur

Gulf of Kutch Gulf of Cambay Surat Bharuch Satpura Range

Diu Daman DAMAN, DADRA NAGAR HAVELI Nasik MAHARASHTRA Amraoti Wardha

BOMBAY Thana Pune (Poona) Ahmadnagar Sholapur ANDHRA PRADESH Hyderabad

Kolhapur Sangli Bijapur Gulbarga Belgaum GOA Hubli

Continuation Southwards on same scale

Dharwar Gadag Kurnool Adoni Erramala Hills

GOA Hubli Hospet Bellary KARNATAKA Cuddapah Nellore

Mangalore Bangalore Kolar Gold Fields Vellore Madras

Mysore Salem Pondicherry Cuddalore

Calicut (Kozhikode) Coimbatore TAMIL NADU Thanjavur

KERALA Tiruchchirappalli Karikal Nagappattinam

Ernakulam Madurai Palk Strait Jaffna

Alleppey Rajapalaiyam Palk Bay Trincomalee

Quilon Tirunelveli Gulf of Mannar Adam's Bridge

Trivandrum Nagercoil Cape Comorin

SRI LANKA Colombo Kandy Moratuwa Galle Dondra Head

1:15 000 000

HONSHU, SHIKOKU AND KYUSHU

1:7 500 000

REFERENCE TO PREFECTURES

1 Aomori	16 Tokyo	32 Shimane
2 Akita	17 Saitama	33 Hiroshima
3 Iwate	18 Yamanashi	34 Yamaguchi
4 Yamagata	19 Shizuoka	35 Kagawa
5 Miyagi	20 Aichi	36 Tokushima
6 Fukushima	21 Gifu	37 Kochi
7 Niigata	22 Fukui	38 Ehime
8 Ishikawa	23 Shiga	39 Oita
9 Toyama	24 Mie	40 Fukuoka
10 Nagano	25 Nara	41 Saga
11 Gunma	26 Wakayama	42 Nagasaki
12 Tochigi	27 Osaka	43 Kumamoto
13 Ibaraki	28 Kyoto	44 Miyazaki
14 Chiba	29 Hyogo	45 Kagoshima
15 Kanagawa	30 Tottori	46 Hokkaido
	31 Okayama	

COPYRIGHT. GEORGE PHILIP & SON. LTD.

1:15 000 000

100 0 100 200 300 miles
100 0 100 200 300 400 500 km

PHILIPPINES

LUZON
MANILA

Quezon City

Mindoro
Panay
CEBU
Samar
Leyte
Mindanao
Davao

SULU SEA

CELEBES SEA

BORNEO

SABAH (NORTH BORNEO)
BRUNEI
SARAWAK
Kuching

MALAYSIA
PENINSULAR MALAYSIA
Kuala Lumpur
SINGAPORE

SOUTH CHINA SEA

THAILAND (SIAM)
BANGKOK

BURMA

CAMBODIA
Phnom Penh

LAOS

VIETNAM
HO CHI MINH CITY (SAIGON)
Da Nang (Tourane)

Paracel Islands

Spratly I.

Palawan Islands

SULAWESI (CELEBES)
Menado
Makasar

CERAM SEA
BANDA SEA
Ambon
Buru
Halmahera
MOLUCCAS

Gorontalo

FLORES SEA
Nusa Tenggara
Sumba (Sandalwood)
Sumbawa
Lombok
Bali
Lesser Sunda Islands

Greater Sunda Islands

JAVA
JAKARTA
SURABAYA
Madura
Bandung
Semarang

SUMATRA
Palembang
Padang
Medan

Banda Aceh (Kutaraja)

INDIAN OCEAN

Equator

East from Greenwich

Projection: Mercator

m / ft
6000 4500 3000 1500 1000 600 200 0
2000 1500 1000 400 200 0
ft / m

1:80 000 000

400   0   400   800   1200   1600 miles
400   0   400   800 1200 1600 2000 2400 km

JULY
TEMPERATURE

25°
20°
15°
20°

Atlas Mountains
Ethiopian Highlands
Congo Basin
Drakensberg
Highveld
S a h a r a
35°
25°
25°
25°

Tropic of Cancer
Equator
Tropic of Capricorn

July Isotherms
reduced to Sea-level
°Celsius

January Isotherms
reduced to Sea-level
°Celsius

ACTUAL
SURFACE
TEMPERATURE
°C   °F
35   95
30   86
25   77
20   68
15   59
10   50
5   41
0   32

JANUARY
TEMPERATURE

15°
20°
25°
25°

Atlas Mountains
Ethiopian Highlands
Congo Basin
Drakensberg
Highveld
S a h a r a
30°
35°
25°
20°
15°
20°
25°

Tropic of Cancer
Equator
Tropic of Capricorn

RAINFALL
May to October
(Winter–South of Equator)
1024 July Isobars
       in millibars
→   Prevailing Winds

1000
1000
1004
1008
1012
1016
1020
1024
1020
1016
HIGH
1024
LOW
HIGH

Tropic of Cancer
Equator
Tropic of Capricorn
Atlas Mountains
Ethiopian Highlands
Congo Basin
Drakensberg
Highveld
S a h a r a

RAINFALL
November to April
(Summer–South of Equator)
1012 January Isobars
       in millibars
→   Prevailing Winds

RAINFALL
mm   inches
2000   80
1500   60
1000   40
750   30
500   20
250   10
125   5

HIGH
1020
1016
1012
LOW
800
1016
1012
1016
1020
1016
1012
HIGH
20 1016

Tropic of Cancer
Equator
Tropic of Capricorn
Atlas Mountains
Ethiopian Highlands
Congo Basin
Drakensberg
Highveld
S a h a r a

COPYRIGHT GEORGE PHILIP & SON LTD

Projection: Sanson-Flamsteed's Sinusoidal

1:40 000 000

ANNUAL RAINFALL
1:80 000 000

mm	inches
3000	120
2000	80
1000	40
500	20
250	10

Projection: Lambert's Equivalent Azimuthal

COPYRIGHT. GEORGE PHILIP & SON LTD.

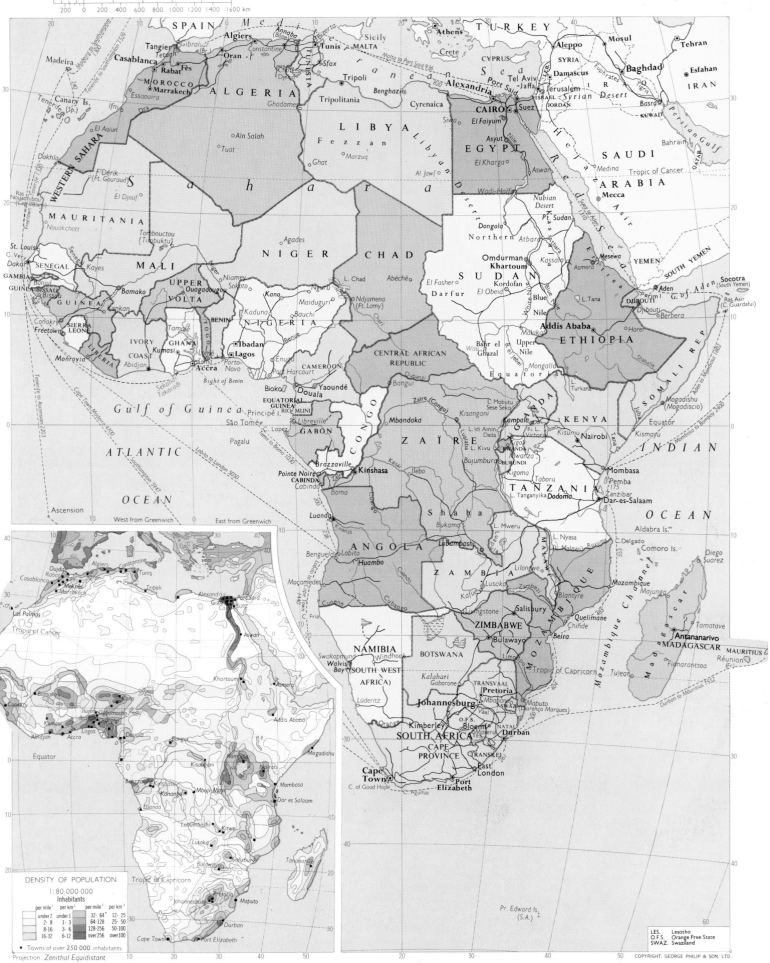

1:40 000 000

200   0   200   400   600   800   1000 miles
200   0   200   400   600   800 1000 1200 1400 1600 km

DENSITY OF POPULATION
1:80 000 000
Inhabitants

per mile²	per km²	per mile²	per km²
under 2	under 1	32- 64	12- 25
2- 8	1- 3	64-128	25- 50
8-16	3- 6	128-256	50-100
16-32	6-12	over 256	over 100

■ Towns of over 250 000 inhabitants

Projection: Zenithal Equidistant

LES.   Lesotho
O.F.S. Orange Free State
SWAZ. Swaziland

1:15 000 000

MEDITERRANEAN SEA

TURKEY

SYRIA

LIBYA

EGYPT

SUDAN

CHAD

CENTRAL AFRICAN REPUBLIC

ETHIOPIA

ZAÏRE

KENYA

SAUDI ARABIA

IRAQ

1:40 000 000

GRASS VEGETATION

Mixed dry Woodland and low Grass Savanna

Tropical Grassland and Savanna, with tall grass and scattered low trees and bushes (baobab, acacia)

Tropical Grassland and Savanna, with low grass

Temperate and Mountain Grassland

Marsh Vegetation

STEPPE AND DESERT VEGETATION

Kalahari Sandveld and Thorn Bush (acacia)

Halfa Grass Steppe and Semi-desert

Karoo Thorn Bush, Steppe (aloe, euphorbia)

Semi-desert with acacia shrubs and bunch grass

Desert Shrub

Salt Desert Shrub

South-West African Namib Desert (occasional succulent shrubs)

Sahara Sandy and Stony Desert with little or no vegetation

Alpine (above Timber Line)

FOREST VEGETATION

Tropical Rain Forest (pandanus, oil palm, rubber, bamboos, tree-ferns, lianas, epiphytes)

Mangrove Swamp Forest

Sub-tropical and Temperate Forest (podocarpus, dum and deleb palm, bananas, lianas, ferns, mosses, epiphytes)

Cape (and South European) Evergreen Trees and Maquis (with bulbous plants)

North African and South European Oak, Pine and Cedar Forest

Oases and Nile Valley (date and dum palms, tamarisk, acacia)

Thorn Forest and Thorn Bush (acacia, euphorbia)

South-East African Sub-tropical Bush (with scattered palms)

South African Bushveld and Woodland

European Mountain Forest, mainly Coniferous (fir, pine, spruce), sometimes with lower belt of broad-leaved Forest (oak, beech, chestnut)

European Mixed Broad-leaved and Coniferous Woodland and Meadow (oak, beech, fir, etc.)

———— Limits of Date Palm (Phoenix dactylifera)

——— Limits of Oil Palm (Elaeis guineensis)

········· Limits of Juniperus procera

·········· North and South Limits of Baobab (Adansonia)

– – – Extreme South Limit of Palms

NATURAL VEGETATION
after Engler, Pole Evans, Schimper
Shantz and others

Projection: Zenithal Equidistant

COPYRIGHT. GEORGE PHILIP & SON. LTD.

ACTUAL
SURFACE
TEMPERATURE
°C	°F
35	95
30	86
25	77
20	68
15	59
10	50
5	41

**JANUARY
TEMPERATURE**

— January Isotherms
reduced to Sea-level
°Celsius

NEW ZEALAND
on same scale

ACTUAL
SURFACE
TEMPERATURE
°C	°F
25	77
20	68
15	59
10	50
5	41
0	32

**JULY
TEMPERATURE**

— July Isotherms
reduced to Sea-level
°Celsius

NEW ZEALAND
on same scale

SUMMER RAINFALL

November to April

	mm	inches
	1000	40
	750	30
	500	20
	250	10
	125	5

1016   January Isobars
in millibars

→ Prevailing Winds

NEW ZEALAND
on same scale

WINTER RAINFALL

May to October

	mm	inches
	1000	40
	750	30
	500	20
	250	10
	125	5

1020   July Isobars
in millibars

→ Prevailing Winds

NEW ZEALAND
on same scale

Projection: Bonne

1:30 000 000
100   0   100   200   300   400   500 miles
100 0   200   400   600   800 km

AUSTRALIA

FOREST VEGETATION

Tropical Rain Forest (" Brush ")—soft woods (palms, cypress, hoop pines), tree-ferns, lianas, epiphytes—mangrove swamps on coast

Eastern Sub-tropical and Temperate Rain Forest—eucalypt hardwoods (gum trees), palms, tree-ferns, epiphytes, and in Tasmania, conifers and beech

Sub-tropical and Temperate Woodland (eucalypts, brigalow scrub)

Evergreen Forest and Xerophilous Woodland plants { of Mediterranean type—eucalypts (in W. Australia, jarrah, karri and tuart), " maquis " scrub, bulbous and tuberous plants

—— Southern Limit of Palms

GRASS AND SCRUB VEGETATION

Tropical Savanna (grassland with scattered trees and scrub—the Queensland " Bush "—low eucalypts and brigalow scrub)

Tropical and Sub-tropical Grassland
Temperate Grassland
Seasonal Grassland
Mallee Scrub and Seasonal Grassland
Dry Semi-desert (mulga and other scrub)
Dry Semi-desert (sand, bare rock and spinifex scrub)
Alpine, above timber line

NEW ZEALAND

Sub-tropical and Temperate Rain Forest—conifers (totara, matai, kauri pine, rimu, kahikatea), tree-ferns, epiphytes, lianas, orchids—southern beech (nothofagus) in upper belt and in south. Mangrove on coast north of Hauraki Gulf

Grassland (tussocks)
Scrub and Moor
Alpine above timber line
········· Southern limit of kauri pine

North I.
South I.
TASMAN SEA
PACIFIC OCEAN
Southern Alps
Canterbury Plains

On same scale as general map

Map labels (main map)

BANDA SEA
FLORES SEA
Nassau Ra.
Owen Stanley Ra.
TIMOR SEA
Torres Str.
G. of Carpentaria
INDIAN OCEAN
GREAT DIVIDE
AUSTRALIAN BASIN
DESERT
"Warburton's Desert"
Macdonnell Ra.
"Gibson's Desert"
Musgrave Mts.
"Victoria Desert"
EUCLA
Nullarbor Plain
Flinders Ra.
Lofty Ra.
MURRAY RIVER
Liverpool Ra.
Blue Mts.
Australian Alps
COASTAL PLAIN
Darling Range
Great Australian Bight
Tropic of Capricorn
TASMAN SEA
Bass Strait
East from Greenwich

········· Boundaries of Artesian Basins
(The so-called " Deserts " of the Old Explorers are becoming in many districts pastoral regions by boring for water in the Artesian Basins)
—— 10-inch Annual Isohyet   Salt Pans and Lakes

PRINCIPAL SCRUB FORMATIONS
Brigalow   Mulga
Mallee

Projection : *Bonne*

ANNUAL RAINFALL 1:60 000 000

Equator
Port Moresby
Townsville
Tropic of Capricorn
Toowoomba
Brisbane
Gold Coast
Perth
Newcastle
Sydney
Wollongong
Adelaide
Canberra
Ballarat
Geelong
Melbourne
Launceston
Hobart

NEW ZEALAND on same scale
Auckland
Hamilton
Wellington
Hutt
Christchurch
Dunedin

mm	inches
3000	120
2000	80
1000	40
500	20
250	10
125	5

DENSITY OF POPULATION 1:50 000 000

Port Moresby
Townsville
Tropic of Capricorn
Toowoomba
Brisbane
Gold Coast
Perth
Newcastle
Sydney
Wollongong
Adelaide
Canberra
Ballarat
Geelong
Melbourne
Launceston
Hobart

NEW ZEALAND on same scale
Auckland
Manukau
Hamilton
Wellington
Hutt
Christchurch
Dunedin

Inhabitants	per mile²	per km²
	under 2	under 1
	2– 8	1– 3
	8– 16	3– 6
	16– 32	6– 12
	32– 64	12– 25
	64–128	25– 50
	128–256	50–100
	over 256	over 100

○ Towns of 50–100 000 inhabitants
■ „ over 100 000 „

Projection of Insets : *Mollweide's Homolographic*

Boundaries of Artesian basins - - - - - -

East from Greenwich

1:12 000 000

100   0   100   200 miles
100   0 100 200 300 400 km

AUSTRALASIA POLITICAL
1:80 000 000

200 0 200 400 600 800 1000 miles
200 0 200 400 600 800 1000 km

Thursday I.   Banks I.
Prince of Wales I.   C. York
Newcastle B.
P. Endeavour Str.
Shelburne B.
P. Musgrave   C. Grenville
Cape   Temple B.
Duifken Pt.   Wenlock   C. Weymouth
Albatross B. Weipa   York   C. Direction
Archer   Peninsula
C. Keer-Weer   Mellwraith Ra.
Holroyd
Coleman   Coral Sea Basin

Wessel Is.
sh Co. Is.
Wilberforce
Melville B.
Nhulunbuy
P. Bradshaw
aledon B.
Grey
Mud B.
angula
Groote Eylandt
C. Beatrice

Gulf of
69

Carpentaria

Edward Pellew Group
Vanderlin I.
oloola
Mornington   C. van
I.   Diemen
Wellesley Is.
Bentinck I.

Duchess
Urandangi
Dajarra
Camooweal
Mount Isa
Mary Kathleen
Cloncurry

Leichhardt
Dobbyn
Kajabbi
Selwyn
Selwyn Range

Burketown
Normanton
Georgetown
Croydon
Forsayth
Einasleigh

Chillagoe   Mareeba
Normanby
C. Flattery
Laura   C. Bedford
Cooktown
C. Tribulation
Mossman   **Trinity Bay**
Cairns   C. Grafton
Battle Frere
Innisfail

Hinchinbrook I.
Ingham   Palm Is.
Halifax B.
Townsville   C. Cleveland
C. Bowling Green
Home Hill
Bowen   Whitsunday Is.
Proserpine   Cumberland Is.
Collinsville   Repulse B.
Netherdale   Mackay
Palmerston

Richmond   Charters
Pentland   Towers
Hughenden
Winton   Muttaburra

QUEENSLAND

Boulia
Aramac
Clermont
Emerald
Rockhampton
Keppel B.
C. Capricorn
Curtis I.
P. Curtis
Bustard Head
Gladstone
Biloela
Burnett
Bundaberg
Hervey Bay
Sandy C.
Fraser I.

Bedourie
L. Machattie
Longreach
Ilfracombe Barcaldine Alpha
Blackall
Jundah   Yaraka
Windorah

Birdsville

Charleville
Augathella
Injune
Mitchell   Roma
Quilpie   Condamine
Toowoomba
Ipswich   **Brisbane**
N. Stradbroke I.

NEW SOUTH WALES

VICTORIA   **MELBOURNE**
Ballarat
Geelong

TASMANIA   **Hobart**

PAPUA NEW GUINEA

1:12 000 000

1:6 000 000

20 0 20 40 60 80 100 miles
20 0 40 80 120 160 km

NEW ZEALAND & DEPENDENCIES
1:60 000 000

200 0 200 400 600 800 miles
200 0 400 800 1200 km

New Zealand Territory
Self-governing Territory

SAMOA ISLANDS
1:12 000 000

FIJI AND TONGA ISLANDS
1:12 000 000

50 0 50 100 150 miles
50 0 50 100 150 200 250 km

Projection : Conical with two standard parallels

COPYRIGHT. GEORGE PHILIP & SON. LTD.

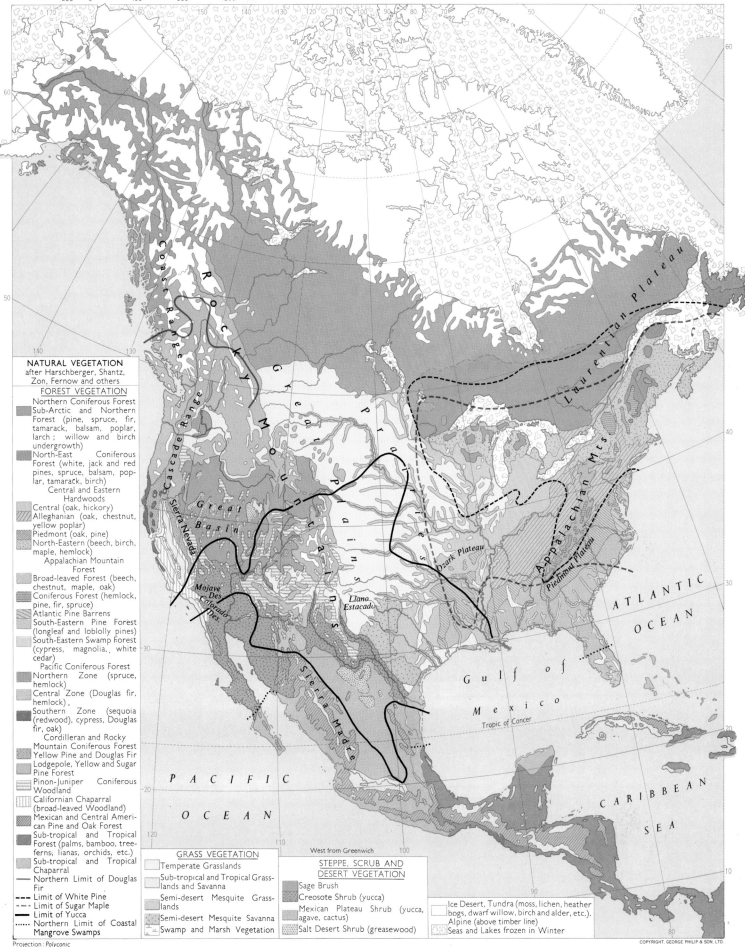

1:32 000 000

200   0   200   400   600   800 miles
200   0   400   800   1200 km

NATURAL VEGETATION
after Harschberger, Shantz,
Zon, Fernow and others

FOREST VEGETATION

Northern Coniferous Forest
Sub-Arctic and Northern
Forest (pine, spruce, fir,
tamarack, balsam, poplar,
larch ; willow and birch
undergrowth)

North-East Coniferous
Forest (white, jack and red
pines, spruce, balsam, poplar, tamarack, birch)

Central and Eastern
Hardwoods

Central (oak, hickory)

Alleghanian (oak, chestnut,
yellow poplar)

Piedmont (oak, pine)

North-Eastern (beech, birch,
maple, hemlock)

Appalachian Mountain
Forest

Broad-leaved Forest (beech,
chestnut, maple, oak)

Coniferous Forest (hemlock,
pine, fir, spruce)

Atlantic Pine Barrens

South-Eastern Pine Forest
(longleaf and loblolly pines)

South-Eastern Swamp Forest
(cypress, magnolia, white
cedar)

Pacific Coniferous Forest

Northern Zone (spruce,
hemlock)

Central Zone (Douglas fir,
hemlock)

Southern Zone (sequoia
(redwood), cypress, Douglas
fir, oak)

Cordilleran and Rocky
Mountain Coniferous Forest

Yellow Pine and Douglas Fir

Lodgepole, Yellow and Sugar
Pine Forest

Pinon-Juniper Coniferous
Woodland

Californian Chaparral
(broad-leaved Woodland)

Mexican and Central American Pine and Oak Forest

Sub-tropical and Tropical
Forest (palms, bamboo, tree-
ferns, lianas, orchids, etc.)

Sub-tropical and Tropical
Chaparral

——— Northern Limit of Douglas
Fir

– – – Limit of White Pine

–·–·– Limit of Sugar Maple

———— Limit of Yucca

·········· Northern Limit of Coastal
Mangrove Swamps

Projection: Polyconic

GRASS VEGETATION

Temperate Grasslands

Sub-tropical and Tropical Grasslands and Savanna

Semi-desert Mesquite Grasslands

Semi-desert Mesquite Savanna

Swamp and Marsh Vegetation

West from Greenwich

STEPPE, SCRUB AND
DESERT VEGETATION

Sage Brush

Creosote Shrub (yucca)

Mexican Plateau Shrub (yucca,
agave, cactus)

Salt Desert Shrub (greasewood)

Ice Desert, Tundra (moss, lichen, heather
bogs, dwarf willow, birch and alder, etc.),
Alpine (above timber line)

Seas and Lakes frozen in Winter

COPYRIGHT. GEORGE PHILIP & SON. LTD.

1 : 40 000 000

200 0 200 400 600 800 1000 miles
200 0 200 400 600 800 1000 1200 1400 1600 km

COPYRIGHT GEORGE PHILIP & SON LTD

January Temperature (inset map)

Appalachian Mts.
prairies
Great Plains
Rocky Mountains
Coast Mts.
Cascade Ra.
Sierra Nevada
Sa. Madre
Tropic of Cancer

ACTUAL SURFACE TEMPERATURE
°C 20 10 -10 -20 -30
°F 68 50 32 14 -4 -22

JANUARY TEMPERATURE
January Isotherms
reduced to Sea-level
°Celsius
1:80 000 000

July Temperature (inset map)

Appalachian Mts.
Prairies
Great Plains
Rocky Mountains
Coast Mts.
Cascade Ra.
Sierra Nevada
Sa. Madre
Tropic of Cancer

ACTUAL SURFACE TEMPERATURE
°C 30 20 10 -10
°F 86 68 50 32 14

JULY TEMPERATURE
July Isotherms
reduced to Sea-level
°Celsius
1:80 000 000

Main Physical Map

Denmark Str.
Mt. Forel 3880
Greenland
3700
Baffin Bay
Baffin Island
Ellesmere Isl.
Smith Sd.
Devon I.
Queen Elizabeth Isls.
Parry Is.
Melville I.
Banks I.
Victoria I.
Prince of Wales Isl.
Boothia Pen.
Gulf of Boothia
Melville Pen.
Southampton I.
Foxe Basin
Foxe Chan.
Hudson Str.
Cumberland Sd.
Frobisher Bay
Resolution Isl.
Labrador
Newfoundland
Belle Isle Str.
Anticosti I.
Gaspé Pen.
G. of St. Lawrence
Cabot Str.
C. Breton I.
Nova Scotia
C. Sable
B. of Fundy
C. Cod
Long I.
Delaware B.
Chesapeake B.
C. Hatteras
Bermudas
ATLANTIC OCEAN
Bahamas
Watling I.
Puerto Rico
Mona Pass.
Hispaniola 3175
Cordillera de Merida
Jamaica
Caribbean Sea
Brooks Ra.
Alaska Pen.
Kodiak
Cook Inlet
Alaska Ra.
Mt. McKinley 6194
Mt. St. Elias 5489
St. Elias Mts.
Mt. Fairweather 4663
Alexander Arch.
Queen Charlotte Is.
Vancouver I.
Mt. Waddington 3994
Coast Range
Mt. Olympus 2428
Mt. Rainier 4392
Columbia
Mt. Shasta 4317
Cascade Ra.
C. Mendocino
Golden Gate
Mt. Whitney 4418
Sa. Nevada
S. Gorgonio 3506
Salton Sea
C. San Lucas
Revilla Gigedo Is. 1129
Clipperton
PACIFIC OCEAN
Tropic of Cancer
G. of California
Californian Pen.
Great Basin
Wasatch Ra.
Colorado Plat.
Gila
Mt. Elbert 4399
Gannett Pk. 4202
Evans 4364
Pikes Pk. 4301
Black Hills 2207
Rocky Mountains
Great Plains
Great Central Plains
Mt. Robson 3954
Peace R.
Athabasca
Gr. Slave L.
Gt. Bear L.
Mackenzie
Beaufort Sea
Pt. Barrow
Bering Str.
Norton Sd.
Yukon
Porcupine
Liard
Nelson
L. Winnipeg
Churchill
Reindeer L.
Saskatchewan
Missouri
Platte
Kansas
Arkansas
Red R.
Brazos
Colorado
Rio Grande
Pecos
Llano Estacado
Mexican Plateau
Sierra Madre
Anahuac
Popocatepetl 5452
R. de las Balsas
Rio Grande de Santiago
C. Corrientes
Isthmus of Tehuantepec
Central American Cordillera 3837
Yucatan
Campeche Bk.
Gulf of Mexico
Florida
Str. of Florida
Gulf Plains
Gulf Coastal Plain
Mississippi
Tennessee
Ohio
Illinois
Wisconsin
L. Superior
L. Michigan
L. Huron
L. Erie
L. Ontario
Ottawa
St. Lawrence
L. Nipigon
Laurentian Plateau
James B.
Gt. Whale
Eastmain
Albany
Severn
Hudson Bay
Chesterfield Inlet
Back
Great Central Plains
Appalachian Mts.
Allegheny Mts.
Blue Ridge
Atlantic Coastal Plain
Cumberland Plat.
Alabama
Chattahoochee
Denver
Nicaragua
G. of Honduras
Yucatan Chan.
Cayman Deep
Bartlett Deep
Cuba 2000
Mt. Logan 6050
Arctic Circle
Davis Str.
Hudson Str.
Kuujjuaq

m 4000 3000 2000 1500 1000 600 400 200 0 -200 -600
ft 12000 9000 6000 4500 3000 1200 600 0 600 2000 4000 6000 12000 18000 24000

West from Greenwich

Projection : Lambert's Equivalent Azimuthal.

ALASKA

1 : 30 000 000

100   0   100   200   300 miles

100   0   200   400 km

Projection: Bonne

West from Greenwich

HAWAII
1:10 000 000

Projection: Albers' Equal Area with two standard parallels

West from Greenwich

1:12 000 000

50   0   50   100   150   200   250   300 miles
50   0   50   100   150   200   250   300   350   400   450 km

1:6 000 000

50   0   50   100   150 miles

50   0   50   100   150   200 km

Port Cartier   West Pt.   Anticosti I.   Jupiter   Heath Pt.

556 ▲   Chibougamau   Chibougamau I.   Pipmuacan L.   Rivière au Renard   South Pt.   ▼ 572

Cap Chat   1310 ▲   Gaspé   C. Gaspé

Matane   Shickshock Mts.   Gaspé Peninsula   GULF OF

Gouin Res.   Dolbeau   Peribonca   Mont Joli   Brion I.

St. Félicien   Lac   Rimouski   Miscou I.   **ST. LAWRENCE**

Roberval   St. Jean   Chicoutimi   Saguenay   Dalhousie   Baie de Chaleur   Shippigan   Magdalen Is. (Quebec)   Grindstone I.   St. Paul I. N.   Ingonish

Chambord   Jonquière   Toddoussac   Campbellton   Bathurst   Tracadie   Tignish   **PRINCE EDWARD**   St. Paul I. S.

Lac Bouchette   Bagotville   Trois Pistoles   NEW   North Pt.   **ISLAND**   Cape Breton Island

Parent   Lac Edouard   Rivière du Loup   819 ▲   St. Leonard   Miramichi B.   Newcastle   Chatham   Summerside   Charlottetown   Georgetown   532 ▲   Inverness   **Glace Bay**

La Tuque   Edmundston   Fort Kent   Grand Falls   **BRUNSWICK**   Richibucto   Souris   East Pt.   Port Hood   **Sydney**

La Malbaie   Baie St. Paul   Montmagny   Caribou   Chipman   Buctouche   Murray Hbr.   Bras d'Or

B E C   Quebec   Levis   Presque Isle   **Moncton**   Shediac   Pictou   New Glasgow   Madame I.

960 ▲   Grand'Mère   Shawinigan   Houlton   Woodstock   Grand L.   Springhill   Stellarton   Chedabucto B.

Gatineau   Trois Rivières   Plessisville   Mt. Katahdin   Fredericton   Sussex   Chignecto B.   Parrsboro   Canso

Joliette   Victoriaville   1606 ▲   **Saint**   Minas Basin   Truro   N O V A   Sherbrooke

St. Jérôme   Sorel   Drummondville   Thetford Mines   Moosehead L.   **John**   Minas Basin

Hawkesbury   St. Hyacinthe   Mégantic   St. Stephen   Windsor   Sheet Hbr.

Lachute   **MONTREAL**   Sherbrooke   M A I N E   Calais   **Dartmouth**

Ottawa   St. Jean   Magog   Coaticook   Bangor   Bay of Fundy   Annapolis Royal   **Halifax**

Ottawa   Valleyfield   Newport   Rangeley   Machias   Eastport   Digby   S C O T I A   Bridgewater

Cornwall   Plattsburg   Waterville   Belfast   Ellsworth   Grand Manan I.   L. Rossignol   Mahone Bay   Lunenburg

Ogdensburg   L. Champlain   Burlington   Augusta   Mt. Desert   St. Mary Bay   Shelburne

Watertown   Montpelier   Barre   Farmington   Penobscot B.   Yarmouth   C. Sable

Adirondack Mts.   1629 ▲   L. George   1917 ▲   Auburn   Lewiston   Rockland

Rutland   Lancaster   Berlin   **Portland**   Biddeford

Rome   Utica   Glens Falls   Saratoga Sps.   Concord   Rochester   Dover

Syracuse   Schenectady   Amsterdam   Keene   Manchester   Nashua   Portsmouth

Y O R K   Watervliet   Troy   Bennington   Fitchburg   Haverhill   **Lawrence**   Lowell

Albany   Pittsfield   Gardner   Clinton   Salem   Lynn   **Massachusetts** Bay

Binghamton   Catskill Mts.   Hudson   **Worcester**   Newton   **BOSTON**   Quincy   C. Cod

1281 ▲   Kingston   Holyoke   **Cambridge**   Brockton   Cape Cod B.

Springfield   Woonsocket   Pawtucket   Fall River   New Bedford

Poughkeepsie   Torrington   Hartford   **Providence**   Bristol   Nantucket Sd.

Newburgh   New Britain   Waterbury   Meriden   R.I.   Newport   Nantucket I.

Wilkes Barre   Middletown   New Haven   New London   Block I.   Martha's Vineyard

Hazleton   Peekskill   Bridgeport   Stamford   Greenwich   Montauk Pt.

Bethlehem   Paterson   Yonkers   Long Island

Allentown   Newark   **NEW YORK**   Jersey City

Reading   Elizabeth   Perth Amboy

PHILADELPHIA   Trenton   **NEW JERSEY**

Camden   Chester   Wilmington

Bridgeton   Atlantic City

DELAWARE   Dover   Cape May

Cape Charles   Salisbury

A T L A N T I C   O C E A N

West from Greenwich

DENSITY OF POPULATION

1:50 000 000

Vancouver   Edmonton   Winnipeg   Montreal   Ottawa   Boston

Seattle   Portland   St. Paul   Buffalo   New York

San Francisco   Denver   Omaha   Chicago   Pitts.   Philadelphia

Los Angeles   Kansas City   St. Louis   Ind.   Cin.   Washington

San Diego   Oklahoma City   Memphis   Atlanta

Fort Worth   Dallas   Jacksonville

Houston   New Orleans   Miami

Monterrey   Tropic of Cancer   Havana   Port au Prince

Guadalajara   Mexico   Puebla   Guatemala

Inhabitants

	per mile²	per km²
	under 2	under 1
	2–8	1–3
	8–16	3–6
	16–32	6–12
	32–64	12–25
	64–128	25–50
	128–256	50–100
	256–512	100–200
	over 512	over 200

■ Towns of over 500 000 Inhabitants

1:15 000 000

100   0   100   200   300   400 miles

100   0   100   200   300   400   500   600 km

BERMUDA
1:750 000
0   5   10 km

St. George   St. George's I.   St. David's I.
Spanish   The   Castle Harb.
Pt.   Flatts   Tucker's Town
Ireland I.   North Village
Somerset   Hamilton
Somerset I.

64   45

32   15

NORTH AMERICA
ANNUAL RAINFALL
1:80 000 000

Arctic Circle

Coast Mts.
Rocky Mountains
Great Plains
Prairies
Sierra Nevada
Sa. Madre
Appalachian Mts.

Tropic of Cancer

REFERENCE
TO COLOURING

mm	inches
3000	120
2000	80
1000	40
500	20
250	10

Columbia
tlanta
Macon   Augusta
umbus   Charleston
Savannah
Altamaha
C. Fear
Long Bay
C. Royal

Jacksonville
hassee
Daytona Beach

Orlando   C. Canaveral
Tampa   Lakeland
sburg
Sarasota   L. Okeechobee
Miami
West Palm Beach
Fort Lauderdale
Freeport   Gt. Abaco I.
Grand Bahama I.

C. Sable

Key West

Florida Str.

BAHAMAS

Eleuthera I.
New Providence I.
Nassau   Cat I.
Andros I.
S. Salvador
or Watlings I.

Tropic of Cancer

Havana
rianao
Matanzas   Cárdenas
Colón
Sta. Clara
Sagua la Grande
Caibarién
G. of   Batabanó
ane Batabanó
Cienfuegos
Trinidad
Sancti Spiritus
I. of Pines

Long I.

Mayaguana

Acklins I.
Caicos I. (Br.)
Turks Is. (Br.)

Gt. Inagua

Port de Paix
Cap Haitien
Monte Cristi
Pto. Plata

S. Francisco de Macoris

PUERTO RICO (U.S.A.)

St. Thomas (U.S.A.)
Charlotte Amalie (U.S.A.)
Virgin Is. (Br.)

Sombrero (Br.)
Anguilla
St. Martin (Fr. & Neth.)
St. Kitts (St. Christopher)
Barbuda

Antigua
St. John's

Montserrat
Plymouth

Guadeloupe (Fr.)
Pointe à Pitre
Marie Galante (Fr.)
DOMINICA
Roseau

Martinique (Fr.)

Fort de France   Castries
ST. LUCIA

Windward
ST. VINCENT   Barbados
Kingstown   Bridgetown
Islands   The Grenadines
Grenada
St. George's

Tobago
Port of Spain
Trinidad
San Fernando

Camagüey   Nuevitas
Morón
Ciego de Avila
Jucaro   Martí
Manzanillo
Campechuela
Bayamo   2000
Antilla
Holguin
Guantánamo
Boracoa
Baracoa
Santiago
de Cuba

GREATER

Santiago

Gonaives
St. Marc

La Vega   1338
DOMINICAN
REP.

Valverde
Santiago
Sánchez

La Romana
S. Pedro de Macoris
Santo Domingo

Grand Cayman
(Br.)

Montego Bay
St. Ann's Bay
P. Antonio

Savanna la Mar
Kingston
Spanish Town

JAMAICA

Jérémie   Léogane
Les Cayes

HAITI
Jacmel
Port au Prince
Duverge
Barahona

Hispaniola

ANTILLES

LESSER

Windward Passage

Mona Passage

Aguadilla   Arecibo
San Juan
Mayagüez   Vieques
Ponce
Guayama
Caguas
Basseterre
Charlestown   Nevis
St. Croix
(U.S.A.)
Christiansted

Leeward
Islands

Caratasca Lagoon

C. Gracias á Dios

Puerto Cabezas

Providencia
(Col.)

San Andrés
(Col.)

Bluefields
agua

CARIBBEAN SEA

ANTILLES

Mosquito Coast

Pta. Gallinas
Pen. de la
Guajira
Santa Marta
Ríohacha
Barranquilla
Cartagena
Soledad
Calamar
Sierra Nevada
de Santa Marta   5800
Sincelejo   Plato
Mompós
Corozal   El Banco
Calera

Gulf of Venezuela

Aruba (Neth.)
Curaçao (Neth.)
Willemstad
Bonaire (Neth.)

Pen. de
Paraguaná
Coro
Dabajuro
Pto. Cabello

La Blanquilla
(Ven.)

Margarita
La Asunción
La Tortuga
(Ven.)   Carúpano
Cumaná
G. of
Paria

Maiquetía
CARACAS
Maracay
Valencia
Barcelona
Maracaibo
Cabimas
San Felipe
Barquisimeto
L. de
Maracaibo   Trujillo
Valera

Cariaco
Caripito
Maturín
Las Mercedes   El Tigre
Calabozo
Tucupita

Delta of the
Orinoco

Cord. de Mérida
5007

Portuguesa
Guanare
San Fernando
de Apure

Orinoco
Ciudad
Guayana
Ciudad Bolívar

GUYANA

Georgetown
New
Amsterdam
Wismar

Bluefields
Vol. Irazú
RICA
3374
Vol. Chiriqui
Limón
Colón
Panama
PANAMA
Chitré
Pearl Is.
Azuero Pen.
Coiba
G. of
Panama

David
3374
La Palma
El Real
Turbo
Jatún
Antioquia
Atrato
G. of Cupica
Quibdó

Apure   Arauca
Arauca
San Cristóbal
Pto. Páez

VENEZUELA

Pto. Carreño
Pto. Ayacucho

Caicara

El Callao
Tumeremo

Caura
2560
Roraima
2810

Sierra Pacaraima

Barticy
Cuyuni

Potaro

Essequibo

SURINAM

1280

Cúcuta
Pamplona
Rubio
San Cristóbal

Pto. Wilches
Bucaramanga

Medellín
Pto. Berrio
Barrancabermeja
El Dorado

Manizales
Pereira
Cartago
Armenia
Buga
Palmira
Cali
5750
Neiva
Popayán
4646

COLOMBIA

Ibagué
Tunja
Honda
Zipaquirá
Bogotá
Olima   5215
Girardot

Guaviare

Meta

Casiquiare

BRAZIL

West from Greenwich

COPYRIGHT. GEORGE PHILIP & SON, LTD.

1 : 40 000 000

JULY TEMPERATURE
1 : 80 000 000

JANUARY TEMPERATURE
1 : 80 000 000

ACTUAL SURFACE TEMPERATURE		
°C	°F	
30	86	
25	77	
20	68	
15	59	
10	50	
5	41	
0	32	

Isotherms
Isotherms reduced to Sea-level

RAINFALL May to October
1 : 80 000 000
1020 July Isobars in millibars
→ Prevailing Winds

RAINFALL November to April
1 : 80 000 000
1020 January Isobars in millibars
→ Prevailing Winds

RAINFALL	
mm	inches
1500	60
1000	40
750	30
500	20
250	10
125	5

COPYRIGHT GEORGE PHILIP & SON, LTD.

NATURAL VEGETATION
after Engler, Denis and others

FOREST VEGETATION
Selvas Tropical Forest (hevea rubber, palms, castanha, lianas)
Andean Tropical Forest (cinchona, palms, tree-fern, maquis)
Brazilian Montane Tropical Forest (palms, tree-fern, bamboos)
Andean Temperate Rain Forest (araucaria, beech, epiphytes)
Catinga Xerophilous Forest (mimosa, cacti)
Chilean Sclerophyllous Woodland (cypress, acacias, laurels, cacti)
Chaco Xerophilous Woodlands (quebracho, mimosa scrub)
Cerrados Sub-tropical Forest (araucaria—in south)
North Chaco Savanna
Marsh subject to inundation
--- Limit of Araucaria brasiliensis
— South Limit of Quebracho
— South Limit of Hevea (wild rubber)

GRASS VEGETATION
Tropical Grasslands (llanos and campos, with gallery woods)
Sub-tropical and Temperate Grasslands

STEPPE, SCRUB AND DESERT VEGETATION
Xerophilous Scrub, Steppe (thorn and other drought-resisting plants)
Patagonian Steppe (thorn bushes)
Andean Plateau Steppe
Paramos Steppe
Dry Puna Steppe
Arid Tola Steppe
Atacama Lomas (subject to sea-fogs; occasional pasturage)
Atacama Desert
Salt Swamps
Sub-antarctic Steppe and Andean Ice Desert

Projection - Lambert's Equivalent Azimuthal

Brazilian Highlands

Plateau of Mato Grosso

Plateau of Bolivia

A n d e s

Equator

Tropic of Capricorn

Catinga

Campos

Cerrados

Gran Chaco

Pampa

Llanos

Selvas

Cordillera de los Andes

Puna de Atacama

Atacama Desert

Tropic of Capricorn

West from 60° Greenwich

ATLANTIC OCEAN

CARIBBEAN SEA

LESSER ANTILLES

Windward Is.

BRAZIL

VENEZUELA

COLOMBIA

ECUADOR

PERU

BOLIVIA

GUYANA

SURINAM

FR. GUIANA

Guiana Highlands

Mato Grosso

Plateau of Mato Grosso

CARACAS
BOGOTÁ
QUITO
LIMA
La Paz
Sucre
Brasília
RECIFE (PERNAMBUCO)
SALVADOR (BAHIA)
BELO HORIZONTE
Fortaleza
Natal
Belém (Pará)
Manaus
Maracaibo
Medellín
Cali
Guayaquil
Iquitos
Cuzco
Arequipa
Santa Cruz
Cochabamba
Oruro
Goiânia
Teresina
Feira de Santana
Aracaju
Campina Grande
João Pessoa
Maceió
Vitória
Gov. Valadares
Uberlândia
Uberaba
Ribeirão Prêto
S. José do Rio Prêto
Barranquilla
Cartagena
Sta. Marta
Bucaramanga
Cúcuta
Valencia
Barquisimeto
Cumaná
Ciudad Bolívar
Ciudad Guayana
Trinidad
Barbados
St. Lucia
St. Vincent
Grenada
Martinique (Fr.)
Aruba (Neth.)
Curaçao (Neth.)

Amazon
Orinoco
Negro
Madeira
Tapajós
Xingu
Tocantins
São Francisco
Marañón
Ucayali
Purús
Juruá
Putumayo
Napo
Branco

Equator

FED. DIST.

MINAS GERAIS
SÃO PAULO
MATO GROSSO
RONDÔNIA
ACRE
AMAPÁ
RORAIMA
PARÁ
MARANHÃO
CEARÁ
RIO GRANDE DO NORTE
PARAÍBA
PERNAMBUCO
ALAGOAS
SERGIPE
BAHIA

1:50 000 000

200   0   200   400   600   800 miles
200 0   400   800   1200 km

PROGRESS OF EXPLORATION
Coasts explored before 1800
" " between 1800 and 1850
" " 1850 and 1900
" " since 1900
Nansen 1895   Highest latitudes reached by explorers, with date
Unexplored regions: most of Antarctica and the interior of Greenland

Northern map

West from Greenwich

PACIFIC OCEAN
Qn. Charlotte Is.
Vancouver I.
G. of Alaska
Bering Strait
St. Lawrence I.
Kolyma
SIBERIA
New Siberian Is.
Wrangel I.
Pt. Barrow
Beaufort Sea
ASIA
Lena
Taimyr Peninsula
C. Chelyuskin
Severnaya Zemlya
ARCTIC OCEAN
Amundsen's Airship Route (1926)
Nansen 1895
North Pole
Peary 1909
Peary 1906 ×
Franz Josef Land
Kara Sea
Novaya Zemlya
Yenisei
Ob
Irtysh
L. Balkhash
Tobol
Alaska
Yukon
Oklowik
M'Clure Str.
Banks I.
Pr. Patrick I.
Parry Is.
Sverdrup Is.
Dolphin & Union Str.
Victoria I.
Bathurst I.
Pr. of Boothia
Magnetic N. Pole
Wilkes
Ellesmere I.
Smith Sd.
Barents Sea
Svalbard
Bear I.
Jan Mayen I.
Greenland Sea
Kola
White Sea
Dvina
Syr Darya
L. Aral
Caspian Sea
Rocky Mountains
Fraser
Pr. Rupert
Mackenzie
Gt. Bear L.
Gt. Slave L.
Athabaska
Edmonton
Saskatchewan
S. Saskatchewan
NORTH AMERICA
Regina
Winnipeg
Nelson
Churchill
Hudson Bay
Hudson Str.
Foxe Basin
Baffin I.
Baffin Bay
Thule
Davis Str.
GREENLAND
Petermann's Pk. 2940
Mt. Forel 3360
Denmark Str.
Iceland
Arctic Circle
Faroe Is.
Scandinavia
G. of Bothnia
Baltic Sea
Leningrad
Moscow
Volga
Don
Dnepr
Caucasus
Black Sea
Ankara
Istanbul
Danube
Belgrade
Vienna
Warsaw
Berlin
Hamburg
North Sea
Edinburgh
British Isles
C. Farewell
Mississippi
L. Michigan
Chicago
L. Superior
L. Huron
L. Erie
Toronto
Moosonee
Labrador
EUROPE

Southern map (ANTARCTICA)

South Sandwich Is.
Antarctic Circle
Molodezhnaya
Showa
Enderby Land
Mawson
C. Darnley
Pr. Charles Mts.
South Georgia
Novolazarevskaya
Sanae
Princess Martha Coast
Queen Maud Land
Norwegian
Australian Highland
American Davis
Mirny
Drygalski I.
South Orkney Is.
British Antarctic Territory
Weddell Sea
Halley Bay
Coats Land
Pionerskaya
Oasis
Vostok
Komsomolskaya
Wilkes Land
Wilkes
Falkland Is.
Elephant I.
S. Shetland Is.
Hope Bay
Antarctic Peninsula
Graham Land
Palmer Land
Shackleton
Ellsworth
General Belgrano
Pensacola Mts.
South Ice
ANTARCTICA
South Pole
Scott 1912 2800
Byrd 1929
Amundsen 1911
Polar Sub-Glacial Basin
Australian Dependency
Berkner I.
Vostok
Adélie Land
Magnetic S. Pole
Dumont d'Urville
Charcot
Alexander I.
Ellsworth Land
Beardmore Glacier
Shackleton 1909
Mt. Markham 4349
Wilkes Sub-Glacial Basin
Byrd Sub-Glacial Basin
Byrd
Byrd Land
Little Rockford
Little America
Ross Ice Shelf
Roosevelt I.
Mt. Erebus
McMurdo
Bay of Whales
Victoria Land
George V Coast
Oates Coast
Charcot
Bellingshausen Sea
Peter 1st I. (Nor)
Ross Sea
C. Adare
Hallett
Scott I.
Ross Dependency
Antarctic Circle
SOUTH AMERICA
Tierra del Fuego
Horn
Drake Passage
C. Magellan Str.
SOUTHERN OCEAN
Macquarie I.
Tasmania
Hobart
Auckland Is.
Campbell I.
West from Greenwich
East from Greenwich

Legend

- Sea open all the year
- Average minimum limit of pack ice (Autumn)
- Average maximum limit of pack ice (Spring)
- Average extreme limit of drift ice
- Tundra
- Ice Caps
- Cold Currents
- Warm Currents
- Outlines of Subglacial Basins

Projection: Zenithal Equidistant

COPYRIGHT. GEORGE PHILIP & SON. LTD.

A.R. – Autonomous Region
A.S.S.R. – Autonomous Soviet Socialist Republic
Afghan. – Afghanistan
Afr. – Africa
Ala. – Alabama
Alg. – Algeria
Amer. – America
Ang. – Angola
Antarc. – Antarctic
arch. – Archipelago
Arg. – Argentina
Ark. – Arkansas
Atlant. – Atlantic
Austral. – Australia
B. – Bay, Bight, (Baie, Baia, Bahia)
Bangla. – Bangladesh
Belg. – Belgium
Br. – British
Braz. – Brazil
Bur. – Burma
C. – Cape (Cabo)
Cal. – California
Cam. – Cameroon
Can. – Canada, Canal
Cap. – Capital
Cent. – Central
Chan. – Channel
Ches. – Cheshire
Cn. – Canton
Co. – County
Col. – Colony, Colombia
Corn. – Cornwall
Cr. – Creek
Cumbs. – Cumberland
Cy. – City
Cz.-slov. – Czechoslovakia
D.C. – District of Columbia
Dan. – Danish

Del. – Delaware
Den. – Denmark
Des. – Desert
Dept. – Department
Dist. – District
Div. – Division
Dom. Rep. – Dominican Republic
E. – East
Eng. – England
Eur. – Europe
F. – Firth
Fd. – Fjord, Fiord
Fed. – Federal
Fin. – Finland
Fla. – Florida
For. – Forest
Fr. – French, France
Fs. – Falls
G. – Gulf, Gebel
Ga. – Georgia
Ger. – Germany
Gr. – Greater, Greece
Gt. – Great
Guin.-B. – Guinea-Bissau
Guat. – Guatemala
Hants. – Hampshire
Hd. – Head
Herts. – Hertfordshire
Hr. – Harbour, Harbor
Hs. – Hills
Hts. – Heights
Hung. – Hungary
Hunts. – Huntingdonshire
I(s). – Island(s), Isle, Ile(s)
I.O.M. – Isle of Man
I.O.W. – Isle of Wight
Ice. – Iceland
Ill. – Illinois
Ind. – Indian, Indiana

Indon. – Indonesia
Ire. – Ireland
Isth. – Isthmus
It. – Italy
Jap. – Japan
Junc. – Junction
Kan. – Kansas
Ky. – Kentucky
L. – Lake, Loch, Lough, Lago
La. – Louisiana
Lag. – Lagoon, Lagoa, Laguna
Lancs. – Lancashire
Ld. – Land
Leb. – Lebanon
Leics. – Leicestershire
Lincs. – Lincolnshire
Lit. – Little
Lr. – Lower
Lux. – Luxembourg
Madag. – Madagascar
Mad. P. – Madhya Pradesh
Md. – Maryland
Me. – Maine
Medit. – Mediterranean
Mex. – Mexico
Mich. – Michigan
Minn. – Minnesota
Miss. – Mississippi
Mo. – Missouri
Mong. – Mongolia
Mozam. – Mozambique
Mt(s). – Mountain(s), Mount(s)
Mte. – Monte
N. – North, Northern
N.B. – New Brunswick
N.C. – North Carolina
N.H. – New Hampshire
N.J. – New Jersey
N.S.W. – New South Wales

N.Y. – New York
N.Z. – New Zealand
Neb. – Nebraska
Neth. – Netherlands
Newf. – Newfoundland
Nicar. – Nicaragua
Nor. – Norway
Northants. – Northamptonshire
O. – Oasis
O.F.S. – Orange Free State
Oc. – Ocean
Ont. – Ontario
Ore. – Oregon
Okla. – Oklahoma
P. – Pass, Paso, Passo
Pa. – Pennsylvania
Pac. Oc. – Pacific Ocean
Pak. – Pakistan
Pan. – Panama
Papua N.G. – Papua New Guinea
Para. – Paraguay
Pen. – Peninsula
Phil. – Philippines
Pk. – Peak
Pl. – Plain, Planina
Plat. – Plateau
Pol. – Poland
Port. – Portuguese, Portugal
Pref. – Prefecture
Prov. – Province
Pt. Pte. – Point, Pointe
R. – River, Rio
R.I. – Rhode Island
Ra. – Range
Reg. – Region
Res. – Reservoir
Rhod. – Rhodesia
Rum. – Rumania
S. – South, Sea

S.C. – South Carolina
S.D. – South Dakota
S.S.R. – Soviet Socialist Republic
S., St., Ste., Sta., Sto. – Sao, Saint, Sainte, Santa, Santo
Sa. – Sierra, Serra
Salop. – Shropshire
Scot. – Scotland
Sd. – Sound
Si Arabia – Saudi Arabia
Som. – Somerset
St. – State
Staffs. – Staffordshire
Str. – Strait
Switz. – Switzerland
Span. – Spanish
Tenn. – Tennessee
Terr. – Territory
Tex. – Texas
Thail. – Thailand
Tipp. – Tipperary
Trans. – Transvaal
Tur. – Turkey
U.S.A. – United States of America
U.S.S.R. – Union of Soviet Socialist Republics
Va. – Virginia
Val. – Valley
Ven. – Venezuela
Vic. – Victoria
Vol. – Volcano
Vt. – Vermont
W. – West, Western, Wadi, Wady
W.I. – West Indies
Wilts. – Wiltshire
Wis. – Wisconsin
Y.-slav. – Yugoslavia
Yorks. – Yorkshire

The latitudes and longitudes are intended primarily as a guide to finding the places on the map and in some cases are only approximate.

A

9 Aabenraa, Denmark 55 7N 9 20E
4 Aachen, Germany 50 49N 6 6E
4 Aalborg, Denmark 57 1N 9 45E
5 Aalen, Germany 48 50N 10 6E
4 Aalma ech Chaab, Leb. 33 6N 35 10E
4 Aalsmeer, Neth. 52 16N 4 45E
4 Aalst, Belgium 50 57N 4 3E
4 Aalten, Neth. 51 56N 6 35E
5 Aarau, Switzerland 47 24N 8 3E
5 Aarberg Switzerland 47 3N 7 17E
5 Aare, R., Switzerland 47 16N 7 45E
5 Aargau, Canton, Switz. 47 25N 8 10E
4 Aarhus, Denmark 56 9N 10 13E
4 Aarschot, Belgium 50 59N 4 50E
2 Aba, Nigeria 5 10N 7 19E
2 Abadan, Iran 30 22N 48 19E
2 Abadla, Algeria 31 0N 2 25w
1 Abakan, U.S.S.R. 53 59N 91 20E
8 Abancay, Peru 13 45s 72 45w
2 Abashiri, Japan 43 55N 144 15E
2 Abau, Papua N.G. 10 0s 148 50E
4 Abaya, L., Ethiopia 6 30N 37 50E
3 Abbeville, France 50 7N 1 50E
4 Abbeyfeale, Ireland 52 23N 9 19w
3 Abbeyside, Ireland 52 5N 7 36w
4 Abbottabad, Pakistan 34 10N 73 15E
2 Abéché, Chad 14 0N 20 40E
2 Abeokuta, Nigeria 7 0N 3 23E
5 Aberaeron, Wales 52 14N 4 16w
5 Abercarn, Wales 51 39N 3 9w
5 Aberchirder, Scotland 57 34N 2 40w
4 Abercorn, see Mbala
5 Abercrave, Wales 51 48N 3 42w
3 Abercorn, Wales 51 43N 3 28w
3 Aberdare, Wales 51 43N 3 28w
3 Aberdeen, Australia 32 5s 150 50E
5 Aberdeen, S. Africa 32 26s 24 2E
0 Aberdeen, S. Dakota, U.S.A. 45 32N 98 30w
0 Aberdeen, Wash., U.S.A. 47 0N 123 47w
1 Aberdour, Scotland 56 2N 3 18w
5 Aberdovey, Wales 52 33N 4 2w
5 Aberdulais, Wales 51 41N 3 46w
1 Aberfeldy, Scotland 56 37N 3 50w
0 Aberfoyle, Scotland 56 11N 4 22w
5 Abergavenny, Wales 51 49N 3 0w
5 Abergele, Wales 53 18N 3 35w
5 Aberkenfig, Wales 51 33N 3 36w
5 Abersychan, Wales 51 43N 3 4w
5 Abertillery, Wales 51 43N 3 8w
5 Aberystwyth, Wales 52 24N 4 4w
2 Abha, Saudi Arabia 18 0N 42 34E
2 Abidjan, Ivory Coast 5 20N 3 58w
2 Abilene, U.S.A. 32 28N 99 45w
2 Abingdon, England 51 40N 1 16w
1 Abington, Scotland 55 30N 3 42w
9 Abitibi, L., Canada 49 40N 79 40w
1 Abkhaz, A.S.S.R., U.S.S.R. 43 0N 41 0E
9 Abo, see Turku
4 Abo, Congo (Fr.) 0 10N 13 10E
2 Abolo, Benin 7 5N 2 5E
9 Abong Mbang, Cameroon 4 0N 13 8E
3 Abou Deia, Chad 11 20N 19 20E
0 Aboyne, Scotland 57 5N 2 50w
2 Abqaiq, Saudi Arabia 26 0N 49 45E
7 Abrantes, Portugal 39 28N 8 10w
8 Abri, Sudan 20 45N 30 27E
8 Abrolhos Arch., Brazil 17 50s 38 35w

47 Abrud, Rumania 46 20N 23 0E
40 Abruzzi, Region, Italy 42 10N 14 0E
90 Absaroka Ra., U.S.A. 44 40N 110 0w
63 Abu Dhabi, U.A.E. 24 27N 54 18E
73 Abu Dist., Sudan 19 15N 33 38E
73 Abu Hamed, Sudan 19 35N 33 37E
73 Abu Matariq, Sudan 11 0N 26 10E
73 Abu Tig, Egypt 27 4N 31 15E
73 Abu Zabad, Sudan 12 28N 28 45E
72 Abuja, Nigeria 9 16N 7 2E
73 Abwong, Sudan 9 2N 32 14E
94 Acaponeta, Mexico 22 30N 105 20w
94 Acapulco, Mexico 17 0N 99 57w
72 Accra, Ghana 5 32N 0 12w
26 Accrington, England 53 46N 2 23w
65 Achak Gomba, China 33 35N 96 20E
35 Achill, Ireland 53 59w
35 Achill Hd. & I., Ireland 53 58N 10 17w
61 Achinsk, U.S.S.R. 56 20N 90 20E
95 Acklin's I., Bahamas 22 15N 74 15w
99 Aconcagua, Arg. 32 37s 70 2w
43 Acqui, Italy 44 42N 8 29E
63 Acre, Israel 32 56N 35 4E
98 Acre, R., Brazil 10 45s 69 30w
98 Acre, st., Brazil 9 0s 71 0w
63 Ad Dam, Saudi Arabia 20 25N 44 30E
83 Adaminaby, Australia 36 0s 148 50E
64 Adam's Bridge, Sri Lanka 9 15N 79 30E
64 Adam's Pk., Sri Lanka 6 40N 80 40E
51 Adana, Turkey 37 10N 35 18E
51 Adapazari, Turkey 40 48N 30 25E
73 Adarama, Sudan 17 8N 34 58E
83 Adavale, Australia 25 46s 144 30E
43 Adda, R., Italy 45 15N 9 50E
74 Addis Ababa, Ethiopia 9 2N 38 43E
45 Adelboden, Switzerland 46 28N 7 36E
83 Adelaide, Australia 34 55s 138 43E
76 Adelaide, S. Africa 32 26s 24 2E
88 Adelaide, Pen., Canada 67 60N 98 0w
100 Adélie Ld., Antarctica 67 0s 140 0E
62 Aden, S. Yemen 12 45N 45 3E
62 Aden, G. of, Arabia 12 0N 48 0E
63 Adh Dharma, Si. Arabia 24 35N 46 12E
80 Adieu, C., Australia 32 0s 132 0E
64 Adilabad, India 19 50N 78 30E
93 Adirondack Mts., U.S.A. 43 50N 74 30w
72 Admer, Algeria 20 23N 5 20E
80 Admiralty G., Australia 14 20s 126 0E
82 Admiralty Is., Papua N.G. 2 0s 146 40E
64 Adoni, India 15 45N 77 20E
42 Adour, R., France 43 47N 0 50w
37 Adra, Spain 36 45N 3 1w
46 Adraj, Saudi Arabia 20 1N 51 0E
40 Adrano, Sicily, Italy 37 40N 14 49E
72 Adrar, Algeria 27 40N 0 12w
72 Adrar des Iforas, Plat., Mali 19 40N 1 40E
73 Adré, Chad 13 40N 22 20E
40 Adriatic Sea, Europe 43 0N 15 0E
73 Adwa, Ethiopia 14 13N 39 0E
27 Adwick le Street, Eng. 53 35N 1 12w
51 Adzhar, A.S.S.R., U.S.S.R. 42 0N 42 0E
9 Æbeltoft, Denmark 56 12N 10 41E
41 Ægean Sea, Medit. S. 38 0N 25 0E
62 Afars & Issas, Fr. Terr. of, Africa, see Djibouti
72 Affreville, France see Khemis Miliana.
32 Affric, Glen & R., Scot. 57 16N 5 0w
64 Afghanistan, Asia 33 0N 66 0E

62 Afif, Saudi Arabia 23 53N 42 59E
70 Africa, Continent
63 Afula, Israel 32 36N 37 17E
51 Afyonkarahisar, Turkey 38 46N 30 33E
72 Agadès, Niger 16 58N 7 59E
72 Agadir, Morocco 30 32N 9 45w
65 Agartala, India 23 47N 91 15E
61 Agata, U.S.S.R. 66 50N 98 10E
72 Agboville, Ivory Coast 5 55N 4 15w
43 Agde, France 43 20N 3 28E
43 Agen, France 44 13N 0 37E
51 Agincourt, France 50 29N 2 7E
64 Agra, India 27 17N 78 0E
51 Agri, see Karaköse
40 Agrigento, Sicily 37 19N 13 33E
41 Agrinion, Greece 38 37N 21 27E
94 Agua Prieta, Mexico 31 25N 109 30w
94 Aguas Calientes, Mexico 22 0N 102 12w
95 Aguadilla, Puerto Rico 18 28N 67 5w
37 Aguilas, Spain 37 27N 1 39w
76 Agulhas C., S. Africa 34 50s 20 5E
63 Agur, Israel 31 41N 34 55E
84 Ahaura, N.Z. 42 20s 171 36E
44 Ahaus, Germany 52 6N 7 0E
84 Ahipara B., N.Z. 35 10s 173 0E
64 Ahiri, India 19 30N 80 0E
64 Ahmadabad, India 23 2N 72 30E
64 Ahmadnagar, India 19 0N 74 40E
64 Ahmadpur E., Pak. 29 0N 71 40E
36 Ahoghill, N. Ireland 54 52N 6 23w
62 Ahvaz, Iran 31 25N 48 40E
49 Ahvenanmaa, Is., Fin. 60 15N 20 0E
62 Ahwar, South Yemen 13 33N 46 37E
67 Aichi, Pref., Japan 35 0N 137 15E
45 Aigle, Switzerland 46 19N 6 58E
67 Aihun, China 49 59N 127 30E
65 Aijal, India 23 50N 92 55E
30 Ailsa Craig, I., Scotland 55 15N 5 6w
61 Aim, U.S.S.R. 59 0N 133 55E
72 Ain, Dépt., France 46 5N 5 30E
72 Ain Beida, Algeria 35 50N 7 29E
72 Ain Salah, Algeria 27 10N 2 32E
73 Ain Sefra, Algeria 32 46N 0 35w
73 Aine Galakka, Chad 18 5N 18 30E
72 Air, Mts., Niger 18 0N 8 20E
33 Aird, The, Scotland 57 26N 4 30w
31 Airdrie, Scotland 55 52N 3 59w
42 Aire, France 43 40N 0 20w
26 Aire, R., England 53 54N 2 0w
42 Aisne, Dépt., France 49 42N 3 40E
43 Aisne, R., France 49 25N 4 0E
82 Aitape, Papua N.G. 3 0s 142 5E
33 Aith, Scotland 59 8N 2 38w
46 Aitos, Bulgaria 42 40N 27 18E
43 Aix, France 43 32N 5 26E
43 Aix-les-Bains, France 45 40N 5 55E
41 Aíyina, tn. & G., Greece 37 40N 23 30E
41 Aíyion, Greece 38 15N 22 5E
43 Ajaccio, Corsica, Fr. 41 55N 8 40E
64 Ajanta Ra., India 20 0N 75 20E
43 Ajaccio, Corsica, Fr. 41 55N 8 40E
64 Ajanta Ra., India 20 0N 75 20E
62 Ajibba, Saudi Arabia 27 28N 44 28E
63 'Ajlun, Jordan 32 20N 35 50E
64 Ajmer, India 26 30N 74 39E
49 Akershus, Norway 60 0N 11 0E
74 Aketi, Zaïre 2 38N 23 47E
41 Akhisar, Turkey 38 56N 27 48E
73 Akhmîm, Egypt 26 31N 31 47E
67 Akita, & Pref., Japan 39 45N 140 6E

72 Akjoujt, Mauritania 19 45N 14 10w
88 Aklavik, Canada 67 50N 135 0w
74 Akoafim, Cameroon 2 20N 12 50E
73 Akobo, Sudan 7 50N 33 1E
64 Akola, India 20 55N 76 59E
48 Akranes, Iceland 64 18N 21 53w
92 Akron, Ohio, U.S.A. 41 14N 81 31w
51 Aksaray, Turkey 38 19N 34 12E
61 Aksenovo Zilovskoye, U.S.S.R. 53 20N 117 40E
73 Aksum, Ethiopia 14 5N 38 40E
51 Aktyubinsk, U.S.S.R. 50 20N 57 10E
72 Aku, Nigeria 6 40N 7 18E
72 Akure, Nigeria 7 15N 5 5E
48 Akureyri, Iceland 65 40N 18 3E
65 Akyab, Burma 20 12N 92 58E
73 Al Bu'ayrat, Libya 31 20N 16 0E
62 Al Ghaidha, South Yemen 16 16N 52 7E
62 Al Hafr, Saudi Arabia 28 30N 46 0E
62 Al Hair, Saudi Arabia 24 18N 46 44E
62 Al Hamar, Saudi Arabia 22 23N 46 5E
62 Al Haribia, Si. Arabia 28 7N 35 15E
62 Al Hatataba, Saudi Arabia 19 30N 44 11E
72 Al Hoceima, Morocco, 35 8N 3 58w
63 Al Husn, Jordan 32 30N 35 50E
73 Al Jarzirah, Libya 25 55N 21 0E
73 Al Jawf, Libya 24 15N 23 30E
62 Al Jawf, Saudi Arabia 29 55N 39 37E
63 Al Jazir, Oman 18 30N 56 31E
63 Al Jiftalik, Jordan 32 10N 35 30E
63 Al Karak, Jordan 31 10N 35 42E
63 Al Khabura, Oman 23 57N 57 5E
63 Al Khalaf, Oman 20 30N 57 56E
63 Al Khobar, Saudi Arabia 30N 50 15E
73 Al Khums, Libya 32 32N 14 20E
63 Al Kuwayt, Kuwait 29 20N 48 0E
63 Al Lubban, Jordan 32 5N 35 14E
73 Al Marj (Barce), Libya 32 30N 20 50E
63 Al Masira, I. Oman 20 30N 58 0E
63 Al Mazra, Jordan 31 18N 35 32E
73 Al Muwaylih, Si. Arabia 27 35N 35 40E
73 Al Qatrun, Libya 24 45N 15 2E
62 Al Qunfidha, Si. Arabia 19 20N 41 10E
63 Al Qunaytirah, Syria 33 7N 35 50E
62 Al'Ula, Saudi Arabia 26 35N 38 0E
73 Al Uquaylah, Libya 30 10N 18 50E
63 Al Yarmuk, Syria 32 45N 35 40E
66 Ala Kul, L., U.S.S.R. 46 15N 81 50E
66 Ala Shan, Mts., China 39 45N 103 20E
66 Ala Tau, Mts., Asia 45 30N 80 40E
91 Alabama, st., & R., U.S.A. 32 40N 87 0w
98 Alagoas, st., Brazil 9 45s 35 47w
95 Alajuela, Costa Rica 10 0N 84 20w
90 Alamogordo, U.S.A. 32 55N 105 55w
90 Alamosa, U.S.A. 37 35N 105 55w
49 Aland Is., see Ahvenanmaa
49 Åland Str., Finland 60 10N 19 30E
51 Alanya, Turkey 36 36N 32 0E
51 Alapayevsk, U.S.S.R. 57 55N 62 0E
51 Alasehir, Turkey 38 20N 28 37E
88 Alaska, st., U.S.A. 65 0N 150 0w
88 Alaska, G. of, U.S.A. 58 0N 145 0w
43 Alassio, Italy 44 0N 8 10E
83 Alawoona, Australia 34 45s 140 30E
43 Alba, Italy 44 45N 8 0E
37 Alba, Sa. de, mts., Spain 43 5N 4 40w
47 Alba-Iulia, Rumania 46 2N 23 54E

37 Albacete, Spain 38 59N 1 53w
41 Albania, Europe 41 10N 20 0E
80 Albany, Australia 35 0s 117 52E
91 Albany, Georgia, U.S.A. 31 35N 84 16w
93 Albany, N.Y., U.S.A. 42 37N 73 50w
90 Albany, Oregon, U.S.A. 44 38N 123 0w
89 Albany, R., Canada 51 20N 86 30w
91 Albemarle Sd., U.S.A. 36 2N 76 0w
43 Albenga, Italy 44 4N 8 15E
43 Albert, France 50 0N 2 40E
83 Albert L., Australia 35 40s 139 20E
74 Albert L. see Mobutu Sese Seko, L.
88 Alberta, Prov., Canada 54 30N 115 0w
74 Albertville, see Kalemie
43 Albertville, France 45 40N 6 20E
43 Albi, France 43 57N 2 9E
37 Alboran I., Spain 35 58N 3 0w
90 Albuquerque, U.S.A. 35 3N 106 36w
80 Alburquerque, Spain 39 13N 6 55w
83 Albury, Australia 36 6s 146 59E
37 Alcalá de Henares, Spain 40 30N 3 19w
40 Alcamo, Sicily 38 0N 12 58E
37 Alcañiz, Spain 41 0N 0 10w
37 Alcántara, Spain 39 42N 6 54w
37 Alcaraz, Sa. de, mts., Spain 38 30N 2 30w
37 Alcaudete, Spain 37 38N 4 7w
37 Alcázar de S. Juan, Spain 39 33N 3 15w
37 Alcira, Spain 39 10N 0 30w
37 Alcobaça, Portugal 39 30N 9 0w
37 Alcoy, Spain 38 42N 0 29w
71 Aldabra Is., Indian Ocean 9 30s 46 15E
61 Aldan, U.S.S.R. 58 40N 125 30E
61 Aldan, R., U.S.S.R. 62 30N 135 30E
61 Aldanski Perezov, U.S.S.R. 62 5N 135 15E
23 Aldeburgh, England 52 9N 1 37E
22 Alderbury, England 51 4N 1 45w
42 Alderney I., Channel Is. 49 45N 2 15w
23 Aldershot, England 51 16N 0 43w
72 Aleg, Mauritania 17 15N 14 10w
98 Alegrete, Brazil 29 40s 56 0w
99 Aleisk, U.S.S.R. 52 40N 83 0E
51 Alexandrov Gai, U.S.S.R. 50 30N 48 10E
61 Aleksandrovsk, U.S.S.R. 50 50N 142 10E
61 Aleksandrovsky Zavod, U.S.S.R. 50 40N 117 50E
60 Aleksandrovskoye, U.S.S.R. 60 35N 77 50E
42 Alençon, France 48 25N 0 1E
37 Alentejo Alto, Prov., Portugal 39 0N 7 55w
37 Alentejo Baixo, Prov., Portugal 38 0N 8 20w
51 Aleppo (Halab), Syria 36 30N 37 22E
43 Alès, France 44 9N 4 5E
43 Alessandria, Italy 44 47N 8 40E
48 Ålesund, Norway 62 28N 6 5E
88 Aleutian Is., Pacific Oc. 52 0N 175 0w
75 Alexander B., S. Africa 28 20s 16 40E
100 Alexander I., Antarctica 68 0s 70 0w
63 Alexander, R., Israel 32 34N 34 55E
83 Alexandra, Australia 37 8s 145 40E
88 Alexandria, B.C., Can. 52 55N 122 20w
76 Alexandria, S. Africa 28 20s 16 25E
73 Alexandria, Egypt 31 5N 29 45E
30 Alexandria, Scotland 55 59N 4 34w
91 Alexandria La, U.S.A. 31 17N 92 29w
92 Alexandria, Va., U.S.A. 38 50N 77 5w

83 Alexandrina, L., Austral. 35 32s 139 12E
41 Alexandroúpolis, Greece 40 50N 25 55E
63 Aley, Lebanon 33 50N 35 36E
27 Alford, England 53 16N 0 10E
27 Alfreton, England 53 7N 1 24w
48 Alftanes, Iceland 64 29N 22 10w
37 Algarve, Prov., Portugal 37 20N 8 35w
37 Algeciras, Spain 36 11N 5 28w
37 Algemesi, Spain 39 15N 0 29w
72 Algeria, N. Africa 33 40N 3 0E
72 Algiers (Alger), Algeria 36 45N 3 5E
76 Algoa B., S. Africa 33 50s 26 0E
37 Alhama de Murcia, Spain 37 50N 1 30w
64 Alikhel, Afghanistan 33 50N 69 30E
74 Alibo, Ethiopia 9 52N 37 5E
37 Alicante, Spain 38 22N 1 28w
82 Alice, R., Australia 23 50s 145 0E
80 Alice Springs, Australia 23 42s 133 58E
75 Alicedale, S. Africa 33 16s 26 2E
64 Aligarh, India 27 42N 78 2E
65 Aling Kangri, Ra., Tibet, China 32 45N 81 5E
49 Alingsas Sweden 57 57N 12 36E
64 Alipur, Pakistan 29 25N 70 50E
64 Alipur Duar, India 26 35N 89 30E
47 Alitus, U.S.S.R. 54 20N 24 0E
37 Aljustrel, Portugal 37 55N 8 10w
44 Alkmaar, Netherlands 52 38N 4 44E
65 Allahabad, India 25 25N 81 50E
61 Allakh Yun, U.S.S.R. 60 50N 137 5E
31 Allan, Bridge of, Scotland 56 9N 3 56w
92 Alleghany Mts., U.S.A. 39 0N 79 0w
92 Allegheny, R., U.S.A. 42 0N 79 0w
35 Allen, Bog of, Ireland 53 13N 7 20w
36 Allen, L., Ireland 54 8N 8 2w
63 Allenby Bridge, see Hussein Bridge
27 Allendale, England 54 55N 2 16w
93 Allentown, U.S.A. 40 40N 75 25w
64 Alleppey, India 9 35N 76 25E
90 Alliance, Neb., U.S.A. 42 8N 102 55w
42 Allier, Dépt., France 46 25N 3 0E
43 Allier, R., France 44 50N 3 42E
31 Alloa, Scotland 56 7N 3 47w
60 Alma Ata, U.S.S.R. 43 20N 76 50E
37 Almada, Portugal 38 45N 9 10w
82 Almaden, Australia 17 22s 144 40E
37 Almadén, Spain 38 48N 4 48w
37 Almansa, Spain 38 50N 1 0w
37 Almazan, Spain 41 30N 2 30w
44 Almelo, Netherlands 52 21N 6 42E
37 Almendralejo, Spain 38 43N 6 28w
37 Almeria, Spain 36 53N 2 33w
24 Almondsbury, England 51 33N 2 34w
44 Aln, R., England 55 24N 1 57w
33 Alness, & R., Scotland 57 45N 4 20w
27 Alnwick, England 55 25N 1 42w
65 Alon, Burma 22 15N 95 10E
61 Alor, & I., Indonesia 8 10s 124 50E
68 Alor Star, Malaya 6 3N 100 25E
92 Alpena, U.S.A. 45 0N 83 35w
42 Alpes Maritimes, Dépt., Fr. 44 5N 7 0E
24 Alphington, England 50 41N 3 32w
41 Alpi Pennine, Mts., Switz. 46 4N 7 35E
90 Alpine, Texas, U.S.A. 30 25N 103 42w
41 Alps, The, Europe 46 to 47 0N 6 to 10 0E
43 Alsace, Dist., France 48 30N 7 30E
36 Alsager, England 53 7N 2 20w
37 Alsdorf, Germany 50 48N 6 10E
32 Alsh, L., Scotland 57 17N 5 40w
26 Alston, England 54 49N 2 28w
66 Altai Mts., Central Asia 48 0N 90 0E
91 Altamaha, R., U.S.A. 31 45N 81 45w
61 Altanbulag, Mongolia 50 15N 106 25E
45 Altdorf, Switzerland 46 53N 8 38E
48 Alte Fjord, Norway 70 0N 23 25E
37 Altea, Spain 38 38N 0 1w
43 Altkirch, France 47 40N 7 15E
75 Alto Molocue, Mozam. 15 50s 37 35E
23 Alton, England 51 8N 0 59w
92 Alton, U.S.A. 38 54N 90 3w
46 Altona, Germany 53 34N 9 51E
92 Altoona, U.S.A. 40 32N 79 27w
26 Altrincham, England 53 24N 2 23w
45 Altstätten, Switzerland 47 23N 9 33E
90 Altus, U.S.A. 34 30N 99 25w
66 Altyn Tagh, Mts., Tibet 39 0N 89 0E
31 Alva, Scotland 56 9N 3 48w
94 Alvarado, Mexico 18 45N 95 50w
27 Alvechurch, England 52 22N 1 58w
49 Alvesta, Sweden 56 57N 14 30E
81 Alvie, Australia 38 15s 143 30E
49 Älvkarleby, Sweden 60 32N 17 40E
49 Alvsborg, Co., Sweden 58 0N 12 30E
49 Älvsby, Sweden 65 42N 21 0E
64 Alwar, India 27 43N 76 40E
31 Alyaty Pristan, U.S.S.R. 39 59N 49 28E
31 Alyth, Scotland 56 38 N 3 14w
47 Alytus, U.S.S.R. 54 25N 24 0E
73 Am-Dam, Chad 12 40N 20 35E
73 Am Djeress, Chad 16 15N 22 50E
73 Am Guereda, Chad 12 53N 21 14E
73 Am Timan, Chad 11 0N 20 10E
80 Amadeus, L., Australia 24 45s 130 45E
74 Amadi, Sudan 5 29N 30 25E
89 Amadjuak & L., Canada 64 0N 72 40w
67 Amagasaki, Japan 34 45N 135 0E
49 Amakusa B. & I., Japan 32 45N 130 5E
49 Amal, Sweden 59 5N 12 35E
64 Amalner, India 21 0N 74 58E
67 Amami O Shima, Is., Japan 27 0N 129 0E
60 Amangeldy, U.S.S.R. 50 10N 65 10E
98 Amapa, st., Brazil 2 0N 52 0w
62 Amara, Iraq 31 58N 47 5E
64 Amaravati, see Amraoti
90 Amarillo U.S.A. 35 6N 101 57w

40 Amaro, Mte., Italy 42 4N 14 5E
51 Amasya, Turkey 40 45N 36 10E
98 Amazon, R., Brazil 1 0s 59 0w
98 Amazonas, st., Brazil 4 30s 64 0w
64 Ambala, India 30 28N 76 50E
74 Amban, Cameroon 2 20N 11 15E
75 Ambanja, Madagascar 13 40s 48 27E
61 Ambarchik, U.S.S.R. 69 40N 162 20E
98 Ambato, Ecuador 1 40s 78 30w
75 Ambatolampy, Madag. 19 0s 47 35E
75 Ambatondrazaka, Madag. 17 55s 48 28E
46 Amberg, Germany 49 27N 11 52E
23 Amberley, England 50 55N 0 33w
75 Ambikapur, India 23 10N 83 5E
75 Ambilobé, Madagascar 13 10s 49 3E
26 Ambleside, England 54 26N 2 56w
68 Ambon, Indonesia 3 50s 128 15E
75 Ambositra, Madagascar 20 30s 47 25E
68 Amboyna, I., S. China Sea 7 0N 113 10E
75 Ambré, C'd', Madagascar 12 0s 49 20E
74 Ambriz, Angola 8 0s 13 20E
*74 Ambriʐete, Angola 7 18s 12 52E
60 Amderma, U.S.S.R. 69 45N 62 0E
94 Ameca, Mexico 20 36N 104 5w
44 Ameland, I., Netherlands 53 27N 5 45E
61 Amen, U.S.S.R. 68 50N 179 59E
1 America, N. and S., Continents
44 Amersfoort, Netherlands 52 10N 5 24E
23 Amersham, England 51 40N 0 38w
88 Amery, Canada 56 35N 94 5w
92 Ames, U.S.A. 42 3N 93 42w
61 Amga, R., U.S.S.R. 61 0N 132 0E
23 Amesbury, England 51 10N 1 46w
61 Amgu, U.S.S.R. 45 45N 137 15E
61 Amgun, R., U.S.S.R. 52 50N 138 0E
65 Amherst, Burma 16 0N 97 64E
89 Amherst, Canada 45 50N 64 30w
40 Amiata, Mt., Italy 42 49N 11 30E
43 Amiens, France 49 52N 2 15E
5 Amirante Is., Ind. Ocean 6 30s 53 0E
62 Amman, Jordan 31 57N 35 56E
25 Ammanford, Wales 51 48N 4 0w
61 Amoy, China 24 25N 118 15E
75 Ampanihy, Madagascar 24 40s 44 45E
51 Amran, Yemen 15 43N 43 57E
64 Amraoti, India 20 53N 77 15E
64 Amreli, India 21 40N 71 5E
64 Amritsar, India 31 40N 75 20E
64 Amroha, India 29 0N 78 25E
44 Amsterdam, Netherlands 52 23N 4 53E
76 Amsterdam, S. Africa 26 35s 30 40E
93 Amsterdam, U.S.A. 42 58N 74 6w
63 Amu Darya, R., U.S.S.R. 40 30N 62 0E
51 Amul, Iran 36 25N 52 10E
89 Amundsen Gulf, Canada 70 30N 123 0w
61 Amur, R., U.S.S.R. 52 0N 126 30E
61 Amurang, Indonesia 1 15N 124 30E
62 An Nafud, Des., Arabia 28 40N 42 0E
62 An Najaf, Iraq 32 0N 44 20E
62 An Nasiriyah, Iraq 31 0N 46 15E
68 An Nhon, Vietnam 13 40N 109 20E
36 An Uaimh, Ireland 53 40N 6 42w
63 Anabta, Jordan 32 19N 35 7E
90 Anaconda, U.S.A. 46 8N 112 58w
61 Anadyr & G., U.S.S.R. 64 40N 178 0E
61 Anadyr R., U.S.S.R. 65 0N 170 0E
90 Anaheim, U.S.A. 33 50N 118 0w
62 Anaiza, Saudi Arabia 26 44N 44 8E
64 Anakapalle, India 17 25N 82 50E
75 Analalava, Madagascar 14 35s 48 0E
68 Anambas Is., Indonesia 3 0N 106 0E
51 Anamur, Turkey 36 8N 32 58E
99 Anatuya, Argentina 28 20s 62 45w
42 Anaye, Niger. 19 28N 13 9E
88 Anchorage, Alaska 61 10N 150 0w
98 Anchohuma, Mt., Bolivia 16 0s 68 50w
40 Ancón, Panama Canal Zone (inset)
40 Ancona, Italy 43 38N 13 34E
99 Ancud & G., Chile 42 5s 73 48w
99 Andalgala, Argentina 27 50s 66 30w
48 Åndalsnes, Norway 62 35N 7 43E
37 Andalusia, Prov., Spain 37 20N 5 0w
37 Andalusia, U.S.A. 31 16N 86 30w
99 Andam, Wadi, Oman 21 30N 58 20E
55 Andaman Is., Indian Oc. 12 0N 92 40E
75 Andara, S.W. Africa 18 2s 21 9E
45 Andermatt, Switzerland 46 38N 8 37E
92 Anderson, Ind., U.S.A. 40 1N 85 40w
91 Anderson, S.C., U.S.A. 34 27N 82 36w
96 Andes, Mts., S. America 7 0N to 53 0s 65 0 to 80 0w
64 Andhra Pradesh, st., India 17 0N 81 0E
41 Andikithira I., Greece 35 40N 23 16E
60 Andizhan, U.S.S.R. 41 0N 72 37E
37 Andorra, Europe 42 28N 1 30E
23 Andover, England 51 12N 1 29w
88 Andreanof Is., Alaska 51 30N 178 0w
40 Andria, Italy 41 11N 16 17E
95 Andros I., Bahamas 24 40N 78 15w
41 Andros I., Greece 37 50N 24 53E
37 Andujar, Spain 38 0N 4 5w
72 Anécho, Togo 6 8N 1 32E
61 Angara, R., Siberia 58 0N 97 0E
61 Angarsk, U.S.S.R. 52 30N 104 0E
83 Angaston, Australia 34 28s 139 5E
49 Ånge, Sweden 62 31N 15 35E
94 Angel de la Guarda, Mexico 29 20N 113 35w
49 Ångelholm, Sweden 56 15N 12 58E
83 Angellala, Australia 26 20s 146 50E
65 Angenong, China 31 55N 94 10E
42 Angers, France 47 30N 0 38w
25 Anglesey I., Wales 53 20N 4 20w

* Renamed Nzeto

89 Angmagssalik, Greenland 65 40N 37 20w
74 Ango, Zaïre 4 10N 26 5E
99 Angol, Chile 38 0s 72 45w
75 Angola, Port. Terr., Afr. 12 0s 19 0E
43 Angoulême, France 45 40N 0 10E
43 Angoumois, Dist., Fr. 45 43N 0 15E
75 Angren, U.S.S.R. 41 0N 69 10E
95 Anguilla I., W. Indies 18 0N 63 0w
33 Angus, Braes of, Scotland 56 45N 2 55w
49 Anholt, I., Denmark 56 43N 11 25E
66 Anhwei, Prov., China 32 0N 117 0E
64 Anjidiv I., India 14 45N 74 10E
42 Anjou, Prov., France 47 20N 0 50w
75 Anjozorobe, Madagascar 18 22s 47 52E
72 Anka, Nigeria 12 13N 5 58E
51 Ankara, Turkey 39 58N 32 28E
75 Ankazoabo, Madagascar 22 15s 44 45E
75 Ankazobe, Madagascar 18 17s 47 2E
66 Anking, China 30 40N 117 2E
46 Anklam, Germany 53 50N 13 40E
74 Ankoro, Zaïre 6 43s 26 45E
92 Ann Arbor, U.S.A. 42 12N 83 48w
72 Annaba (Bône), Algeria 36 55N 7 45E
68 Annam, reg., Vietnam 16 0N 107 0E
31 Annan, Scotland 55 0N 3 17w
31 Annandale, Dist. & R., Scotland 55 15N 3 25w
92 Annapolis, Md., U.S.A. 39 0N 76 15w
93 Annapolis Royal, Canada 44 45N 65 42w
43 Annecy, France 45 46N 6 5E
26 Annfield Plain, England 54 52N 1 45w
51 Anniston, U.S.A. 33 45N 85 50w
71 Annobon, I. see Pagalu
43 Annonay, France 45 15N 4 40E
94 Annotto Bay, Jamaica 18 17N 76 43w
83 Annuello, Australia 34 55s 142 55E
45 Anoka, U.S.A. 45 14N 93 29w
45 Ansbach, Germany 49 21N 10 37E
66 Anshan, China 41 2N 122 10E
66 Ansi, China 40 37N 95 50E
72 Ansongo, Mali 15 50N 0 25E
22 Anstey, England 52 41N 1 14w
31 Anstruther, Scotland 56 13N 2 41w
51 Antakya, Turkey 36 10N 36 15E
75 Antalaha, Madagascar 14 57s 50 20E
51 Antalya & G., Turkey 37 0N 30 43E
37 Antequera, Spain 37 4N 4 31w
72 Anti Atlas, Mts., Morocco 30 0N 7 0w
43 Antibes, France 43 40N 7 10E
93 Anticosti, I., Canada 49 30N 63 0w
72 Antigo, U.S.A. 45 10N 89 11w
95 Antigua, I., W. Indies 17 12N 61 45w
94 Antilla, Cuba 20 50N 75 50w
62 Antioch, see Antakya
98 Antioquia, Columbia 6 40N 76 0w
4 Antipodes I., S. Pac. Oc. 50 0s 178 0E
99 Antofagasta, Chile 23 45s 70 18w
75 Antonio Enes, Mozam. 16 8s 39 50E
36 Antrim, & Co., N. Ireland 54 42N 6 12w
36 Antrim, Mts. of N. Ire. 54 57N 6 10w
75 Antsalova, Madagascar 18 40s 44 37E
75 Antsirabe, Madagascar 19 55s 47 2E
75 Antsohihy, Madagascar 14 50s 47 50E
67 Antung, China 40 9N 124 22E
44 Antwerp, & Prov., Belg. 51 13N 4 25E
64 Anupgarh, India 29 10N 73 5E
64 Anuradhapura, Sri Lanka 8 20N 80 23E
80 Anxious B., Australia 33 20s 134 40E
66 Anyang, China 36 15N 114 35E
61 Anzhero-Sudzhensk, U.S.S.R. 56 10N 85 40E
43 Anzin, France 50 20N 3 30E
40 Anzio, Italy 41 28N 12 37E
67 Aomori, & Pref., Japan 40 40N 140 40E
41 Aosta, Italy 45 46N 7 20E
72 Aoulef Arab, Algeria 27 0N 1 0E
91 Apalachee B., U.S.A. 30 0N 84 0w
91 Apalachicola, U.S.A. 29 47N 85 5w
68 Aparri, Philippines 18 15N 121 50E
44 Apeldoorn, Netherlands 52 13N 5 58E
40 Apennines, Mts., Italy 43 0N 13 0E
80 Apia, Upolu I., Samoa (Inset)
73 Apollonia (Marsa Susa), Libya 32 52N 21 59E
44 Apostle Is., U.S.A. 47 0N 90 45w
92 Appalachians, Mts., U.S.A. 37 0N 80 20w
44 Appenzell, & Cn., Switz. 47 20N 9 24E
44 Appingedam, Netherlands 53 17N 6 45E
26 Appleby, England 54 35N 2 30w
23 Appledore, Devon, England 51 3N 4 12w
23 Appledore, Kent, England 51 2N 0 47E
92 Appleton, U.S.A. 44 17N 88 27w
40 Apulia, Reg., Italy 40 40N 17 20E
95 Apure, R., Venezuela 7 30N 69 15w
98 Apurimac, R., Peru 13 0s 73 0w
73 Aqaba, & Gulf, Jordan 29 0N 35 0E
62 Ar Rutbah, Iraq 33 0N 40 10E
62-63 Arab Emirates, Union of 23 50N 52 30E
72 Araba, Nigeria 13 7N 5 0E
62 Arabia, Asia 15 0 to 30 0N; 35 0 to 59 0E
73 Arabian Des., Egypt 28 0N 32 20E
57 Arabian Sea, Indian Oc. 17 0N 65 0E
98 Aracaju, Brazil 11 0s 37 0w
43 Aracati, Brazil 4 20s 37 45w
37 Aracena, Spain 37 53N 6 36w
98 Araçuai, Brazil 17 30s 42 0w
43 Arad, Israel 31 16N 35 13E
47 Arad, Rumania 46 10N 21 13E
65 Arakan Coast Dist., Bur. 20 43N 93 20E

65 Arakan Yoma, Mts., Burma 20 0N 94 0E
51 Araks, R., Asia 39 0N 47 30E
60 Aral Sea, Cent. Asia 45 0N 59 0E
60 Aralsk, U.S.S.R. 46 50N 61 20E
82 Aramac, Australia 22 58s 145 14E
36 Aran I., Ireland 55 0N 8 32w
34 Aran Is, Ireland 53 5N 9 35w
75 Aranjuez, Spain 40 1N 3 38w
75 Aranos, S.W. Afr. 24 9s 19 7E
91 Aransas Pass, U.S.A. 27 55N 97 0w
72 Araouane, Mali 19 0N 3 30w
51 Araq, Iran 34 0N 49 50E
31 Ararat, Australia 37 30s 142 37E
51 Ararat, Mt., Turkey 39 40N 44 25E
98 Araripe, Sa. do, plat., Brazil 7 0s 40 0w
31 Arbroath, Scotland 56 33N 2 36w
42 Arcachon, France 44 39N 1 13w
37 Arcos, Spain 36 44N 5 47w
64 Arcot, India 12 50N 79 26E
100 Arctic Ocean
88 Arctic Red R., Canada 67 15N 134 0w
32 Ardcharnich, Scotland 57 52N 5 5w
36 Ardee, Ireland 53 51N 6 32w
42 Ardennes, Dépt., France 49 35N 4 50E
44 Ardennes, Mts., Belg.-Fr. 50 0N 5 30E
51 Ardestan, Iran 33 22N 52 24E
36 Ardfinnan, Ireland 52 20N 7 53w
36 Ardglass, N. Ireland 54 15N 5 56w
32 Ardhasig, Scotland 57 55N 6 51w
36 Ardkeen, N. Ireland 54 27N 5 53w
35 Ardmore & Hd., Ire. 51 58N 7 44w
90 Ardmore, U.S.A. 34 11N 97 9w
34 Ardnacrusha, Ireland 52 42N 8 38w
32 Ardnamurchan Pt., Scot. 56 46N 6 14w
30 Ardrossan, Scotland 55 39N 4 49w
49 Arendal, Norway 58 28N 8 43E
42 Arenig Fach, Mt., Wales 52 57N 3 46w
98 Arequipa, Peru 16 30s 71 25w
42 Arès, France 44 46N 1 10w
40 Arévalo, Spain 41 0N 4 45w
40 Arezzo, Italy 43 29N 11 54E
42 Argentan, France 48 43N 0 2w
42 Argentat, France 45 8N 2 0E
96 Argentina, S. Amer. 30 0s 65 0w
99 Argentino, L., Argentina 50 30s 72 54w
42 Argenton, France 46 35N 1 30E
41 Argolis, G. of, Greece 37 44N 22 54E
41 Argos, Greece 37 39N 22 42E
72 Argungu, Nigeria 12 55N 4 30E
30 Argyll, Dist., Scot. 56 20N 5 25w
98 Arica, Chile 18 37s 70 18w
80 Arid, C., Australia 34 0s 123 20E
51 Ariège, Dépt., France 43 20N 1 30E
94 Arima, Trinidad 10 40N 61 15w
98 Arinos, R., Brazil 12 0s 57 0w
98 Aripuana, R., Brazil 7 30s 60 0w
51 Arisaig & Sd. of, Scot. 56 54N 5 48w
90 Arizona, st., U.S.A. 34 0N 111 30w
48 Arjeplog, Sweden 66 0N 18 0E
37 Arkaig, L., Scotland 56 58N 5 10w
90 Arkansas, st., U.S.A. 35 0N 92 0w
91 Arkansas, R., U.S.A. 35 0N 92 0w
91 Arkhangelsk, U.S.S.R. 64 35N 40 50E
35 Arklow, & Hd., Ireland 52 47N 6 9w
43 Arles, France 43 10N 4 42E
44 Arlon, Belgium 49 41N 5 49E
31 Armadale, Scotland 55 54N 3 42w
36 Armagh & Co., N. Ire. 54 20N 6 38w
51 Armavir, U.S.S.R. 45 0N 41 7E
51 Armenia, S.S.R. 40 0N 45 0E
43 Armentières, France 50 40N 2 55E
83 Armidale, Australia 30 30s 151 40E
48 Arnar Fjord, Iceland 65 45N 23 50w
48 Arnes, Iceland 66 2N 22 32w
44 Arnhem, Netherlands 51 59N 5 55E
80 Arnhem B., Austral. 12 15s 136 4E
80 Arnhem Ld., Australia 13 15s 133 30E
40 Arno, R., Italy 43 41N 10 40w
48 Arnold, England 53 0N 1 8w
92 Arnprior, Canada 45 28N 76 26w
76 Aroab, S.W. Afr. 26 41s 19 39E
37 Aroche, Spain 37 58N 7 0w
43 Arona, Italy 45 48N 8 33E
51 Arqa, S. Yemen 13 35N 47 22E
65 Arrah, India 25 40N 84 38E
94 Arraijan, Panama 8 57N 79 38w
51 Arran I., Scotland 55 35N 5 15w
43 Arras, France 50 17N 2 40E
72 Arrecife, Canary Is. 28 58N 13 35w
43 Arrée, Mts. d', France 48 25N 3 35w
51 Arrow L., Ireland 54 3N 8 19w
67 Arshan, China 47 20N 119 55E
41 Arta, Greece 39 10N 20 59E
61 Artem, U.S.S.R. 43 50N 131 55E
52 Artemovsk, U.S.S.R. 48 25N 38 5E
61 Artemovski, U.S.S.R. 54 45N 93 35E
43 Artois, Prov., France 50 30N 2 20E
51 Artvin, Turkey 41 10N 41 3E
74 Arua, Uganda 3 1N 30 58E
95 Aruba I., Neth. W. Indies 12 30N 70 0w
65 Arunachal Pradesh, st., India 28 0N 95 0E
23 Arundel, England 50 52N 0 33w
74 Arusha, Tanzania 3 10s 36 30E
74 Aruwimi, R., Zaïre 1 30N 25 0E
45 Arve, R., France 45 56N 6 40E

49 Arvika, Sweden 59 43N 12 34E
60 Arys, U.S.S.R. 42 20N 68 30E
52 Arzamas, U.S.S.R. 55 30N 43 45E
72 Arzew, Algeria 35 50N 0 40w
63 As Rabbah, Jordan 31 10N 35 45E
62 As Sabya, Saudi Arabia 17 10N 42 37E
63 As Salt, Jordan 32 1N 35 44E
63 As Sohar, Oman 24 20N 56 40E
63 As Zahiriyah, Jordan 31 24N 34 56E
67 Asahigawa, Japan 43 50N 142 20E
5 Ascension I., Atlantic Oc. 7 55s 14 0w
45 Aschaffenburg, Germany 49 58N 9 10E
40 Ascoli Piceno, Italy 42 54N 13 37E
23 Ascot, England 51 24N 0 41w
74 Aseb, Ethiopia 13 5N 42 38E
74 Asela, Ethiopia 8 0N 39 0E
44 Asfeld, France 49 27N 4 5E
25 Ash, England 51 16N 0 18w
62 Ash Shihr, S. Yemen 14 50N 49 35E
62 Ashaira, Saudi Arabia 21 40N 40 40E
27 Ashbourne, England 53 1N 1 44w
24 Ashburton, England 50 31N 3 46w
84 Ashburton, N.Z. 53 59s 171 52E
80 Ashburton R., Australia 22 20s 115 12E
25 Ashby-de-la-Zouch, Eng. 52 45N 1 30w
63 Ashdod, Israel 31 49N 34 38E
63 Ashdod Yam, Israel 31 47N 34 39E
23 Ashdown Forest, Eng. 51 4N 0 10E
23 Asheville, U.S.A. 35 40N 82 33w
23 Ashford, England 51 8N 0 52E
67 Ashikaga, Japan 36 25N 139 20E
25 Ashington, England 55 12N 1 35w
63 Ashkhabad, U.S.S.R. 38 5N 58 22E
92 Ashland, Ky., U.S.A. 38 30N 82 42w
92 Ashland, Wis., U.S.A. 46 30N 91 0w
63 Ashquelon, Israel 31 40N 34 35E
92 Ashtabula, U.S.A. 41 55N 80 47w
26 Ashton-in-Makerfield, England 53 29N 2 39w
26 Ashton-under-Lyne, Eng. 53 30N 2 8w
5 Asia, Continent
51 Asia Minor, see Anatolia
72 Asilah, Morocco 35 30N 6 0w
63 Asino, U.S.S.R. 57 0N 86 0E
62 Asir, Dist., Saudi Arabia 18 25N 43 0E
49 Askersund, Sweden 58 58N 14 8E
74 Asmera, Ethiopia 15 20N 38 49E
23 Aspatria, England 54 45N 3 20w
84 Aspiring, Mt., N.Z. 44 31s 168 41E
65 Assam, st., India 25 20N 93 0E
44 Asse, Belgium 50 55N 4 12E
44 Assen, Netherlands 53 0N 6 35E
88 Assiniboia, Canada 49 36N 106 4w
88 Assiniboine R., Canada 49 45N 99 0w
72 Assinie, Ivory Coast 5 9N 3 15w
40 Assisi, Italy 43 5N 12 38E
40 Assynt, L. & Dist., Scot. 58 10N 5 1w
40 Asti, Italy 44 54N 8 15E
92 Astorga, Spain 42 28N 6 8w
90 Astoria, U.S.A. 46 10N 123 45E
52 Astrakhan, U.S.S.R. 46 25N 48 8w
37 Asturias, Prov., Spain 43 20N 5 50E
99 Asunción, Paraguay 25 25s 57 35E
73 Aswan, Egypt 24 12N 32 59E
73 Asyut, Egypt 27 15N 31 0s
72 Atacama Des., Chile 25 0s 70 0w
72 Atakpame, Togo 7 35N 1 0E
72 Atar, Mauritania 20 30N 13 0w
61 Atara, U.S.S.R. 63 10N 129 10E
60 Atasu, U.S.S.R. 48 30N 71 0E
73 Atbara, Sudan 17 20N 35 0E
73 Atbara, R., Sudan 13 50N 36 0E
91 Atbasar, U.S.S.R. 51 50N 68 5E
91 Atchison, U.S.A. 39 31N 95 10w
44 Ath, Belgium 50 39N 3 48E
88 Athabasca, Canada 54 48N 113 15w
88 Athabasca L. & R., Can. 59 20N 109 30w
35 Athboy, Ireland 53 38N 7 5w
34 Athenry, Ireland 53 19N 8 45w
41 Athens, Greece 37 59N 23 42E
91 Athens, Georgia, U.S.A. 33 57N 83 29w
92 Athens, Ohio, U.S.A. 39 28N 82 12w
91 Athens, Tenn., U.S.A. 35 29N 84 42w
22 Atherstone, England 52 35N 1 32w
82 Atherton, Australia 16 54s 145 3E
26 Atherton, England 53 32N 2 30w
34 Athleague, Ireland 53 34N 8 17w
34 Athlone, Ireland 53 27N 7 55w
33 Athol, Forest of, Scot. 56 51N 4 0w
41 Athos, Mt., Greece 40 9N 24 23E
35 Athy, Ireland 53 0N 7 0w
73 Ati, Chad 13 25N 17 0E
92 Atikokan, Canada 48 45N 91 43w
52 Atkarsk, U.S.S.R. 51 55N 45 3E
91 Atlanta, U.S.A. 33 45N 84 25w
93 Atlantic City, U.S.A. 39 24N 74 28w
10 Atlantic Ocean, N. 35 0N 40 0w
10 Atlantic Ocean, S. 20 0s 10 0w
72 Atlas Mts., Morocco 33 0N 7 0w
44 Attigny, France 49 29N 4 35E
27 Attleborough, England 52 32N 1 1E
64 Attock, Pakistan 33 58N 72 32E
68 Attopeu, Laos 14 50N 107 0E
64 Attur, India 11 35N 78 30E
43 Aubagne, France 43 20N 5 30E
42 Aube, Dépt., France 48 30N 4 0E
43 Aube, R., France 48 35N 4 30E
43 Aubenas, France 44 38N 4 24E
43 Aubenton, France 49 50N 4 11E
43 Aubigny, France 47 30N 2 25E
45 Aubonne, Switzerland 46 31N 6 42E
93 Auburn, Me., U.S.A. 44 0N 70 10w
93 Auburn, N.Y., U.S.A. 42 55N 76 38w
43 Auch, France 43 39N 0 32E

Auchinleck, Scotland 55 28N 4 18W
Auchterarder, Scotland 56 18N 3 43W
Auchterderran, Scotland 56 9N 3 16W
Auchtermuchty, Scotland 56 18N 3 15W
Auchtertyre, Scotland 57 17N 5 35W
Auckland, N.Z. 36 50s 174 42E
Auckland Is., S. Ocean 51 0s 168 0E
Aude, Dépt., France 43 2N 2 25E
Aude, R., France 42 47N 2 9E
Audierne, France 48 2N 4 38W
Aughnacloy, N. Ireland 54 26N 6 59W
Aughrus More, Ireland 53 34N 10 10W
Augsburg, Germany 48 26N 10 53E
Augusta, Australia 34 18s 115 12E
Augusta, Italy 37 14N 15 12E
Augusta, Me., U.S.A. 44 20N 69 45W
Augusta, Ga., U.S.A. 33 30N 82 0W
Augustow, Poland 53 51N 22 58E
Augustus, Mt., Australia 24 8s 117 0E
Aulnoye, France 50 11N 3 50E
Aunis, Dist., France 46 9N 0 57W
Aurangabad, India 19 55N 75 30E
Auray, France 47 40N 3 0W
Aurillac, France 44 58N 2 27E
Aurora, Ill., U.S.A. 41 48N 88 15W
Aus, S.W. Africa 26 43s 16 12E
Aust-Agder, Co., Norway 59 0N 8 30E
Austin, Minn., U.S.A. 43 39N 92 59W
Austin, Tex., U.S.A. 30 20N 97 46W
Austral Downs, Australia 20 45s 137 40E
Austral Is., Pacific Ocean 23 0s 150 0W
Australia, Commonwealth of, 25 0s 135 0E
Australian Alps, Australia 37 0s 148 0E
Australian Cap. Terr., Australia 35 15N 149 8E
Austria, Europe 47 30N 13 20E
Austvågöy, I., Norway 68 25N 14 45E
Autun, France 47 1N 4 20E
Auvergne, Prov., France 45 30N 3 0E
Auvergne Monts d', France 45 30N 3 0E
Auxerre, France 47 48N 3 33W
Avakubi, Zaïre 1 16N 27 30E
Avallon, France 47 34N 3 49E
Aveh, Iran 35 40N 49 15E
Aveiro, Portugal 40 39N 8 39W
Avellino, Italy 41 0N 14 42E
Aversa, Italy 41 0N 14 10E
Avesnes, France 50 9N 3 55E
Avesta, Sweden 60 13N 16 8E
Aveyron, Dépt., France 44 10N 2 45E
Aviá Terai, Argentina 26 30s 60 45W
Avignon, France 43 58N 4 54E
Avila, Spain 40 39N 4 41W
Aviles, Spain 43 33N 6 0W
Avoca, Ireland 52 51N 6 12W
Avon, Co., England 51 25N 2 35W
Avon, R., Hants, Eng. 51 8N 1 48W
Avon, R., Warwick, Eng. 52 22N 1 25W
Avon, R., Scotland 57 15N 3 23W
Avon Downs, Australia 19 58s 137 25E
Avonmouth, England 51 30N 2 43W
Avranches, France 48 42N 1 18W
Awash, Ethiopia 8 9N 40 7E
Awe, L. & R., Scotland 56 17N 5 15W
Awjilah, Libya 29 8N 21 7E
Axar, Fd., Iceland 66 20N 16 45W
Axbridge, England 51 17N 2 50W
Axe, R., England 51 17N 2 50W
Axe Edge, England 53 13N 1 58W
Axim, Ghana 4 58N 2 6W
Axminster, England 50 46N 3 0W
Ayacucho, Peru 12 58s 74 5W
Ayaguz, U.S.S.R. 48 10N 80 0E
Ayamonte, Spain 37 15N 7 24W
Ayan, U.S.S.R. 56 0N 137 0E
Aydin, Turkey 37 55N 27 55E
Ayios Evstratios, I., Gr. 39 30N 24 59E
Aylesbury, England 51 49N 0 48W
Aylesford, England 51 18N 0 29E
Aylsham, England 52 48N 1 16E
Ayr, Australia 19 36s 147 25E
Ayr, Scotland 55 27N 4 37W
Ayre, Pt. of, Isle of Man 54 25N 4 22W
Ayton, England 54 15N 0 29W
Ayutla, Mexico 17 0N 99 5W
Ayutthaya, Thailand 14 30N 100 40E
Ayvalik, Turkey 39 20N 26 50E
Azamgarh, India 26 15N 83 16E
Azare, Nigeria 11 55N 10 10E
Azerbaijan, S.S.R., U.S.S.R. 40 20N 48 0E
Azores Is., Atlantic Oc. 39 0N 29 0W
Azov, U.S.S.R. 47 3N 39 20E
Azov, S. of U.S.S.R. 45 53N 35 35E
Azpeitia, Spain 43 19N 2 14W
Azua, Dominican Rep. 18 15N 70 40W
Azuaga, Spain 38 16N 5 42W
Azul, Argentina 36 25s 59 40W

B

Ba'abda, Lebanon 33 50N 35 32E
Ba'labakk (Baalbek), Leb. 34 0N 36 12E
Baarle-Nassau, Neth. 51 27N 4 57E
Baarn, Neth. 52 13N 5 17E
Bab el Mandeb Str. 12 37N 43 22E
Babar Is., Indonesia 8 2s 128 58E
Babinda, Australia 17 25N 146 0E
Babine L., Canada 54 40N 126 10W
Baboua, Central Africa 5 49N 14 58E
Babul, Iran 36 40N 52 40E
Babushkin, U.S.S.R. 55 50N 38 0E
Babuyan Is., Philippines 19 20N 121 45E

Bacan Gr., Is., Indonesia 0 30s 127 0E
Bacau, Rumania 46 30N 26 59E
Baccarat, France 48 30N 6 45E
Bachelina, U.S.S.R. 57 45N 67 20E
Backnang, Germany 48 57N 9 26E
Bacolod, Philippines 10 40N 123 2E
Bacuit, Philippines 11 0N 119 25E
Bacup, England 53 44N 2 13W
Bad Hersfeld, Germany 50 50N 9 40E
Bad Homburg, Germany 50 15N 8 36E
Bad Ischl, Austria 47 40N 13 39E
Bad Kissingen, Germany 50 10N 10 10E
Bad Kreuznach, Germany 49 51N 7 50E
Bad Lands, U.S.A. 43 30N 102 10W
Bad Mergentheim, Ger. 49 29N 9 46E
Badagara, India 11 35N 75 35E
Badagri, Nigeria 6 25N 2 55E
Badajoz, Spain 38 50N 6 59W
Badakhshan, Dist., Afghanistan 36 40N 70 0E
Badalona, Spain 41 28N 2 30E
Badampahar, India 22 10N 86 10E
Baddo, R., Pak. 28 0N 65 0E
Baden, Austria 48 0N 16 46E
Baden, Switzerland 47 29N 8 18E
Baden-Baden, Germany 48 44N 8 18E
Badenoch, Dist., Scot. 57 5N 4 0W
Baden-Württemburg, Länd, Germany 48 45N 9 0E
Badgastein, Austria 47 7N 13 9E
Badrinath, India 30 45N 79 25E
Badulla, Sri Lanka 6 48N 81 7E
Baffin B. & I., Canada 73 0N 70 0W
Bafia, Cameroon 4 40N 11 0E
Bafoulabe, Mali 13 45N 11 0W
Bafq, Iran 31 40N 55 28E
Bafwasende, Zaïre 1 20N 27 20E
Bagansiapiapi, Indonesia 2 5N 101 0E
Bagé, Brazil 31 10s 54 0W
Bagenalstown, see Muine Bheag
Baghdad, Iraq 33 23N 44 30E
Bagh nam Faoileann, B., Scotland 57 22N 7 10W
Bagnères de Bigorre, Fr. 43 0N 0 5E
Bagnères de Luchon, Fr. 42 45N 0 35E
Bagotville, Canada 48 28N 70 58W
Bagrach Kol, China 42 0N 87 0E
Bagshot, England 51 21N 0 39W
Baguio, Philippines 16 17N 120 47E
Bahama Is., W. Indies 26 0N 77 30W
Bahawalpur, Pak. 29 0N 72 0E
Bahia Prov., Brazil 12 0s 42 0W
Bahia Blanca, Argentina 38 45s 62 25W
Bahias, C. dos, Argentina 45 0s 65 30W
Bahr el Abyad (White Nile), Sudan 13 30N 33 0E
Bahr el Azraq (Blue Nile), Sudan 14 30N 33 0E
Bahr el Ghazal, R., Sudan 9 0N 30 0E
Bahr el Jebel, R., Sudan 7 30N 30 35E
Bahra, Saudi Arabia 21 15N 39 30E
Bahraich, India 27 48N 81 30E
Bahrain I., Persian G. 26 0N 50 23E
Bahu Kalat, Iran 25 40N 61 15E
Baia Mare, Rumania 47 40N 23 32E
Baie Comeau, Canada 49 25N 68 20W
Baikit, U.S.S.R. 61 40N 96 5E
Baikonur, U.S.S.R. 47 48N 66 4E
Baildon, England 53 52N 1 46W
Baillieborough, Ireland 53 56N 6 59W
Bain, France 47 52N 1 40W
Bainbridge, U.S.A. 31 0N 84 30W
Baird Mts. Alaska 60 45N 160 0W
Bairnsdale, Australia 38 0s 147 32E
Baitadi, Nepal, India 29 35N 80 25E
Baja, Hungary 46 10N 19 0E
Bakala, Central Africa 6 15N 20 20E
Baker, Ore., U.S.A. 44 45N 117 50W
Baker Lake, Canada 64 20N 96 0W
Baker, Mt., U.S.A. 48 45N 121 45W
Baker's Dozen, Is., Can. 56 45N 79 20W
Bakersfield, Calif., U.S.A. 35 22N 119 0W
Bakewell, England 53 12N 1 40W
Bakkagerdi, Iceland 65 33N 13 58W
Bakony Forest, Hungary 47 30N 18 0E
Baku, U.S.S.R. 40 27N 49 48E
Bala, U.S.S.R. 66 40N 133 5E
Bala, tn. & L., Wales 52 55N 3 37W
Ba'labakk, Lebanon 34 0N 36 12E
Balaghat Ra., India 18 58N 76 0E
Balaguer, Spain 41 50N 0 50E
Balaklava, Australia 34 2s 138 20E
Balaklava, U.S.S.R. 44 37N 33 44E
Balangir, India 20 50N 83 25E
Balashikha, U.S.S.R. 55 47N 37 59E
Balashov, U.S.S.R. 51 35N 43 5E
Balasore, India 21 31N 87 10E
Balaton, L., Hungary 46 47N 17 40E
Balbeggie, Scotland 56 26N 3 19W
Balboa, Panama Canal Zone (Inset)
Balbriggan, Ireland 53 37N 6 11W
Balchik, Bulgaria 43 23N 28 11E
Balclutha, N.Z. 46 15s 169 50E
Baldock, England 51 59N 0 11W
Baldy Pk., U.S.A. 33 50N 109 30W
Baldzhikan, U.S.S.R. 49 20N 110 30E
Balearic I., Spain 39 40N 3 0E
Baleshare I., Scotland 57 31N 7 21W
Balfouriya, Israel 32 38N 35 17E
Balfron, Scotland 56 4N 4 20W
Bali, Cameroon 5 54N 10 0E
Bali, I., Indonesia 8 30s 115 20E
Balikesir, Turkey 39 40N 28 2E

Balikpapan, Indonesia 1 10s 116 55E
Balintore, Scotland 57 45N 3 55W
Balipara, India 26 54N 92 51E
Balkan Mts., Bulgaria 42 50N 24 50E
Balkhash, L., U.S.S.R. 46 30N 76 0E
Balkh, Afghanistan 36 44N 66 47E
Balla, Bangladesh 24 10N 91 35E
Ballachulish, Scot., see N. Ballachulish
Ballaghaderreen, Ireland 53 55N 8 34W
Ballantrae, Scotland 55 6N 5 0W
Ballarat, Australia 37 37s 143 50E
Ballater, Scotland 57 3N 3 3W
Ballina, Australia 28 48s 153 40E
Ballina, Mayo, Ireland 54 8N 9 10W
Ballina, Tipperary, Ire. 52 50N 8 27W
Ballinalee, Ireland 53 46N 7 40W
Ballinamore, Ireland 54 7N 7 48W
Ballinasloe, Ireland 53 20N 8 13W
Ballincollig, Ireland 51 52N 8 35W
Ballindaggin, Ireland 52 34N 6 41W
Ballindine, Ireland 53 40N 8 57W
Ballineen, Ireland 51 44N 8 57W
Ballingarry, Limerick, Ire. 52 29N 8 50W
Ballingarry, Tipp., Ire. 53 1N 8 3W
Ballinlough, Ireland 53 45N 8 39W
Ballinluig, Scotland 56 38N 3 39W
Ballinrobe, Ireland 53 37N 9 12W
Ballintoy, Ireland 55 13N 6 20W
Ballintra, Ireland 54 35N 8 9W
Balloch, Scotland 56 0N 4 35W
Ballon, Ireland 52 44N 6 47W
Ballybay, Ireland 54 8N 6 52W
Ballybofey, Ireland 54 48N 7 47W
Ballybunion, Ireland 52 31N 9 40W
Ballycanew, Ireland 52 37N 6 18W
Ballyconnell, Ireland 54 7N 7 35W
Ballycotton, Ireland 51 50N 8 0W
Ballycroy, Ireland 54 2N 9 49W
Ballydavid, Ireland 52 13N 10 21W
Ballydehob, Ireland 51 34N 9 29W
Ballyduff, Kerry, Ire. 52 27N 9 40W
Ballyduff, Waterford, Ire. 52 9N 8 2W
Ballyforan, Ireland 53 28N 8 16W
Ballygar, Ireland 53 33N 8 20W
Ballygarrett, Ireland 52 34N 6 15W
Ballygawley, N. Ireland 54 27N 7 2W
Ballyhaise, Ireland 54 3N 7 20W
Ballyhalbert, N. Ireland 54 30N 5 33W
Ballyhaunis, Ireland 53 47N 8 47W
Ballyheige, Ireland 52 24N 9 50W
Ballyjamesduff, Ireland 53 52N 7 11W
Ballylanders, Ireland 52 23N 8 21W
Ballylongford, Ireland 52 34N 9 30W
Ballylynan, Ireland 52 56N 7 3W
Ballymahon, Ireland 53 33N 7 47W
Ballymoe, Ireland 53 41N 8 28W
Ballymore, Ireland 53 29N 7 40W
Ballymore Eustace, Ire. 53 8N 6 38W
Ballynacargy, Ireland 53 35N 7 32W
Ballynahinch, N. Ireland 54 25N 5 54W
Ballynure, N. Ireland 54 47N 5 59W
Ballyragget, Ireland 52 47N 7 20W
Ballyroan, Ireland 52 57N 7 20W
Ballysadare, Ireland 54 12N 8 30W
Ballyshannon, Ireland 54 30N 8 10W
Ballyvaughan, Ireland 53 7N 9 9W
Ballywalter, N. Ireland 54 33N 5 30W
Balmoral Castle, Scotland 57 2N 3 14W
Balquhidder, Scotland 56 22N 4 22W
Balrampur, India 27 25N 82 20E
Balranald, Australia 34 40s 143 35E
Balsas, R., Mexico 18 30N 102 0W
Balsthal, Switzerland 47 19N 7 42E
Baltic Sea, Europe 57 0N 19 30E
Baltiisk, U.S.S.R. 54 40N 19 10E
Baltimore, Ireland 51 29N 9 20W
Baltimore, U.S.A. 39 25N 76 40W
Baluchistan, Reg., Pak. 27 30N 65 0E
Bam, Iran 29 5N 58 23E
Bamako, Mali 12 30N 7 45W
Bamba, Mali 17 0N 1 0W
Bambari, Central Africa 5 40N 20 35E
Bambaroo, Australia 18 57s 146 15E
Bamberg, Germany 49 53N 11 14E
Bamburgh, England 55 37N 1 42W
Bamian, Afghanistan 35 0N 67 53E
Bampton, England 51 44N 1 33W
Bampur, Iran 27 8N 60 8E
Ban Aranyaprathet, Thailand 13 40N 102 35E
Ban Khemmarat, Thail. 16 0N 105 20E
Banagher, Ireland 53 12N 8 0W
Banalia, Zaïre 1 40N 25 20E
Banaras, India see Varanasi
Banat, Dist., Rumania 45 27N 21 35E
Banbridge, N. Ireland 54 20N 6 16W
Banbury, England 52 4N 1 20W
Banchory, Scotland 57 3N 2 30W
Bancroft, Zambia, see Chililabombwe
Banda Aceh, Indonesia 5 35N 95 25E
Banda Sea, East Indies 6 0s 127 30E
Bandaisan, Mt., Japan 37 40N 140 30E
Bandama, R., Ivory Coast 7 0N 5 0W
Bandar Abbas, Iran 27 15N 56 23E
Bandar Rig, Iran 29 27N 50 47E
*Bandar Shapur, Iran 30 10N 48 40E
Bandiagara, Mali 14 12N 3 29W
Bandirma, Turkey 40 21N 27 58E
Bandon, Ireland 51 44N 8 44W
Bandundu, Zaïre 3 12s 17 12E

* *Renamed Bandar Khomeyni*

Bangung, Indonesia 6 48s 107 45E
Banff, Canada 51 14N 115 38W
Banff, Scotland 57 41N 2 32W
Banfora, Volta 10 40N 4 40W
Bangalore, India 12 58N 77 30E
Bangassou, Central Africa 4 50N 22 48E
Banggai, Arch., Indonesia 1 15s 123 0E
Bangka, I., Indonesia 2 20s 106 0E
Bangkalan, Indonesia 7 10s 112 50E
Bangkok, Thailand 13 55N 100 30E
Bangladesh, South Asia 24 0N 90 0E
Bangor, N. Ireland 54 39N 5 39W
Bangor, Me., U.S.A. 44 48N 68 40W
Bangor, Wales 53 14N 4 7W
Bangui, Central Africa 4 23N 19 20E
Bangweulu, L., Zambia 11 30s 30 5E
Banias, Syria 35 7N 36 2E
Banja Luka, Yugoslavia 44 45N 17 0E
Banjarmasin, Indonesia 3 20s 114 25E
Banjul, Gambia 13 20N 16 40W
Bankfoot, Scotland 56 30N 3 31W
Baninah, Libya 32 10N 20 15E
Banja Bystrica, Cz.-slov. 48 46N 19 54E
Bankura, India 23 15N 85 5E
Banningville, see Bandundu
Bannockburn, Scotland 56 5N 3 55W
Bannu, Pakistan 33 0N 70 18E
Banská Bystrica, Cz.-slov. 48 46N 19 14E
Banská Stiavnica, Cz.-slov. 48 26N 18 54E
Banteer, Ireland 52 8N 8 53W
Bantry, & B., Ireland 51 1N 9 27W
Banyo, Cameroon 6 58N 11 5E
Banzyville (Mobayi), Zaïre 4 15N 21 8E
Bapatla, India 15 50N 80 30E
Bapaume, France 50 8N 2 49E
Baquba, Iraq 33 45N 44 50E
Bar, Yugoslavia 42 4N 19 7E
Bar Harbor, U.S.A. 44 20N 68 17W
Bar-le-Duc, France 48 45N 5 8E
Bar-s.-Aube, France 48 18N 4 45E
Bar-s.-Seine, France 48 6N 4 28E
Barabinsk, U.S.S.R. 55 30N 78 35E
Baraboo, U.S.A. 43 30N 89 48W
Baracoa, Cuba 20 20N 74 20W
Barahona, Dom. Rep. 18 0N 71 2W
Barail Ra., India 25 15N 93 0E
Barakhola, India 25 0N 92 40E
Barakula, Australia 26 30s 150 33E
Baramula, Kashmir 34 15N 74 25E
Baran, India 25 3N 76 30E
Baranof I., Alaska 57 0N 135 0W
Baranovichi, U.S.S.R. 53 10N 26 0E
Barbacena, Brazil 21 10s 43 0W
Barbados I., W. Indies 13 15N 59 30W
Barberton, Transvaal 25 42s 31 1E
Barbezieux, France 45 30N 0 12W
Barcaldine, Australia 23 30s 145 17E
Barce (Al Marj), Libya 32 30N 20 50E
Barcelona, Spain 41 24N 2 9E
Barcelona, Venezuela 10 12N 64 45W
Barcelonnette, France 44 20N 6 35E
Bardai, Chad 21 15N 17 40E
Bardiyah, Libya 31 45N 25 0E
Bardney, England 53 13N 0 19W
Bardonecchia, Italy 45 5N 6 40E
Bareilly, India 28 22N 79 27E
Barents Sea, Arctic Oc. 73 0N 42 0E
Barentu, Ethiopia 15 2N 37 35E
Barfleur, France 49 40N 1 20W
Barhi, India 24 20N 85 20E
Bari, Italy 41 7N 16 52E
Bari Doab, Pakistan 30 20N 73 0E
Bari Sadri, India 24 28N 74 25E
Baring C., Canada 70 0N 116 30W
Baringo, L., Kenya 0 35N 36 0E
Barisal, Bangladesh 22 50N 90 32E
Barisan Mts., Indonesia 4 0s 103 0E
Barking, Greater London, England 51 32N 0 5E
Barkly Tableland, Australia 19 40s 138 30E
Barkol, China 44 18N 90 48E
Barlby, England 53 48N 1 3W
Barlee L., Australia 29 10s 119 28E
Barletta, Italy 41 18N 16 20E
Barmby Moor, England 53 55N 0 47W
Barmedman, Australia 34 0s 147 16E
Barmer, India 25 49N 71 32E
Barmoor Castle, England 55 38N 2 0W
Barmouth, Wales 52 43N 4 3W
Barna, Ireland 53 14N 9 10W
Barnard Castle, England 54 33N 1 56W
Barnato, Australia 31 35s 145 0E
Barnaul, U.S.S.R. 53 10N 83 40E
Barnes, Australia 36 2s 144 40E
Barnet, Greater London, England 51 40N 0 11W
Barneveld, Neth. 52 7N 5 36E
Barneville, France 49 23N 1 46W
Barnoldswick, England 53 55N 2 11W
Barnsley, England 53 34N 1 29W
Barnstaple, England 51 5N 4 2W
Barnstaple or Bideford Bay, England 51 5N 4 20W
Baro, Nigeria 8 50N 6 25E
Baroda, see Vadodara
Barotse, Prov., Zambia 15 30s 23 30E
Barpeta, India 26 20N 91 0E
Barquisimeto, Venezuela 9 55N 69 15W

Barr, France 48 20N 7 20E
Barra, Brazil 10 30s 42 28W
Barra I., & Sd., Scotland 57 0N 7 30W
Barraba, Australia 30 12s 150 40E
Barrackpore, India 22 45N 88 30E
Barrancos, Portugal 38 10N 7 0W
Barranquilla, Colombia 10 49N 74 45W
Barre, U.S.A. 44 28N 72 25W
Barreiro, Portugal 38 42N 8 56W
Barren Is., Madagascar 18 30s 44 0E
Barrhead, Scotland 55 47N 4 24W
Barrie, Canada 44 30N 79 45W
Barrow, England 54 8N 3 12W
Barrow I., Australia 20 47s 115 25E
Barrow Ra., Mts., Austral. 26 0s 128 0E
Barrow upon Humber, England 53 41N 0 22W
Barrowford, England 53 51N 2 14W
Barry, Wales 51 24N 3 17W
Barsoi, India 25 48N 87 57E
Bartlesville, U.S.A. 36 48N 96 15W
Bartlett Deep, W. Indies 20 0N 85 0W
Barton-upon-Humber, England 53 41N 0 27W
Baruch, India 21 50N 73 10E
Bas-Rhin, Dépt., France 48 45N 7 35E
Bashkir, A.S.S.R., U.S.S.R. 54 0N 56 0E
Basilan, I., Philippines 6 40N 122 0E
Basildon, England 51 34N 0 29E
Basilicata, Prov., Italy 40 30N 16 0E
Basingstoke, England 51 16N 1 5W
Baskerville, C., Australia 17 10s 122 5E
Basle, & Cn., Switzerland 47 33N 7 34E
Basoka, Zaïre 1 20N 23 38E
Basque Provinces, Spain 43 20N 2 20W
Basra, Iraq 30 30N 47 50E
Bass Str., Australia 39 30s 146 0E
Bassano, Canada 50 45N 112 30W
Bassas da India, Is., Ind. Oc. 21 45s 37 38E
Basse Terre, Guadeloupe 16 0N 61 45W
Bassein, Burma 17 0N 94 58E
Basses Alpes, Dépt., Fr. 44 40N 6 20E
Basses-Pyrénées, Dépt.. France 43 17N 0 57W
Bassigny, Dist., France 48 3N 5 23E
Bastar, India 19 15N 81 40E
Basti, India 26 45N 82 58E
Bastia, Corsica 42 40N 9 20E
Bastogne, Belgium 50 5N 5 40E
Baston, England 52 43N 0 19W
Basutoland, see Lesotho
Bat Shelomo, Israel 32 36N 35 0E
Bat Yam, Israel 32 0N 34 44E
Bata, Rio Muni 1 57N 9 50E
Batabano, G., Cuba 22 20N 82 40W
Batalha, Portugal 39 40N 8 52W
Batan Is., Philippines 20 25N 122 5E
Batang, China 30 20N 98 25E
Batangas, Philippines 13 50N 121 5E
Batavia, U.S.A. 43 0N 78 2W
Bataysk, U.S.S.R. 47 5N 39 45E
Bateman's Bay, Australia 35 40s 150 12E
Bath, England 51 24N 2 22W
Bath, Me., U.S.A. 43 57N 69 58W
Batha, Wadi, Oman 22 30N 59 0E
Bathgate, Scotland 55 55N 3 38W
Bathurst, Australia 33 28s 149 30E
Bathurst, Canada 47 37N 65 49W
Bathurst, Gambia see Banjul
Bathurst Inlet, Canada 67 30N 109 0W
Batley, England 53 44N 1 38W
Batlow, Australia 35 33s 148 10E
Batna, Algeria 35 32N 6 20E
Baton Rouge, U.S.A. 30 22N 90 50W
Batongafo, Central Africa 7 30N 18 20E
Batouri, Cameroon 4 30N 14 25E
Battambang, Cambodia 13 5N 103 8E
Batticaloa, Sri Lanka 7 50N 81 31E
Battle, England 50 55N 0 29E
Battle Creek, U.S.A. 42 17N 85 10W
Battle Harbour, Canada 52 13N 55 42W
Battleford, Canada 52 40N 108 12W
Batu Is., Indonesia 0 20s 98 5E
Batu, Mt., Ethiopia 6 50N 39 50E
Batumi, U.S.S.R. 41 40N 41 30E
Baturaja, Indonesia 4 10s 104 10E
Baturite, Brazil 4 0s 38 40W
Baudouinville (Moba), Zaïre 7 0s 29 48E
Bauge, France 47 35N 0 10W
Baume les Dames, France 47 21N 6 21E
Baurú, Brazil 22 12s 49 8W
Bauska, U.S.S.R. 56 24N 24 15E
Bautzen, Germany 51 14N 14 23E
Bavaria, land, Germany 49 0N 12 0E
Bawku, Ghana 11 3N 0 19W
Bawlake, Burma 19 0N 97 30E
Bay Cy., Mich. U.S.A. 43 38N 83 48W
Bayamo, Cuba 20 25N 76 40W
Bayan Khara Shan Mts., China 34 0N 98 0E
Bayanhongor, Mts., Mongolia 46 35N 99 45E
Bayanga, Central Africa 2 55N 16 15E
Bayble, Scotland 58 12N 6 13W
Bayeux, France 49 20N 0 44W
Bayhan Aul, U.S.S.R. 50 50N 75 50E
Baykal, L., U.S.S.R. 53 0N 108 0E
Bayonne, France 43 30N 1 30W
Bayreuth, Germany 49 57N 11 32E
Baza, Spain 37 31N 2 46W
Bazarnyy Syzgan, U.S.S.R. 53 45N 46 45E

83 Beachport, Australia 37 30N 140 0E
23 Beachy Hd., England 50 44N 0 17E
23 Beaconsfield, England 51 36N 0 39w
99 Beagle Chan, Chile 55 0s 68 30w
22 Beaminster, England 50 48N 2 46w
90 Bear, L. & R., U.S.A. 42 0N 111 20w
100 Beardmore, Antarc. 83 30s 175 0E
100 Beardmore Glacier, Antarctica 84 30s 170 0E
42 Béarn, Prov., France 43 20N 0 40w
30 Bearsden, Scotland 55 55N 4 19w
91 Beatrice, U.S.A. 40 20N 96 46w
31 Beattock, Scotland 55 19N 3 27w
43 Beaucaire, France 43 50N 4 35E
83 Beaudesert, Australia 28 0s 152 50E
68 Beaufort, Malaysia 5 25N 115 50E
100 Beaufort Sea, Arctic Oc. 75 0N 160 0w
43 Beaujolais, Dist., France 46 10N 4 30E
33 Beauly, & Firth, Scot. 57 28N 4 28w
25 Beaumaris, Wales 53 17N 4 6w
91 Beaumont, U.S.A. 30 4N 94 10w
43 Beaune, France 47 2N 4 50E
43 Beauvais, France 49 26N 2 2E
88 Beauval, Canada 55 10N 107 55w
91 Beaverdam, U.S.A. 43 30N 88 50w
26 Bebington, England 53 25N 3 1w
23 Beccles, England 52 28N 1 36E
41 Becejo, Yugoslavia 45 33N 20 2E
72 Bechar, Algeria 31 40N 2 17w
31 Beckfoot, England 54 50N 3 25w
27 Beckingham, England 53 24N 0 49w
92 Beckley, U.S.A. 37 44N 81 42w
27 Bedale, England 54 18N 1 35w
43 Bédarieux, France 43 40N 3 10E
23 Bedford, & Co., England 52 8N 0 28w
92 Bedford, Ind., U.S.A. 39 6N 86 37w
23 Bedford Level, England 52 50N 0 15w
27 Bedlington, England 55 9N 1 35w
25 Bedwas, England 51 36N 3 10w
22 Bedworth, England 52 28N 1 29w
83 Beenleigh, Australia 27 52s 153 0E
27 Beeston, England 52 55N 1 11w
54 Befale, Zaïre 0 5N 21 0E
36 Beg, L., N. Ireland 54 48N 6 25w
83 Bega, Australia 36 48s 149 55E
25 Begelly, Wales 51 45N 4 44w
61 Begichev I., U.S.S.R. 74 20N 112 30E
65 Beharigani, India 25 40N 87 0E
73 Beida (Al Bayda), Libya 32 35N 21 25E
62 Bebairat al Daula, South Yemen 14 45N 45 15E
75 Beira, Mozambique 19 45s 35 0E
37 Beira-Alta, Prov., Port. 40 35N 7 35w
37 Beira-Baixa, Prov., Port. 40 0N 7 30w
37 Beira-Litoral Prov., Port. 40 5N 8 30w
63 Beirut (Bayrut), Lebanon 33 55N 35 30E
63 Beit Alfa, Israel 32 31N 35 25E
63 Beit Eddine, Lebanon 33 42N 35 35E
63 Beit Hanun, Israel 31 32N 34 31E
63 Beit Shean, Israel 32 30N 35 30E
63 Beit Yosef, Israel 32 34N 35 33E
75 Beitbridge, Rhodesia 22 12s 30 0E
30 Beith, Scotland 55 45N 4 38w
38 Beja, Portugal 38 2N 7 51w
72 Beja, Tunisia 36 55N 9 5E
72 Bejaia (Bougie), Algeria 36 49N 5 7E
72 Békéscaba, Hungary 46 40N 21 0E
41 Bela Crkva, Y.-slav. 44 54N 21 22E
54 Belawan, Indonesia 3 45N 98 45E
51 Belaya Tserkov, U.S.S.R. 49 40N 30 10E
89 Belcher Is., Canada 56 0N 80 30w
50 Belebei, Russia 54 10N 54 5E
98 Belem (Pará), Brazil 1 25s 48 20w
37 Belem, Portugal 38 40N 9 10w
52 Belev, U.S.S.R. 53 50N 36 5E
36 Belfast, & L., N. Ireland 54 35N 5 57w
93 Belfast, Me., U.S.A. 44 15N 69 0w
43 Belfort, France 47 41N 6 54E
42 Belfort, Dépt., France 47 38N 6 52E
64 Belgaum, India 15 42N 74 40E
44 Belgium, Europe 51 0N 4 10E
52 Belgorod, U.S.S.R. 50 30N 36 40E
51 Belgorod Dnestrovski, U.S.S.R. 46 11N 30 23E
41 Belgrade (Beograd), Yugoslavia 44 48N 20 33E
68 Beliton, I., Indonesia 3 0s 108 0E
94 Belize, St., Cent. America 17 0N 88 40w
94 Belize, Belize 17 28N 88 20w
83 Bell Bay, Australia 41 2s 146 48E
31 Bell Rock, Scot., 56 26N 2 24w
98 Bell Ville, Argentina 32 30s 62 50w
88 Bella Coola, Canada 52 25N 126 40w
36 Bellaghy, N. Ireland 54 50N 6 31w
43 Bellágio, Italy 45 55N 9 20E
92 Bellaire, Ohio, U.S.A. 40 1N 80 48w
36 Bellanagare, Ireland 53 49N 8 21w
36 Bellananagh, Ireland 53 59N 7 28w
64 Bellary, India 15 12N 77 5E
83 Bellata, Australia 29 58s 149 55E
36 Bellavary, Ireland 53 54N 9 10w
90 Belle Fourche R., U.S.A. 44 40N 104 0w
89 Belle I., Canada 52 10N 55 18w
42 Belle Ile, France 47 20N 3 12w
36 Belleek, N. Ireland 54 30N 8 6w
43 Bellegarde, France 46 4N 5 46E
89 Belleville, Canada 44 15N 77 37w
92 Belleville, Ill., U.S.A. 38 30N 90 7w
43 Belley, France 45 45N 5 45E
83 Bellingen, Australia 30 25s 152 50E
26 Bellingham, Eng., 55 9N 2 16w
90 Bellingham, U.S.A. 48 45N 122 48w
100 Bellingshausen Sea, Antarctica 65 0s 80 0w
45 Bellinzona, Switzerland 46 12N 9 1E

40 Belluno, Italy 46 8N 12 12E
37 Belmez, Spain 38 15N 5 15w
83 Belmont, Australia 33 0s 151 35E
94 Belmopan, Br. Honduras 17 12N 88 0w
35 Belmullet, Ireland 54 13N 9 58w
98 Belo Horizonte, Brazil 19 55s 44 0w
75 Belo sur Tsiribihina, Madagascar 19 40s 44 30w
50 Belomorsk, U.S.S.R. 64 35N 34 30E
50 Beloretsk, U.S.S.R. 54 0N 58 0E
50 Belovo, U.S.S.R. 54 35N 86 27E
50 Beloye L., U.S.S.R. 60 10N 37 35E
27 Belper, England 53 2N 1 28w
27 Belton (Lincs.), England 53 33N 0 49w
23 Belton (Suff.), England 52 35N 1 39E
91 Belton, Texas, U.S.A. 31 30N 97 30w
36 Beltra, Sligo, Ireland 54 12N 8 36w
47 Beltsy, U.S.S.R. 47 48N 28 0E
36 Belturbet, Ireland 54 6N 7 25w
22 Bembridge, England 50 41N 1 4w
61 Bemidji, U.S.A. 47 30N 94 58w
33 Ben Alder, Scotland 56 49N 4 30w
33 Ben Avon, Scotland 57 7N 3 18w
31 Ben Chonzie, Scotland 56 27N 4 0w
30 Ben Cruachan, Scotland 56 27N 5 5w
33 Ben Dearg, Perth, Scot. 56 54N 3 50w
33 Ben Dhorain, Scotland 58 7N 3 50w
33 Ben Dorain, Scotland 56 30N 4 42w
33 Ben Hope, Scotland 58 26N 4 33w
30 Ben Lawers, Scotland 56 31N 4 17w
30 Ben Lomond, Scotland 56 10N 4 30w
33 Ben Loyal, Scotland 58 24N 4 25w
30 Ben Lui, Scotland 56 24N 4 45w
33 Ben Macdhui, Scotland 57 3N 3 30w
32 Ben Mhor, Lewis, Scot. 57 58N 6 31w
32 Ben Mhor, S. Uist., Scotland 57 16N 7 18w
30 Ben More, Perth, Scot. 56 20N 4 30w
33 Ben More Assynt, Suth., Dist., Scotland 58 9N 4 53w
33 Ben Nevis, Scotland 56 46N 5 0w
33 Ben Sgeirach, Scotland 58 4N 4 39w
32 Ben Sgritheall, Scotland 57 9N 5 34w
30 Ben Stack, Scotland 58 20N 4 58w
30 Ben Venue, Scotland 56 13N 4 28w
30 Ben Vorlich, Scotland 56 22N 4 15w
33 Ben Wyvis, Scotland 57 41N 4 40w
72 Bena, Nigeria 11 20N 5 50E
83 Benalla, Australia 36 34s 146 0E
83 Benanee, Australia 34 26s 142 56E
65 Benares, see Varanasi
34 Benbaun, Mt., Ireland 53 30N 9 50w
32 Benbecula I., Scotland 57 26N 7 20w
80 Bencubbin, Australia 30 56s 118 5E
90 Bend, U.S.A. 44 3N 121 15w
47 Bendery, U.S.S.R. 46 50N 29 28E
83 Bendigo, Australia 36 48s 144 13E
72 Benei Berag, Israel 32 5N 34 50E
40 Benevento, Italy 41 8N 14 50E
68 Benghazi, Libya 32 10N 20 5E
68 Bengkalis, Indonesia 1 38N 102 9E
75 Benguela, Angola 12 20s 13 10E
72 Beni Abbès, Algeria 30 10N 2 0w
72 Beni Mazàr, Egypt 28 32N 30 44E
72 Beni Mellal, Morocco 32 21N 6 14w
73 Beni Suef, Egypt 29 2N 30 58E
72 Beni Ulid, Libya 31 50N 14 20E
72 Benin, W. Africa 9 0N 2 0E
72 Benin City, Nigeria 6 20N 5 31E
68 Bengkulu, Indonesia 3 40s 102 40E
88 Bennett, Canada 59 50N 135 0w
61 Bennett I., U.S.S.R. 76 30N 150 0E
35 Bennettsbridge, Ireland 52 36N 7 12w
93 Bennington, U.S.A. 42 55N 73 16w
63 Bennt Jbail, Lebanon 33 7N 35 26E
76 Benoni, Trans. S. Africa 26 11s 28 18E
49 Bensheim, Germany 49 41N 8 36E
73 Bentiu, Sudan 9 10N 29 30E
27 Bentley, Yorks., England 53 33N 1 9w
92 Benton Harbor, U.S.A. 42 8N 86 28w
72 Benue R., Nigeria 8 0N 7 30E
41 Beograd, see Belgrade
67 Beppu, Japan 33 15N 131 35E
94 Bequia, W. Indies 13 0N 61 15w
72 Ber Rechid, Morocco 33 0N 7 35E
36 Beragh, N. Ireland 54 34N 7 10w
41 Berat, Albania 40 40N 20 0E
45 Berber, Sudan 18 2N 34 2E
45 Berbera, Somali Rep. 10 30N 45 25E
45 Bercher, Switzerland 46 43N 6 43E
51 Berdichev, U.S.S.R. 49 50N 28 45E
47 Berdyansk, U.S.S.R. 46 42N 36 47E
47 Bereza, U.S.S.R. 52 45N 25 0E
47 Berezniki, U.S.S.R. 59 25N 56 5E
50 Berezovo, U.S.S.R. 64 5N 65 0E
41 Bergama, Turkey 39 6N 27 20E
40 Bergamo, Italy 45 42N 9 40E
49 Bergen, Norway 60 21N 5 22E
44 Bergen Binnen, Neth. 52 40N 4 40E
44 Bergen-op-Zoom, Neth. 51 30N 4 17E
44 Bergerac, France 44 53N 0 26E
44 Bergum, Netherlands 53 12N 5 59E
76 Bergville, S. Africa 28 40s 29 20E
64 Berhampore, India 24 10N 88 20E
65 Berhampur, India 19 24N 84 50E
54 Bering Sea, Pacific Ocean 57 0N 173 0E
37 Berja, Spain 36 45N 3 0w
23 Berkeley, England 51 42N 2 27w
90 Berkeley, U.S.A. 38 6N 122 0w
23 Berkhamsted, England 51 45N 0 33w
22 Berks. Downs, England 51 30N 1 20w
22 Berkshire, Co., England 51 25N 1 15w

46 Berlin, Germany 52 31N 13 20E
93 Berlin, N.H., U.S.A. 44 28N 71 11w
100 Bermejo, R., Arg. 25 40s 59 40w
42 Bermeo, Spain 43 26N 2 46w
95 Bermuda Is., Atlantic Oc. 32 20N 65 0w
45 Bern and Cn., Switz. 46 57N 7 27E
44 Bernay, France 49 5N 0 32E
46 Bernburg, Germany 51 40N 11 42E
45 Berner Alpen, Mts., Switzerland 46 25N 7 30E
32 Berneray, I., Scotland 56 47N 7 40w
80 Bernier I., Australia 24 58s 113 0E
45 Bernina, Mt., Switzerland 46 22N 9 50E
37 Beror Hayil, Israel 31 34N 34 39E
75 Beroroha, Madagascar 21 40s 45 10E
46 Beroun, Cz.-slov. 50 0N 14 5E
83 Berri, Australia 34 12s 140 38E
33 Berriedale, Scotland 58 10N 3 31w
83 Berry, Australia 34 48s 150 48E
43 Berry, Prov., France 46 48N 2 5E
74 Bertoua, Cameroon 4 30N 13 45E
48 Beru Fjord, Iceland 64 40N 14 15w
48 Berufjordur, Iceland 64 47N 14 28w
31 Berwick-upon-Tweed, England 55 47N 2 2w
25 Berwyn Mts., Wales 52 54N 3 25w
75 Besalampy, Madagascar 16 43s 44 29E
43 Besançon, France 47 18N 6 0E
47 Beskids, E., Mts., Eur. 49 30N 22 10E
47 Beskids, W., Mts., Eur. 49 8N 19 0E
53 Bessarabia, reg., U.S.S.R. 47 0N 28 20E
36 Bessbrook, N. Ireland 54 11N 6 23w
45 Bessèges, France 44 20N 4 2E
92 Bessemer, U.S.A. 46 30N 90 0w
73 Betaré-Oya, Cameroon 5 40N 14 15E
63 Bethanien, S.W. Africa 26 32s 17 11E
63 Bethlehem, Jordan 31 42N 35 12E
76 Bethlehem, S. Africa 28 5s 28 30E
93 Bethlehem, Pa., U.S.A. 40 25N 75 30w
76 Bethulie, S. Africa 30 30s 26 0E
43 Béthune, France 50 30N 2 40E
75 Betioky, Madag. 23 48s 44 20E
75 Betroka, Madag. 23 16s 46 0E
23 Betteshanger, England 51 13N 1 20E
65 Bettiah, India 26 59N 84 38E
64 Betul, India 21 50N 77 50E
64 Betws-y-Coed, Wales 53 5N 3 50w
44 Beveren, Belgium 51 14N 4 16E
80 Beverley, Australia 32 2s 116 58E
27 Beverley, England 53 50N 0 27w
44 Beverwijk, Netherlands 52 28N 4 38E
44 Bex, Switzerland 46 16N 7 2E
23 Bexhill, England 50 50N 0 27E
23 Bexley, Gt. London, Eng. 51 26N 0 10E
41 Beykoz, Turkey 41 6N 29 8E
72 Beyla, Guinea 8 35N 8 30w
51 Beypazari, Turkey 40 11N 31 50E
51 Beysehir Gölü L., Tur. 37 50N 31 30E
50 Bezhitsa, U.S.S.R. 53 25N 34 18E
43 Beziers, France 43 27N 3 15E
64 Bhachau, India 23 20N 70 16E
65 Bhadrakh, India 21 0N 86 30E
65 Bhagalpur, India 25 12N 86 52E
76 Bhamo, Burma 24 16N 96 50E
65 Bhamragarh, India 19 30N 80 30E
64 Bhandara, India 21 8N 79 40E
64 Bharatpur, India 27 18N 77 50E
65 Bhatpara, India 23 0N 88 30E
72 Bhavnagar, India 21 59N 72 19E
64 Bhima, R., India 17 25N 76 0E
65 Bhimavaram, India 16 30N 81 30E
64 Bhiwandi, India 19 15N 72 55E
65 Bhola, Bangladesh 22 45N 90 35E
65 Bhubaneswar, India 20 10N 85 50E
65 Bhuj, India 23 10N 69 45E
64 Bhusawal, India 21 10N 75 56E
64 Bhutan, Asia 27 30N 90 20E
74 Biafra, B. of, see Bonny, B. of
47 Biala Podlaska, Poland 52 2N 23 0E
47 Bialystok, Poland 53 4N 23 12E
42 Biarritz, France 43 30N 1 32w
45 Biasca, Switzerland 46 22N 8 59E
45 Biberach, Germany 48 5N 9 45E
72 Bibiani, Ghana 6 30N 2 8w
82 Biboohra, Australia 16 35s 145 27E
22 Bibury, England 51 46N 1 50w
22 Bicester, England 51 55N 1 9w
25 Bicton, England 52 43N 2 47w
72 Bida, Nigeria 9 2N 6 12E
64 Bidar, India 17 58N 77 35E
48 Biddenden, England 51 7N 0 40E
26 Biddulph, England 53 8N 2 11w
22 Bideford, England 51 1N 4 13w
22 Bidford on Avon, Eng. 52 9N 1 53w
72 Bidon 5, see Poste Maurice Cortier
75 Bié, Angola 12 16s 16 55E
75 Bié Plateau, Angola 13 0s 16 40E
46 Biel, Switzerland 47 9N 7 15E
46 Bielefeld, Germany 52 2N 8 17E
46 Bieler See, Switzerland 47 7N 7 18E
47 Bielsko, Poland 49 50N 19 10E
68 Bien Hoa, Vietnam 11 0N 107 0E
88 Big Belt, Mts., U.S.A. 46 40N 111 30w
90 Big Spring, U.S.A. 32 14N 101 32w
91 Big Stone L., U.S.A. 30 30N 96 30w
89 Big Trout L., Canada 54 30N 90 0w
72 Bigbury, tn. & B., England 50 17N 3 52w
88 Biggar, Canada 52 6N 108 0w
31 Biggar, Scotland 55 38N 3 31w
83 Biggenden, Australia 25 30s 152 0E
23 Biggleswade, England 52 5N 0 17w
22 Bighorn, Mts., U.S.A. 44 30N 107 30w
45 Bignasco, Switzerland 46 20N 8 36E

40 Bihac, Yugoslavia 44 46N 15 57E
65 Bihar, st., India 23 0N 85 30E
65 Bijapur, Mad. P., India 18 50N 80 50E
64 Bijapur, Mysore, India 16 55N 75 57E
62 Bijar, Iran 32 52N 47 35E
61 Bijeljina, Yugoslavia 44 42N 19 15E
64 Bikaner, India 28 1N 73 40E
61 Bikfaiya, Lebanon 33 55N 35 40E
61 Bikin, U.S.S.R. 46 50N 134 15E
74 Bikoro, Zaïre 0 48s 18 15E
32 Bilara, India 26 20N 73 58E
65 Bilaspur, Mad. P., India 22 2N 82 14E
68 Bilauk Taung Ra., Thail. 13 30N 99 15w
37 Bilbao, Spain 43 16N 2 53w
48 Bildudalur, Iceland 65 20N 23 40w
51 Bilecik, Turkey 40 16N 29 52E
23 Bilir, U.S.S.R. 65 40N 131 20E
23 Billericay, England 51 38N 0 25E
33 Billesdon, England 52 38N 0 56w
23 Billingham, England 54 36N 1 18w
90 Billings, U.S.A. 45 58N 108 30w
73 Bilma, Niger 18 5N 13 20E
82 Biloela, Australia 24 25s 150 35E
91 Biloxi, U.S.A. 30 32N 89 0w
22 Bilston, England 52 34N 2 7w
73 Biltine, Chad 14 40N 20 50E
41 Bilyana, Australia 18 5s 145 50E
72 Bimbéreke, Benin 10 11N 2 43E
44 Bina-Etawah, India 24 11N 78 12E
44 Binche, Belgium 50 25N 14 12E
81 Binda, Australia 27 50s 147 28E
75 Bindura, Rhodesia 17 15s 31 20E
83 Bingara, Australia 29 40s 150 40E
27 Bingham, England 52 57N 0 55w
93 Binghampton, U.S.A. 42 5N 75 48w
27 Bingley, England 53 51N 1 50w
68 Binh-dinh, see An Nhon
68 Binjai, Indonesia 3 30N 98 30E
99 Bio Bio, R., Chile 37 45s 71 30w
64 Bir, India 19 4N 75 58E
73 Bir Atrun, Sudan 28 15N 26 40E
62 Bir Terfawi, Egypt 22 7N 28 10E
42 Bir Ungat, Egypt 22 8N 33 48E
84 Bir Zeit, Jordan 31 59N 35 11E
73 Birao, Central Africa 10 20N 22 40E
23 Birch, England 51 50N 0 54E
80 Birdsville, Australia 25 58s 139 20E
80 Birdum, Australia 15 30s 133 0E
63 Birjand, Iran 32 52N 59 7E
41 Birkdale, England 53 38N 3 2w
41 Birkenhead, England 53 23N 3 3w
41 Birlad, Rumania 46 15N 27 38E
22 Birmingham, England 52 29N 1 54w
91 Birmingham, U.S.A. 33 37N 86 45w
65 Birmitrapur, India 22 30N 84 10E
72 Birnin-Kebbi, Nigeria 12 10N 4 0E
61 Birobidzhan, U.S.S.R. 48 50N 132 50E
50 Birsk, U.S.S.R. 55 23N 55 35E
31 Birtley, England 54 55N 1 33w
27 Birtley, England 55 2N 2 12w
64 Birur, India 13 30N 75 55E
40 Birzebbuga, Malta 35 52N 14 31E
27 Biscay, B. of, Atlantic Oc. 45 20N 2 0w
27 Bishop Auckland, Eng. 54 40N 1 41w
23 Bishop's Cleeve, England 51 56N 2 3w
24 Bishop's Nympton, Eng. 50 58N 3 44w
23 Bishop's Stortford, Eng. 51 53N 0 10E
23 Bishopsteignton, Eng. 50 32N 3 32w
72 Biskra, Algeria 34 50N 5 45E
82 Bismarck Arch., Papua N.G. 2 0s 148 0E
82 Bismarck Sea, Papua N.G. 4 30s 149 0E
72 Bissagos Is., Guinea-B., 11 0N 16 0w
72 Bissau, Guinea-Bissau 11 50N 15 37w
47 Bistrita, Rumania 47 7N 24 32E
44 Bitburg, Germany 49 59N 6 32E
51 Bitlis, Turkey 38 30N 42 17E
41 Bitola (Monastir) Y.-slav. 41 5N 21 14E
73 Bitter Lakes, Egypt 30 10N 32 0E
90 Bitterroot Ra., U.S.A. 46 30N 115 0w
75 Bitterfontein, S. Africa 31 0s 18 32E
90 Biwa, L., Japan 35 15s 135 45E
60 Biysk, U.S.S.R. 52 40N 85 0E
76 Bizana, S. Africa 30 55s 29 50E
72 Bizerte, Tunisia 37 20N 9 45E
48 Bjargtangar, Iceland 65 30N 24 30w
48 Bjarnanes, Iceland 64 18N 15 10w
40 Bjelovar, Yugoslavia 46 0N 16 45E
49 Blaavands Huk, Denmark 55 33N 8 2E
22 Blaby, England 52 34N 1 10w
47 Black Crisul, R., Rumania 46 40N 22 0E
26 Black Fell, Mt., England 54 47N 2 34w
45 Black Forest, see Schwarzwald, Ger.
27 Black Hills, England 53 33N 1 45w
90 Black Hills, U.S.A. 44 0N 104 0w
33 Black Isle, Scotland 57 35N 4 15w
25 Black Mt., see Mynydd du
25 Black Mts., Wales 51 52N 3 5w
72 Black (Da) R., Viet Nam 21 30N 104 0E
90 Black Range, Mts., U.S.A. 33 0N 107 45w
51 Black Sea, Europe 43 0N 34 0E
72 Black Volta R., W. Africa 10 0N 3 0w
72 Blackall, Australia 24 20s 145 30E
84 Blackball, New Zealand 42 20s 171 35E
27 Blackbull, Australia 18 0s 141 7E
27 Blackburn, England 53 46N 2 30w
26 Blackdown Hills, Eng. 50 57N 3 15w
90 Blackfoot, U.S.A. 43 14N 112 22w
31 Blackford, Scotland 56 15N 3 48w
24 Blackmoor Vale, England 50 54N 2 18w
26 Blackpool, England 53 50N 3 3w

82 Blackwater, Australia 23 35s 149 0E
35 Blackwater, Ireland 52 27N 6 20w
34 Blackwater, R., Cork, Ire. 52 6N 8 30E
23 Blackwater, R., England 51 47N 0 38E
36 Blackwater, R., N. Ireland 54 26N 7 5w
31 Blackwood, Scotland 55 40N 3 56w
25 Blaenavon, Wales 51 46N 3 5w
51 Blagodarnoye, U.S.S.R. 45 0N 43 45E
61 Blagoveshchensk, U.S.S.R. 50 30N 127 55E
42 Blain, France 47 30N 1 42w
25 Blaina, Wales 51 46N 3 10w
42 Blainville, France 49 5N 1 32w
82 Blair Athol, Australia 22 50s 147 0E
33 Blair Atholl, Scotland 56 46N 3 50w
31 Blairgowrie, Scotland 56 36N 3 20w
88 Blairmore, Canada 49 40N 114 25w
23 Blakeney, Norfolk, England 52 57N 1 1E
72 Blanc, C., Mauritania 20 40N 17 0w
83 Blanche, L., Australia 29 15s 139 40E
94 Blanchisseuse, Trinidad 10 45N 61 18w
44 Blankenberge, Belgium 51 18N 3 8E
95 Blanquilla I., Venezuela 12 0N 64 30w
75 Blantyre, Malawi 15 50 35 1E
34 Blarney, Ireland 51 58N 8 35w
27 Blaydon, England 54 56N 1 47w
42 Blaye, France 45 8N 0 40w
83 Blayney, Australia 33 35s 149 10E
60 Blednaya, Mt., U.S.S.R. 75 50N 65 30E
46 Bleiburg, Austria 46 40N 14 55E
49 Blekinge, Co., Sweden 56 27N 15 10E
84 Blenheim, New Zealand 41 38s 174 5E
23 Bletchley, England 52 0N 0 45w
72 Blida, Algeria 36 30N 2 50E
72 Blitar, Indonesia 8 12s 112 25E
93 Block I., U.S.A. 41 12N 71 32w
76 Bloemfontein, S. Africa 29 12s 26 15E
76 Bloemhof, S. Africa 27 30s 25 36E
23 Blofield, England 52 38N 1 25E
48 Blois, France 47 37N 1 19E
48 Blonduós, Iceland 65 40N 20 12w
45 Bloody Foreland, Ireland 55 9N 8 17w
92 Bloomington, Ill., U.S.A. 40 28N 88 59w
92 Bloomington, Ind., U.S.A. 39 10N 86 32w
90 Blue Mts., see Katoomba
90 Blue Mts., U.S.A. 45 0N 119 5w
80 Blue Mud B., Australia 13 30s 136 10E
73 Blue Nile, Dist., Sudan 12 40N 33 30E
73 Blue Nile, R., N.E. Africa 10 0N 35 0E
91 Blue Ridge Mts., U.S.A. 35 0N 82 0w
92 Bluefield, U.S.A. 37 28N 81 4w
95 Bluefields, Nicaragua 12 0N 83 45w
36 Blue Stack, Mt., Ireland 54 45N 8 9w
84 Bluff, New Zealand 46 32s 168 20E
99 Blumenau, Brazil 27 0s 49 0w
23 Blundeston, England 52 33N 1 42E
27 Blyth, England 55 7N 1 1w
31 Blyth Bridge, Scotland 55 41N 3 22w
27 Blyth R., England 55 6N 1 56w
23 Blythburgh, England 52 19N 1 36E
91 Blytheville, U.S.A. 35 56N 89 58w
72 Bo, Sierra Leone 7 55N 11 50w
98 Boa Vista, Brazil 2 5N 60 15w
95 Bobbili, India 18 35s 83 30E
43 Bobbio, Italy 44 50N 9 25E
72 Bobo-Dioulasso, Volta 11 30N 4 0w
46 Bobr, R., Poland 51 30N 15 28E
50 Bobruysk, U.S.S.R. 53 0N 30 0E
72 Bocanda, Ivory Coast 7 5N 4 31w
74 Bocaranga, Central Africa 7 0N 15 35w
46 Bocholt, Germany 51 5N 6 37E
44 Bochum, Germany 51 30N 7 15E
74 Boda, Central Africa 4 19N 17 26E
61 Bodaibo, U.S.S.R. 57 50N 114 0E
33 Boddam, Scotland 57 28N 1 46w
32 Boddam, Shetland Is., Scotland 59 55N 1 16w
40 Boden, Sweden 65 48N 21 45E
45 Bodensee, L., Germany 47 33N 9 30E
64 Bodhan, India 18 45N 77 50E
24 Bodmin Moor, England 50 33N 4 36w
48 Bodø, Il, Norway 67 21N 14 20E
74 Bodrog, R., Hungary 48 20N 21 45E
74 Boende, Zaïre 0 15s 21 12E
91 Bog of Allen, Ireland 53 13N 7 20w
91 Bogalusa, U.S.A. 30 51N 89 56w
82 Bogan, R., Australia 31 0s 147 2E
83 Bogan Gate, Australia 33 0s 147 52E
75 Bogenfels, S.W. Africa 27 31s 15 33E
82 Boggabilla, Australia 28 40s 150 20E
83 Boggabri, Australia 30 45s 150 0E
82 Boggeragh, Mts., Ireland 52 2s 8 55w
72 Boghé, Mauritania 16 45N 14 10w
83 Bognor Regis, England 50 47N 0 40w
72 Bogor, Indonesia 6 30s 106 58E
72 Bogoro, Nigeria 9 37N 9 29E
98 Bogota, Colombia 4 38N 74 15w
60 Bogotol, U.S.S.R. 56 15N 89 50E
65 Bogra, Bangladesh 24 48N 89 24E
44 Bohain, France 49 59N 3 28E
46 Bohemia dist., Cz. 49 50N 13 0E
46 Bohemian For., Cz. 49 15N 13 20E
68 Bohol, I., Philippines 9 45N 124 20E
90 Boise, U.S.A. 43 54N 116 12w
72 Bojador, C., Span. Sahara 26 20N 14 55E
72 Boké, Guinea 10 56N 14 17w
49 Bokna Fd., Norway 59 12N 5 30E
74 Bokote, Zaïre 0 12s 21 8E
74 Bokungu, Zaïre 0 39s 23 12E
72 Bolama, Guinea-B. 11 30N 15 35w
46 Bolbec, France 49 59N 0 30E
46 Bolesawiec, Poland 51 17N 15 37E
72 Bolgatanga, Ghana 10 48N 0 52w
38 Boli, U.S.S.R. 45 40N 28 40E
99 Bolivar, Argentina 36 0s 61 0w
98 Bolivia, South America 16 0s 64 30w

Böllnäs, Sweden 61 24N 16 27E
Bollon, Australia 28 0s 147 36E
Bolobo, Zaïre 2 6s 16 20E
Bologna, Italy 44 29N 11 23E
Bologoye, U.S.S.R. 57 55N 34 5E
Bolomba, Zaïre 0 35N 19 0E
Bolsena, L., Italy 42 40N 12 0E
Bolshereche, U.S.S.R. 56 5N 74 40E
Bolshevik I., U.S.S.R. 78 30N 102 0E
Bolshoi I., U.S.S.R. 73 30N 142 0E
Bolshoi Altym, U.S.S.R. 62 25N 66 50E
Bolshoi Mamyr, U.S.S.R. 56 20N 102 55E
Bolsward, Netherlands 53 4N 5 31E
Bolt Hd., England 50 13N 3 48w
Boltigen, Switzerland 46 37N 7 24E
Bolton, England 53 25N 2 25w
Bolton Abbey, England 53 59N 1 53w
Bolton-by-Bowland, Eng. 53 56N 2 21w
Bolu, Turkey 40 46N 31 38E
Bolus Hd., Ireland 51 47N 10 21w
Bolvadin, Turkey 38 45N 31 57E
Bolzano, Italy 46 30N 11 20E
Boma, Zaïre 5 57s 12 40E
Bomaderry, Australia 34 55s 150 35E
Bombala, Australia 37 0s 149 3E
Bombay, India 18 55N 73 0E
Bomda, China 30 10N 95 10E
Bomongo, Zaïre 1 27N 18 21E
Bon, C., Tunisia 37 0N 11 0E
Bona Mt., Canada 61 20N 140 0w
Bonaire I., Neth. W.I. 12 12N 68 15w
Bonang, Australia 37 15s 150 35E
Bonaparte Arch., Austral. 13 0s 124 0E
Bonarbridge, Scotland 57 53N 4 20w
Bonavista, Canada 48 42N 53 5w
Bône, Algeria, see Annaba
Bone, G. of, Indonesia 4 38s 120 10E
Bo'ness, Scotland 56 1N 3 5w
Bongandanga, Zaïre 1 30N 21 0E
Bongor, Chad 10 35N 15 20E
Bonifacio, & Str., of, Medit. 41 18N 9 10E
Bonin Is., Pacific Oc. 27 0N 142 0E
Bonn, W. Germany 50 43N 7 7E
Bonneville, France 46 0N 6 30E
Bonnie Rock, Australia 30 10s 118 5E
Bonny, B. of, W. Africa 3 40N 9 30E
Bonnyrigg, Scotland 55 52N 3 8w
Bonthé, Sierra Leone 7 30N 12 33w
Bontoc, Philippines 17 10N 121 0E
Boom, Belgium 51 5N 4 22E
Boonah, Australia 28 0s 152 27E
Boorindal, Australia 30 25s 146 0E
Boorowa, Australia 34 26s 148 47E
Boot, England 54 24N 3 18w
Boothia, G. & Pen., Can. 70 0N 90 0w
Bootle, Cumberland, Eng. 54 17N 3 24w
Bootle, Lancs., England 53 28N 3 0w
Booué, Gabon 0 5s 11 55E
Bor, Yugoslavia 44 16N 22 3E
Boras, Sweden 57 46N 12 55E
Borazjan, Iran 29 22N 51 10E
Bordeaux, France 44 45N 0 38w
Borders, Reg., Scotland 55 30N 2 50w
Bordertown, Australia 36 21s 140 50E
Bordeyri, Iceland 65 12N 21 6w
Bordighera, Italy 43 50N 7 40E
Bordj-in-Eker, Algeria 24 5N 5 10E
Borehamwood, England 51 40N 0 15w
Borgarnes, Iceland 64 33N 21 55w
Börgefjell Mts., Norway 65 20N 13 30E
Borger, Netherlands 52 55N 6 46E
Borger, U.S.A. 35 43N 101 25w
Borgholm, Sweden 56 16N 16 40E
Boris Vilktski Strait, U.S.S.R. 77 40N 105 0E
Borislav, U.S.S.R. 49 5N 23 26E
Borisoglebsk, U.S.S.R. 51 21N 42 5E
Borisov, U.S.S.R. 54 14N 28 20E
Borken, Germany 51 50N 6 50E
Borkum I., Germany 53 38N 6 41E
Borlänge, Sweden 60 28N 14 33E
Bormio, Italy 46 30N 10 20E
Borneo, I. Asia 1 0N 114 30E
Bornholm I., Denmark 55 9N 14 55E
Boromo, Volta 11 56N 2 50w
Bororoen, Australia 24 13s 151 33E
Borovichi, U.S.S.R. 58 25N 33 58E
Borris, Ireland 52 36N 6 57w
Borris-in-Ossory, Ire. 52 57N 7 40w
Borrisokane, Ireland 53 0N 8 8w
Borrisoleigh, Ireland 52 48N 7 58w
Borroloola, Australia 16 7s 136 28E
Borrowdale, England 54 30N 3 9w
Bort, France 45 20N 2 30E
Borth, Wales 52 29N 4 3w
Borve, Scotland 58 25N 6 28w
Borzya, U.S.S.R. 50 25N 116 0E
Bosa, Sardinia, Italy 40 20N 8 25E
Bosanska Gradiska, Yugoslavia 45 20N 17 20E
Bosna, R., Yugoslavia 45 0N 18 10E
Bosnia, & Hercegovina, Fed. Unit, Yugoslavia 44 20N 17 40E
Bosobolo, Zaïre 4 14N 19 50E
Bosporus, Turkey 41 10N 29 10E
Bossangoa, Central Africa 6 35N 17 30E
Bossembélé, Cen. Africa 5 25N 17 40E
Boston, England 53 0N 0 3w
Boston, U.S.A. 42 18N 71 0w
Boston Mts., U.S.A. 36 0N 94 0w
Bothnia, G. of, Europe 62 0N 19 30E
Bothwell, Australia 42 28s 147 2E
Botosani, Rumania 47 42N 26 42E

75 Botswana, Africa 22 30s 24 0E
27 Bottesford, England 52 47N 0 48w
72 Botou, Upper Volta 12 45N 2 5E
44 Bottrop, Germany 51 34N 6 59E
72 Bou Arfa, Morocco 33 0N 2 0w
72 Bouaké, Ivory Coast 7 45N 5 0w
42 Bouches du Rhône, Dépt., France 43 28N 5 22E
72 Bougie, Algeria, see Bejaia
72 Bougouni, Mali 11 22N 7 12w
44 Bouillon, Belgium 49 50N 5 2E
80 Boulder, Australia 30 55s 121 28E
90 Boulder, U.S.A. 40 0N 105 0w
82 Boulia, Australia 23 0s 139 50E
43 Boulogne, France 50 42N 1 33E
90 Bountiful, U.S.A. 41 0N 111 58w
4 Bounty I., S. Ocean 48 0s 179 0E
61 Bour Khaya, C., U.S.S.R. 71 50N 133 10E
43 Bourbon Lancy, France 46 39N 3 45E
43 Bourbonnais, Prov., France 46 20N 2 55E
72 Bourem, Mali 17 1N 0 24w
43 Bourg, France 46 14N 5 17E
43 Bourganeuf, France 45 55N 1 46E
43 Bourges, France 47 9N 2 25E
42 Bourgneuf, France 47 5N 1 58w
43 Bourgoin, France 45 38N 5 15E
83 Bourke, Australia 30 8s 145 59E
23 Bourne, England 52 47N 0 21w
22 Bournemouth, England 50 43N 1 54w
22 Bourton-on-the-Water, England 51 53N 1 45w
44 Boussu, Belgium 50 25N 3 42E
72 Boutilimit, Mauritania 17 30N 14 40w
1 Bouvet, Is., S. Atlantic 55 0s 3 30E
24 Bovey Tracey, England 50 36N 3 40w
44 Bovigny, Belgium 50 12N 5 56E
82 Bowen, Australia 19 59s 148 18E
83 Bowen, Mts., Australia 37 5s 148 0E
31 Bowes, England 54 31N 1 59w
92 Bowling Green, U.S.A. 36 59s 186 0E
83 Bowmans, Australia 34 15s 138 10E
30 Bowmore, Scotland 55 45N 6 17w
83 Bowral, Australia 34 27s 150 30E
80 Bowraville, Australia 30 40s 152 40E
23 Box Hill, England 51 16N 0 16w
44 Boxtel, Netherlands 51 37N 5 17E
36 Boyle, Ireland 53 59N 8 20w
41 Bozca 'Ada I., Turkey 39 50N 26 10E
90 Bozeman, U.S.A. 45 45N 111 5w
74 Bozoum, Central Africa 6 25N 16 35E
44 Brabant, N., Netherlands 51 37N 5 0E
44 Brabant, Prov., Belgium 50 47N 4 30E
40 Brac., I., Yugoslavia 43 20N 16 40E
30 Bracadale, Scotland 57 19N 6 30w
40 Bracciano, L., Italy 42 5N 12 15E
73 Brach, Libya 27 50N 14 50E
48 Bräcke, Sweden 62 50N 15 12E
22 Brackley, England 52 3N 1 10w
23 Bracknell, England 51 24N 0 45w
31 Braco, Scotland 56 16N 3 55w
47 Brad, Rumania 46 10N 22 45E
91 Bradenton, U.S.A. 27 30N 82 33w
26 Bradford, Yorks., Eng. 53 48N 1 46w
22 Bradford-on-Avon, Eng. 51 21N 2 15w
23 Bradwell-on-Sea, Eng. 51 44N 0 55E
32 Brae, Scotland 60 23N 1 20w
83 Braemar, Queens., Australia 25 35s 152 15E
83 Braemar, S. Australia 33 15s 139 35E
33 Braemar, Scotland 57 0N 3 24w
33 Braeriach, Mt., Scotland 57 6N 3 45w
31 Braes of Angus, Scotland 56 52N 3 0w
37 Braga, Portugal 41 34N 8 28w
99 Bragança, Brazil 0 56s 47 0w
37 Bragança, Portugal 41 48N 6 51w
64 Brahmani, R., India 20 25N 85 40E
65 Brahmanbaria, Bangla. 23 5N 91 15E
65 Brahmaputra, R., India 26 45N 93 0E
64 Brahmaur, India 32 28N 76 32E
62 Braidwood, Australia 35 28s 149 57E
47 Braila, Rumania 45 18N 27 57E
27 Brailsford, England 52 58N 1 35w
91 Brainerd, U.S.A. 46 16N 94 10w
23 Braintree, England 51 53N 0 33E
76 Brak, R., S. Africa 29 55s 23 12E
64 Bramhapuri, India 20 40N 79 50E
92 Brampton, Canada 43 40N 79 58w
26 Brampton, England 54 57N 2 46w
99 Branco, C., Brazil 7 20s 36 0w
46 Brandenburg, Germany 52 24N 12 31E
33 Branderburgh, Scotland 57 43N 3 17w
76 Brandfort, S. Africa 28 36s 26 28E
88 Brandon, Canada 49 50N 99 57w
47 Braniewo, Poland 54 25N 19 50E
47 Bransk, Poland 52 45N 22 50E
89 Brantford, Canada 43 10N 80 20w
83 Branxholme, Australia 38 0s 141 52E
98 Brasilia (Fed. Dist.), Braz. 16 0s 48 10w
47 Brasov, Rumania 45 35N 25 35E
45 Brasschaat, Belgium 51 17N 4 30E
46 Bratislava, Cz-slov. 48 7N 17 2E
61 Bratsk, U.S.S.R. 56 10N 101 30E
24 Braunton, England 51 6N 4 9w
90 Brawley, U.S.A. 32 58N 115 30w
34 Bray, Ireland 53 11N 6 6w
96 Brazil, S. America 0 to 30 0s; 35 0 to 75 0w
90 Brazos, R., U.S.A. 32 30N 97 30w
74 Brazzaville, Congo (Fr.) 4 7s 15 15E
41 Brcko, Yugoslavia 44 54N 18 46E
30 Breadalbane, Dist., Scot. 56 35N 4 15w
84 Bream, B., & Hd., N.Z. 35 56s 174 35E
31 Brechin, Scotland 56 46N 2 30w
23 Breckland, England 52 30N 1 20w

25 Brecon, Wales 51 57N 3 24w
25 Brecon Beacons, Wales 51 55N 3 30w
44 Breda, Netherlands 51 36N 4 46E
83 Bredbo, Australia 36 0s 148 40E
46 Bregenz, Austria 47 28N 9 45E
48 Breidi Fd., Iceland 65 15N 24 0w
49 Bremen, Germany 53 6N 8 51E
49 Bremerhaven, Germany 53 36N 8 40E
45 Bremgarten, Switzerland 47 21N 8 20E
40 Brenner Pass, Austra-Italy 47 1N 11 30E
45 Breno, Italy 45 57N 10 19E
23 Brent, Gt. London, Eng. 51 33N 0 15w
23 Brentwood, England 51 37N 0 19w
40 Brescia, Italy 45 35N 10 17E
42 Bressanone, Italy 46 43N 11 39E
32 Bressay, I. & Sd., Scot. 60 8N 1 5w
43 Bresse, Dist., France 46 25N 5 10E
42 Brest, France 48 26N 4 32w
47 Brest, U.S.S.R. 52 10N 23 40E
47 Bretcu, Rumania 46 2N 26 10E
84 Brett, C., N.Z. 35 12s 174 20w
42 Bretteville, France 49 18N 1 35w
42 Breuville, France 49 32N 1 40w
83 Brewarrina, Australia 30 0s 146 53E
42 Brewood, England 52 41N 2 10w
43 Briançon, France 44 53N 6 35E
43 Briare, France 47 40N 2 45E
82 Bribie I., Australia 26 55s 153 17E
75 Brickaville, Madagascar 18 49s 49 4E
31 Bridge of Allan, Scotland 56 9N 3 56w
31 Bridge of Earn, Scotland 56 22N 3 21w
30 Bridge of Orchy, Scot. 56 32N 4 46w
25 Bridgend, Wales 51 31N 3 35w
93 Bridgeport, U.S.A. 41 15N 73 13w
92 Bridgeton, U.S.A. 39 30N 75 15w
80 Bridgetown, Australia 33 58s 116 5E
94 Bridgetown, Barbados 13 5N 59 35w
93 Bridgewater, Canada 44 27N 64 30w
24 Bridgwater, England 51 8N 3 1w
22 Bridlington, England 54 7N 0 10w
83 Bridport, Australia 41 0s 147 32E
22 Bridport, England 50 44N 2 46w
43 Brienne, France 48 23N 4 30E
45 Brienz, Switzerland 46 47N 8 2E
42 Brierley Hill, England 52 29N 2 7w
43 Briey, France 49 15N 5 56E
45 Brig, Switzerland 46 20N 8 0E
27 Brigg, England 53 34N 0 30w
90 Brigham City, U.S.A. 41 35N 111 58w
27 Brighouse, England 53 42N 1 46w
23 Brightlingsea, England 51 48N 1 2E
23 Brighton, Australia 35 0s 138 30E
23 Brighton, England 50 49N 0 9w
25 Brimfield, England 52 18N 2 42w
41 Brindisi, Italy 40 40N 17 55E
83 Brinkworth, Australia 33 40s 138 20E
33 Brinyan, Scotland 59 8N 3 0w
93 Brion, I., Canada 47 50N 61 30w
43 Brioude, France 45 18N 3 25E
44 Brionne, France 49 28N 1 39w
83 Brisbane, Australia 27 30s 153 1E
83 Brisbane R., Australia 27 0s 152 30E
22 Bristol, England 51 28N 2 36w
93 Bristol, R.I., U.S.A. 41 40N 71 15w
24 Bristol Chan., England 51 18N 4 30w
100 British Antarctic Terr. 65 0s 50 0w
88 British Columbia, Prov. Canada 54 0N 125 0w
95 British Guiana, see Guyana
94 British Honduras, see Belize
13 British Isles, Europe 55 0N 5 0w
25 Briton Ferry, Wales 51 37N 3 50w
76 Britstown, South Africa 30 33s 23 32E
42 Brittany, Prov., France 48 0N 2 10w
35 Brittas, Ireland 53 14N 6 29w
43 Brive, France 45 10N 1 30E
24 Brixham, England 50 23N 3 32w
83 Brixton, Australia 23 32s 144 52E
23 Brixworth, England 52 20N 0 54w
46 Brno (Brünn), Cz. 49 19N 16 38E
64 Broach, see Baruch
35 Broad Haven, Ireland 54 18N 9 54w
25 Broad Haven, Wales 51 46N 5 6w
31 Broad Law, Mt., Scot. 55 29N 3 22w
82 Broad Sd., Australia 22 10s 149 40E
34 Broadford, Ireland 52 48N 8 38w
23 Broadstairs, England 51 21N 1 27E
22 Broadway, England 52 2N 1 51w
88 Brochet, Manitoba, Can. 57 55N 101 40w
49 Brocken, Mt., Germany 51 48N 10 50E
72 Brockenhurst, England 50 49N 1 34w
93 Brockton, Mass., U.S.A. 42 4N 71 0w
89 Brockville, Canada 44 30N 75 40w
89 Brodeur Pen., Canada 72 0N 88 0w
30 Brodick, Scotland 55 33N 5 8w
47 Brody, U.S.S.R. 50 7N 25 8E
83 Broken Hill, Australia 31 59s 141 25E
75 Broken Hill, see Kabwe
26 Bromborough, England 53 20N 3 0w
23 Bromley, England 51 24N 0 2w
27 Brompton, England 54 22N 1 25w
22 Bromsgrove, England 52 20N 2 1w
22 Bromyard, England 52 12N 2 30w
49 Bronderslev, Denmark 57 17N 9 55E
83 Bronte Park, Australia 42 8s 146 30E
36 Brookeborough, N. Ire. 54 19N 7 23w
91 Brookhaven, U.S.A. 31 48N 90 27w
91 Brookings, S. Dak., U.S.A. 44 25N 96 40w
80 Brookton, Australia 32 15s 117 0E
83 Brooloo, Australia 26 18s 152 30E

80 Broome, Australia 18 8s 122 15E
33 Brora, & R., Scotland 58 0N 3 51w
22 Broseley, England 52 35N 2 28w
34 Brosna, R., Ireland 53 20N 7 50w
36 Broughshane, N. Ireland 54 54N 6 12w
27 Broughton, Lincs., Eng. 55 33N 0 33w
23 Broughton, Northants., England 52 22N 0 45w
27 Broughton, Yorks., Eng. 54 26N 1 8w
31 Broughty Ferry, Scotland 56 27N 2 51w
24 Brown Willy, Mt., Eng. 50 35N 4 35w
22 Brownhills, England 52 38N 1 57w
91 Brownsville, Tex., U.S.A. 26 0N 97 20w
90 Brownwood, U.S.A. 31 42N 99 2w
23 Broxburn, Scotland 55 56N 3 23w
48 Brú, Iceland 65 5N 15 25w
80 Bruce, Mt., Australia 22 40s 117 30E
45 Bruchsal, Germany 49 10N 8 45E
46 Bruck, Austria 47 27N 15 15E
34 Bruff, Ireland 52 29N 8 35w
45 Bruges, Belgium, see Brugge
45 Brugg, Switzerland 47 28N 8 12E
44 Brugge, Belgium 51 12N 3 13E
44 Bruhl, Germany 50 49N 6 51E
68 Brunei, Borneo 4 55N 114 52E
45 Brunig Pass, Switzerland 46 48N 8 10E
46 Brünn, see Brno
46 Brünsbüttel, Germany 53 55N 9 14E
46 Brunswick, Germany 52 17N 10 36E
91 Brunswick, Ga., U.S.A. 31 10N 81 31w
83 Brunswick B., Australia 15 15s 125 0E
83 Bruny I., Australia 43 20s 147 15E
36 Bruree, Ireland 52 35N 8 40w
44 Brussels, Belgium 50 51N 4 22E
44 Bruthen, Australia 37 55s 147 49E
44 Bruxelles, see Brussels
91 Bryan, Texas, U.S.A. 30 17N 96 5w
52 Bryansk, U.S.S.R. 53 25N 34 22E
25 Bryncethin, Wales 51 32N 3 34w
49 Bryne, Norway 58 46N 5 38E
25 Brynmawr, Wales 51 50N 3 8w
47 Brzeg, Poland 50 52N 17 30E
68 Buayan, Philippines 6 5N 125 20E
95 Bucaramanga, Colombia 6 55N 72 58w
72 Buchanan, Liberia 5 57N 10 2w
31 Buchanan, Canada 48 50N 57 30w
47 Bucharest (Bucuresti), Rumania 44 25N 26 2E
45 Buchs, Switzerland 47 10N 9 30E
33 Buck, The, Mt., Scot. 57 9N 3 0w
31 Buckhaven, Scotland 56 10N 3 2w
33 Buckie, Scotland 57 40N 2 58w
23 Buckingham, Canada 45 40N 75 36w
23 Buckingham & Co., Engl 52 0N 0 59w
25 Buckley, Wales 53 10N 3 5w
30 Bucklyvie, Scotland 56 7N 4 20w
33 Bucksburn, Scotland 57 10N 2 10w
93 Buctouche, Canada 46 30N 64 47w
92 Bucyrus, U.S.A. 40 52N 83 0w
47 Budalin, Burma 22 25N 95 5E
47 Budapest, Hungary 47 33N 19 3E
48 Budareyri, Iceland 65 3N 14 10w
64 Budaun, India 28 15N 79 6E
31 Buddon Ness, Scotland 56 28N 2 43w
24 Bude, England 50 50N 4 32w
48 Budir, Iceland 64 48N 23 21w
24 Budjala, Zaïre 2 50N 19 40E
95 Budleigh Salterton, Eng. 50 37N 3 19w
95 Buenaventura, Colombia 3 55N 77 5w
92 Buenos Aires, Argentina 34 50s 58 37w
92 Buffalo, N.Y., U.S.A. 42 57N 78 50w
90 Buffalo, Wyoming, U.S.A. 44 20N 106 42w
47 Bug, R., Poland 52 39N 21 35E
52 Bug., R., U.S.S.R. 48 17N 30 10E
50 Bugulma, U.S.S.R. 54 35N 52 45E
47 Buie, L., Scotland 56 20N 5 53w
25 Builth Wells, Wales 52 8N 3 24w
72 Buitenpost, Netherlands 53 15N 6 6E
61 Bujumbura, Burundi 3 30s 29 30E
74 Bukachacha, U.S.S.R. 52 55N 116 50E
74 Bukama, Zaïre 9 10s 25 50E
74 Bukavu, Zaïre 2 20s 28 52E
74 Bukene, Tanzania 4 0s 33 0E
60 Bukhara, U.S.S.R. 39 50N 64 10E
68 Bukittingi, Malaysia 0 25s 100 25E
74 Bukoba, Tanzania 1 15s 31 50E
66 Bulak, Sinkiang, China 45 0N 82 0E
66 Bulandshahr, India 50 40N 1 34w
75 Bulawayo, Rhodesia 20 7s 28 38E
83 Bulgan, Mongolia 48 45N 103 0E
83 Bulgroo, Australia 25 40s 143 57E
61 Bulgaria, Europe 42 35N 25 0E
61 Bulinski, U.S.S.R. 68 10N 123 5E
61 Bulkur, U.S.S.R. 71 50N 126 30E
45 Bulle, Switzerland 46 35N 7 6E
80 Bullfinch, Australia 31 10s 119 0E
83 Bulli, Australia 34 12s 150 50E
82 Bullock Creek, Australia 17 40s 144 30E
84 Bulls, N.Z. 40 10s 175 21E
64 Bulsar, India 21 28N 72 53E
61 Bulun, U.S.S.R. 70 37N 126 0E
83 Bulwell, England 53 1N 1 12w
65 Bumpha Bum Mt., Burma 26 45N 97 10E
74 Buna, Kenya 2 58N 39 30E
82 Buna, Papua N.G. 8 35s 148 30E
80 Bunbury, Australia 33 18s 115 40E
35 Bunclody (Newtownbarry), Ireland 52 40N 6 38E

36 Buncrana, Ireland 55 8N 7 25w
83 Bundaberg, Australia 24 54s 152 25E
36 Bundoran, Ireland 54 29N 8 16w
23 Bungay, England 52 27N 1 27E
67 Bungo Chan., Japan 33 0N 132 15E
68 Bunguran Is., Indonesia 3 45N 108 15E
74 Bunia, Zaïre 2 0N 30 20E
36 Bunnanaddan, Ireland 54 3N 8 35w
36 Buntingford, England 51 57N 0 1w
23 Bunnanoch, England 52 30N 1 9E
74 Bura, Kenya 1 0s 40 0E
62 Buraida ,Saudi Arabia 26 3N 44 0E
22 Buraimi, U.A.E. 24 15N 55 43E
22 Burbage, Wilts., England 51 21N 1 40w
90 Burbank, U.S.A. 34 14N 118 28w
83 Burcher, Australia 33 30s 147 10E
51 Burdur, Turkey 37 40N 30 17E
65 Burdwan, India 23 18N 87 50E
61 Bureya, R., U.S.S.R. 50 35N 132 0E
62 Burgan, Kuwait 29 0N 47 59E
41 Burgas, Bulgaria 42 36N 27 26E
45 Burgdorf, Switzerland 47 4N 7 38E
46 Burgenland, Prov., Austria 47 20N 16 20E
76 Burgersdorp, South Africa 31 0s 26 20E
23 Burgess Hill, England 50 57N 0 7w
22 Burghclere, England 51 19N 1 20w
37 Burgos, Spain 42 21N 3 42w
49 Burgsvik, Sweden 57 2N 18 14E
43 Burgundy Prov., France 47 0N 4 50E
50 Burguruslan, U.S.S.R. 53 22N 52 22E
42 Burhou Rocks, Channel Is. 49 45N 2 12w
74 Burji, Ethiopia 5 29N 37 51E
82 Burketown, Australia 17 45s 139 33E
27 Burley, England 53 55N 1 46w
90 Burley, U.S.A. 42 30N 113 55w
91 Burlington, Iowa, U.S.A. 41 0N 91 10w
93 Burlington, Vt., U.S.A. 44 30N 73 12w
60 Burlyu-Tyube, U.S.S.R. 46 30N 79 10E
65 Burma, Asia 21 30N 97 0E
23 Burnham, Essex, England 51 37N 0 50E
83 Burnie, Australia 41 0s 146 0E
26 Burnley, England 53 49N 2 16w
31 Burnmouth, Scotland 55 50N 2 4w
88 Burnside, R., Canada 66 20N 110 0w
31 Burntisland, Scotland 56 3N 3 12w
32 Burravoe, Scotland 60 31N 1 5w
33 Burray I., Scotland 58 50N 2 54w
83 Burren, Australia 30 10s 148 55E
25 Burry Port, Wales 51 41N 4 17w
41 Bursa, Turkey 40 8N 29 1E
24 Burton Bradstock, Eng. 50 41N 2 43w
23 Burton Latimer, Eng. 52 23N 0 41w
22 Burton-upon-Trent, Eng. 52 48N 1 38w
83 Burtundy, Australia 33 40s 142 20E
68 Buru, I., Indonesia 3 30s 126 30E
62 Burujird, Iran 33 55N 48 50E
74 Burundi, Africa 3 30s 30 0E
74 Burutu, Nigeria 5 20N 5 29E
26 Bury, England 53 36N 2 18w
23 Bury St. Edmunds, Eng. 52 14N 0 43E
61 Buryat, A.S.S.R., U.S.S.R. 51 0N 104 0E
62 Busaiya, Iraq 30 1N 46 10E
62 Bushire, Iran 29 0N 50 50E
36 Bushmills, N. Ireland 55 14N 6 32w
74 Businga, Zaïre 3 30N 20 50E
49 Buskerud, Co., Norway 60 20N 9 0E
74 Busra, Syria 32 30N 38 27E
80 Busselton, Australia 33 40s 115 20E
44 Bussum, Netherlands 58 5 10E
43 Busto Arsizio, Italy 45 40N 8 50E
74 Buta, Zaïre 2 50N 24 58E
30 Bute, I., & Kyles of, Scotland 55 50N 5 9w
30 Bute, Sd. of, Scotland 55 45N 5 10w
74 Butembo, Zaïre 0 9N 29 18E
63 Butmiya, Syria 32 57N 35 53E
32 Butt of Lewis, Scotland 58 30N 6 16w
90 Butte, Montana, U.S.A. 46 0N 112 32w
31 Buttermere, England 54 32N 3 16w
68 Butterworth, Malaysia 5 28N 100 28E
34 Buttevant, Ireland 52 14N 8 40w
68 Butuan, Philippines 9 0N 125 35E
68 Butung, I., Indonesia 5 0s 122 45E
52 Buturlinovka, U.S.S.R. 50 50N 40 35E
26 Buxton, England 53 16N 1 56w
61 Buyaga, U.S.S.R. 59 50N 127 0E
66 Buyr Nor, L., Mongolia 47 40N 17 40E
47 Buzau, & R., Rumania 45 10N 26 48E
73 Buzaymah, Libya 24 35N 22 0E
50 Buzuluk, U.S.S.R. 52 48N 52 5E
47 Bydgoszcz, Poland 53 7N 17 59E
89 Bylot I., Canada 73 0N 78 0w
100 Byrd, Antarctica 80 0s 120 0w
100 Byrd Basin, Antarctica 80 0s 110 0w
100 Byrd Land, Antarctica 79 30s 125 0w
83 Byrock, Australia 30 40s 146 28E
83 Byron Bay, Australia 28 30s 153 30E
61 Byrranga Mts., U.S.S.R. 75 0N 100 0E
48 Byske, & R., Sweden 64 57N 21 15E
61 Bysyttakh, U.S.S.R. 69 30N 124 10E
47 Bytom, Poland 50 23N 18 58E

C

98 Cabedelo, Brazil 6 45s 35 0w
74 Cabinda, Angola 5 10s 12 10E
74 Cabonge, Res., Canada 47 10N 77 0w
83 Caboolture, Australia 27 5s 152 47E
89 Cabot Str., Canada 47 20N 60 0w
33 Cabrach, Scotland 57 20N 3 0w
37 Cabrera I., Spain 39 8N 2 58E

AIL

41 Cacak, Yugoslavia 43 51N 20 22E
37 Caceres, Spain 39 29N 6 22w
99 Cachoeira, Brazil 30 3s 52 43w
99 Cachoeiro, Brazil 20 45s 41 0w
75 Caconda, Angola 13 40s 15 9E
35 Cadamstown, Ireland 53 7N 7 39w
25 Cader Idris, Mt., Wales 52 40N 3 50w
91 Cadillac, U.S.A. 44 15N 85 28w
37 Cadiz, Spain 36 33N 6 20w
42 Caen, France 49 15N 0 27w
27 Caenby Corner, England 53 23N 0 32w
25 Caerleon, Wales 51 37N 2 57w
25 Caernarfon, Wales 53 9N 4 15w
25 Caernarfon B., Wales 53 4N 4 28w
25 Caerphilly, Wales 51 34N 3 13w
25 Caerwent, Wales 51 37N 2 47w
63 Caesarea, Israel 32 30N 34 54E
68 Cagayan, R., Philippines 17 30N 121 40E
68 Cagayan de Oro, Phil. 8 32N 124 35E
40 Cagliari, & G., Italy 39 19N 9 8E
40 Caguas, Puerto Rico 18 15N 66 0w
35 Caha Mts., Ireland 51 47N 9 40w
34 Caherconlish, Ireland 52 36N 8 30w
35 Cahir, Ireland 52 21N 7 56w
35 Cahirciveen, Ireland 51 57N 10 14w
43 Cahors, France 44 28N 1 21E
98 Caiapó, Sa. do, Mts., Brazil
   17 0s 52 0w
95 Caicos Is., W. Indies 21 45N 72 0w
31 Cairn Gorm Mt., Scot. 57 9N 3 40w
31 Cairn Table, Mt., Scot. 55 30N 4 0w
33 Cairn Toul, Mt., Scotland 57 1N 3 49w
33 Cairngorm Mts., Scotland 57 6N 3 38w
30 Cairnryan, Scotland 54 59N 5 0w
82 Cairns, Australia 17 0s 145 42E
73 Cairo (El Qâhira), Egypt 30 1N 31 14E
91 Cairo, Ill., U.S.A. 37 0N 89 20w
24 Caister-on-Sea, England 52 38N 1 43E
27 Caistor, England 53 31N 0 18w
98 Cajamarca, Peru 7 0s 78 18w
98 Calabar, Nigeria 4 59N 8 23E
40 Calabria, Reg., Italy 39 10N 16 20E
41 Calafat, Rumania 43 59N 22 54E
37 Calahorra, Spain 42 20N 2 0w
43 Calais, France 50 59N 1 55E
93 Calais, U.S.A. 45 6N 67 14w
99 Calama, Chile 22 20s 69 0w
95 Calamar, Colombia 10 0N 75 0w
68 Calamian Group, Phil. 11 30N 120 0E
37 Calamocha, Spain 40 57N 1 8w
68 Calapan, Philippines 13 15N 121 15E
47 Calarasi, Rumania 44 35N 27 25E
37 Calatayud, Spain 41 20N 1 40w
68 Calauag, Philippines 14 0N 122 20E
65 Calcutta, India 22 38N 88 21E
65 Calder Hall, England 54 25N 3 30w
99 Caldera, Chile 27 12s 70 48w
90 Caldwell, Idaho, U.S.A. 43 42N 116 45w
36 Caledon, N. Ireland 54 23N 6 52w
81 Caledon B., Australia 12 57s 136 50E
32 Caledonian Can., Scot. 57 28N 4 22w
26 Calf of Man, Isle of Man 54 4N 4 49w
88 Calgary, Canada 51 2N 114 5w
32 Calgary, Scotland 56 34N 6 17w
94 Cali, Colombia 3 30N 76 45w
65 Calicut, India 11 15N 75 43E
69 California, G. of, Mexico 28 0N 112 0w
90 California, st., U.S.A. 37 0N 120 0w
94 California, Lower, Mex. 28 0N 114 0w
83 Callabonna L., Australia 29 45s 140 0E
35 Callan, Ireland 52 33N 7 23w
31 Callander, Scotland 56 14N 4 12w
98 Callao, Peru 11 48s 77 15w
82 Callide, Australia 24 23s 150 33E
82 Calliope, Australia 24 0s 151 16E
24 Calne, England 51 27N 1 55w
83 Caloundra, Australia 26 45s 153 10E
40 Caltagirone, Italy 37 14N 14 33E
40 Caltanisetta, Italy 37 29N 14 7E
74 Calumbo, Angola 9 0s 13 0E
91 Calumet, U.S.A. 47 18N 88 28w
43 Calvados, Dépt., France 49 5N 0 20w
76 Calvinia, S. Africa 31 29s 19 50E
74 Camabatela, Angola 8 20s 15 26E
95 Camaguey, Cuba 21 17N 78 10w
64 Cambay, & G., India 22 27N 72 42E
23 Camberley, England 51 20N 0 44w
68 Cambodia, S.E. Asia 11 45N 105 0E
24 Camborne, England 50 12N 5 17w
44 Cambrai, France 50 11N 3 13E
25 Cambrian Mts., Wales 52 20N 3 30w
23 Cambridge, Eng. 52 11N 0 8E
23 Cambridge, England 52 15N 0 5E
94 Cambridge, Jamaica 18 16N 77 53w
84 Cambridge, N.Z. 37 52s 175 28E
93 Cambridge, Mass., U.S.A. 42 40N 71 3w
88 Cambridge Bay,' Canada 69 10N 105 0w
80 Cambridge G., Australia 14 30s 128 30E
23 Camden Gr. London, Eng. 51 32N 0 8w
91 Camden, Ark., U.S.A. 33 30N 92 52w
91 Camden, N.J., U.S.A. 39 58N 75 0w
92 Camden Falls, Canada 49 5N 88 16w
74 Cameroon, Mt., Camer. 4 30N 8 55E
74 Cameroon, Africa 6 0N 12 0E
24 Camerton, England 51 18N 2 27w
37 Caminha, Portugal 41 45N 7 35w
83 Camira Creek, Austral. 29 15s 152 58E
98 Camocim, Brazil 2 55s 40 50w
35 Camolin, Ireland 52 37N 6 26w
82 Camooweal, Australia 19 59s 138 8E
99 Campana, Argentina 34 10s 58 40w
99 Campaña I., Chile 48 30s 75 30w
40 Campania, Prov., Italy 40 50N 14 45E
100 Campbell I., Southern Oc. 52 0s 169 0E
83 Campbell Town, Austral. 42 0s 147 50E

93 Campbellton, Canada 48 0N 66 57w
83 Campbelltown, Australia 34 5s 150 48E
30 Campbeltown, Scotland 55 26N 5 37w
94 Campêche, & G., Mexico 19 50N 90 30w
83 Camperdown, Australia 38 11s 143 12E
98 Campina Grande, Brazil 7 15s 36 0w
99 Campinas, Brazil 22 50s 47 0w
74 Campo, Cameroon 2 25N 9 55E
98 Campo Grande, Brazil 20 27s 54 40w
40 Campobasso, Italy 41 37N 14 44E
99 Campos, Brazil 21 45s 41 35w
30 Campsie Fells, Scotland 56 2N 4 20w
83 Camurra, Australia 29 25s 149 58E
68 Can Tho, Vietnam 10 0N 105 40E
88-89 Canada, N. America
   42 0 to 70 0N; 60 0 to 140 0w
83 Canadian, R., U.S.A. 35 15N 102 0w
41 Canakkale, Turkey 40 5N 26 30E
94 Cananea, Mexico 31 0N 110 25w
72 Canary Is., Atlantic Oc. 28 0N 16 0w
98 Canastra, Se. da, Mts., Brazil
   9 30s 46 30w
95 Canaveral, C., U.S.A., see Kennedy, C.
81 Canaway Ra., Australia 25 50s 142 40E
83 Canbelego, Australia 31 32s 146 27E
83 Canberra, Australia 35 15s 149 10E
42 Cancale, France 48 40N 2 0w
40 Candia, Italy, see Iraklion, Greece
98 Cañete, Peru 13 10s 76 25w
37 Cangas, Spain 43 13N 6 31w
98 Canicado, Mozam., 24 45s 33 15E
51 Cankiri, Turkey 40 43N 33 35E
83 Cann River, Australia 37 40s 149 10E
32 Canna I., Scotland 57 5N 6 35w
64 Cannanore, India 11 59N 75 32E
43 Cannes, France 43 35N 0 0E
80 Canning Basin, Austral. 19 50s 124 0E
23 Cannington, England 51 8N 3 4w
22 Cannock, England 52 42N 2 2w
27 Cannock Chase, Hs., Eng. 52 40N 2 0w
88 Canora, Canada 51 48N 102 36w
83 Canowindra, Australia 33 31s 148 50E
93 Canso, & C., Canada 45 30N 61 0w
37 Cantabrian Mts., Spain 43 12N 5 20w
42 Cantal, Dépt., France 45 3N 3 0E
23 Canterbury, England 51 15N 1 6E
84 Canterbury, Dist., N.Z. 44 0s 171 0E
84 Canterbury Bight, N.Z. 44 20s 172 0E
84 Canterbury Plains, N.Z. 43 30s 172 0E
66 Canton, China 23 15N 113 30E
91 Canton, Miss., U.S.A. 32 30N 90 7w
92 Canton, Ohio, U.S.A. 40 48N 81 20w
23 Canvey, Eng., 51 32N 0 35E
94 Cap Chat, Canada 49 3N 66 40w
95 Cap Haitien, Haiti 20 5N 72 20w
94 Cape Barren I. Austral. 40 25s 148 15E
89 Cape Breton I., Canada 46 25N 61 0w
72 Cape Coast, Ghana 5 5N 1 0w
95 Cape Fear, R., U.S.A. 34 30N 78 30w
92 Cape Girardeau, U.S.A. 37 19N 89 38w
55 Cape Johnson Deep, Pacific Ocean
   10 0N 128 0E
76 Cape Province, S. Afr. 32 0s 24 0E
76 Cape Town, S. Africa 33 59s 18 30E
70 Cape Verde Is., Atlantic Oc. 16 0N 24 0w
82 Cape York Pen., Austral. 13 0s 142 30E
25 Capel-Curig, Wales 53 6N 3 55w
82 Capella, Australia 23 2s 148 1E
63 Capernaum, Israel 32 53N 35 34E
40 Capoeiras Falls, Fs., Brazil 7 0s 57 45w
34 Cappamore, Ireland 52 38N 8 20w
34 Cappoquin, Ireland 52 9N 7 49w
40 Capri, I., Italy 40 35N 14 18E
75 Caprivi Strip, S.W. Africa 17 50s 23 0E
83 Captain's Flat, Australia 35 35s 149 30E
98 Caracal, Rumania 44 10N 24 20E
95 Caracas, Venezuela 10 0N 66 50w
83 Caradoc, Australia 30 35s 142 58E
98 Caransebes, Rumania 45 30N 22 15E
98 Caravelas, Brazil 17 45s 39 0w
99 Carbonara, C., Italy 39 10N 9 30E
89 Carbonear, Canada 47 42N 53 13w
43 Carcassonne, France 43 13N 2 22E
88 Carcross, Canada 60 20N 134 40w
64 Cardamon Hills, India 9 30N 77 0E
95 Cardenas, Cuba 23 0s 81 30w
25 Cardiff, Wales 51 29N 3 10w
25 Cardigan, Wales 52 6N 4 38w
25 Cardigan B., Wales 52 30N 4 40w
37 Cardona, Spain 41 56N 1 40E
82 Cardston, Canada 49 15N 113 28w
82 Cardwell, Australia 18 14s 146 2E
47 Carei, Rumania 47 45N 22 33E
42 Carentan, France 49 20N 1 20w
90 Carey, L., Australia 29 5s 122 20E
42 Careysburg, Liberia 6 34N 10 30w
42 Carhaix, France 48 20N 3 4w
80 Caribbean Sea, W. Indies 15 30N 73 0w
91 Caribou, U.S.A. 46 52N 68 2w
44 Carignan, France 49 37N 5 10E
83 Carinda, Australia 30 27s 147 52E
40 Carinthia, Prov., Austria 46 50N 14 0E
22 Carisbrooke, England 50 42N 1 19w
93 Carleton Place, Canada 45 4N 76 7w
76 Carletonville, S. Africa 26 25s 27 15E
36 Carlingford, & L., Ireland 54 2N 6 8w
26 Carlisle, England 54 54N 2 55w
31 Carlops, Scotland 55 47N 3 20w
35 Carlow, & Co., Ireland 52 50s 6 56w
90 Carlsbad, U.S.A. 32 25N 104 13w
27 Carlton, England 52 58N 1 6w
31 Carluke, Scotland 55 44N 3 50w
88 Carmacks, Canada 62 0N 136 0w

88 Carman, Canada 49 30N 98 0w
25 Carmarthen, & Co., Wales 51 52N 4 18w
24 Carmarthen B., Wales 51 37N 4 30w
43 Carmaux, France 44 1N 2 5E
63 Carmel, Mt., Israel 32 45N 35 0E
82 Carmila, Australia 21 53s 149 5E
37 Carmona, Spain 37 28N 5 43w
31 Carmyllie, Scotland 56 36N 2 41w
32 Carn Eige, Mt., Scotland 57 17N 5 9w
33 Carn Glas-choire, Mt., Scotland
   57 18N 3 50w
33 Carn na Caim, Mt., Scotland
   56 54N 4 10w
42 Carnac, France 47 39N 3 3w
80 Carnarvon, Austral. 24 49s 113 40E
76 Carnarvon, S. Africa 31 0s 22 10E
37 Carnatic, Dist., India 12 30N 79 30E
80 Carnegie, L., Australia 26 0s 122 30E
35 Carnew, Ireland 52 43s 6 30w
26 Carnforth, England 54 8N 2 46w
40 Carnic Alps, Italy 46 34N 12 50E
36 Carnlough, N. Ireland 54 59N 6 0w
73 Carnot, Central Africa 5 0N 15 57E
31 Carnoustie, Scotland 56 30N 2 43w
31 Carnwath, Scotland 56 42N 3 38w
5 Caroline Is., Pacific Ocean 6 0N 146 0E
98 Caroni, R., Venezuela 7 0N 63 0w
47 Carpathian Mts., E. Eur. 48 0N 24 0E
82 Carpentaria, G. of, Australia
   15 0s 138 0E
43 Carpentras, France 44 0N 5 0E
83 Carpolac, Australia 36 45s 141 20E
35 Carra, L., Ireland 53 43N 9 15w
43 Carrara, Italy 44 3N 10 9E
83 Carraweena, Australia 29 10s 139 55E
33 Carrbridge, Scotland 57 16N 3 48w
94 Carriacou I., W. Indies 12 30N 61 28w
30 Carrick, Dist., Scotland 55 10N 4 40w
36 Carrick-on-Shannon, Ire. 53 58N 8 5w
35 Carrick-on-Suir, Ireland 52 21N 7 24w
36 Carrickboy, Ireland 53 42N 7 40w
36 Carrickfergus, N. Ireland 54 43N 5 48w
36 Carrickmacross, Ireland 53 59N 6 45w
83 Carrieton, Australia 32 27s 138 30E
34 Carrigaholt, Ireland 52 37N 9 42w
35 Carrigaline, Ireland 51 49N 8 22w
35 Carrigallen, Ireland 53 59N 7 40w
34 Carron & L., R., Scotland 57 22N 5 35w
31 Carronbridge, Scotland 55 16N 3 46w
36 Carryduff, N. Ireland 54 32N 5 52w
90 Carson City, U.S.A. 39 6N 119 37w
90 Carson Sink, L., U.S.A. 39 45N 118 40w
30 Carsphairn, Scotland 55 13N 4 15w
31 Carstairs, Scotland 55 42N 3 40w
78 Cartenz, Mt., New Guinea,
   see Sukarno Pk.
95 Cartagena, Colombia 10 21N 75 35w
37 Cartagena, Spain 37 38N 0 55w
94 Cartago, Colombia 4 30N 76 10w
95 Cartago, Costa Rica 9 50N 83 50w
42 Carteret, France 49 23N 1 48w
92 Carthage, Mo., U.S.A. 37 4N 94 18w
89 Cartwright, Canada 53 40N 56 40w
98 Carúpano, Venezuela 10 40N 63 25w
72 Casablanca, Morocco 33 30N 7 35w
43 Casale, Italy 45 6N 8 32E
90 Cascade Ra., U.S.A. 45 0N 122 0w
37 Cascais, Portugal 38 45N 9 35w
40 Caserta, Italy 41 8N 14 23E
35 Cashel, Ireland 52 30N 7 55w
83 Casino, Australia 29 0s 152 49E
95 Casiquiare, R., Venezuela 2 40N 66 15w
37 Caspe, Spain 41 5N 0 0
90 Casper, U.S.A. 42 57N 106 30w
41 Caspian Sea, U.S.S.R. 42 30N 51 0E
42 Casquets, The, Channel Is. 49 45N 2 20w
75 Cassinga, Angola 15 5s 16 20E
42 Casseljaloux, France 44 20N 0 0
43 Castellammare, Italy 38 1N 12 52E
43 Castelnaudary, France 43 20N 2 0E
83 Castelo Branco, Portugal 39 50N 7 32w
43 Castelsarrasin, France 44 0N 1 5E
43 Castelvetrano, Italy 37 42N 12 47E
83 Casterton, Australia 37 32s 141 25E
37 Castile, New, Prov. Spain 40 0N 3 20w
37 Castile, Old, Prov., Spain 41 30N 3 40w
31 Castle Douglas, Scotland 54 56N 3 57w
36 Castlebellingham, Ireland 53 53N 6 22w
34 Castleblayney, Ireland 54 6N 6 50w
36 Castlebridge, Ireland 52 23N 6 28w
35 Castlecomer, Ireland 52 45N 7 12w
34 Castleconnell, Ireland 52 44N 8 30w
34 Castledawson, N. Ireland 54 47N 6 30w
36 Castlederg, N. Ireland 54 43N 7 40w
34 Castledermot, Ireland 52 55N 6 50w
34 Castlegregory, Ireland 52 15N 10 1w
34 Castleisland, Ireland 52 14N 9 28w
83 Castlemaine, Australia 37 0s 144 15E
34 Castlemaine, Ireland 52 10N 9 44w
35 Castlemaine Hr., Ireland 52 8N 9 52w
36 Castlemartyr, Ireland 51 54N 8 3w
36 Castlepollard, Ireland 53 40N 7 20w
36 Castlereagh, Ireland 53 47N 8 29w
83 Castlereagh R., Australia 31 20s 148 0E
26 Castleton, England 53 24N 1 40w
26 Castletown, I.o.M. 54 4N 4 41w
35 Castletown, Meath, Ire. 53 47N 6 42w
35 Castletown, Laois, Ire. 52 58N 7 30w
35 Castletown, Westmeath, Ireland
   53 26N 7 25w
33 Castletown, Scotland 58 35N 3 22w
34 Castletownroche, Ireland 52 10N 8 28w
34 Castletownshend, Ireland 51 31N 9 11w

36 Castlewellan, N. Ireland 54 16N 5 57w
43 Castres, France 43 40N 2 13E
94 Castries, Windward Is. 14 0N 61 0w
99 Castro, Chile 42 30s 73 40w
37 Castro, Spain 37 46N 4 30w
91 Cat I., Bahamas 24 25N 75 30w
99 Catalão, Brazil 18 8s 47 50w
37 Catalonia, Prov., Spain 41 40N 1 30E
99 Catamarca, Argentina 28 28s 65 47w
68 Catanduanes, Phil. 13 45N 124 20E
40 Catania, Italy 37 33N 15 7E
40 Catanzaro, Italy 38 59N 16 34E
23 Caterham, England 51 16N 0 4w
92 Catlettsburg, U.S.A. 38 28N 82 33w
94 Catoche, C., Mexico 21 45N 87 0w
94 Catorce, Mexico 23 50N 100 55w
93 Catskill, Mts., U.S.A. 42 18N 74 30w
27 Catterick, England 54 23N 1 38w
51 Caucasus, Mts., U.S.S.R. 43 0N 44 0E
42 Caudebec, France 49 20N 1 0E
44 Caudry, France 50 7N 3 22E
74 Caungula, Angola 8 15s 18 50E
64 Cauvery, R., India 11 0N 78 0E
36 Cavan, & Co., Ireland 54 0N 7 21w
83 Cavendish, Australia 37 35s 142 5E
98 Caviana I., Brazil 0 10N 50 10w
32 Cawdor, Scotland 57 32N 3 53w
64 Cawnpore, see Kanpur
99 Caxias, Brazil 4 50s 43 2w
99 Caxias do Sul, Brazil 29 25s 51 10w
92 Cayenne, French Guiana 4 45N 52 15w
92 Cayuga, L., U.S.A. 42 42N 76 35w
36 Ceanannus Mor, Ireland 53 40N 6 55w
98 Ceará, see Fortaleza
98 Ceará, st., Brazil 4 30s 39 30w
68 Cebu & I., Philippines 10 20N 123 50E
83 Cecil Plains, Australia 27 32s 151 4E
91 Cedar City, U.S.A. 37 40N 113 7w
91 Cedar Falls, U.S.A. 42 33N 92 30w
91 Cedar Rapids, U.S.A. 42 0N 91 39w
80 Ceduna, Australia 32 0s 133 54E
40 Cefalu, Italy 38 0N 14 0E
37 Cehegin, Spain 38 6N 1 48w
94 Celaya, Mexico 20 1N 101 0w
36 Celbridge, Ireland 53 20N 6 31w
68 Celebes, I., Indonesia, see Sulawesi
49 Celebes Sea, Indonesia 4 0N 122 0E
41 Celje, Yugoslavia 46 20N 15 20E
46 Celle, Germany 52 39N 10 3E
25 Cemaes Road, Wales 52 39N 3 41w
43 Cenis, Mt., France 45 17N 7 0E
43 Ceno, R., Italy 44 42N 9 48E
31 Central, Reg., Scotland 54 10N 4 5w
*74 Central African Empire, Africa
   7 0N 20 0E
84 Central Auckland, Dist., N.Z.
   37 0s 174 50E
13 Central Massif, mts., Fr. 45 0N 2 30E
64 Central Makran Ra., Pakistan
   26 30N 64 0E
13 Central Russian Uplands, U.S.S.R.
   53 0N 35 0E
61 Central Siberian Plat., U.S.S.R.
   65 0N 105 0E
92 Centralia, Ill., U.S.A. 38 30N 89 10w
90 Centralia, Wash., U.S.A.
   46 40N 122 55w
68 Cephalonia, I., see Kefallinia
68 Ceram, I., Indonesia 3 10s 129 30E
49 Ceram Sea, Indonesia 2 20s 129 0E
43 Cerbère, France 42 25N 3 10E
76 Ceres, Cape Prov., S. Afr. 33 21s 19 18E
43 Cerignola, Italy 41 18N 15 58E
41 Cerigo, I., Greece, see Kithira
40 Cerknica, Yugoslavia 45 47N 14 40E
98 Cernavoda, Rumania 44 20N 28 5E
98 Cerro de Pasco, Peru 10 45s 77 0w
43 Cervera, Spain 41 40N 1 5E
43 Cervione, France 42 17N 9 30E
41 Cesena, Italy 44 10N 12 15E
49 Cesis, U.S.S.R. 57 20N 25 15E
46 Cesky Tesin, Cz-slov. 49 45N 18 39E
83 Cessnock, Australia 33 0s 151 0E
41 Cetinje, Yugoslavia 42 23N 18 59E
72 Ceuta, Morocco 35 50N 5 20w
43 Ceva, Italy 44 25N 8 0E
43 Cevennes, mts., France 44 30N 4 0E
64 Ceylon, see Sri Lanka
98 Chachapoyas, Peru 6 15s 77 35w
68 Chachoengsao, Thailand 13 45N 101 12E
64 Chachran, Pakistan 28 55N 70 30E
99 Chaco Central, Argentina 24 0s 61 0w
73 Chad (Tchad), Afr. 13 0N 14 0E
73 Chad, L., Chad 13 0N 14 30E
90 Chadron, U.S.A. 42 52N 103 4w
63 Chagai Hills, Afghan. 29 40N 64 0E
61 Chagda, U.S.S.R. 58 30N 130 45E
55 Chagos Is., Indian Ocean 6 0s 72 0w
63 Chahar Burjak, Afghan. 30 20N 62 0E
63 Chahbar, Iran 25 20N 60 33E
64 Chaibasa, India 22 42N 85 49E
64 Chakhansur, Prov., Afghan.
   30 0N 62 0E
65 Chakradharpur, India 22 50N 85 40E
94 Chalainor, China 49 25N 117 30E
67 Chalatun, China 48 0N 122 40E
64 Chaleur, B. de, Canada 47 50N 65 40w
23 Chalfont St. Peter, Eng. 51 36N 0 33w
64 Chaliagaon, India 20 30N 75 0E
43 Challans, France 46 50N 1 58w
43 Chalon-Saône, France 46 51N 4 52E
43 Chalonnes, France 47 20N 0 44w
43 Châlons-s-Marne, France 49 0N 4 20E

64 Chaman, Pakistan 30 55N 66 50E
64 Chamba, India 32 35N 76 15E
75 Chamba, Tanzania 11 40s 37 0E
64 Chambal, R., India 26 0N 76 55E
43 Chambéry, France 45 35N 5 54E
93 Chamborn, Canada 48 27N 72 3w
42 Chamborn, France 47 38N 1 30E
66 Ch'amdo, China 31 30N 97 35E
66 Ch'amdo, Prov., China 31 0N 95 0E
66 Chamonix, France 45 55N 6 50E
42 Champagne, Dist., France 49 0N 4 30E
91 Champaign, U.S.A. 40 12N 88 17w
80 Champion Bay, Australia 28 25s 114 0E
93 Champlain, L., U.S.A. 44 30N 73 20w
99 Chanaral, Chile 26 16s 70 45w
64 Chanda, India 19 59N 79 15E
66 Chandigarh, India 30 32N 76 40E
66 Chandpur, Bangladesh 23 6N 90 35E
66 Changchih, China 36 15 113 0E
66 Changchow, Fukien, China
   24 36N 117 40E
67 Changchow, Kiangsu, China
   31 55N 119 50E
66 Changchun, China 43 20N 126 30E
66 Changkin, Sinkiang, China 44 10N 87 0E
67 Changpai Shan, Mts., China
   42 0N 126 30E
66 Changsha, China 28 10N 112 59E
67 Chang Tang, Tibet 34 0N 88 0E
66 Changteh, China 29 2N 111 45E
66 Changyeh, China 39 15N 100 15E
66 Chankiang, see Tsamkong, China
64 Channapatna, India 12 40N 77 5E
22 Channel Is., U.K. 49 20N 2 20w
37 Chantada, Spain 42 40N 7 48w
66 Chanthaburi, Thailand 12 35N 102 5E
66 Chanyi, China 25 50N 103 20E
66 Chaochow, China 23 42N 116 25E
66 Chaotung, China 27 22N 103 34E
60 Chap Kuduk, U.S.S.R. 48 40N 55 5E
98 Chapada dos Veadeiros, plat., Brazil
   15 0s 48 0w
94 Chapala, L. de, Mexico 20 20N 103 10w
50 Chapayevsk, U.S.S.R. 53 0N 49 50E
26 Chapel-en-le-Frith, Eng. 53 19N 1 54w
64 Chapra, India 25 58N 84 39E
63 Charak, Iran 26 40N 54 50E
98 Charaña, Bolivia 17 45s 69 10w
100 Charcot, I., Antarctica 70 0s 78 0w
24 Chard, England 50 52N 2 57w
60 Chardzhou, U.S.S.R. 39 0N 63 15E
42 Charente, Dépt., France 46 0N 0 30E
42 Charente-Maritime, Dépt., France
   46 5N 0 48w
64 Charikar, Afghan. 35 5N 69 0E
66 Charkhlik, China 39 0N 88 10E
44 Charleroi, Belgium 50 25N 4 27E
93 Charles, C., U.S.A. 37 12N 75 43w
91 Charles City, U.S.A. 43 2N 92 43w
91 Charleston, S.C., U.S.A. 32 48N 80 0w
92 Charleston, W. Va., U.S.A.
   38 24N 81 36w
91 Charleston Hr., U.S.A. 32 45N 79 55w
36 Charlestown, Ireland 53 58N 8 48w
95 Charlestown, Nevis, W.I. 17 10N 62 35w
74 Charlesville, Zaïre 5 27s 20 59E
83 Charleville, Australia 26 27s 146 14E
43 Charleville-Mézières, France
   49 46N 4 42E
91 Charlotte, N.C., U.S.A. 35 16N 80 50w
95 Charlotte Amalie, Virgin Is.
   18 0N 65 0w
80 Charlotte Waters, Australia
   25 55s 134 59E
46 Charlottenburg, Ger. 52 31N 13 15E
92 Charlottesville, U.S.A. 38 0N 78 31w
89 Charlottetown, Canada 46 20N 63 22w
83 Charlton, Australia 36 20s 143 30E
89 Charlton I., Canada 52 0N 79 20w
22 Charlton Kings, Eng. 51 52N 2 3w
22 Charnwood Forest, Eng. 52 45N 1 18w
72 Charouin, Algeria 29 10N 0 15w
82 Charters Towers, Austral. 20 0s 146 13E
43 Chartres, France 48 30N 1 33E
61 Chasovnya Uchurskaya, U.S.S.R.
   57 5N 133 20E
45 Château-d'Oex, Switz. 46 28N 7 10E
43 Château du Loir, France 47 40N 0 30E
42 Château Gontier, France 47 40N 0 42w
43 Château la Vallière, Fr. 47 30N 0 15E
44 Château Porcien, France 49 32N 4 14E
43 Château Thierry, France 49 0N 3 28E
42 Châteaubriant, France 47 45N 1 23w
43 Châteaudun, France 48 0N 1 20E
43 Châteauroux, France 46 51N 1 39E
43 Châtellerault, France 46 46N 0 34E
45 Chatel-St.-Denis, Switz. 46 32N 6 55E
89 Chatham, N.B., Canada 47 0N 65 31w
89 Chatham, Ont., Canada 42 20N 82 18w
23 Chatham, England 51 21N 0 32E
4 Chatham Is., Pacific Oc. 44 0s 176 40w
43 Châtillon-s.-Seine, France 47 50N 4 33E
95 Chatrapur, India 19 25s 84 55E
91 Chattahoochee R., U.S.A. 32 0N 85 7w
91 Chattanooga, U.S.A. 35 2N 85 10w
64 Chatteris, England 52 27N 0 3E
31 Chatton, England 55 34N 1 55w
43 Chaulnes, France 49 48N 2 47E
43 Chauny, France 49 49N 3 15E
37 Chaves, Portugal 41 45N 7 35w
75 Chavuma, Zambia 13 10N 22 55E
64 Chayul, Tibet 28 20N 92 50E
26 Cheadle, Ches. Eng. 53 23N 2 14w

* Renamed Central
African Republic

26 Cheadle, Staffs., Eng. 43 0N 1 58W
26 Cheadle Hulme, Eng. 53 22N 2 12W
56 Cheb, Czechoslovakia 50 9N 12 20E
90 Cheboksary, U.S.S.R. 56 8N 47 30E
91 Cheboygan, U.S.A. 45 29N 84 15W
71 Chech, Erg, des., Algeria 25 0N 7 0W
71 Checheno-Ingush, A.S.S.R., U.S.S.R. 43 30N 46 0E
22 Cheddar, England 51 16N 2 47W
26 Cheddleton, England 53 5N 2 2W
65 Cheduba, I., Burma 18 48N 93 43E
83 Cheepie, Australia 26 39s 145 0E
67 Chefoo (Yehtai), China 37 30N 121 25E
70 Chegga, Mauritania 25 15N 5 40W
90 Chehalis, U.S.A. 46 58N 122 55W
67 Cheju, Korea 33 30N 126 20E
67 Cheju Do. I. (Quelpart), Korea 33 20N 126 30E
67 Chekiang, Prov., China 29 10N 120 0E
50 Cheleken, I., U.S.S.R. 39 25N 53 15E
50 Chelkar, U.S.S.R. 47 50N 59 32E
56 Chelm, Poland 51 12N 23 39E
56 Chelmno, Poland 53 20N 18 30E
23 Chelmsford, England 51 44N 0 27E
56 Chelmza, Poland 53 10N 18 45E
22 Cheltenham, England 51 54N 2 4W
50 Chelyabinsk, U.S.S.R. 55 20N 61 15E
90 Chemikovsk, U.S.S.R. 54 55N 56 0E
67 Chengchow, China 34 55N 113 40E
67 Cheng-teh, China 41 0N 118 0E
67 Chengtu, China 30 50N 104 5E
26 Chepstow, Wales 51 39N 2 41W
43 Cher, R. & Dépt., France 47 0N 2 15E
42 Cherbourg, France 49 39N 1 40W
67 Cherchen, China 38 15N 85 27E
56 Cherchen, R., China 39 20N 86 0E
51 Cherdyn, U.S.S.R. 60 20N 56 20E
51 Cheremkhovo, U.S.S.R. 53 8N 103 1E
50 Cherepovets, U.S.S.R. 59 10N 37 50E
50 Cherkassy, U.S.S.R. 49 20N 32 10E
50 Cherkessk, U.S.S.R. 44 25N 42 10E
51 Chernovtsy, U.S.S.R. 48 21N 25 58E
50 Chernoye, U.S.S.R. 70 30N 89 10E
91 Chernyakhovsk, U.S.S.R. 54 29N 21 48E
91 Cherokee, U.S.A. 42 46N 95 39W
65 Cherrapunji, India 25 18N 91 57E
51 Cherskiy Ra., U.S.S.R. 64 0N 145 0E
22 Cherwell, R., England 51 55N 1 18W
27 Chesapeake B., U.S.A. 37 0N 76 0W
23 Chesham, England 51 42N 0 36W
26 Cheshire, Co. & Plain, Eng. 53 15N 2 30W
23 Cheshunt, England 51 42N 0 1W
22 Chesil Beach, England 50 38N 2 35W
26 Chester, England 53 12N 2 53W
26 Chesterfield, England 53 15N 1 26W
81 Chesterfield Inlet, Can. 63 25N 91 0W
81 Chesterfield Is., Pac. Oc. 19 52s 158 0E
27 Chester-le-Street, Eng. 54 52N 1 34W
27 Chesterton Ra., Australia 25 50s 146 55E
31 Cheviot Hills, England 55 20N 2 30W
74 Chew Bahir, L., Ethiopia 4 45N 36 50E
90 Cheyenne, U.S.A. 41 20N 104 57W
90 Cheyenne, R., U.S.A. 44 30N 101 45W
64 Chhatarpur, India 25 0N 78 35E
64 Chhindwara, India 22 6N 78 59E
65 Chiali, China 30 25N 93 0E
65 Chiang Mai, Thailand 19 0N 99 55E
65 Chiang Rai, Thailand 19 30N 99 50E
94 Chiapa, R., Mexico 16 45N 92 58W
40 Chiavari, Italy 44 20N 9 20E
40 Chiavenna, Italy 46 20N 9 26E
67 Chiba, & Pref., Japan 35 40N 140 6E
73 Chibia, Angola 15 10s 13 50E
73 Chibuk, Nigeria 10 52N 12 50E
92 Chicago, U.S.A. 41 50N 87 50W
88 Chichagof I., Alaska 57 50N 136 0W
23 Chichester, England 50 50N 0 47W
67 Chichibu, Japan 35 2N 98 0W
94 Chiclana, Spain 36 23N 6 10W
99 Chiclayo, Peru 7 0s 79 30W
99 Chico, R., Argentina 49 0s 70 0W
75 Chicoa, Mozambique 15 50s 32 40E
93 Chicoutimi, Canada 48 24N 71 2W
64 Chidambaram, India 11 20N 79 40E
75 Chiengi, Zambia 8 38s 29 10E
44 Chiers, R., France 49 39N 5 20E
40 Chieti, Italy 42 21N 14 12E
66 Chihli, G., China 40 0N 116 30E
94 Chihuahua, Mexico 28 47N 106 20W
64 Chik Ballapur, India 13 25N 77 40E
64 Chikmagalur, India 13 20N 75 52E
65 Chilaw, Sri Lanka 7 30N 79 50E
83 Childers, Australia 25 15s 152 17E
91 Childress, U.S.A. 34 25N 100 15W
99 Chile, S. America 17 30s to 55 0s 71 15W
99 Chilecito, Argentina 29 0s 67 40W
50 Chili, U.S.S.R. 44 20N 66 59E
75 Chililabombwe, Zambia 12 10s 28 0E
64 Chilka, L., India 19 40N 85 28E
82 Chillagoe, Australia 17 0s 144 10E
99 Chillán, Chile 36 48s 72 12W
92 Chillicothe, Mo., U.S.A. 39 46N 93 34W
92 Chillicothe, Ohio, U.S.A. 39 28N 83 1W
62 Chiloe, I., Chile 43 0s 73 30W
23 Chiltern Hills, England 51 45N 0 45W
94 Chimai, China 33 30N 100 45E
44 Chimay, Belgium 50 2N 4 20E
99 Chimborazo, Mt. Ecuador 1 10s 79 5W
98 Chimbote, Peru 8 55s 78 33W
50 Chimkent, U.S.S.R. 42 40N 69 25E
66 China, Asia 55 0N to 18 30N; 70 0E to 133 0E
94 Chinandega, Nicaragua 12 34N 87 5W
98 Chincha Alta, Peru 13 20s 76 0W

83 Chinchilla, Australia 26 40s 150 8E
37 Chinchon, Spain 40 10N 3 28W
75 Chinde, Mozambique 18 45s 36 25E
65 Chindwin, R., Burma 25 0N 95 0E
65 Chingkiang, China 32 7N 119 32E
75 Chingola, Zambia 12 31s 27 53E
72 Chinguetti, Mauritania 20 35s 12 25W
64 Chiniot, Pakistan 31 45N 72 55E
65 Chinnampo, Korea 39 10N 126 0E
43 Chinon, France 47 12N 0 15E
65 Chins Division, Burma 22 30N 93 30E
67 Chinsali, Zambia 10 35s 32 3E
74 Chinwangtao, China 39 58N 119 30E
40 Chioggia, Italy 45 13N 12 17E
75 Chipata, Zambia 13 29s 32 36E
91 Chippewa Falls, U.S.A. 44 55N 92 30W
22 Chipping Campden, Eng. 52 4N 1 48W
22 Chipping Norton, Eng. 51 57N 1 33W
64 Chirala, India 15 45N 80 20E
60 Chirchik, U.S.S.R. 41 40N 69 10E
25 Chirk, Wales 52 57N 3 4W
75 Chirmiri, India 23 15N 82 20E
75 Chiromo, Malawi 16 25s 35 12E
75 Chisamba, Zambia 14 55s 28 20E
65 Chisapani Garhi, Nepal 27 30N 84 2E
50 Chistopol, U.S.S.R. 55 22N 50 37E
51 Chita, U.S.S.R. 52 15N 113 50E
75 Chitembo, Angola 13 30s 16 50E
64 Chitorgarh, India 24 58N 74 36E
94 Chitré, Panama 7 50N 80 25W
65 Chittagong, E. Pak. 22 25N 91 43E
64 Chittoor, India 13 15N 79 5E
40 Chiusi, Italy 43 2N 11 56E
43 Chivasso, Italy 45 15N 7 55E
99 Chivilcoy, Argentina 35 0s 60 4W
75 Chobe Swamp, Botswana 18 25s 24 25E
99 Choele Choel, Argentina 39 15s 65 30W
56 Chojnice, Poland 53 44N 17 40E
22 Cholsey, England 51 34N 1 10W
75 Choma, Zambia 16 57s 26 58E
56 Chomutov, Cz-slov. 50 28N 13 23E
67 Chongjin, Korea 41 40N 129 40E
67 Chongnang, China 34 8N 105 0E
67 Chonos Arch., Chile 45 0s 74 0W
26 Chorley, England 53 39N 2 38W
47 Chortkov, U.S.S.R. 49 2N 25 46E
47 Chorzow, Poland 50 20N 19 0E
67 Choshi, Japan 35 50N 140 48E
46 Choszczno, Poland 53 7N 15 25E
64 Chotila, India 22 30N 71 15E
72 Chott Djerid, Tunisia 34 10N 8 0E
72 Chott el Hodna, Algeria 35 30N 4 30E
63 Choueifat, Lebanon 33 48N 35 30E
83 Chowilla, Australia 33 58s 140 45E
66 Chowkow (Shangshui), China 31 10N 105 45E
66 Choybalsan, Mongolia 48 9N 114 30E
66 Chowkow, China 33 40N 115 0E
22 Christchurch, England 50 44N 1 47W
84 Christchurch, N.Z. 43 30s 172 43E
76 Christiana, S. Africa 27 57s 25 8E
95 Christiansted, St. Croix, W. Indies 17 45N 64 45W
5 Christmas I., Indian Oc. 10 0s 105 0E
11 Christmas I., Pac. Oc. 1 58N 157 27W
67 Chüanchow, China 25 0N 118 33E
66 Chuchow, China 27 45N 113 10E
61 Chuckchi or Chukot Sea, U.S.S.R. 69 0N 177 0E
24 Chudleigh, England 50 35N 3 36W
50 Chudskoye L., U.S.S.R. 58 0N 27 30E
68 Chühsien, China 28 55N 119 0E
68 Chukai, Malaysia 4 10N 103 30E
61 Chulman, U.S.S.R. 57 5N 124 50E
61 Chumatien, China 33 0N 114 10E
61 Chumikan, U.S.S.R. 54 45N 135 20E
66 Chumphon, Thailand 10 35N 99 20E
66 Chunking, China 29 32N 106 40E
65 Chungtien, China 27 50N 99 50E
67 Chungwei, China 38 0N 105 0E
74 Chunya, Tanzania 8 30s 34 0E
99 Chuquicamata, Chile 22 30s 69 0W
45 Chur, Switzerland 46 51N 9 32E
22 Church Stretton, Eng. 52 32N 2 49W
22 Churchdown, England 51 53N 2 9W
88 Churchill, & C., Canada 58 45N 94 0W
89 Churchill L., Canada 56 0N 108 30W
89 Churchill Falls, Canada 53 35N 65 20W
88 Churchill R., Canada 55 30N 104 0W
64 Churu, India 28 25N 75 0E
50 Chusovoy, U.S.S.R. 58 15N 57 30E
50 Chusul, Kashmir 33 40N 78 40E
50 Chuvash, A.S.S.R., U.S.S.R. 55 40N 47 0E
47 Ciechanów, Poland 52 55N 20 35E
98 Cienaga, Colombia 11 0N 74 15W
95 Cienfuegos, Cuba 22 13N 80 30W
47 Cieszyn, Poland 49 45N 18 40E
37 Cieza, Spain 38 15N 1 25W
62 Cilician Gates, Turkey 37 20N 34 52E
91 Cimarron, R., U.S.A. 37 10N 102 0W
47 Cimpina, Rumania 45 10N 25 45E
47 Cimpulung, Rumania 45 18N 25 0E
37 Cinca, R., Spain 42 20N 0 10E
92 Cincinnati, U.S.A. 39 17N 84 25W
22 Cinderford, England 51 49N 2 30W
44 Ciney, Belgium 50 19N 5 5E
68 Cirebon, Indonesia 6 5s 108 30E
22 Cirencester, England 51 44N 1 58W
94 Citlaltepetl, Mt., Mexico 19 3N 97 16W
95 Ciudad Bolivar, Venezuela 8 0N 63 30W

94 Ciudad Camargo, Mexico 27 40N 105 10W
94 Ciudad del Carmen, Mex. 18 45N 91 45W
95 Ciudad Guayana, Ven. 8 25N 62 30W
94 Ciudad Juárez, Mexico 31 40N 106 28W
94 Ciudad Madero, Mexico 22 40N 98 10W
94 Ciudad Mante, Mexico 22 40N 99 2W
94 Ciudad Obregon, Mex. 27 40N 109 50W
37 Ciudad Real, Spain 39 0N 3 55W
37 Ciudad Rodrigo, Spain 40 38N 6 33W
94 Ciudad Victoria, Mex. 23 50N 99 0W
40 Civitanova, Italy 43 20N 13 40E
40 Civitavecchia, Italy 42 6N 11 51E
43 Civray, France 46 10N 0 15E
51 Cizre, Turkey 37 27N 42 3E
30 Clachan, Arg., Scot. 55 45N 5 35W
31 Clachan, Invern., Scot. 57 33N 7 20W
31 Clackmannan, Scot. 56 6N 3 45W
23 Clacton-on-Sea, England 51 48N 1 9E
31 Cladich, Scotland 56 21N 5 5W
43 Clamecy, France 47 27N 3 30E
88 Claire L., Canada 58 30N 112 0W
35 Clane, Ireland 53 18N 6 40W
76 Clanwilliam, S. Africa 32 13s 18 59E
35 Clara, Ireland 53 20N 7 38W
83 Clare, Australia 33 47s 138 30E
23 Clare, England 52 5N 0 36E
34 Clare, R., Ireland 53 30N 8 53W
35 Claremorris, Ireland 53 42N 8 58W
84 Clarence, R., N.Z. 42 15s 173 30E
34 Clarinbride, Ireland 53 13N 8 55W
83 Clarke I., Australia 40 32s 148 10E
90 Clark Fork R., U.S.A. 46 45N 114 0W
92 Clarksburg, U.S.A. 39 5N 80 30W
91 Clarksdale, U.S.A. 34 14N 90 33W
91 Clarksville, U.S.A. 36 35N 87 15W
33 Clashmore, Scotland 57 53N 4 8W
36 Claudy, N. Ireland 54 55N 7 10W
23 Claydon, England 52 6N 1 7E
30 Clear, C. & I., Ireland 51 26N 9 30W
91 Clearwater, U.S.A. 28 0N 82 47W
90 Clearwater, L., Canada 56 20N 75 0W
90 Clearwater, R., U.S.A. 46 15N 115 30W
33 Cleat, Scotland 58 45N 2 56W
26 Cleator Moor, England 54 31N 3 32W
91 Cleburne, U.S.A. 32 21N 97 27W
25 Cleddau, R., Wales 51 55N 4 44W
22 Clee Hills, England 52 26N 2 37W
22 Cleethorpes, England 53 33N 0 2W
22 Cleeve Cloud, mt., Eng. 51 57N 2 0W
82 Clermont, Australia 22 45s 147 30E
43 Clermont Ferrand, Fr. 45 46N 3 10E
44 Clervaux, Luxembourg 50 3N 6 2E
27 Cleveland, Australia 27 35s 153 0E
91 Cleveland, Miss., U.S.A. 33 45N 90 50W
92 Cleveland, Ohio, U.S.A. 41 25N 81 40W
91 Cleveland, Tenn., U.S.A. 35 10N 84 35W
27 Cleveland Hills, England 54 25N 1 11W
35 Clew B., Ireland 53 50N 9 45W
36 Clifden, & B., Ireland 53 30N 10 1W
84 Clifden, New Zealand 46 5s 167 30E
36 Cliffony, Ireland 54 27N 8 31W
22 Clifford, England 52 6N 3 6W
34 Cliffs of Moher, Ireland 52 59N 9 25W
31 Clifton, Australia 27 58s 151 40E
76 Clifton Bakoven, S. Africa 33 57s 18 20E
90 Clinch, Mts., U.S.A. 36 30N 83 0W
88 Clinton, Canada 51 0N 121 40W
84 Clinton, New Zealand 46 24s 169 23E
91 Clinton, Iowa, U.S.A. 41 50N 90 15W
90 Clinton, Okla., U.S.A. 35 30N 98 58W
88 Clinton Colden L., Can. 64 0N 107 0W
26 Clitheroe, England 53 52N 2 24W
83 Cloates, Pt., Australia 22 30s 113 40E
34 Clogh, Donegal, Ireland 54 48N 7 57W
34 Clogheen, Ireland 52 17N 8 0W
36 Clogher, N. Ireland 54 25N 7 11W
36 Clogher Hd., Ireland 53 47N 6 13W
34 Cloghjordan, Ireland 52 57N 8 2W
34 Clonakilty, & B., Ireland 51 38N 8 52W
27 Cloncurry, Australia 20 38s 140 30E
35 Clondalkin, Ireland 53 20N 6 25W
35 Clonee, Ireland 53 25N 6 28W
35 Clones, Ireland 54 10N 7 13W
35 Clonkeen, Ireland 51 59N 9 20W
35 Clonmany, Ireland 55 16N 7 24W
34 Clonmel, Ireland 52 27N 7 40W
35 Clonroche, Ireland 52 27N 6 42W
35 Cloonfad, Ireland 53 41N 8 45W
31 Closeburn, Scotland 55 13N 3 45W
90 Clough, N. Ireland 54 18N 5 50W
90 Clovis, U.S.A. 34 25N 103 16W
33 Clowne, England 53 16N 1 16W
34 Cloyne, Ireland 51 52N 8 8W
22 Cluanie, L., Scotland 57 8N 5 6W
47 Cluj, Rumania 46 42N 23 36E
22 Clun, England 52 26N 3 1W
45 Clunes, Australia 37 20s 143 45E
43 Cluny, France 46 23N 4 43E
43 Cluses, France 46 4N 6 35E
45 Clusone, Italy 45 54N 9 58E
84 Clutha, R., N.Z. 45 39s 168 55E
25 Clwyd, Co., Wales 53 5N 3 20W
25 Clwyd, R., Wales 53 15N 3 25W

22 Coalbrookdale, Eng. 52 40N 2 25W
36 Coalisland, N. Ireland 54 33N 6 42W
22 Coalville, England 52 43N 1 21W
88 Coast Mts., Canada 56 0N 130 0W
99 Coast Ra., Chile 24 0s 70 0W
90 Coast Ra., N. America 42 0N 123 0W
80 Coastal Plains Basin, Australia 30 30s 115 30E
31 Coatbridge, Scotland 55 51N 4 2W
93 Coaticook, Canada 45 7N 71 50W
88 Coats I., Canada 62 30N 83 0W
100 Coats Ld., Antarctica 78 0s 25 0W
94 Coatzacoalcos, Mexico 18 7N 94 35W
89 Cobalt, Canada 47 30N 79 42W
34 Cobar, Australia 31 29s 145 45E
34 Cobh, Ireland 51 52N 8 17W
83 Cobham, Australia 30 10s 142 5E
83 Cobram, Australia 35 58s 145 35E
75 Cóbué, Mozambique 12 0s 34 58E
46 Coburg, Germany 50 16N 10 57E
65 Cocanada, India 17 0N 82 10E
98 Cochabamba, Bolivia 17 30s 66 0W
68 Cochin China, Vietnam 10 0N 106 0E
89 Cochrane, Canada 49 12N 81 37W
83 Cockburn, Australia 31 58s 141 8E
99 Cockburn Chan., Chile 54 30s 72 30W
31 Cockburnspath, Scotland 55 56N 2 23W
31 Cockenzie, Scotland 55 58N 2 59W
26 Cockerham, England 53 58N 2 49W
26 Cockermouth, England 54 41N 3 19W
23 Cockfield, England 52 8N 0 47E
98 Coco, R., Cent. Amer., see Wanks R.
5 Cocos Is., Indian Ocean 12 10s 96 50E
94 Cod, C., U.S.A. 42 8N 70 10W
23 Coddenham, England 52 8N 1 8E
94 Codrington. Barbuda, 17 40N 61 11W
82 Coen, Australia 13 55s 143 15E
44 Coesfeld, Germany 51 57N 7 11E
90 Coeur d'Alene, U.S.A. 47 58N 116 57W
44 Coevorden, Netherlands 52 29N 6 45E
83 Coff's Harbour, Austral. 30 17s 152 51E
40 Coghinas, R., Sardinia, It. 40 30N 8 50E
43 Cognac, France 45 42N 0 20W
83 Cohuna, Australia 35 57s 144 8E
94 Coiba, I., Panama 7 30N 81 50W
32 Coigach, Scotland 58 0N 5 10W
64 Coimbatore, India 11 0N 77 0E
37 Coimbra, Portugal 40 17N 8 26W
37 Coin, Spain 36 42N 4 46W
43 Col de Fauille, France 46 21N 6 0E
43 Col de la Perche, Spain 42 30N 2 0E
43 Col di Tenda, France 44 10N 7 30E
83 Colac, Australia 38 18s 143 40E
83 Colbinabbin, Australia 36 40s 144 45E
23 Colchester, England 51 53N 0 55E
26 Cold Fell, Mt., England 54 56N 2 38W
31 Coldingham, Scotland 55 53N 2 29W
31 Coldstream, Scotland 55 40N 2 14W
24 Colebrooke, England 50 45N 3 44W
22 Coleford, England 51 46N 2 38W
88 Coleman, Canada 49 36N 114 30W
83 Coleraine, Australia 37 47s 141 42E
36 Coleraine, N. Ireland 55 7N 6 39W
23 Coleshill, England 52 30N 1 46W
43 Colico, Italy 46 9N 9 24E
94 Colima, & Vol., Mex. 19 30N 103 50W
30 Coll I., Scotland 56 40N 6 35W
83 Collarenebri, Austral. 29 33s 148 36E
83 Collie, Australia 33 18s 116 5E
80 Collier B., Australia 16 0s 124 0E
32 Collier Law, mt., Eng. 54 47N 1 59W
84 Collingwood, N.Z. 40 40s 172 40E
82 Collinsville, Australia 20 35s 147 56E
43 Collioure, France 42 30N 3 0E
36 Collon, Ireland 53 46N 6 29W
43 Colly Blue, Australia 31 30s 150 2E
43 Colmar, France 48 0N 6 43E
46 Colmars, France 44 10N 6 40E
26 Colne, England 53 52N 2 12W
23 Colne, R., England 51 55N 0 45E
46 Cologne (Köln), Germany 50 56N 6 58E
98 Colombia, Rep., S. Amer. 7 40N 75 0W
65 Colombo, Sri Lanka 6 56N 79 58E
95 Colón, Cuba 22 55N 80 55W
94 Colón, Panama 9 20N 79 54W
30 Colonsay I., Scotland 56 4N 6 13W
94 Colorado I., Panama Canal Zone (Inset)
99 Colorado, R., Argentina 39 30s 63 0W
90 Colorado, R., U.S.A. 38 0N 109 30W
90 Colorado, st., U.S.A. 39 15N 105 30W
90 Colorado Springs, U.S.A. 38 57N 104 59W
33 Colpy, Scotland 57 23N 2 35W
92 Columbia, Dist. of, 38 50N 77 0W
91 Columbia, S.C., U.S.A. 33 59N 81 0W
91 Columbia, Tenn., U.S.A. 35 38N 86 59W
90 Columbia Plat., U.S.A. 47 0N 118 0W
90 Columbia R., U.S.A. 46 15N 124 0W
37 Columbretes Is., Spain 39 53 0 45E
91 Columbus, Ga., U.S.A. 32 30N 84 58W
91 Columbus, Miss., U.S.A. 33 31N 88 17W
91 Columbus, Neb., U.S.A. 41 27N 97 20W
92 Columbus, Ohio, U.S.A. 39 57N 83 2W
25 Colwyn, Wales 53 17N 3 43W
25 Colwyn Bay, Wales 53 19N 3 44W
40 Comacchio, Italy 44 42N 12 17E
94 Comayagua, Honduras 14 10N 87 40W
44 Comblain, Belgium 50 27N 5 34E
35 Comeragh Mts., Ireland 52 16N 7 34W
40 Comilla, Bangladesh 23 27N 91 15E
40 Comino I., Malta 36 0N 14 21E
43 Commentry, France 46 20N 2 45E
43 Commercy, France 48 46N 5 30E

83 Commonwealth Territory, Austral. 35 10s 151 0E
45 Como, & L., Italy 45 49N 9 8E
99 Comodoro Rivadavia, Argentina 45 45s 67 30W
64 Comorin, C., India 8 5N 77 40E
71 Comoro Is., Mozam. Chan. 11 30s 43 17E
43 Comox, Canada 49 50N 125 5W
43 Compiègne, France 49 25N 2 49E
21 Compton, France 52 21N 1 19W
83 Compton Downs, Australia 30 30s 146 35E
31 Comrie, Scotland 56 22N 4 0W
83 Conara Junction, Australia 41 50s 147 20E
72 Conakry, Guinea 9 25N 13 56W
42 Concarneau, France 47 55N 3 55W
99 Concepción, Chile 36 48s 73 5W
73 Conception B., S.W. Afr. 23 55s 14 22E
90 Conception Pt., U.S.A. 34 21N 120 40W
99 Conceptión del Uruguay, Argentina 33 0s 58 40W
93 Concord, U.S.A. 43 7N 71 30W
99 Concordia, Argentina 31 0s 57 48W
83 Condamine, Australia 26 55s 150 5E
43 Condé, Calvados, Fr. 48 55N 0 35E
44 Condé, Nord, France 50 25N 3 35E
83 Condobolin, Australia 33 1s 147 13E
68 Condore Is., Vietnam 8 15s 106 0E
23 Condover, England 52 39N 2 46W
43 Conflans, France 49 10N 5 45E
43 Confolens, France 46 0N 0 45E
26 Congleton, England 53 10N 2 12W
74 Congo, Dem. Rep. of, see Zaïre
74 Congo, Africa 0 0 16 0E
74 Congo, R., Africa 2 0N 22 0E
70 Congo Basin, Africa 1 0s 22 0E
26 Conisbrough, England 53 29N 1 12W
26 Coniston Water, Eng. 54 20N 3 7W
82 Conjuboy, Australia 18 35s 144 45E
35 Connacht, Prov., Ireland 53 42N 8 55W
25 Connah's Quay, Wales 53 13N 3 6W
93 Conneaut, U.S.A. 41 57N 80 32W
93 Connecticut, st., U.S.A. 41 35N 72 40W
93 Connellsville, U.S.A. 40 5N 79 33W
34 Connemara, Dist., Ire. 53 27N 9 45W
82 Connors Ra., Australia 21 40s 149 10E
83 Conoble, Australia 33 0s 144 45E
26 Consett, England 54 52N 1 50W
45 Constance, L., Switz.-Ger., see Bodensee
72 Constantine, Algeria 36 21N 6 0E
72 Constanta, Rumania 44 12N 28 39E
37 Constantina, Spain 37 55N 5 43W
99 Constitución, Chile 35 18s 72 30W
98 Contas, R., Brazil 13 40s 40 30W
36 Convoy, Ireland 54 52N 7 40W
91 Conway, U.S.A. 35 5N 92 30W
25 Conwy, & B., Wales 53 18N 3 52W
25 Conwy, R., Wales 53 0N 3 50W
65 Cooch Behar, India 26 30N 89 20E
11 Cook Is., Pacific Ocean 18 0s 164 0W
84 Cook, Mt., N.Z. 43 30s 170 12E
84 Cook Str., N.Z. 41 15s 174 30E
23 Cookham, England 51 33N 0 42W
76 Cookhouse, S. Africa 32 43s 25 45E
82 Cooktown, Australia 15 30s 145 16E
82 Coolabah, Australia 30 52s 146 54E
83 Cooladdi, Australia 26 35s 145 28E
83 Coolah, Australia 31 36s 149 50E
83 Coolamon, Australia 34 46s 147 8E
83 Coolangatta, Australia 28 0s 153 5E
36 Coolaney, Ireland 54 11N 8 35W
80 Coolgardie, Australia 30 55s 121 7E
83 Coolgreany, Ireland 52 46N 6 14W
83 Cooma, Australia 36 13s 149 10E
83 Coonabarabran, Austral. 31 1s 149 50E
83 Coonamble, Australia 31 0s 148 21E
64 Coondapoor, India 13 30N 74 40E
83 Coongie, Australia 27 10s 140 5E
83 Coongoola, Australia 27 48s 146 0E
83 Cooper Cr., Australia 27 30s 139 17E
83 Cooroy, Australia 26 18s 152 50E
83 Cootamundra, Australia 34 40s 148 2E
36 Cootehill, Ireland 54 6N 7 3W
83 Cooyar, Australia 27 15s 151 48E
99 Copenhagen, Denmark 55 40N 12 35E
99 Copiapó, Chile 27 15s 70 20W
83 Copley, Australia 30 35s 138 30E
89 Coppercliff, Canada 46 25N 81 6W
80 Coppermine, Canada 68 0N 116 0W
27 Coquet, R. & I., England 55 18N 1 45W
74 Coquilhatville, see Mbandaka
99 Coquimbo, Chile 29 50s 71 27W
47 Corabia, Rumania 43 45N 24 30E
98 Coracora, Peru 15 0s 73 40W
91 Coral Gables, U.S.A. 25 46N 80 16W
82 Coral Sea, Australasia 18 0s 152 30E
40 Corato, Italy 41 10N 16 27E
43 Corbeil, France 48 38N 2 30E
26 Corbridge, England 54 58N 2 6W
22 Corby, Lincs., England 52 49N 0 31W
22 Corby, Northants., Eng. 52 30N 0 41W
37 Corcubión, Spain 42 55N 9 14W
91 Cordele, U.S.A. 31 58N 83 50W
99 Cordoba, Argentina 31 22s 64 12W
37 Cordoba, Spain 37 54N 4 48W
99 Cordoba, Sierra de, Arg. 31 30s 65 0W
88 Cordova, Alaska 60 36N 145 45W
22 Corfe Castle, England 50 38N 2 3W
22 Corfe Mullen, England 50 45N 2 0W
82 Corfield, Australia 21 40s 143 21E
41 Corfu, see Kérkira
40 Corigliano, Italy 39 37N 16 32E

41 Corinth, Greece 37 40N 22 58E
91 Corinth, U.S.A. 34 54N 88 35W
34 Cork, & Co., Ireland 51 54N 8 28W
34 Cork Harbour, Ireland 51 48N 8 16W
89 Corner Brook, Canada 49 0N 58 0W
83 Cornwall, Australia 41 35s 148 0E
93 Cornwall, Canada 45 2N 75 10W
34 Cornwall Co., England 50 20N 4 50W
95 Coro, Venezuela 11 23N 69 45W
98 Corocoro, Bolivia 17 25s 68 25W
34 Corofin, Ireland 52 52N 9 11W
84 Coromandel, N.Z. 36 33s 175 28E
64 Coromandel Coast, India 13 0N 80 20E
88 Coronation G., Canada 68 0N 110 0W
90 Coronel Pringles, Arg. 38 0s 61 30W
83 Corowa, Australia 36 7s 146 30E
94 Corozal, Belize 17 20N 88 30W
91 Corpus Christi, U.S.A. 27 50N 97 28W
99 Corral, Chile 40 0s 73 40W
42 Corrèze Dépt., France 45 28N 2 5E
35 Corrib, Lough, Ire. 53 30N 9 20W
22 Corrientes, Argentina 27 15s 58 45W
98 Corrientes, C., Columbia 5 30N 77 30W
94 Corrientes, C., Mexico 20 20N 105 40W
27 Corringham, England 53 25N 0 41W
30 Corryvreckan, G. of, Scot. 56 10N 5 44W
42 Corse, C., Corsica 43 0N 9 0E
42 Corse-du-Sud, Dépt. Fr. 42 0N 9 0E
22 Corsham, England 51 25N 2 11W
43 Corsica I., Mediterranean 42 0N 9 0E
91 Corsicana, U.S.A. 32 5N 96 31W
31 Corsock, Scotland 55 4N 3 56W
43 Corte, France 42 17N 9 8E
90 Cortez, U.S.A. 37 25N 108 45W
93 Cortland, U.S.A. 42 35N 76 12W
40 Cortona, Italy 43 19N 12 1E
51 Corum, Turkey 40 35N 35 5E
98 Corumba, Brazil 19 0s 57 20W
37 Corunna, see La Coruña, Spain
22 Corve, R., Eng. 52 27N 2 43W
25 Corwen, Wales 52 58N 3 22W
22 Coseley, England 52 33N 2 6W
40 Cosenza, Italy 39 20N 16 13E
22 Cosham, England 50 51N 1 3W
43 Cosne, France 47 22N 2 58E
95 Costa Rica, Cen. Amer. 10 0N 84 0W
34 Costelloe, Ireland 53 17N 9 33W
33 Costessey, England 52 40N 1 11E
68 Cotabato, Philippines 7 0N 124 10E
43 Côte d'Or, Dépt. & Dist., France 47 40N 4 45E
91 Coteau des Prairies, U.S.A. 45 0N 95 30W
43 Cotentin, Dist., France 49 20N 1 30W
43 Côtes du Nord, Dépt., Fr. 48 25N 2 45W
72 Cotonou, Benin 6 25N 2 20E
98 Cotopaxi Vol., Ecuador 0 40s 78 30W
22 Cotswold Hills, England 51 45N 2 10W
46 Cottbus, Germany 51 45N 14 24E
22 Cottenham, England 52 18N 0 8E
43 Cottian Alps, France 44 40N 6 50E
22 Cottingham, England 53 47N 0 25W
43 Coulommiers, France 48 46N 3 5E
91 Council Bluffs, U.S.A. 41 22N 95 50W
31 Coupar Angus, Scotland 56 33N 3 15W
95 Courentyne, R., S. Amer. 6 0N 57 3W
42 Courmayeur, Italy 45 47N 7 0E
45 Courtelary, Switzerland 47 10N 7 5E
34 Courtmacsherry, Ire. 51 38N 8 41W
35 Courtown, Ire. 52 37N 6 14W
42 Coutainville, France 49 2N 1 32W
33 Cove Bay, Scotland 57 5s 2 5W
22 Coventry, England 52 25N 1 31W
37 Covilha, Portugal 40 2N 7 27W
92 Covington, U.S.A. 39 0N 84 38W
80 Cowal, Dist., Australia 31 50s 121 50E
83 Cowangie, Australia 35 20s 141 25E
25 Cowbridge, Wales 51 27N 3 28W
31 Cowdenbeath, Scotland 56 7N 3 20W
83 Cowell, Australia 33 35s 136 50E
22 Cowes, England 50 46N 1 18W
22 Cowley, England 51 43N 1 12W
83 Cowra, Australia 33 50s 148 37E
65 Cox's Bazaar, Bangladesh 21 30N 92 5E
92 Cozumel I. de, Mexico 20 30N 87 0W
83 Craboon, Australia 32 2s 149 30E
76 Cradock, S. Africa 32 25s 25 38E
36 Craigavon, N. Ireland 54 28N 6 20W
31 Crail, Scotland 56 16N 2 38W
47 Craiova, Rumania 44 20N 23 49E
27 Cramlington, England 55 5N 1 37W
83 Cranbrook, Australia 42 0s 147 10E
88 Cranbrook, Canada 49 28N 115 58W
23 Cranbrook, England 51 6N 0 33E
23 Cranleigh, England 51 8N 0 29W
31 Cranshaws, Scotland 55 51N 2 30W
22 Cranwell, England 53 2N 0 28W
44 Craonne, France 49 27N 3 42E
98 Crateus, Brazil 5 5s 40 43W
33 Crathie, Scotland 57 2N 3 13W
98 Crato, Brazil 7 0s 39 12W
34 Craughwell, Ireland 53 14N 8 44W
22 Craven Arms, England 52 24N 2 45W
31 Crawford, Scotland 55 28N 3 39W
23 Crawley, England 51 7N 0 12W
33 Creag Meagaidh, Scot. 56 57N 4 37W
43 Crécy, France 50 17N 1 53E
44 Crécy s. Serre, France 49 43N 3 35E
22 Credenhill, England 52 6N 2 48W
22 Crediton, England 50 48N 3 39W
44 Creil, France 49 18N 2 30E
40 Crema, Italy 45 22N 9 40E
40 Cremona, Italy 45 10N 10 1E
44 Crépy, France 49 37N 3 32E

40 Cres, I., Yugoslavia 44 50N 14 25E
83 Cressy, Australia 38 10s 143 48E
43 Crest, France 44 40N 5 0E
91 Creston, U.S.A. 41 2N 94 21W
37 Crete, I., Greece 35 15N 25 0E
37 Creus, C., Spain 42 18N 3 21E
42 Creuse, Dépt., France 45 57N 1 53E
43 Creuse, France 46 40N 1 20E
26 Crewe, England 53 8N 2 23W
43 Crewkerne, England 50 54N 2 48W
30 Crianlarich, Scotland 56 23N 4 36W
25 Crickhowell, Wales 51 52N 3 8W
22 Cricklade, England 51 39N 1 51W
31 Crieff, Scotland 56 23N 3 51W
31 Criffel, Mt., Scotland 54 57N 3 45W
51 Crimea, Pen., U.S.S.R. 45 30N 34 0E
30 Crimond, Scotland 57 35N 1 53W
94 Cristobal, Panama Canal Zone (Inset)
46 Crisul, Black, R., Rum. 46 40N 22 0E
47 Crisul, White, R., Rum. 46 20N 22 0E
47 Crna, R., Yugoslavia 41 20N 21 59E
41 Crna Gora Mts., Y.-Slav. 42 20N 21 30E
35 Croaghpatrick, Mt., Ire. 53 45N 9 42W
40 Croatia, Fed. unit, Y.-slav. 45 30N 16 0E
32 Comalt Hill, Scotland 58 0N 5 0W
31 Cromarty, Scotland 57 41N 4 2W
33 Cromarty Firth, Scot. 57 40N 4 10W
33 Cromer, England 52 57N 1 19E
84 Cromwell, New Zealand 45 0s 169 12E
22 Crondall, England 51 14N 0 52W
83 Cronulla, Australia 33 58s 151 4E
27 Crook, England 54 44N 1 45W
83 Crookwell, Australia 34 30s 149 28E
34 Croom, Ireland 52 31N 8 44W
31 Crosby, Cumb., Eng. 54 45N 3 25W
26 Crosby, Lancs., Eng. 53 28N 3 2W
88 Cross Sd., Alaska 58 20N 136 30W
36 Crossakiel, Ireland 53 43N 7 1W
36 Crossgar, N. Ireland 54 24N 5 46W
34 Crosshaven, Ireland 51 48N 8 17W
34 Crossmolina, Ireland 54 6N 9 19W
40 Crotone, Italy 39 5N 17 6E
23 Crouch, R., England 51 39N 0 40E
23 Crowborough, England 51 4N 0 9W
83 Crowes, Australia 38 55s 143 22E
27 Crowle, England 53 36N 0 50W
88 Crows Nest P., Canada 49 35N 115 0W
82 Croydon, Australia 18 30s 142 15E
23 Croydon, England 51 21N 0 6W
5 Crozet Is., Indian Ocean 46 0s 51 0E
42 Crozon, France 48 24N 4 30W
33 Cruden Bay, Scotland 57 24N 1 51W
30 Crummock Water L., Eng. 54 34N 3 19W
34 Crusheen, Ireland 52 57N 8 54W
98 Cruzeiro do Sul, Brazil 7 30s 72 60W
83 Crystal Brook, Ausfralia 33 20s 138 7E
47 Csongrad, Hungary 46 43N 20 12E
47 Csorna, Hungary 47 38N 17 18E
74 Cuango, Congo 6 20s 16 50E
53 Cuba, West Indies 21 30N 79 30W
75 Cubango, R., Angola 15 30s 18 0E
73 Cuchi, Angola 14 40s 17 5E
23 Cuckfield, England 51 1N 0 9W
27 Cudworth, England 53 34N 1 26W
98 Cúcuta, Colombia 7 40N 72 40W
64 Cuddalore, India 11 42N 79 50E
64 Cuddapah, India 14 30N 78 50E
83 Cudgewa, Australia 36 10s 147 48E
80 Cue, Australia 27 25s 118 0E
98 Cuenca, Ecuador 2 46s 79 10W
37 Cuenca, Spain 40 8N 2 5W
37 Cuenca, Sa. de, mts., Spain 40 20N 1 50W
91 Cuero, U.S.A. 29 20N 97 30W
98 Cuiaba, Brazil 15 30s 56 6W
36 Cuilcagh, Mt., Ireland 54 16N 8 0W
32 Cuillin Hills & Sd., Scot. 57 13N 6 6W
73 Cuima, Angola 13 0s 15 30E
83 Culcairn, Australia 35 40s 147 0E
26 Culdaff, Ireland 55 16N 7 8W
37 Culebra, Sa. de la, mts., Spain 42 0N 6 30W
94 Culiacan, Mexico 24 49N 107 20W
33 Cullen, Scotland 57 42N 2 48W
37 Cullera, Spain 39 10N 0 15W
35 Cullin, L., Ireland 53 57N 9 11W
33 Cullivoe, Scotland 60 42N 1 1W
33 Culloden Moor, Scotland 57 29N 4 8W
22 Cullompton, England 50 52N 3 23W
45 Cully, Switzerland 46 30N 6 44E
43 Culoz, France 45 50N 5 50E
31 Culross, Scotland 56 3N 3 38W
33 Cults, Scotland 57 7N 2 10W
34 Culvain Mt., Scotland 56 55N 5 19W
95 Cumanà, Venezuela 10 30N 64 10W
88 Cumberland, Canada 49 34N 125 0W
26 Cumberland, Co., see Cumbria
92 Cumberland, U.S.A. 39 45N 78 57W
82 Cumberland Is., Austral. 20 25s 149 0E
89 Cumberland Pen., Can. 67 0N 65 0W
91 Cumberland Plat., U.S.A. 36 0N 84 40W
89 Cumberland Sd., Canada 65 0N 65 0W
31 Cumbernauld, Scotland 55 57N 3 59W
30 Cumbrae, Is., Scot. 55 46N 4 55W
26 Cumbria, Co., England 54 30N 3 0W
83 Cumnock, Australia 32 55s 148 40E
30 Cumnock, Scotland 55 27N 4 16W
22 Cumnor, England 51 44N 1 21W
31 Cumwhinton, England 54 51N 2 49W
75 Cunene, R., Angola 17 0s 15 0E
43 Cuneo, Italy 44 23N 7 32E
83 Cunnamulla, Australia 28 0s 145 42E
30 Cunninghame, Dist., Scot. 55 40N 4 25W

31 Cupar, Scotland 56 19N 3 2W
95 Curaçao, I., Neth. W. I. 12 12N 69 0W
99 Curicó, Chile 35 0s 71 15W
99 Curitiba, Brazil 52 25s 49 45W
34 Currane, L., Ireland 51 50N 10 8W
83 Curraweena, Australia 30 45s 145 55E
31 Currie, Scotland 55 53N 3 17W
83 Curtis I., Australia 23 45s 151 17E
94 Curundu, Panama Can. Zone (Inset)
36 Cushendall, N. Ireland 55 5N 6 4W
43 Cusset, France 46 10N 3 30E
65 Cuttack, India 20 30N 85 57E
49 Cuxhaven, Germany 53 54N 8 42E
98 Cuzco, Peru 13 30s 72 8W
25 Cwmbran, Wales 51 39N 3 0W
25 Cwrt, Wales 52 35N 3 45W
37 Cyclades, Is., see Kikladhes
83 Cygnet, Tasmania 43 5s 147 3E
62 Cyprus I., Medit. Sea 35 0N 33 0E
73 Cyrenaica, Prov., Libya 28 0N 22 0E
73 Cyrene (Shahhat), Libya 32 39N 21 18E
46-47 Czechoslovakia, Eur. 49 0N 17 0E
47 Czegléd, Hungary 47 5N 19 45E
47 Czeremcha, Poland 52 32N 23 20E
47 Czestochowa, Poland 50 49N 19 4E

D

68 Da Lat, Vietnam 12 0N 108 30E
68 Da-Nang (Tourane), Vietnam 16 2N 108 0E
63 Daal, Syria 32 45N 36 8E
62 Dabat, Ethiopia 13 0N 37 50E
46 Dabie, Poland 53 27N 14 45E
72 Dabola, Guinea 10 50N 11 5W
74 Dabra Tabor, Ethiopia 11 50N 38 0E
47 Dabrowa, Poland 50 10N 21 0E
65 Dacca, Bangladesh 23 40N 90 25E
64 Dadu, Pakistan 26 45N 67 35E
68 Daet, Philippines 14 3N 122 59E
72 Dafina, Saudi Arabia 23 11N 42 0E
72 Dagana, Sénégal 16 30N 15 20W
51 Dagestan, A.S.S.R., U.S.S.R. 43 0N 47 0E
68 Dagupan, Philippines 16 0N 120 20E
72 Dahlak Arch., Red Sea 16 0N 40 10E
72 Dahomey, see Benin
35 Daingean (Philipstown), Ireland 53 19N 7 18W
67 Dairen-Port Arthur, China, see Lü-ta
67 Dairut, Egypt 27 34N 30 43E
67 Daishoji, Japan 36 15N 136 16E
82 Dajarra, Australia 21 47N 139 20E
72 Dakar, Sénégal 14 45N 17 8W
72 Dakhla, W. Sahara 23 55N 15 50W
72 Dakhla Oasis, Egypt 25 55N 27 30E
51 Dakhovskaya, U.S.S.R. 44 15N 40 15E
90 Dakota N. & S., see N. & S. Dakota
41 Dakovica, Yugoslavia 42 25N 20 26E
51 Dakra, Sénégal 15 30N 15 20W
49 Dal, R., Sweden 60 12N 16 40E
66 Dalai Nor, L., China 48 0N 116 30E
66 Dalandzadagad, Mong. 43 55N 104 10E
49 Dalarö, Sweden 59 10N 18 23E
64 Dalbandin, Pakistan 29 0N 64 23E
31 Dalbeattie, Scotland 54 56N 3 50W
83 Dalby, Australia 27 6s 151 18E
33 Dalhalvaig, Scotland 58 27N 3 52W
89 Dalhousie, Canada 48 0N 66 21W
31 Dalkeith, Scotland 55 53N 3 4W
83 Dallarnil, Australia 25 25s 152 0E
91 Dallas, Oregon, U.S.A. 44 50N 123 20W
91 Dallas, Texas, U.S.A. 32 44N 96 55W
31 Dalmally, Scotland 56 24N 4 58W
40 Dalmatia, Prov., Y.-slav. 43 10N 17 10E
30 Dalmellington, Scotland 55 19N 4 24W
61 Dalnegorsk, U.S.S.R. 44 30N 135 57E
61 Dalnerechensk, U.S.S.R. 45 50N 133 50E
30 Dalry, Scotland 55 43N 4 43W
26 Dalton, Lancs., England 54 12N 3 12W
27 Dalton, Yorks., England 54 28N 1 32W
48 Dalvik, Iceland 66 2N 18 20W
80 Daly, R., Australia 14 0s 130 50E
80 Daly Waters, Australia 16 5s 133 30E
64 Daman, India 20 20N 72 59E
75 Damara, Dist., S.W. Africa 22 25s 17 0E
63 Damascus (Esh Sham), Syria 33 30N 36 18E
74 Damba, Angola 6 44s 15 29E
74 Dambacha, Ethiopia 10 40N 37 10E
62 Damghan, Persia 36 5N 54 20E
73 Damietta, Egypt 31 30N 31 32E
62 Damman, Saudi Arabia 26 27N 50 3E
64 Damoh, India 23 58N 79 30E
80 Dampier Arch., Austral. 20 30s 116 40E
80 Dampier Downs, Austral. 18 5s 124 10E
82 Dampier Str., Australia 20 30s 131 15E
72 Dan Gora, Nigeria 11 30N 8 7E
64 Dandeli, India 15 5N 74 30E
65 Dandeldhura, Nepal 29 25N 80 30E
83 Dandenong, Australia 38 10s 145 14E
79 Dankhar Gompa, India 32 8N 78 10E
49 Dannemora, Sweden 60 13N 17 50E
84 Dannevirke, N.Z. 40 8s 176 10E
93 Dansville, U.S.A. 42 35N 77 40W
47 Danube, R., Europe 45 0N 28 0E
92 Danville, Ill., U.S.A. 40 10N 87 35W
92 Danville, Ken., U.S.A. 37 40N 84 50W
74 Dar es Salaam, Tanzania 6 48s 39 12E
73 Daraj, Libya 30 5N 10 30E
63 Dareiya, Syria 33 28N 36 14E
64 Dargai, India 26 15N 71 50E

60 Dargan Ata, U.S.S.R. 40 40N 62 20E
84 Dargaville, N.Z. 36 0s 173 59E
94 Darien, Panama Canal Zone (Inset)
95 Darien, G. of, Colombia 9 0N 77 0W
65 Darjeeling, India 27N 88 18E
22 Darlaston, England 52 35N 2 1W
83 Darling Downs, Australia 27 45s 150 0E
81 Darling, R., Australia 32 0s 143 0E
80 Darling Ra., Australia 32 0s 116 0E
27 Darlington, England 54 33N 1 34W
46 Darlowo, Poland 54 13N 16 19E
45 Darmstadt, Germany 49 52N 8 40E
73 Darnah, Libya 32 40N 22 25E
100 Darnley, C., Antarctica 68 0s 70 0E
82 Darr, Australia 24 34s 144 52E
24 Dart, R., England 50 28N 3 45W
24 Dartford, England 51 26N 0 13E
24 Dartmoor, England 50 39N 3 55W
93 Dartmouth, Canada 44 50N 63 30W
24 Dartmouth, England 50 21N 3 35W
27 Darton, England 53 36N 1 32W
31 Darvel, Scotland 55 37N 4 20W
26 Darwen, England 53 42N 2 28W
80 Darwin, Australia 12 28s 131 0E
62 Darya yi Namak, L., Iran 34 40N 51 30E
63 Dasht-i-Kavir, Des., Iran 35 0N 55 0E
63 Dasht-i-Lut, Des., Iran 31 0N 58 30E
64 Dasht-i-Margo, Des., Afghan. 30 40N 62 30E
50 Daugavpils, U.S.S.R. 56 0N 26 30E
64 Daukara, U.S.S.R. 45 55N 59 30E
64 Daulat Yar, Afghan. 34 35N 65 40E
63 Daulatabad, Afghanistan 32 46N 62 34E
64 Daulatabad, Iran 28 20N 56 38E
88 Dauphin, Canada 51 13N 100 3W
43 Dauphiné, Prov., France 45 5N 5 30E
68 Davao, & G., Philippines 7 15N 125 35E
92 Davenport, U.S.A. 41 33N 90 34W
22 Daventry, England 52 15N 1 10W
100 Davis, Antarctica 69 0s 79 0E
89 Davis Str., N. America 67 0N 58 0W
45 Davos-Platz, Switzerland 46 50N 9 50E
62 Dawasir, Si. Arabia 20 25N 45 30E
24 Dawlish, England 50 35N 3 29W
65 Dawna Ra., Burma 16 30N 98 30E
88 Dawson, Canada 64 10N 139 30W
88 Dawson Cr., Canada 55 45N 120 15W
82 Dawson Ra., Australia 24 45s 149 55E
43 Dax, France 43 41N 1 0W
92 Dayton, Ohio, U.S.A. 39 47N 84 12W
91 Daytona Beach, U.S.A. 29 7N 81 2W
76 De Aar, S. Africa 30 46s 23 54E
80 De Grey, R., Australia 20 32s 120 0E
61 De Long Is., U.S.S.R. 77 0N 155 0E
63 Dead Sea, Jordan-Israel 31 30N 35 25E
80 Deakin, Australia 30 34s 129 0E
22 Dean, Forest of, England 51 47N 2 35W
88 Dease Arm, Canada 66 45N 120 6W
88 Dease, R. & L., Canada 59 10N 129 50W
91 Death Valley, U.S.A. 36 0N 117 0W
43 Deauville, France 49 20N 0 0
72 Deba Habe, Nigeria 10 14N 11 20E
41 Debar, Yugoslavia 41 30N 20 30E
23 Deben, R., England 52 12N 1 13E
74 Debre Markos, Ethiopia 10 20N 37 45E
47 Debrecen, Hungary 47 7N 21 54E
91 Decatur, Alabama, U.S.A. 34 29N 86 43W
91 Decatur, Georgia, U.S.A. 33 42N 84 21W
92 Decatur, Ill., U.S.A. 39 53N 88 56W
43 Decazeville, France 44 37N 2 15E
64 Deccan, Reg., India 17 0N 78 30E
72 Dedougou, Volta 12 35N 3 40W
33 Dee, R., Scotland 57 7N 2 10W
25 Dee, R., Wales 52 50N 3 30W
83 Deepwater, Australia 29 25s 151 55E
64 Deesa, India 24 25N 72 20E
25 Deganwy, Wales 53 18N 3 49W
49 Degerfors, Sweden 64 10N 19 50E
45 Deggendorf, Germany 48 49N 12 59E
63 Deh Titan, Afghan. 33 45N 63 50E
63 Dehra Dun, India 30 20N 78 4E
72 Dehibat, Tunisia 32 0N 10 10E
63 Deim Zubeir, Sudan 7 47N 26 20E
44 Deinze, Belgium 50 59N 3 30E
63 Deir Abu Sa'id, Jordan 32 30N 35 42E
51 Deir ez Zor, Syria 35 19N 40 15E
90 Del Rio, U.S.A. 29 22N 100 55W
62 Delami, Sudan 11 50N 30 25E
91 Delaware, R., U.S.A. 40 0N 75 15W
91 Delaware, st. & B., U.S.A. 38 45N 75 20W
83 Delegate, Australia 37 14N 148 58E
45 Delemont, Switzerland 47 20N 7 20E
74 Delgado, C., Mozambique 10 40s 40 43E
64 Delgo, Sudan 20 30N 30 20E
64 Delhi, India 28 42N 77 20E
51 Delice, R., Turkey 39 45N 34 15E
94 Delicias, Mexico 28 25N 105 0W
80 Deloraine, Australia 41 30s 146 45E
76 Deloornshoop, S. Africa 28 25s 24 20E
35 Delvin, Ireland 53 37N 7 4W
37 Demanda, Sa. de la, mts., Spain 42 8N 3 0W
41 Demavend, Mt., Iran 35 50N 52 12E
74 Demidolo, Ethiopia 8 34N 34 50E
44 Demer, R., Belgium 51 0N 5 10E
90 Deming, U.S.A. 32 17N 107 48W
44 Den Burg, Netherlands 53 5N 4 47E
44 Den Helder, Netherlands 52 58N 4 46E

44 Denain, France 50 20N 3 22E
25 Denbigh, Wales 53 11N 3 26W
65 Denchin, China 31 35N 95 10E
37 Denia, Spain 38 50N 0 5E
83 Deniliquin, Australia 35 31s 144 59E
51 Denizli, Turkey 37 57N 28 41E
48 Denmark, Europe 55 45N 10 20E
100 Denmark Str., N. Atlantic Ocean 66 0N 30 0W
31 Denny, Scotland 56 1N 3 55W
26 Denton, Lancs., England 53 26N 2 10W
23 Denton, Leics., England 52 55N 0 42W
23 Denton, Sussex, England 50 48N 0 5E
91 Denton, U.S.A. 33 10N 97 14W
82 D'Entrecasteaux Is., Papua N.G. 9 30s 151 0E
90 Denver, U.S.A. 39 50N 104 57W
65 Deoghar, India 24 40N 86 40E
64 Deolali, India 19 55N 73 43E
65 Deoria, India 26 35N 83 50E
64 Dera Ghazi Khan, Pak. 30 5N 70 53E
64 Dera Ismail Khan, Pak. 31 46N 70 54E
62 Deraheib, Sudan 21 58N 35 7E
51 Derbent, U.S.S.R. 42 0N 48 23E
80 Derby, Australia 17 18s 123 40E
26 Derby, & Co., England 52 56N 1 28W
35 Derg, L., Ireland 53 0N 8 18E
36 Derg, L. & R., Ireland 54 40N 7 40W
65 Dergaon, India 26 40N 94 0E
36 Derry, N. Ireland, see Londonderry
36 Derrygonnelly, N. Ire. 54 25N 7 50W
34 Derryrush, Ireland 53 9N 9 40W
36 Derryveagh Mts., Ireland 55 0N 8 3W
73 Derudub, Sudan 17 30N 36 30E
27 Derwent, R., Derby, Eng. 53 15N 1 38W
27 Derwent, R., Yorks., Eng. 53 50N 1 0W
26 Derwent Water, L., Eng. 54 35N 3 9W
91 Des Moines, & R., U.S.A. 41 30N 93 34W
74 Dese, Ethiopia 10 58N 39 45E
99 Deseado, R., Argentina 47 0s 68 0W
94 Désirade, I., Leeward Is. 16 15N 61 0W
61 Desna, R., U.S.S.R. 51 30N 30 30E
99 Desolación I., Chile 53 0s 74 30W
22 Dessa, Niger 14 44N 1 6E
46 Dessau, Germany 51 41N 12 14E
46 Detmold, Germany 51 55N 8 50E
92 Detroit, U.S.A. 42 22N 83 7E
48 Dettifoss, Iceland 65 50N 16 0W
44 Deurne, Belgium 51 13N 4 27E
44 Deurne, Netherlands 51 27N 5 47E
42 Deux Sèvres, Dépt., Fr. 46 30N 0 30W
47 Deva, Rumania 45 55N 22 50E
64 Devakottai, India 9 55N 78 40E
44 Deventer, Netherlands 52 16N 6 10E
31 Deveron, R., Scotland 57 22N 3 0W
22 Devizes, England 51 21N 1 59W
24 Devon, Co., England 50 47N 3 40W
89 Devon Island, Canada 4 30N 85 0W
83 Devonport, Australia 41 8s 146 30E
24 Devonport, England 50 22N 4 10W
84 Devonport, N.Z. 36 49s 174 49E
64 Dewas, India 23 0N 76 0E
27 Dewsbury, England 53 42N 1 38W
61 Dezhneva, C., U.S.S.R. 66 0N 170 0W
62 Dhaba, Saudi Arabia 27 25N 35 50E
62 Dhahran, Saudi Arabia 26 20N 50 10E
64 Dhamtari, India 20 45N 81 30E
65 Dhanbad, India 23 50N 86 30E
65 Dhangarhi, Nepal 28 55N 80 40E
63 Dhank, Oman 23 33N 56 5E
65 Dhankuta, Nepal 27 0N 87 10E
64 Dhar, India 22 40N 75 5E
64 Dharmapuri, India 12 10N 78 5E
64 Dharwar, India 15 39N 75 59E
65 Dhaulagiri, Mt., Nepal 28 45N 83 25E
65 Dhenkanal, India 20 35N 85 30E
41 Dhidhimotikhon, Greece 41 18N 26 33E
64 Dhikti, Mt., Crete 35 5N 25 34E
63 Dhilban, Jordan 31 30N 35 47E
63 Dhofar, Prov., Oman 17 0N 54 10E
63 Dholpur, India 26 45N 77 58E
63 Dhour Chouer, Lebanon 33 53N 35 42E
64 Dhrol, India 22 40N 70 25E
65 Dhubri, India 26 3N 89 58E
62 Dhula, South Yemen 15 10N 48 0E
64 Dhulia, India 21 0N 74 56E
94 Diablo Heights, Panama Canal Zone (Inset)
72 Diafarabe, Mali 14 17N 4 57W
90 Diamante, Argentina 32 0s 60 40W
98 Diamantina, Brazil 18 11s 43 45W
81 Diamantina, R., Australia 24 48s 140 0E
98 Diamantino, Brazil 14 25s 56 40W
64 Dibaya, Zaïre 6 30s 23 0E
74 Dibaya-Lubue, Zaïre 4 12s 19 54E
22 Dibden, England 50 53N 1 24W
65 Dibrugarh, India 27 38N 94 55E
90 Dickinson, U.S.A. 46 55N 102 53W
75 Diebougou, Volta 11 0N 5 0W
75 Diego Suarez, Madagascar 12 25s 49 20E
44 Diekirch, Luxembourg 52 6N 6 10E
44 Dielette, France 49 33N 1 54W
44 Diepenbeek, Belgium 50 55N 5 22E
44 Dieppe, France 49 58N 1 13E
44 Dieren, Netherlands 52 3N 6 6E
44 Diest, Belgium 50 59N 5 4E
44 Differdange, Luxembourg 49 32N 5 53E
90 Digby, Canada 44 45N 65 40W
44 Digne, France 44 6N 6 12E
44 Diganes, C., Iceland 66 4N 14 37W
65 Dihang, R., India 28 30N 95 0E
43 Dijon, France 47 20N 5 1E
61 Dikemda, U.S.S.R. 59 0N 121 35E
44 Diksmuide, Belgium 51 3N 2 52E

73 Dikwa, Nigeria 12 6N 14 0E
62 Dilam, Saudi Arabia 23 55N 47 10E
68 Dili, Portuguese Timor 8 45s 125 30E
74 Dimbelenge, Zaïre 5 28s 23 5E
72 Dimbokro, Ivory Coast 6 45N 4 30w
83 Dimboola, Australia 36 29s 142 2E
61 Dimitri Laptev Str., U.S.S.R.
  73 0N 140 0E
41 Dimitrovgrad, Bulgaria 42 5N 25 35E
68 Dinagat I., Philippines 10 10N 125 35E
65 Dinajpur, Bangladesh 25 40N 88 32E
74 Dinan, Belgium 50 17N 4 56E
40 Dinant, Belgium 50 17N 4 56E
40 Dinaric Alps, Y-slav. 44 0N 16 0E
74 Dinas Powis, Wales 51 25N 3 14w
74 Dincha, Ethiopia 6 15N 37 32E
64 Dindigul, India 10 22N 78 0E
34 Dingle, & B., Ireland 52 9N 10 16w
82 Dingo, Australia 23 40s 149 27E
51 Dinguiraye, Guinea 11 30N 10 35w
33 Dingwall, Scotland 57 36N 4 26w
72 Diourbel, Sénégal 14 40N 15 30w
68 Dipolog, Philippines 8 35N 123 25E
62 Dir, Pakistan 35 25N 71 45E
75 Dirico, Angola 17 52s 20 40E
80 Dirk Hartog I., Austral. 25 50s 113 0E
83 Dirranbandi, Australia 28 29s 148 18E
80 Disappointment, L., Australia
  23 20s 123 10E
83 Discovery B., Australia 38 10s 140 40E
89 Disko B. & I., Greenland 69 0N 53 0w
23 Diss, England 52 22N 1 7E
23 Ditchling, Village & Beacon, England
  55 50N 0 7w
25 Ditton Priors, England 52 29N 2 35w
62 Diu, India 20 48N 71 0E
91 Dixon, U.S.A. 41 51N 89 18w
62 Diyala, R., Iraq 34 0N 45 0E
64 Diyarbakir, Turkey 37 58N 40 25E
64 Dizak, Iran 27 20N 62 3E
62 Dizful, Iran 32 30N 48 33E
73 Djado, Niger 21 10N 12 5E
72 Djambala, Congo (Fr.) 2 25s 14 45E
72 Djanet, see Fort Charlet
73 Djang, Cameroon 5 30N 10 5E
72 Djelfa, Algeria 34 39N 3 14E
73 Djema, Central Africa 6 3N 25 0E
72 Djenne, Mali 14 0N 4 30w
73 Djerada, Morocco 34 16N 2 4w
72 Djerba I., Tunisia 33 50N 10 50E
72 Djibo, Volta 14 15N 1 35w
62 Djibouti, St., Africa 11 35N 43 0E
72 Djibouti, Djibouti 11 30N 43 5E
72 Djidjelli, Algeria 36 45N 5 0E
73 Djolu, Zaïre 0 45N 22 5E
72' Djougou, Benin 9 40N 1 45E
63 Djounie (Juniyah), Leb. 33 58N 35 39E
74 Djugu, Zaïre 1 50N 30 40E
89 Djupivogur, Iceland 64 38N 14 14w
52 Dneprodzerzhinsk, U.S.S.R.
  48 32N 34 30E
52 Dnepropetrovsk, U.S.S.R. 48 25N 34 55E
51 Dnepr, R., U.S.S.R. 47 0N 33 0E
51 Dnestr, R., U.S.S.R. 48 30N 25 0E
74 Doba, Chad 8 40N 16 50E
92 Dobbyn, Australia 19 40s 139 58E
47 Dobrógea, Reg., Rum. 44 30N 28 20E
21 Docking, England 52 55N 0 39E
90 Dodge City, U.S.A. 37 50N 100 4w
41 Dodecanese Is., Greece 36 40N 27 0E
74 Dodoma, Tanzania 6 0s 35 50E
44 Doetinchem, Neth. 51 58N 6 18E
18 Dogger Bank, North Sea 54 45N 2 0E
64 Dogi, Afghanistan 32 20N 62 50E
69 Dogo I., Japan 36 15N 133 20E
62 Doha, Qatar 25 15N 51 32E
64 Dohad, India 22 57N 74 20E
62 Dohazari, Bangladesh 22 10N 92 7E
41 Dojran, Yugoslavia 41 10N 22 45E
44 Dokkum, Netherlands 53 20N 6 1E
89 Dolbeau, Canada 48 25N 72 18w
43 Dôle, France 47 6N 5 30E
74 Dolgellau, Wales 52 44N 3 54w
67 Dolinsk, U.S.S.R. 47 25N 142 48E
74 Dolisie, Congo (Fr.) 4 0s 13 10E
31 Dollar, Scotland 56 9N 3 40w
40 Dolomites, Italy 46 30N 11 40E
99 Dolores, Argentina 36 15s 57 50w
88 Dolphin & Union Str., Can.
  70 0N 120 0w
31 Dolphinton, Scotland 55 42N 3 28w
51 Dolya, U.S.S.R. 69 45N 132 0E
75 Dombe Grande, Angola 13 0s 13 0E
40 Domfront, France 48 35N 0 40w
95 Dominica, I., W. Indies 15 25N 61 20w
95 Dominican Rep., W.I. 19 0N 70 30w
43 Domodossola, Italy 46 6N 8 19E
43 Domrémy, France 48 40N 5 40E
34 Don, R., England 53 30N 1 15w
33 Don, R., Scotland 57 15N 2 15w
52 Don, R., U.S.S.R. 50 0N 42 0E
37 Don Benito, Spain 38 55N 5 50w
36 Donaghadee, N. Ireland 54 38N 5 32w
36 Donald, Australia 36 25s 142 57E
45 Donaueschingen, Ger. 47 58N 8 31E
47 Donauwörth, Germany 48 42N 10 47E
27 Doncaster, England 53 31N 1 8w
74 Dondo, Angola 9 45s 14 32E
75 Dondo, Mozambique 19 32s 34 45E
64 Dondra Hd., Sri Lanka 6 0N 80 40E
36 Donegal, & B., Ireland 54 39N 8 6w
36 Donegal, Co., Ireland 54 52N 8 0w
51 Donets, R., U.S.S.R. 48 48N 39 0E
52 Donetsk, U.S.S.R. 48 0N 37 30E

80 Dongara, Australia 29 15s 114 59E
73 Dongola, Sudan 19 8N 20 23E
74 Dongou, Congo 2 4N 17 57E
48 Donna I., Norway 66 5N 12 40E
84 Donnelly's Crossing, N.Z.
  35 38s 173 33E
34 Donoughmore, Ireland 52 0N 8 50w
30 Doon, L. & R., Scotland 55 15N 4 22w
34 Doonbeg, R., Ireland 52 44N 9 31w
63 Dor, Israel 32 36N 34 55E
80 Dora, L., Australia 22 0s 122 50E
43 Dora Baltea, R., Italy 45 42N 8 0E
42 Dorchester, Dorset, Eng. 50 42N 2 26w
42 Dordogne, Dépt., France 45 0N 0 7E
42 Dordogne, R., France 44 50N 0 30E
46 Dordrecht, Netherlands 51 47N 4 40E
33 Dores, Scotland 57 22N 4 20w
72 Dori, Volta 14 0N 0 5w
33 Dorking, England 51 14N 0 20w
33 Dornoch, & F., Scotland 57 53N 4 2w
47 Dorohoi, U.S.S.R. 47 55N 26 30E
74 Dorrigo, Australia 30 22s 152 28E
27 Dorset, Co. & Hs., Eng. 50 45N 2 25w
44 Dorsten, Germany 51 40N 6 55E
44 Dortmund, Germany 51 30N 7 28E
74 Doruma, Zaïre 4 50N 27 33E
72 Dosso, Niger 13 0N 3 13E
91 Dothan, U.S.A. 31 13N 85 26w
43 Douai, France 50 22N 3 3E
42 Douala, Cameroon 4 0N 9 45E
42 Douarnenez, France 48 5N 4 20w
42 Doubs, Dépt., France 47 16N 6 35E
43 Doubs, R., France 47 0N 5 30E
72 Douentza, Mali 14 58N 2 48w
31 Douglas, Scotland 55 33N 3 50w
90 Douglas, U.S.A. 31 25N 109 35w
74 Douglas & Hd., I. of Man 54 9N 4 31w
74 Doumé, Cameroon 4 10N 13 30E
31 Doune, Scotland 56 12N 4 3w
31 Dounreay, Scotland 58 35N 3 45w
37 Douro, R., Portugal 41 8N 8 0w
37 Douro Litoral, Prov., Port.
  41 10N 8 20w
27 Dove, R., & Dale, Eng. 53 5N 1 38w
83 Dover, Australia 43 26s 147 0E
23 Dover, & Str., England 51 7N 1 19E
93 Dover, Del., U.S.A. 39 19N 75 23w
93 Dover, N.H., U.S.A. 43 13N 70 55w
23 Dovey, R., Wales 52 31N 4 0w
48 Dovrefjell, mts., Norway 62 25N 9 10E
75 Dowa, Malawi 13 38s 33 58E
35 Down, Co., N. Ireland 54 22N 5 55w
23 Downham, England 52 26N 0 14E
23 Downham Market, Eng. 52 36N 0 22E
35 Downpatrick, N. Ireland 54 19N 5 41w
35 Downpatrick Hd., Ire. 54 19N 9 21w
36 Dowra, Ireland 54 11N 8 2w
65 Doyung, China 33 40N 99 30E
44 Dra, Wadi, Morocco 29 0N 8 0w
41 Dragoman P., Bulgaria 43 0N 22 57E
98 Dragons' Mouths,
  Venezuela-Trinidad 10 40N 61 40w
43 Draguignan, France 43 38N 6 28E
100 Drake Pass, S. America 57 0s 65 0w
76 Drakensberg, mts., S. Afr. 30 0s 29 0E
41 Drama, Greece 41 9N 24 10E
49 Drammen, Norway 59 45N 10 14E
84 Dranga Jökul, mt., Ice. 66 12N 22 15w
36 Draperstown, N. Ireland 54 48N 6 50w
47 Drava, R., Yugoslavia 45 50N 18 0E
44 Drenthe, Prov., Neth. 52 53N 6 40E
46 Dresden, Germany 51 5N 13 41E
43 Dreux, France 48 42N 1 25E
27 Driffield, England 54 1N 0 27w
41 Drina, R., Yugoslavia 44 30N 19 5E
49 Drobak, Norway 59 39N 10 48E
36 Drogheda, Ireland 53 43N 6 20w
47 Drogobych, U.S.S.R. 49 28N 23 30E
35 Droichead Nua (Newbridge), Ireland
  53 11N 6 48w
22 Droitwich, England 52 15N 2 10w
36 Dromara, N. Ireland 54 27N 6 1w
42 Drôme, Dépt., France 44 50N 5 10E
36 Dromore, N. Ireland 54 25N 6 8w
36 Dromore West, Ireland 54 15N 8 50w
82 Dronfield, Australia 21 12s 140 3E
27 Dronfield, England 53 18N 1 29w
36 Drum, Ireland 54 7N 7 4w
31 Drumbeg, Scotland 58 15N 5 12w
88 Drumheller, Canada 51 27N 112 58w
36 Drumlish, Ireland 53 50N 7 47w
93 Drummond Ra., Austral. 23 0s 147 15E
93 Drummondville, Can. 45 54N 72 30w
36 Drumquin, N. Ireland 54 38N 7 30w
36 Drumshanbo, Ireland 54 2N 8 2w
36 Drumsna, Ireland 53 57N 8 0w
100 Drygalski I., Antarctica 68 0s 91 0E
30 Drymen, Scotland 56 4N 4 28w
80 Drysdale R., Australia 15 0s 126 50E
92 Du Bois, U.S.A. 61 6N 78 48w
74 Duaringa, Australia 23 42s 149 42E
36 Dubawnt, L. & R., Can. 63 0N 101 30w
83 Dubbo, Australia 32 15s 148 37E
35 Dublin (Baile Atha Cliath), Ireland
  53 20N 6 18w
35 Dublin, Co., Ireland 53 25N 6 20w
91 Dublin, U.S.A. 32 32N 82 59w
52 Dubno, U.S.S.R. 50 24N 25 47E
52 Dubréka, Guinea 9 46N 13 31w
47 Dubrovitsa, U.S.S.R. 51 31N 26 35E
41 Dubrovnik, Yugoslavia 42 40N 18 6E
52 Dubrovskoye, U.S.S.R. 58 55N 111 0E
92 Dubuque, U.S.A. 42 30N 90 45w

82 Duchess, Australia 21 15s 139 57E
1 Ducie, I., Pacific Ocean 25 0s 125 0w
23 Duddington, England 52 36N 0 32w
61 Dudinka, U.S.S.R. 69 30N 86 0E
22 Dudley, England 52 30N 2 4w
27 Duero, R., Spain 41 31N 4 20w
27 Duffield, England 52 59N 1 30w
33 Dufftown, Scotland 57 28N 3 7w
47 Dugi Otok, I., Y.-slav. 44 0N 15 0E
76 Duiwelskloof, S. Africa 23 38s 30 5E
73 Duk Fadiat, Sudan 7 49N 31 31E
73 Duki, Pakistan 30 14N 68 25E
26 Dukinfield, England 53 28N 2 6w
27 Dukla P., Poland-Cz-slov. 49 25N 21 40E
72 Duku, Nigeria 10 43N 10 43E
99 Dulce, R., Argentina 28 30s 63 30w
36 Duleek, Ireland 53 40N 6 25w
82 Dululu, Australia 23 48s 150 15E
74 Duluth, U.S.A. 46 48N 92 10w
24 Dulverton, England 51 2N 3 33w
65 Dum Duma, India 27 35N 95 40E
39 Dumbarton, Scotland 55 57N 4 33w
31 Dumfries, Scot. 55 4N 3 35w
31 Dumfries and Galloway, Reg.,
  Scotland 55 10N 4 0w
100 Dumont d'Urville, Antarctica
  67 0s 140 0E
35 Dun Laoghaire, Ireland 53 15N 6 10E
47 Dunaujvaros, Hungary 47 3N 18 58E
84 Dunback, N.Z. 45 23s 170 36E
31 Dunbar, Scotland 56 0N 2 31w
31 Dunblane, Scotland 56 11N 3 57w
33 Dunboyne, Ireland 53 25N 6 30w
33 Duncansby Hd., Scotland 58 38N 3 2w
36 Dunchurch, England 52 21N 1 18w
36 Dundalk, & B., Ireland 54 0N 6 23w
80 Dundas Str., Australia 11 0s 131 40E
36 Dundee, Scotland 56 27N 2 58w
36 Dundonald, N. Ireland 54 36N 5 50w
36 Dundrum, & B., Ireland 53 17N 6 15w
84 Dunedin, New Zealand 45 51s 170 31E
36 Dunfanaghy, Ireland 55 11N 7 59w
31 Dunfermline, Scotland 56 4N 3 27w
36 Dungannon, N. Ireland 54 31N 6 47w
36 Dungarvan & Hr., Ire. 52 5N 7 38w
23 Dungeness, England 50 54N 0 58E
36 Dungiven, N. Ireland 54 56N 6 55w
36 Dungloe, Ireland 55 0N 8 25w
82 Dungog, Australia 32 27s 151 34E
74 Dungu, Zaïre 3 48N 28 37E
36 Dunkeld, Scotland 56 34N 3 35w
73 Dunkerque, France 51 2N 2 21E
24 Dunkery Beacon, Eng. 51 11N 3 35w
72 Dunkwa, Ghana 6 0N 1 5w
35 Dunlavin, Ireland 53 3N 6 40w
35 Dunleary, see Dunlaoghaire, Ireland
36 Dunleer, Ireland 53 49N 6 22w
34 Dunloe, Gap. of, Ireland 52 0N 9 40w
34 Dunlop, Scotland 55 43N 4 32w
34 Dunmanway, Ireland 51 43N 9 6w
36 Dunmore, Ireland 53 37N 8 45w
35 Dunmore, E., Ireland 52 9N 7 0w
33 Dunnet, Scotland 58 37N 3 20w
31 Dunnet B., & Hd., Scot. 58 37N 3 23w
31 Dunning, Scotland 56 18N 3 37w
83 Dunolly, Australia 36 58s 143 44E
36 Dunoon, Scotland 55 57N 4 55w
73 Dunqul Oasis, Egypt 23 38N 31 3E
31 Duns, Scotland 55 46N 2 19w
31 Dunscore, Scotland 55 8N 3 48w
36 Dunshaughlin, Ireland 53 31N 6 31w
23 Dunstable, England 51 54N 0 31w
84 Dunstan Mts., N.Z. 44 50s 169 30E
24 Dunster, England 51 11N 3 28w
32 Dunton Green, England 51 17N 0 11E
32 Dunvegan, Scotland 57 26N 6 35w
32 Dunvegan Head, Scot. 57 32N 6 45w
36 Dura, Jordan 31 30N 35 2E
80 Durack Ra., Australia 17 0s 127 30E
43 Durance, R., France 44 0N 6 0E
94 Durango, Mexico 24 12N 105 15w
37 Durango, Spain 43 15s 2 40w
90 Durango, U.S.A. 37 20N 107 55w
91 Durant, U.S.A. 33 58N 96 27w
99 Durazno, Uruguay 33 30s 56 50w
76 Durban, S. Africa 29 57s 30 59E
22 Düren, Germany 50 49N 6 29E
65 Durg, India 21 12N 81 20E
84 Durham, & Co., England 54 47N 1 36w
91 Durham, U.S.A. 36 0N 78 53w
41 Durmitor, Mt., Y.-slav. 43 20N 19 10E
31 Durness, & Kyle of, Scot. 58 34N 4 45w
41 Durres, Albania 41 20N 19 29E
74 Durrie, Australia 25 35s 140 15E
34 Durrus, Ireland 51 37N 9 32w
35 Dursey Hd., & I., Ire. 51 36N 10 16w
22 Dursley, England 51 42N 2 22w
84 D'Urville, I., N.Z. 40 55s 173 50E
51 Dushak, U.S.S.R. 37 20N 60 10E
60 Dushanbe, U.S.S.R. 38 20N 68 30E
66 Dutulun Shan, mts., Mongolia
  48 45N 111 30E
95 Duverge, Dom. Rep. 18 15N 71 25w
50 Dvina B., U.S.S.R. 65 0N 39 30E
50 Dvina, R., U.S.S.R. 63 0N 42 45E
50 Dvina W., R., U.S.S.R. 56 35N 25 30E
64 Dwarka, India 22 20N 69 0E
76 Dwyka, S. Africa 33 10s 21 30E
91 Dyersburg, U.S.A. 35 5N 89 10w
89 Dyer, C., Canada 67 0N 61 0w

25 Dyfed, Co., Wales 52 0N 4 30w
31 Dysart, Scotland 56 7N 3 6w
52 Dzerzhinsk, U.S.S.R. 56 15N 43 15E
60 Dzhailma, U.S.S.R. 51 30N 61 50E
60 Dzhalal Abad, U.S.S.R. 41 0N 73 0E
61 Dzhalinda, U.S.S.R. 53 40N 124 0E
60 Dzhambul, U.S.S.R. 43 10N 71 0E
51 Dzankoi, U.S.S.R. 45 40N 34 30E
61 Dzhelinde, U.S.S.R. 70 0N 114 0E
60 Dzhetygara, U.S.S.R. 52 10N 61 0E
60 Dzhezkazgan, U.S.S.R. 47 10N 67 40E
61 Dzhugdzhur Ra., U.S.S.R.
  57 30N 138 0E
66 Dzungaria, Dist., China 44 20N 88 0E
66 Dzuunmod, Mongolia 47 55N 107 0E

E

88 Eagle, Alaska 64 44N 141 29w
90 Eagle Pass, U.S.A. 28 45N 100 28w
83 Eaglehawk, Australia 36 43s 144 16E
30 Eaglesham, Scotland 55 44N 4 18w
27 Eakring, England 53 9N 0 59w
22 Ealing, Gr. London, Eng. 51 30N 0 19w
25 Eardisland, England 52 14N 2 50w
31 Earl Shilton, England 52 35N 1 20w
31 Earls Colne, England 51 56N 0 43E
31 Earlsferry, Scotland 56 11N 2 50w
31 Earlston, Scotland 55 39N 2 40w
84 Earnslaw, Mt., N.Z. 44 37s 168 28E
27 Earsdon, England 55 4N 1 30w
31 Easington Colliery, Eng. 54 49N 1 19w
31 Easington, England 54 50N 1 24w
36 Easingwold, England 54 8N 1 11w
36 Easky, Ireland 54 17N 8 55w
84 East C., New Zealand 37 42s 178 58E
91 East Pt., U.S.A. 33 38N 84 29w
23 East Anglian Hts., Eng. 52 20N 0 42E
65 East Bengal, reg., Bangla. 24 30N 90 0E
47 East Beskids, Mts., Eur. 49 8N 22 10E
74 East China Sea, Asia 29 30N 125 0E
84 East Coast, Dist., N.Z. 38 30s 177 50E
22 East Cowes, England 50 45N 1 17w
23 East Dereham, England 52 41N 0 57E
27 East Fen, England 53 5N 0 5E
23 East Grinstead, England 51 7N 0 3w
68 East Indies, reg., Asia 0 0 120 0E
31 East Kirby, England 53 5N 1 15w
31 East Linton, Scotland 56 0N 2 40w
93 East London, S. Africa 32 31s 27 58E
24 East Looe, England 50 22N 4 28w
27 East Retford, England 53 20N 0 56w
92 East St. Louis, U.S.A. 38 36N 90 3w
61 East Siberian Sea, U.S.S.R.
  73 0N 160 0E
23 East Sussex, Co., England 50 55N 0 15E
83 East Toorale, Australia 30 30s 145 25E
31 East Wemyss, Scotland 56 8N 3 5w
23 Eastbourne, England 50 46N 0 16E
84 Eastbourne, N.Z. 41 50s 174 47E
23 Eastchurch, England 51 23N 0 53E
4 Easter I., Pacific Ocean 27 0s 108 30w
84 Easter Ross, dist., Scot. 57 37N 4 30w
64 Eastern Ghats, Mts., India 13 30N 79 0E
61 Eastern Sayan, Mts., U.S.S.R.
  54 0N 96 0E
22 Eastleigh, England 50 58N 1 21w
36 Eastmain, & R., Canada 52 20N 78 30w
22 Easton, Dorset, England 50 30N 2 28w
22 Easton, Somerset, Eng. 51 28N 2 45w
93 Easton, Pa., U.S.A. 40 42N 75 16w
23 Eastry, England 51 15N 1 19E
23 Eastwood, England 53 1N 1 16w
92 Eaton Socon, England 52 13N 0 18w
92 Eau Claire, U.S.A. 44 49N 91 30w
84 Eaval, Mt., Scotland 57 33N 7 12w
45 Ebbw Vale, Wales 5J 47N 3 13w
45 Eberbach, Germany 49 30N 9 0E
46 Eberswalde, Germany 52 50N 13 50E
67 Ebi Nor, L., China 45 0N 82 30E
40 Eboli, Italy 40 38N 15 0E
74 Ebolowa, Cameroon 3 0N 11 11E
37 Ebro, R., Spain 41 0N 0 30E
31 Ecclefechan, Scotland 55 4N 3 16w
26 Eccles, England 53 29N 2 20w
35 Eccleshall, England 52 52N 2 14w
88 Echo Bay, Canada 66 10N 117 40w
31 Echt, Scotland 57 8N 2 21w
44 Echternach, Luxembourg 49 50N 6 15E
83 Echuca, Australia 36 3s 144 50E
37 Ecija, Spain 37 30N 5 9w
27 Eckington, England 53 21N 1 22w
98 Ecuador, S. Amer. 2 30N 78 0w
74 Ed Damer, Sudan 17 27N 34 0E
73 Ed Debba, Sudan 17 7N 31 12E
73 Ed Dueim, Sudan 13 55N 32 20E
73 Ed Dzong, Tibet 32 10N 90 20E
44 Edam, Netherlands 52 31N 5 3E
32 Eday I. & Sd., Scotland 59 12N 2 47w
73 Edd, Ethiopia 14 0N 41 30E
33 Edderton, Scotland 57 50N 4 10w
33 Eddrachillis, B., Scot. 58 19N 5 8w
44 Ede, Netherlands 52 5N 5 40E
83 Eden, Australia 37 0s 149 55E
26 Eden, R., England 54 56N 2 48w
23 Edenbridge, England 51 12N 0 4E
76 Edenburg, S. Africa 29 42s 25 58E
35 Edenderry, Ireland 53 21N 7 3w
36 Ederny, N. Ireland 54 32N 7 40w
73 Edeyin, Erg, des., Libya 27 0N 10 0E
22 Edge Hill, England 52 9N 1 35w
41 Edhessa, Greece 40 50N 22 5E

84 Edievale, New Zealand 45 20s 169 19E
31 Edinburgh, Scotland 55 57N 3 12w
41 Edirne, Turkey 41 41N 26 36E
82 Edithburgh, Australia 35 2s 137 35E
82 Edmonton, Australia 16 55s 145 45E
88 Edmonton, Canada 53 40N 113 30w
89 Edmundston, Canada 47 22N 68 22w
45 Edolo, Italy 46 11N 10 20E
41 Edremit & G., Turkey 39 35N 27 2E
88 Edson, Canada 53 35N 115 58w
74 Edward, L., see Idi Amin Dada, L.
90 Edwards Plateau, U.S.A. 30 30N 100 40w
13 Edzell, Scotland 56 49N 2 39w
44 Eekloo, Belgium 51 11N 3 34E
76 Eersterus, S. Africa 25 45s 28 15E
47 Eger, Hungary 47 57N 20 23E
80 Egerton, Mt., Australia 24 40s 118 0E
23 Egham, England 51 25N 0 33w
33 Egilsay I., Scotland 59 9N 2 56w
75 Egito, Angola 12 15s 13 18E
84 Egmont, C., N.Z. 39 12s 173 45E
84 Egmont, Mt., N.Z. 39 13s 174 7E
76 Egremont, England 54 28N 3 33w
51 Egridir, Turkey 37 55N 30 50E
73 Egypt, N.E. Africa 26 0N 30 0E
67 Ehime, Pref., Japan 33 30N 132 30E
49 Eidsvoll, Norway 60 19N 11 17E
89 Eidsvold, Australia 25 19s 151 10E
49 Eidsvoll, Norway 60 19N 11 17E
44 Eifel, Mts., Germany 50 5N 6 35E
49 Eigersund, Norway 58 26N 6 3E
32 Eigg, I. & Sd. of, Scot. 56 52N 6 15w
80 Eighty Mile Beach, Australia
  19 30s 121 0E
32 Eil, L., Scotland 56 50N 5 10w
83 Eildon, L., Australia 37 16s 146 0E
92 Einasleigh, Australia 18 45s 144 15E
44 Eindhoven, Netherlands 51 27N 5 29E
45 Einsiedeln, Switzerland 47 9N 8 45E
46 Eisenach, Germany 50 59N 10 21E
84 Eketahuna, N.Z. 40 34s 175 40E
61 Ekimchan, U.S.S.R. 53 0N 133 0E
72 El Aaiun, Western Sahara 20 0N 13 0w
63 El Aal, Syria 32 38N 35 43E
72 El 'Alamein, Egypt 30 40N 29 0E
62 El 'Allâqi, Egypt 23 10N 32 54E
73 El Arish, Egypt 31 3N 33 40E
72 El Asnam (Orleansville), Algeria
  36 2N 1 22E
62 El Bawiti, Egypt 28 27N 29 0E
72 El Bayadh (Géryville), Algeria
  33 45N 1 0E
63 El Bira, Jordan 31 55N 35 13E
90 El Centro, U.S.A. 32 40N 115 38w
94 El Cuyo, Mexico 21 35N 87 50w
94 El Diaz, Mexico 21 10N 87 30w
62 El Dirr, Egypt 22 40N 32 0E
72 El Djouf, Desert, Mauritania
  21 0N 8 0w
91 El Dorado, Ark., U.S.A. 33 14N 92 43w
91 El Dorado, Kan., U.S.A. 37 48N 96 56w
37 El Escorial, Spain 40 38N 4 11w
62 El Faiyum, Egypt 29 30N 30 59E
73 El Fasher, Sudan 13 37N 25 20E
94 El Fuerte, Mexico 26 36N 108 30w
95 El Gallo, Nicaragua 13 5N 84 15w
73 El Geneina, Sudan 13 27N 22 45E
73 El Geteina, Sudan 14 54N 32 30E
73 El Gezira, Prov., Sudan 15 0N 33 0E
62 El Giza, Egypt 30 0N 31 0E
73 El Golea, Algeria 30 40N 3 0E
73 El Gusbat, Libya 32 30N 14 1E
73 El Iskandariya, see Alexandria
72 El Jadida, Morocco 33 11N 8 17w
73 El Jebelein, Sudan 12 40N 32 55E
72 El Kab, Sudan 19 30N 32 46E
63 El Khalil, see Hebron
73 El Khandaq, Sudan 18 43N 30 38E
73 El Kharga, Egypt 25 30N 30 33E
73 El Mansura, Egypt 31 10N 31 20E
73 El Minya, Egypt 28 12N 30 30E
73 El Niabo, Ethiopia 4 30N 39 56E
73 El Obeid, Sudan 13 15N 30 45E
73 El Odaiya, Sudan 12 0N 27 5E
72 El Oued, Algeria 33 20N 6 40E
72 El Ouig, Mali 19 25N 0 25E
90 El Paso, U.S.A. 31 56N 106 25w
73 El Qâhira, Egypt, see Cairo
62 El Qantara, Egypt 31 0N 32 20E
73 El Qasr, Egypt 25 40N 28 42E
62 El Qattara, Egypt 30 10N 27 15E
95 El Real, Panama 8 0N 77 40w
90 El Reno, U.S.A. 35 30N 98 0w
62 El Tur, Egypt 28 14N 33 39E
74 El Wak, Kenya 3 0N 41 0E
62 El Wasta, Egypt 29 25N 31 10E
25 Elan, R., Wales 52 18N 3 34w
51 Elâzig, Turkey 38 37N 39 18E
40 Elba, I., Italy 42 50N 10 20E
41 Elbasan, Albania 41 8N 20 8F
44 Elbe, R., Germany 53 5N 8 50E
43 Elbeuf, France 49 17N 0 58E
47 Elblag, Poland 54 10N 19 22E
51 Elbrus, Mt., U.S.S.R. 43 45N 43 0E
51 Elburz, Mts., Iran 36 0N 51 30E
37 Elche, Spain 38 15N 0 42w
74 Eldoret, Kenya 0 20N 35 40E
90 Electra, U.S.A. 34 2N 98 55w
52 Elektrostal, U.S.S.R. 55 46N 38 30E
100 Elephant I., Falkland Is.,
  Dependency 61 0s 54 0w
91 Eleuthera I., Bahamas 25 0N 76 30w
33 Elgin, Scotland 57 39N 3 20w

92 Elgin, U.S.A. 42 2N 88 15W
74 Elgon, Mt., Kenya-Uganda
　　1 30N 34 50E
23 Elham, England 51 9N 1 7E
31 Elie, Scotland 56 11N 2 50W
74 Elila, R., Zaïre 3 0S 27 0E
75 Elisabethville, see Lubumbashi
51 Elista, (Stepnoi), U.S.S.R.
　　46 28N 44 20E
93 Elizabeth, U.S.A. 40 35N 74 8W
57 Elizabeth C., U.S.S.R. 54 0N 143 0E
91 Elizabeth City, U.S.A. 36 17N 76 12W
49 Elk, Poland 53 50N 22 20E
92 Elkhart, U.S.A. 41 39N 85 48W
90 Elko, U.S.A. 40 58N 115 48W
27 Elland, England 53 41N 1 49W
90 Ellensburg, U.S.A. 47 2N 120 32W
26 Ellesmere Port, England 53 17N 2 55W
100 Ellesmere I., Canada 79 0N 80 0W
11 Ellice Is., see Tuvalu
64 Ellichpur (Achalpur), India
　　21 12N 77 30E
31 Ellington, England 55 14N 1 34W
33 Ellon, Scotland 57 23N 2 3W
100 Ellsworth, Antarctica 78 02 41 0W
100 Ellsworth Land, Antarctica
　　74 30S 85 0W
51 Elmali, Turkey 36 20N 30 0E
92 Elmira, U.S.A. 42 15N 76 54W
36 Elphin, Ireland 53 51N 8 11W
32 Elphin, Scotland 58 4N 5 3W
23 Elstree, England 51 38N 0 16W
84 Eltham, N.Z. 39 25S 174 20E
65 Eluru, India 16 50N 81 0E
37 Elvas, Portugal 38 52N 7 13W
49 Elverum, Norway 60 55N 11 34E
23 Ely, & Isle of, England 52 23N 0 16E
60 Emba, U.S.S.R. 47 0N 55 45E
60 Emba, R., U.S.S.R. 48 0N 56 0E
43 Embrun, France 44 37N 6 29E
74 Embu, Kenya 0 30S 37 30E
44 Emden, Germany 53 22N 7 12E
82 Emerald, Australia 23 30S 148 1E
88 Emerson, Canada 49 0N 97 10W
73 Emi Koussi, Mt., Chad 20 0N 19 0E
40 Emilia-Romagna, Reg., It.
　　44 33N 10 40E
34 Emly, Ireland 52 28N 8 20W
44 Emmeloord, Netherlands 52 43N 5 46E
44 Emmen, Netherlands 52 46N 6 50E
44 Emmerich, Germany 51 52N 6 18E
82 Emmet, Australia 24 45S 144 30E
73 Em Nahud, Sudan 12 33N 28 35E
76 Empageni, South Africa 28 43S 31 52E
91 Emporia, Kansas, U.S.A.
　　38 25N 96 16W
46 Ems, R., Germany 52 47N 7 18E
23 Emsworth, England 50 51N 0 56W
83 Encounter B., Australia 35 50S 139 0E
82 Endeavour Str., Austral. 11 0S 142 0E
22 Enderby, England 52 35N 1 15W
100 Enderby Ld., Antarctica 67 0S 52 0E
41 Enez, Turkey 40 40N 26 5E
23 Enfield, Gr. London, Eng. 51 39N 0 4W
45 Engadin, Dist., Switz. 46 45N 10 10E
45 Engelberg, Switzerland 46 48N 8 24E
52 Engels, U.S.S.R. 51 28N 46 6E
29 England, United Kingdom. Europe
　　53 0N 2 0W
65 English Bazar, India 24 58N 88 21E
13 English Channel, Europe 50 0N 2 30W
90 Enid, U.S.A. 36 25N 97 52W
44 Enkhuizen, Netherlands 52 42N 5 17E
26 Ennerdale Water, L., Eng. 54 32N 3 24W
83 Enngonia, Australia 29 24S 146 0E
34 Ennis, Ireland 52 51N 8 59W
91 Ennis, U.S.A. 32 21N 96 45W
35 Enniscorthy, Ireland 52 32N 6 43W
34 Enniskean, Ireland 51 44N 8 54W
35 Enniskerry, Ireland 53 12N 6 10W
36 Enniskillen, N. Ireland 54 19N 7 37W
34 Ennistymon, Ireland 52 57N 9 20W
44 Enschede, Netherlands 52 13N 6 53E
94 Ensenada, Mexico 31 45N 116 40W
22 Enstone, England 51 55N 1 25W
74 Entebbe, Uganda 0 3N 32 32E
99 Entre Rios, Prov., Arg. 31 0S 59 0W
80 Entrecasteaux, Pt. d', Australia
　　34 48S 116 0E
72 Enugu, Nigeria 6 35N 7 30E
44 Epe, Netherlands 52 22N 5 59E
43 Épernay, France 49 3N 3 56E
43 Épinal, France 48 15N 6 25E
41 Epirus, Prov., Greece 39 50N 20 20E
23 Epping, & Forest, Eng. 51 40N 0 6E
23 Epsom, England 51 19N 0 16W
75 Epukiro, & R., S.W. Africa
　　21 30S 19 0E
73 Equatoria, Dist., Sudan 6 0N 30 0E
71 Equatorial Guinea, Afr. 23 0N 10 0W
73 Er Rahad, Sudan 12 50N 30 47E
62 Er Roda, Egypt 27 45N 30 58E
73 Er Roseires, Sudan 11 55N 34 30E
62 Erbil, Iraq 36 12N 44 7E
61 Ercha, U.S.S.R. 69 40N 147 5E
39 Erciyas Dagi, Turkey 38 30N 35 10E
100 Erebus, Mt., Antarctica 77 0S 166 0E
51 Eregli, Turkey 41 18N 31 25E
62 Eregli, Turkey 38 30N 34 7E
46 Erfurt, Germany 50 59N 11 0E
66 Erhlien, China 43 55N 111 45E
33 Eriboll, L., Scotland 58 33N 4 38W
33 Ericht, L., Scotland 56 45N 4 25W
92 Erie, U.S.A. 42 6N 80 6W
92 Erie, L., N. America 42 0N 81 0W

32 Eriskay, & Sd. of, Scot. 57 4N 7 18W
62 Eritrea, Prov., Ethiopia 15 0N 40 0E
45 Erlangen, Germany 49 38N 11 3E
76 Ermelo, S. Africa 26 30S 29 59E
41 Ermoupolis, Greece 37 10N 24 50E
64 Ernakulam, India 9 58N 76 15E
36 Erne, L. & R., N. Ireland
　　54 28N 7 50W
36 Erne, Upper L., N. Ire. 54 13N 7 32W
64 Erode, India 11 24N 77 45E
36 Errigal, Mt., Ireland 55 5N 8 12W
35 Erris Hd., Ireland 54 19N 10 0W
46 Erz Gebirge (Ore Mts.), Germany
　　50 30N 13 0E
51 Erzincan, Turkey 39 49N 39 40E
51 Erzurum, Turkey 39 58N 41 20E
49 Esbjerg, Denmark 55 30N 8 29E
92 Escanaba, U.S.A. 45 47N 87 5W
44 Esch, Luxembourg 49 30N 6 0E
64 Eschweiler, Germany 50 49N 6 14E
94 Escobal, Panama Canal Zone (Inset)
94 Escuinapa, Mexico 22 45N 105 30W
62 Esfahan, Iran 32 40N 51 30E
76 Eshowe, S. Africa 28 54S 31 30E
62 Esh Shuna, Jordan 32 36N 35 35E
27 Esk, R. (Yorks.), England 54 27N 0 52W
31 Esk, R., Scotland 55 12N 3 15W
48 Eskifjördur, Iceland 65 5N 13 55W
49 Eskilstuna, Sweden 59 20N 16 30E
51 Eskisehir, Turkey 39 20N 30 10E
37 Esla, R., Spain 42 30N 5 20W
60 Espe, U.S.S.R. 44 5N 74 0E
80 Esperance, & B., Australia
　　33 50S 121 57E
99 Espinhaço, Sa. do, mts., Brazil
　　19 0S 43 45W
99 Espirito Santo, st., Brazil
　　19 30S 40 30W
88 Esquimalt, Canada 48 30N 123 50W
72 Essaouira, Morocco 31 40N 9 45W
44 Essen, Belgium 51 27N 4 26E
44 Essen, Germany 51 25N 7 0W
98 Essequibo, R., Guyana 6 50N 58 30W
23 Essex, Co., England 51 45N 0 25E
44 Esslingen, Germany 48 45N 9 15E
42 Essonne, Dépt., France 48 30N 2 15E
45 Estavaver-le-Lac, Switz. 46 51N 6 52E
76 Estcourt, S. Africa 29 0S 29 55E
88 Estevan, Canada 49 12N 103 0W
27 Eston, England 54 34N 1 9W
49 Estonia, S.S.R., U.S.S.R. 58 50N 25 40E
37 Estrela, Sa. da., mts., Port.
　　40 20N 7 20W
37 Estremadura, Prov., Port. 39 0N 8 35W
37 Estremadura, Old Prov., Spain
　　39 20N 6 20W
99 Estrondo, Sa. do, hs., Brazil
　　8 0S 48 45W
47 Esztergom, Hungary 47 49N 18 42E
43 Étampes, France 48 26N 2 6E
43 Étaples, France 50 38N 1 40E
64 Etawah, India 26 54N 79 4E
71 Etchingham, England 51 0N 0 27E
71 Ethiopia, E. Africa 8 0N 40 0E
40 Etna, Mt., Italy 37 42N 15 0E
23 Eton, England 51 29N 0 37E
75 Etosha Pan, S.W. Africa 18 45S 16 20E
44 Ettelbrück, Luxembourg 49 51N 6 6E
45 Ettlingen, Germany 48 55N 8 22E
31 Ettrick Water, R., Scot. 55 31N 2 55W
43 Eu, France 50 0N 1 30E
41 Eubœa, see Evvoia, Greece
92 Euclid, U.S.A. 41 39N 81 32W
83 Eucumbene, L., Australia 36 5S 148 40E
90 Eugene, U.S.A. 44 6N 123 8W
83 Eugowra, Australia 33 5S 148 27E
44 Eupen, Belgium 50 38N 6 3E
62 Euphrates, R., Iraq 34 0N 42 40E
42 Eure, Dépt., France 49 0N 1 20E
42 Eure-et-Loire, Dépt., Fr. 48 15N 1 20E
90 Eureka, U.S.A. 40 48N 124 0W
83 Euroa, Australia 36 49S 145 34E
75 Europa, I., Indian Oc. 23 0S 40 30E
37 Europa Pt., Gibraltar 36 2N 6 32E
44 Europoort, Netherlands 51 57N 4 10E
46 Euskirchen, Germany 50 39N 6 47E
49 Eutin, Germany 54 7N 10 38E
92 Evanston, U.S.A. 42 9N 87 43W
92 Evansville, U.S.A. 38 3N 87 27W
80 Everard, L., Australia 31 30S 135 0E
65 Everest, Mt., Himalaya, Nepal-Tibet
　　28 3N 87 7E
90 Everett, U.S.A. 48 0N 122 13W
91 Everglades, The, region, U.S.A.
　　26 0N 80 30W
22 Evesham, England 52 5N 1 57W
37 Évora, Portugal 38 37N 7 55W
43 Évreux, France 49 1N 1 5E
41 Evvoia (Eubœa), I., Greece
　　38 30N 23 50E
23 Ewell, England 51 20N 0 15W
94 Ewarton, Jamaica 18 10N 77 2W
83 Excelsior, Australia 33 5S 150 0E
24 Exe, R., England 50 45N 3 31W
24 Exeter, England 50 44N 3 32W
84 Featherston, N.Z. 41 1S 175 23E
24 Exminster, England 50 40N 3 29W
24 Exmoor, England 51 10N 3 43W
24 Exmouth, England 50 37N 3 25W
80 Exmouth G., Australia 22 0S 114 20E
74 Eyasi, L., Tanzania 3 30S 35 0E
31 Eyemouth, Scotland 55 52N 2 5W
48 Eyja Fjord, Iceland 66 5N 18 27W
33 Eynhallow Sd., Scotland 59 8N 3 7W
32 Eynort, L., Scotland 57 13N 7 20W

48 Eyrarbakki, Iceland 63 5N 21 2W
80 Eyre, Australia 32 13S 126 20E
83 Eyre, L., Australia 29 20S 137 25E
80 Eyre Pen., Australia 33 30S 135 40E
48 Eyrecourt, Ireland 53 12N 8 8W
48 Eyriks Jökull, mt., Iceland
　　64 45N 20 20W
62 Ez Zeidab, Sudan 17 30N 33 45E

F

40 Fabriano, Italy 43 20N 12 50E
72 Fachi, Niger 19 5N 11 0E
72 Fada, Chad 17 18N 21 35E
72 Fada N'Gourma, Volta 12 5N 0 30E
40 Faenza, Italy 44 19N 11 54E
49 Fagaras, Rumania 45 50N 24 58E
49 Fagernes, Norway 61 1N 9 5E
49 Fagersta, Sweden 60 1N 15 46E
18 Fair I., British Is. 59 30N 1 40W
22 Fairford, England 51 42N 1 48W
88 Fairbanks, Alaska 64 59N 148 10W
22 Fairford, England 51 42N 1 48W
84 Fairlie, New Zealand 44 5S 170 48E
91 Fairmont, Minn., U.S.A.
　　43 40N 94 30W
91 Fairmont, W. Va., U.S.A. 39 30N 80 6W
88 Fairweather, Mt., Alaska
　　58 50N 137 40W
63 Faizabad, Afghanistan 37 18N 70 45E
65 Faizabad, India 26 50N 82 10E
22 Fakenham, England 52 50N 0 51E
65 Falam, Burma 22 58N 93 50E
49 Faldingworth, England 53 21N 0 22W
49 Falkenberg, Sweden 56 56N 12 30E
31 Falkirk, Scotland 55 59N 3 47W
31 Falkland, Scotland 56 15N 3 13W
99 Falkland Is., S. Atlantic 52 0S 60 0W
100 Falkland Is. Dependencies
　　55 0S 35 0W
49 Falköping, Sweden 58 10N 13 30E
93 Fall River, U.S.A. 41 43N 71 9W
94 Falmouth, Antigua 17 0N 61 47W
24 Falmouth, & B., Eng. 50 9N 5 4W
94 Falmouth, Jamaica 18 30N 77 42W
49 False B., S. Africa 34 15S 18 40E
49 Falster, I., Denmark 54 50N 11 55E
49 Falsterbo, Sweden 55 21N 13 3E
49 Falun, Sweden 60 38N 15 32E
51 Famagusta, Cyprus 35 10N 33 58E
99 Famatina, Mt., Arg. 28 30S 67 0W
36 Fanad Hd., Ireland 55 15N 7 37W
73 Fangak, Sudan 9 0N 30 50E
32 Fannich, L., Scotland 57 39N 5 0W
40 Fano, Italy 43 50N 13 4E
63 Fanuch, Iran 26 35N 59 38E
64 Faradje, Zaïre 4 0N 29 52E
64 Farah, Afghanistan 32 22N 62 7E
64 Farah Prov., Afghan. 32 0N 62 5E
64 Farah Rud R., Afghan. 32 30N 62 20E
72 Faranah, Guinea 10 3N 10 45W
22 Farasan Is., Red Sea 17 0N 42 0E
22 Fareham, England 50 53N 1 12W
89 Farewell, C., Greenland
　　60 0N 44 0W
84 Farewell, C., N.Z. 40 30S 172 40E
91 Fargo, U.S.A. 46 57N 96 47W
63 Faria, Well, Jordan 32 12N 35 25E
91 Faribault, U.S.A. 44 16N 93 20W
72 Farim, Guinea-Bissau 12 27N 15 17W
22 Faringdon, England 51 39N 1 34W
91 Farmington, U.S.A. 44 40N 70 8W
23 Farnborough, Eng. 51 17N 0 46W
22 Farne I., England 55 38N 1 37W
23 Farnham, England 51 13N 0 48W
26 Farnworth, England 53 33N 2 33W
37 Faro, Portugal 37 5N 7 54W
49 Farö, Sweden 58 0N 19 10E
13 Faroe Is., Atlantic 62 0N 7 0W
34 Farranfore, Ireland 52 10N 9 32W
82 Farrell Flat, Australia 33 50S 139 40E
41 Farsala, Greece 39 20N 22 28E
49 Farsund, Norway 58 3N 6 42E
62 Fasa, Iran 28 57N 53 35E
30 Faslane, Scotland 56 4N 4 49W
35 Fastnet Rock, Ireland 51 23N 9 37W
64 Fatehgarh, India 27 25N 79 35E
64 Fatehpur, Rajasthan, India
　　27 57N 74 55E
65 Fatehpur, U.P., India 26 0N 80 50E
66 Fatshan, China 23 7N 113 10E
31 Fauldhouse, Scotland 55 50N 3 44W
40 Favara, Italy 37 20N 13 40E
40 Faversham, England 51 18N 0 53E
40 Favignana, Italy 37 55N 12 20E
22 Fawley, England 50 49N 1 20W
48 Faxa Flói, Iceland 64 27N 23 0W
91 Fayetteville, N.C., U.S.A.
　　35 1N 78 58W
91 Fayetteville, Ark., U.S.A. 36 0N 94 5W
91 Fazeley, England 52 36N 1 42W
64 Fazilka, India 30 30N 74 2E
72 F'Dérik (Fort Gouraud), Mauritania
　　22 40N 12 45W
91 Fear, C., U.S.A. 33 59N 78 0W
31 Fearn, Scotland 57 44N 4 0W
84 Featherston, N Z. 41 1S 175 23E
49 Fécamp, France 49 47N 0 21E
46 Fehmarn I., Germany 54 27N 11 10E
46 Fehmarn Belt, Str., Den. 54 35N 11 20E
84 Feilding, New Zealand 40 12S 175 30E
75 Feira, Zambia 15 30S 30 15E
45 Feldkirch, Austria 47 12N 9 35E
23 Felixstowe, England 51 58N 1 23E
23 Felpham, England 50 47N 0 38W

48 Femunden L., Norway 62 30N 11 55E
66 Fenglingtu, China 34 40N 110 20E
27 Fenny Bentley, Eng. 53 4N 1 43W
22 Fenny Compton, Eng. 52 9N 1 20W
23 Fenny Stratford, Eng. 51 59N 0 42W
23 Fens, The, Eng. 52 45N 0 2E
51 Feodosiya, U.S.S.R. 45 2N 35 28E
34 Ferbane, Ireland 53 17N 7 50W
60 Fergana, U.S.S.R. 40 30N 71 55E
34 Fergus, R., Ireland 52 45N 9 0W
91 Fergus Falls, U.S.A. 46 25N 96 0W
40 Ferla, Italy 37 5N 14 55E
36 Fermanagh, Co., N. Ire. 54 22N 7 40W
34 Fermoy, Ireland 52 9N 8 15W
74 Fernando Poo., I., see Macias Nguema
　　Biyoga
23 Fernhurst, England 51 3N 0 43W
90 Fernie, Canada 49 30N 115 0W
32 Fernilea, Scotland 57 18N 6 24W
64 Ferozepore, India 30 55N 75 20E
37 Ferrara, Italy 44 50N 11 35E
37 Ferrol, Spain 43 32N 8 13W
27 Ferryhill, England 54 42N 1 32W
33 Fès, Morocco 34 5N 5 0W
35 Fethard, Ireland 52 28N 7 43W
33 Fetlar I., Scotland 60 35N 0 50W
33 Fettercairn, Scotland 56 50N 2 33W
25 Ffestiniog, Wales 52 58N 3 56W
75 Fianarantsoa, Madagascar 21 30S 47 0E
46 Fichtel Gebirge. Mts., Germany
　　50 0N 12 0E
76 Ficksburg, S. Africa 28 48S 27 55E
35 Fiddown, Ireland 52 20N 7 20W
31 Fife, Reg., Scotland 56 10N 3 10W
31 Fife Ness, Scotland 56 17N 2 35W
43 Figeac, France 44 40N 2 0E
37 Figueira da Foz, Portugal 40 7N 8 54W
37 Figueras, Spain 42 17N 3 0E
72 Figuig, Morocco 32 38N 1 20W
84 Fiji, Pac. Oc. 18 0S 178 0E
23 Filby, England 52 40N 1 39E
27 Filey, & B., England 54 14N 0 18W
41 Filiatra, Greece 37 5N 21 35E
45 Filipstad, Sweden 59 42N 14 5E
45 Filisur, Switzerland 46 40N 9 40E
41 Filskivotn, Dist., Ice. 64 50N 20 45W
24 Filton, England 51 29N 2 34W
33 Findhorn, & R., Scot. 57 40N 3 36W
92 Findlay, U.S.A. 41 0N 83 32W
23 Finedon, England 52 20N 0 40W
75 Fingoé, Mozambique 14 55S 32 10E
43 Finistère, Dépt., France 48 13N 4 4W
37 Finisterre, C., Spain 42 51N 9 19W
23 Finland, Europe 62 20N 26 30E
50 Finland, G. of, Europe 60 0N 26 0E
30 Finnart, Scotland 56 7N 4 48W
36 Finn, R., Ireland 54 50N 7 55W
49 Finnmark, Norway 70 0N 22 0E
82 Finschhafen, Papua N.G.
　　6 33S 147 48E
33 Finstown, Scotland 59 0N 3 8W
36 Fintona, N. Ireland 54 30N 7 20W
63 Fiq, Syria 32 47N 35 41E
62 Firat (Euphrates), R., Turkey
　　39 0N 38 30E
64 Firozabad, India 27 5N 78 20E
73 First Cataract of Nile, Egypt
　　24 0N 32 50E
62 Firyuza, U.S.S.R. 38 10N 57 45E
13 Fisher Bank, Europe 61 0N 10 0W
25 Fishguard & B., Wales 51 59N 4 58W
91 Fitzgerald, U.S.A. 31 40N 83 10W
80 Fitzgerald, Australia 34 50S 114 48E
90 Flagstaff, U.S.A. 35 12N 111 38W
49 Flam, Norway 60 52N 7 14E
27 Flamborough Hd., Eng. 54 9N 0 5W
44 Flandre Occidentale, Belg. 51 0N 3 0E
44 Flandre Orientale, Belg. 51 0N 3 0E
48 Flasjön, L., Sweden 64 0N 15 40E
48 Flatey I., Iceland 65 22N 22 57W
48 Flatey I., Iceland 66 10N 17 50W
48 Flateyri, Iceland 66 5N 23 30W
82 Flattery, C., Australia 15 0S 145 30E
90 Flattery, C., U.S.A. 48 30N 124 56W
23 Flatts, The, Bermuda 32 20N 64 44W
44 Flavy le Martel, France 49 43N 3 13E
23 Fleet, England 51 16N 0 50W
31 Fleet, L. & R., Scotland 57 56N 4 2W
26 Fleetwood, England 53 56N 3 2W
48 Flekkefjord, Norway 58 18N 6 39E
49 Flensburg, Germany 54 45N 9 27E
43 Fletton, England 52 34N 0 13W
45 Fleurier, Switzerland 46 55N 6 35E
44 Fleurus, Belgium 50 30N 4 30E
88 Flin Flon, Canada 54 58 101 58W
80 Flinders B., Australia 34 25S 115 20E
83 Flinders I., Australia 40 0S 148 0E
82 Flinders R., Australia 20 35S 142 30E
82 Flinders Ras., Australia 31 0S 139 0E
92 Flint, U.S.A. 42 59N 83 45W
91 Flint R., U.S.A. 31 15N 84 15W
25 Flint, Wales 53 16N 3 9W
27 Flodden, England 55 37N 2 8W
40 Florence (Firenze), Italy
　　43 48N 11 18E
91 Florence, Ala., U.S.A. 34 51N 87 35W
91 Florence, S.C., U.S.A. 34 5N 79 47W
98 Florencia, Colombia 1 50N 75 50W
44 Florennes, Belgium 50 15N 4 35E
68 Flores, I., Indonesia 8 35S 121 30E
68 Flores Sea, Indonesia 6 50S 122 0E

44 Florenville, Belgium 49 40N 5 19E
99 Florianopolis, Brazil 27 35S 48 25W
91 Florida, st., U.S.A. 28 30N 81 30W
99 Florida, Uruguay 34 10S 56 25W
91 Florida Keys, Is. & B., U.S.A.
　　25 0N 80 30W
49 Florö, Norway 61 36N 5 0E
33 Flotta, I., Scotland 58 50N 3 8W
45 Fluela Pass, Switz. 46 48N 9 44E
44 Flushing (Vlissingen), Netherlands
　　51 27N 3 35E
82 Fly R., Papua N.G. 8 0S 142 0E
33 Fochabers, Scotland 57 38N 3 5W
47 Focsani, Rumania 45 39N 27 13E
40 Foggia, Italy 41 27N 15 37E
43 Foix, France 42 58N 1 30E
48 Folda fd., Norway 67 35N 15 25E
49 Folgefonni, Norway 60 0N 6 15E
40 Foligno, Italy 42 58N 12 48E
23 Folkestone, England 51 5N 1 11E
88 Fond du Lac, Canada 59 28N 107 5W
92 Fond du Lac, Wis., U.S.A.
　　43 50N 88 30W
94 Fonseca, G. of, Central America
　　13 15N 87 40W
44 Fontainebleau, France 48 20N 2 40E
42 Fontevrault, France 47 17N 0 0
67 Foochow, China 26 10N 119 20E
45 Forbach, France 49 10N 6 52E
83 Forbes, Australia 33 24S 148 1E
30 Ford, Scotland 56 10N 5 27W
35 Ford, Ireland 52 32N 6 15W
26 Forden, England 52 34N 3 8W
22 Fordingbridge, England 50 56N 1 48W
33 Fordyce, Scotland 57 40N 2 45W
86 Forel, Mt., Greenland 67 0N 34 0W
24 Foreland Pt., England 51 14N 3 45W
27 Forest, Guernsey 49 26N 2 35W
26 Forest of Bowland, Eng. 54 0N 2 30W
22 Forest of Dean, England 51 48N 2 35W
23 Forest Row, England 51 6N 0 3E
83 Forestier Pen., Australia 43 0S 148 0E
31 Forfar, Scotland 56 40N 2 53W
40 Forli, Italy 44 14N 12 7E
33 Formartine, Dist., Scot. 57 20N 2 15W
26 Formby, & Pt., England 53 34N 3 4W
41 Formentera I., Spain 38 40N 1 33E
99 Formosa, Argentina 26 10S 58 25W
74 Formosa B., Kenya 2 50S 40 10E
67 Formosa (Taiwan) I., China
　　24 0N 121 0E
67 Formosa Str., China 24 0N 119 0E
43 Fornovo, Italy 44 42N 10 10E
33 Forres, Scotland 57 37N 3 36W
80 Forrest, Australia 30 50S 128 2E
82 Forsayth, Australia 18 50S 143 45E
48 Fors, Sweden 63 1N 16 38E
33 Forsinard, Scotland 58 22N 3 54W
46 Forst, Germany 51 45N 14 40E
83 Forster, Australia 32 12N 152 0E
89 Fort Albany, Ont., Can. 52 10N 81 50W
73 Fort Archambault, Chad 9 0N 18 18E
33 Fort Augustus, Scotland 57 9N 4 40W
76 Fort Beaufort, S. Africa 32 44S 26 42E
73 Fort Bretonnet, Chad 10 40N 16 50E
72 Fort Charlet (Djanet), Algeria
　　24 35N 9 20E
89 Fort Chimo, Canada 58 40N 67 10W
88 Fort Chipewyan, Can. 58 50N 111 0W
90 Fort Collins, U.S.A. 40 28N 105 10W
73 Fort Crampel, Cent. Africa
　　7 2N 19 18E
75 Fort Dauphin, Madagascar
　　25 0S 46 57E
94 Fort Davis, Panama Canal Zone (Inset)
95 Fort de France, Martinique
　　14 33N 61 2W
91 Fort Dodge, U.S.A. 42 32N 94 11W
88 Fort Ferera, Canada 58 32N 93 25W
72 Fort Gouraud, see F'Dérik
65 Fort Hertz, see Putao
75 Fort Jameson, see Chipata
70 Fort Johnston, see Mangoche
72 Fort Lallemand, Algeria 31 30N 6 35E
73 Fort Lamy, see Ndjamena
72 Fort Laperrine (Tamanrasset), Algeria
　　22 45N 5 30E
91 Fort Lauderdale, U.S.A. 26 5N 80 5W
72 Fort Miribel, Algeria 29 30N 3 0E
91 Fort Myers, U.S.A. 26 39N 81 48W
88 Fort Nelson, & R., Can. 58 50N 123 0W
88 Fort Norman, Canada 65 0N 125 30W
90 Fort Peck L., U.S.A. 47 40N 107 0W
91 Fort Pierce, U.S.A. 27 35N 80 25W
74 Fort Portal, Uganda 0 40N 30 20E
88 Fort Providence, Can., 61 20N 117 30W
74 Fort Rosebery, see Mansa
74 Fort Rousset, Congo (Fr.) 0 35S 16 5E
88 Fort St. John, Can. 56 15N 120 50W
91 Fort Scott, U.S.A. 37 50N 94 44W
51 Fort Shevchenko, U.S.S.R.
　　44 37N 50 30E
88 Fort Simpson, Can. 61 45N 121 30W
88 Fort Smith, North West Territories,
　　Canada 60 0N 112 25W
91 Fort Smith, U.S.A. 35 10N 94 30W
88 Fort Vermilion, Can. 58 15N 115 57W
75 Fort Victoria, Rhodesia 20 3S 30 50E
92 Fort Wayne, U.S.A. 41 0N 85 3W
92 Fort William, see Thunder Bay
32 Fort William, Scotland 56 49N 5 6W
90 Fort Worth, U.S.A. 32 50N 97 20W
88 Fort Yukon, Alaska 66 35N 145 12W
99 Fortaleza (Ceará), Brazil 3 48S 38 38W

*75 Forte Roçadas, Angola 16 38s 15 22E
80 Fortescue R., Australia 22 5s 117 0E
31 Forth, Scotland 55 45N 3 42w
31 Forth, Firth of, Scotland 56 10N 2 45w
33 Forth, R., Scotland 56 8N 4 15w
33 Fortrose, Scotland 57 36N 4 8w
92 Fostoria, U.S.A. 41 8N 83 10w
91 Fothergill, England 54 43N 3 30w
89 Fotheringhay, England 52 32N 0 25w
18 Foula, I., Scotland 60 8N 2 7w
36 Foxford, Ireland 53 59N 9 7w
84 Foumban, Cameroon 5 50N 10 58E
43 Fourmies, France 50 0N 4 0E
41 Fournoi I., Greece 37 38N 26 50E
72 Fouta Djalon, Mt., Guinea
     11 30N 12 0w
84 Foveaux Str., N.Z. 46 45s 168 15E
24 Fowey, & R., England 50 20N 4 39w
80 Fowler's B., Australia 32 0s 132 50E
18 Foxdale, I., of Man 54 12N 4 38w
89 Foxe Basin, Canada 66 30N 77 0w
89 Foxe Pen., Canada 65 0N 76 0w
36 Foxford, Ireland 53 59N 9 7w
84 Foxton, New Zealand 40 31s 175 13E
79 Foyle, L. & R., N. Ire. 55 5N 7 10w
34 Foynes, Ireland 52 37N 9 5w
89 Framlingham, England 52 12N 1 21E
41 Francavilla Fontana, It. 40 30N 17 34E
43 France, Europe 47 0N 3 0E
33 Frances, Australia 36 40s 140 55E
74 Franceville, Gabon 1 55s 13 40E
75 Francistown, Botswana 21 6s 27 32E
45 Franeker, Netherlands 53 12N 5 33E
45 Frankenthal, Germany 49 32N 8 20E
92 Frankfort, Ind., U.S.A. 40 18N 86 31w
92 Frankfort, Ken., U.S.A. 38 10N 84 50w
46 Frankfurt-on-Main, Ger. 50 5N 8 42E
46 Frankfurt-on-Oder, Ger. 52 20N 14 32E
88 Franklin B., Canada 70 0N 126 0w
90 Franklin D. Roosevelt L., U.S.A.
     48 30N 119 0w
88 Franklin, Mts., U.S.A. Can. 66 0N 125 0w
88 Franklin Str., Canada 72 0N 96 0w
88 Franklin Terr., Canada 71 0N 100 0w
83 Frankston, Australia 38 15s 145 10E
23 Frant, England 51 5N 0 17E
100 Franz Josef Ld. U.S.S.R.
     81 0N 60 0E
83 Fraser or Gt. Sandy I., Australia
     25 0s 154 0E
88 Fraser R., Canada 53 30N 120 30w
33 Fraserburgh, Scotland 57 42N 2 0w
45 Frauenfeld, Switzerland 47 34N 8 54E
99 Fray Bentos, Uruguay 33 19s 58 25w
45 Fredericia, Denmark 55 36N 9 43E
89 Fredericton, Canada 45 50N 66 40w
89 Frederikshaab, Greenland
     62 0N 49 30w
49 Frederikshavn, Den. 57 26N 10 19E
92 Fredonia, U.S.A. 42 25N 79 20w
49 Fredrikstad, Norway 59 10N 10 57E
95 Freeport, Bahama Is. 25 55N 78 20w
92 Freeport, U.S.A. 42 16N 89 42w
72 Freetown, Sierra Leone 8 20N 13 5w
83 Freevater Forest, Scot. 57 52N 4 43w
46 Freiburg, Germany 47 59N 7 53E
46 Freising, Germany 48 30N 11 40E
46 Freistadt, Austria 48 38N 9 30E
43 Fréjus, France 43 12N 6 45E
80 Fremantle, Australia 32 6s 115 50E
91 Fremont, U.S.A. 41 33N 96 28w
96 French Fuiana, S. Amer. 4 0N 53 0w
72 French Somal., see Djibouti
62 French Territory of Afars and Issas,
     see Djibouti
36 Frenchpark, Ireland 53 53N 8 25w
90 Fresno, U.S.A. 36 42N 119 48w
33 Freswick, Scotland 58 35N 3 5w
31 Freuchie, Scotland 56 14N 3 8w
81 Freycinet Pen., Australia 42 0s 148 15E
75 Fria, C., S.W. Africa 18 34s 12 0E
45 Fribourg, & Cn., Switz. 46 49N 7 9E
45 Friedrichshafen, Ger. 47 38N 9 30E
44 Friendly Is., see Tonga Is. (Inset)
44 Friesland, Prov., Neth. 53 5N 5 50E
94 Frijoles, Panama (Inset)
23 Frimley, England 51 18N 0 43w
89 Frinton-on-Sea, England 51 50N 1 16E
99 Frio, C., Brazil 22 50s 41 50w
46 Frisian Is., Neth.-Ger. 53 30N 6 0E
40 Friuli-Venezia Giulia, Reg., Italy
     46 15N 12 50E
26 Frizington, England 54 33N 3 30w
89 Frobisher & B., N.W. Terr., Canada
     63 45N 68 30w
88 Frobisher, L., Canada 56 40N 108 20w
89 Frodsham, England 53 17N 2 45w
24 Frome, England 51 15N 2 19w
81 Frome, L., Australia 30 45s 139 45E
22 Frome, R., England 50 44N 2 33w
90 Front Ra., U.S.A. 40 0N 105 10w
41 Frosinone, Italy 41 40N 13 29E
98 Frostisen Mt., Norway 68 17N 17 0E
99 Froward C.. Chile 55 0s 71 0w
60 Frunze, U.S.S.R. 42 55N 75 0E
45 Frutigen, Switzerland 46 34N 7 38E
94 Fuego, Vol., Guatemala
     14 20N 91 15w
37 Fuenteovejuna, Spain 38 16N 5 28w
37 Fuentes de Onoro, Spain 40 37N 6 45w
37 Fundao, Portugal 40 10N 7 30w
94 Fuerte, R., Mexico 26 0N 108 30w
48 Fuerteventura, I., Canary Is.
     28 25N 14 0w
48 Fuglö Sound, Norway 70 0N 20 0E
* Renamed Xangongo

67 Fujiyama, Mt. Japan 35 30N 139 0E
66 Fukien, Prov., China 25 50N 118 0E
67 Fukui, & Pref., Japan 36 4N 136 8E
67 Fukue Shima, Japan 32 30N 128 40E
67 Fukuoka, & Pref., Japan 33 36N 130 27E
67 Fukushima, & Pref., Japan
     37 30N 140 30E
46 Fulda, Germany 50 37N 9 40E
26 Fulwood, England 53 47N 2 41w
44 Fumay, France 49 59N 4 43E
44 Funchal, Madeira 32 40N 16 50E
89 Fundy, B. of, Canada 45 0N 66 0w
83 Furneaux Group, Austral. 40 0s 148 0E
26 Furness, Dist., England 54 18N 3 8w
45 Furth, Germany 49 29N 10 58E
67 Fusin, China 42 0N 121 40E
67 Fushun, China 42 1N 123 59E
67 Futuna, I., Pacific Ocean 14 3s 178 3E
67 Fuyu, China 45 15N 125 15E
30 Fyne, Loch, Scotland 56 0N 5 20w

G

74 Gabela, Angola 10 50s 14 27E
73 Gabes, Tunisia 33 53N 10 4E
74 Gabon, Africa 1 55s 12 0E
76 Gaborone, Botswana 24 38s 25 50E
41 Gabrovo, Bulgaria 42 50N 25 25E
64 Gadag, India 15 10N 75 45E
64 Gadarwara, India 22 58N 78 50E
91 Gadsden, U.S.A. 34 5N 85 59w
64 Gadwal, India 16 8N 77 56E
40 Gaeta, Italy 41 18N 13 35E
43 Gaillac, France 43 58N 1 56E
27 Gainsborough, Eng. 53 25N 0 47w
82 Gairdner, L., Australia 31 30s 136 0E
33 Gairloch, Scotland 57 43N 5 47w
75 Galangue, Angola 13 38s 16 0E
4 Galapagos Is., Pac. Oc. 0 30s 91 0w
31 Galashiels, Scotland 55 37N 2 50w
47 Galati, Rumania 45 28N 28 2E
41 Galatina, Italy 40 10N 18 10E
34 Galbally, Ireland 52 28N 8 17w
49 Galdhöpiggen, Mt., Nor. 61 40N 8 20E
94 Galeana, Mexico 30 7N 107 30w
91 Galesburg, U.S.A. 40 54N 90 20w
50 Galich, U.S.S.R. 58 22N 42 12E
37 Galicia, Old Prov., Spain 42 45N 8 0w
63 Galilee, Dist., Israel 32 52s 35 20E
63 Galilee, Sea of, see Kinneret, L.
62 Gallabat, Sudan 13 10N 36 30E
62 Galle, Sri Lanka 6 2N 80 13E
37 Gallego, R., Spain 42 20N 0 30w
34 Galley Hd., Ireland 51 31N 8 57w
98 Gallinas, Punta, Colombia
     12 28N 71 37w
41 Gallipoli, Italy 40 1N 18 0E
41 Gallipoli, Turkey, see Gelibolu
48 Gällivare, Sweden 67 10N 20 32E
30 Galloway, Mull of, Scot. 54 37N 4 52w
90 Gallup, U.S.A. 35 28N 108 50w
83 Galong, Australia 34 40s 148 30E
62 Galoya, Sri Lanka 8 10N 80 55E
92 Galt, Canada 43 25N 80 20w
34 Galty Mts., Ireland 52 22N 8 13w
34 Galtymore Mt., Ireland 52 15N 8 4w
91 Galveston, U.S.A. 29 15N 95 0w
34 Galway, & Co., Ireland 53 18N 9 3w
72 Gambaga, Ghana 10 35N 0 25w
72 Gambia, & R., West Africa
     13 50N 15 0w
94 Gamboa, Panama Canal Zone (Inset)
74 Gamboma, Congo (Fr.) 1 45s 16 0E
48 Gamlakarleby, see Kokkola, Finland
64 Gandak, R., India 28 0N 84 56E
64 Gandava, Pakistan 28 40N 67 20E
89 Gander, Newf., Canada 49 1N 54 53w
72 Gandi, Nigeria 12 55N 5 49E
65 Ganga (Ganges), R., India &
     Pakistan 24 30N 88 20E
64 Ganganagar, India 29 55N 73 50E
65 Gangtok, Sikkim 27 20N 88 30E
43 Gannat, France 46 8N 3 12E
90 Gannett Pk., U.S.A. 43 10N 110 0w
76 Ganspan, S. Africa 27 55s 24 45E
72 Ganta, Liberia 7 15N 8 59w
72 Gao, Mali 16 20N 0 10w
72 Gaoua, Volta 10 20N 3 15w
72 Gaoual, Guinea 11 35N 13 25w
43 Gap, France 44 35 6 5E
34 Gap of Dunloe, Ireland 52 0N 9 40w
64 Gar Dzong, China 32 29N 79 55E
36 Gara, L., Ireland 53 54N 8 27w
43 Gard, Dépt., France 44 3N 4 20E
40 Garda, L., Italy 45 40N 10 40E
62 Gardala, Ethiopia 5 40N 36 40E
90 Garden City, U.S.A. 38 0N 100 47w
64 Gardez, Afghanistan 33 40N 69 0E
73 Gardian, Chad 15 45N 19 40E
93 Gardner, U.S.A. 42 35N 72 0w
27 Garforth, England 53 48N 1 22w
40 Gargano, Mt., Italy 41 50N 16 5E
76 Garies, S. Africa 30 31s 18 0E
40 Garigliano, R., Italy 41 18N 13 50E
30 Garliestown, Scotland 54 47N 4 22w
60 Garm, U.S.S.R. 39 0N 70 20E
45 Garmisch Partenkirchen, Germany
     47 30N 11 6E
33 Garmouth, Scotland 57 40N 3 8w
43 Garonne, R., France 43 20N 1 20E
74 Garoua Malaba, Cam. 9 16N 13 25E
36 Garrison, Ireland 54 25N 8 5w

88 Garry, L., Canada 66 0N 100 0w
88 Garry, L., Scotland 57 5N 4 52w
74 Garsen, Kenya 2 25s 40 20E
26 Garstang, England 53 53N 2 45w
64 Gartok, Tibet, China 31 33N 80 30E
68 Garut, Java, Indonesia 7 20s 108 0E
36 Garvagh, N. Ireland 55 0N 6 41w
84 Garvie, Mts., N.Z. 45 30s 169 0E
91 Gary, U.S.A. 41 36N 87 10w
60 Gasan Kuli, U.S.S.R. 37 40N 54 20E
72 Gascony, Prov., France 43 40N 0 10E
80 Gascoyne, R., Australia 25 0s 115 0E
72 Gashaka, Nigeria 7 30N 11 30E
89 Gaspé, C., Canada 48 50N 64 5w
37 Gata, Cabo de, Spain 36 42N 2 6w
37 Gata, Sa. de, mts., Spain 40 30N 6 0w
27 Gateshead, England 54 58N 1 38w
93 Gatineau, R., Canada 47 0N 75 50w
89 Gatley, England 53 25N 2 15w
94 Gatun, & L., Panama Canal Zone
     (Inset)
65 Gaud-i-Zirreh, Afghan. 29 45N 62 0E
65 Gauhati, Assam, India 26 12N 91 50E
49 Gaula, R., Norway 63 5N 10 15E
49 Gausta, Mt., Norway 59 48N 8 40E
49 Gauja, R., U.S.S.R. 57 15N 24 50E
49 Gävle, Sweden 60 40N 17 4E
49 Gävleborg, Co., Sweden 61 0N 16 30E
83 Gawler, Australia 34 39s 138 45E
64 Gawilgarh Hills, India 21 15N 76 30E
65 Gaya, India 24 42N 85 0E
83 Gayndah, Australia 25 38s 151 40E
63 Gaza (Ghazzah), Israel 31 30N 34 28E
72 Gaziantep, Turkey 37 10N 37 30E
76 Gcuwa, S. Africa 32 20s 28 5E
47 Gdansk, Poland 54 19N 18 40E
47 Gdov, U.S.S.R. 58 40N 27 55E
47 Gdynia, Poland 54 38N 18 39E
72 Geashill, Ireland 53 14N 7 20w
74 Gedo, Ethiopia 9 0N 37 0E
49 Gedser, Denmark 54 35N 11 55E
44 Geel, Belgium 51 9N 4 59E
83 Geelong, Australia 38 8s 144 20E
44 Geeraardsbergen, Belg. 50 46N 3 53E
73 Geidam, Nigeria 12 57N 11 57E
45 Geislingen, Germany 48 37N 9 47E
74 Geita, Tanzania 2 40s 32 18E
40 Gela, Italy 37 6N 14 18E
44 Gelderland, Prov., Neth. 52 6N 6 10E
44 Geldermalsen, Neth. 51 53N 5 17E
44 Geldrop, Netherlands 51 24N 5 32E
72 Gelhak, Sudan 11 14N 32 45E
41 Gelibolu (Gallipoli), Turkey
     40 30N 26 55E
44 Gelsenkirchen, Germany 51 32N 7 4E
68 Gemas, Malaya 2 35N 102 50E
44 Gembloux, Belgium 50 34N 4 41E
74 Gemena, Zaïre 3 20N 19 40E
44 Gemmi P., Switzerland 46 25N 7 39E
100 General Belgrano, Antarc. 78 0s 38 0w
99 Gen. Pico, Argentina 35 40s 63 45w
45 Geneva, & Cn., Switz. 46 12N 6 9E
45 Geneva, L. of Europe, see Lac Leman
44 Genk, Belgium 50 58N 5 30E
40 Genoa, Australia 37 30s 149 30E
40 Genoa, & G. (Genova), It.
     44 25N 8 58E
44 Gent (Ghent), Belgium 51 5N 3 40E
76 Genyesa, S. Africa 26 30s 24 10F
82 Geographe Chan., Austral.
     24 20s 113 15E
76 George, S. Africa 34 0s 22 15E
83 George, L., Australia 35 0s 149 0E
74 George, L., Uganda 0 0 30 15E
91 George, L., U.S.A. 29 20N 81 30w
93 George, L., N.Y., U.S.A. 43 30N 73 33w
83 George Town, Australia 41 5s 148 55E
68 George Town, Malaya 5 28N 100 5E
72 Georgetown, Gambia 13 30N 14 47w
94 Georgetown, Guyana 6 40N 58 15w
91 Georgetown, s., U.S.A. 33 0N 83 0w
51 Georgia S.S.R., U.S.S.R. 42 0N 44 30E
82 Georgian B., Canada 45 0N 80 30w
51 Georgievsk, U.S.S.R. 44 10N 43 17E
80 Georgiu-Dezh, U.S.S.R. 51 3N 39 20E
46 Gera, Germany 50 53N 12 6E
80 Geraldton, Australia 28 48s 114 38E
46 Gerar, R., Israel 31 23N 34 50E
43 Gérardmer, France 48 0N 6 50E
46 Germany, East Europe 52 0N 13 0E
46 Germany, West Europe 51 0N 9 0E
46 Germiston, S. Africa 26 18s 28 12E
44 Gerolstein, Germany 50 12N 6 24E
37 Gerona, Spain 41 58N 2 50E
23 Gerrards Cross, England 51 35N 0 32w
42 Gers, Dépt., France 43 31N 0 10E
92 Géryville, Algeria see El Bayadh
92 Gettysburg, U.S.A. 39 50N 77 18w
63 Gevaudan, Dist., France 44 45N 3 30E
48 Geyser, Springs, Ice. 64 22N 20 15w
63 Gezer, Israel 31 51N 34 55E
62 Gezira, Sudan 16 20N 34 0E
72 Ghadames, Libya 30 18N 9 5E
65 Ghaghara (Gogra), R., India
     26 40N 82 40E
72 Ghana, Africa 8 0N 1 30w
63 Ghar, Wadi, Jordan 31 30N 35 20E
73 Gharyan, Libya 32 10N 13 0E
72 Ghat, Libya 25 0N 10 20E

65 Ghats, Eastern, Mts., India
     13 30N 79 0E
65 Ghats, Western, Mts., India
     17 0N 74 0E
72 Ghazaouet (Nemours), Algeria
     35 1N 1 48w
64 Ghaziabad, India 28 35N 77 45E
65 Ghazipur, India 25 39N 83 28E
63 Ghazir, Lebanon 34 1N 35 39E
44 Ghent, Belgium, see Gent
65 Giamda Dzong, China 30 2N 93 0E
36 Giant's Causeway, N. Ire. 55 13N 6 31w
40 Giarre, Italy 37 44N 15 10E
75 Gibeon, S.W. Africa 25 11s 17 48E
37 Gibraltar, & Str., Europe 36 10N 5 20w
37 Gibraltar Pt., England 53 7N 0 19E
80 Gibson Des., Australia 24 0s 126 0E
46 Giessen, Germany 50 37N 8 42E
67 Gifu, & Pref., Japan 35 30N 136 54E
48 Gigglewick, England 54 5N 2 19w
30 Gigha I., Scotland 55 42N 5 43w
37 Gijon, Spain 43 32N 5 43 w
90 Gila, R., U.S.A. 33 0N 113 0w
*11 Gilbert Is., Pacific Oc. 1 0s 173 0E
82 Gilbert R., Australia 17 0s 141 30E
36 Gilford, N. Ireland 54 22N 6 21w
83 Gilgandra, Australia 31 32s 148 37E
64 Gilgit, Kashmir 35 58N 74 27E
82 Gill, L., Ireland 54 14N 8 15w
82 Gilliatt, Australia 20 40s 141 28E
23 Gillingham, England 51 22N 0 33E
44 Gilly, Belgium 50 25N 4 25E
48 Gilsbakki, Iceland 64 42N 21 2w
48 Gilsland, England 55 0N 2 34w
25 Gilwern, Wales 51 49N 3 5w
41 Gimbi, Ethiopia 9 3N 35 42E
41 Giona, Mt., Greece 38 40N 22 10E
51 Giresun, Turkey 40 53N 38 19E
65 Giridih, India 24 10N 86 15E
42 Gironde, Dépt., France 44 50N 0 22E
82 Giru, Australia 19 30s 147 5E
30 Girvan & R., Scotland 55 15N 4 50w
84 Gisborne, N.Z. 38 39s 178 5E
43 Gisors, France 49 20N 1 45E
47 Giurgiu, Rumania 43 53N 25 56E
63 Giv'atayim, Israel 32 4N 34 49E
44 Givet, France 50 8N 4 49E
72 Gizhiga, U.S.S.R. 62 0N 160 27E
47 Gizycko, Poland 54 5N 21 50E
49 Gjøvik, Norway 60 47N 10 43E
93 Glace Bay, Canada 46 25N 60 0w
90 Glacier National Park, U.S.A.
     48 45N 114 0w
82 Gladstone, Queensland, Australia
     24 0s 151 15E
83 Gladstone, S. Australia 33 5s 138 10E
49 Glama, R., Norway 61 0N 11 30E
48 Glama Jökull, Mt., Ice. 65 47N 23 0w
31 Glamis, Scotland 56 37N 3 0w
34 Glanaruddery, Mts., Ire. 52 20N 9 27w
36 Glandore, Ireland 51 33N 9 7w
34 Glanworth, Ireland 52 11N 8 21w
45 Glarner Alpen, Mts., Switzerland
     46 54N 9 1E
45 Glarus, Cn., Switzerland 44 55N 9 0E
30 Glas Maol, Mt., Scotland 56 52N 3 20w
30 Glasgow, Scotland 55 52N 4 14w
92 Glasgow, U.S.A. 37 0N 85 55w
36 Glasslough, Ireland 54 20N 6 53w
24 Glastonbury, England 51 18N 2 42w
46 Glauchau, Germany 50 49 12 31E
50 Glazov, U.S.S.R. 58 9N 52 30E
32 Glen Affric, Scotland 57 16N 5 0w
30 Glen Coe, Scotland 56 40N 5 0w
93 Glen Falls, U.S.A. 43 25N 73 40w
32 Glen Garry, Scotland 57 4N 5 10w
83 Glen Innes, Australia 29 42s 151 45E
33 Glen Mor, Scotland 57 15N 4 30w
30 Glen Orchy, Scotland 56 27N 4 52w
30 Glen Shiel, Scotland 57 8N 5 20w
34 Glenamaddy, Ireland 53 40N 8 35w
35 Glenamoy, Ireland 54 14N 9 40w
35 Glenart Castle, Ireland 52 48N 6 12w
36 Glenarm, N. Ireland 54 58N 5 58w
76 Glencairn, S. Africa 34 10s 18 25E
90 Glendale, U.S.A. 34 15N 118 20w
82 Glenden, U.S.A. 47 10N 104 45w
35 Glenealy, Ireland 52 59N 6 10w
32 Glenelg, Scotland 57 13N 5 36w
83 Glenelg, R., Australia 37 25N 141 30E
30 Glenken, The, reg., Scot. 55 10N 4 15w
30 Glenluce, Scotland 54 53N 4 49w
83 Glenmorgan, Australia 27 15s 149 30E
83 Glenorchy, Australia 42 49s 147 18E
31 Glenrothes, Scotland 56 12N 3 11w
48 Glettinganes, Iceland 65 30N 13 30w
34 Glin, Ireland 52 34N 9 17w
35 Glinsk, Ireland 53 29N 9 49w
47 Gliwice, Poland 50 20N 18 52E
90 Globe, U.S.E. 33 30N 111 0w
46 Glockner, Gr., mt., Austria
     47 0N 12 30E
47 Glogow, Poland 51 35N 16 10E
63 Glorieuses Is., Ind. Oc. 11 30N 47 20w
26 Glossop, England 53 27N 1 56w
83 Gloucester, Australia 31 58s 151 56E
24 Gloucester, England 51 52N 2 15w
93 Gloversville, U.S.A. 43 4N 74 25w
46 Glückstadt, Germany 53 48N 9 29E
46 Gmund, Austria 48 45N 15 0E
46 Gmunden, Austria 47 56N 13 46E
47 Gniezno, Poland 52 30N 17 35E
* Renamed Kiribati

22 Gnosall, England 52 48N 2 15w
68 Go Cong, Vietnam 10 25N 106 50E
65 Goa, India 15 30N 74 0E
76 Goageb, S.W. Africa 26 40s 17 15E
30 Goalpara, India 26 10N 90 40E
74 Goat Fell, mt., Scotland 55 37N 5 15w
74 Goba, Ethiopia 7 1N 39 59E
75 Goba, Mozambique 26 1s 32 10E
75 Gobabis, S.W. Africa 22 1s 19 0E
66 Gobi (Shamo) Desert, Mongolia
     44 0N 108 0E
44 Goch, Germany 51 42N 6 10E
23 Godalming, England 51 10N 0 36w
65 Godavari, R., India 19 20N 76 0E
47 Godeanu, Mt., Rumania 45 25N 22 15E
64 Godhra, India 22 45N 73 50E
89 Gods Lake, Canada 54 40N 94 10w
89 Godthaab, Greenland 64 10N 51 35w
44 Goeree I., Netherlands 51 50N 3 55E
44 Goes, Netherlands 51 31N 3 55E
44 Gogango, Australia 23 40s 150 2E
44 Goggingen, Germany 48 20N 10 52E
73 Gogra, R., see Ghaghara, R., India
99 Goiânia, Brazil 16 17s 48 16w
99 Goiás, Brazil 15 55s 50 10w
30 Goil, L., Scotland 56 8N 4 54w
64 Gojra, Pakistan 31 5N 72 35E
41 Gökçeade, I., Turkey 40 10N 26 0E
72 Gold Coast, reg., Austral. 28 0s 153 25E
49 Goldap, Poland 54 18N 22 22E
34 Golden, Ireland 52 30N 8 0w
84 Golden B., N.Z. 40 40s 172 50E
90 Golden Gate, U.S.A. 37 58N 122 30w
34 Golden Vale, Ireland 52 30N 8 0w
91 Goldsboro, U.S.A. 35 26N 77 59w
46 Goleniów, Poland 53 35N 14 50E
31 Golspie, Scotland 57 58N 3 59w
74 Goma, Zaïre 1 40s 29 42E
50 Gomel, U.S.S.R. 52 28N 31 5E
30 Gometra I., Scotland 56 30N 6 18w
94 Gomez (Palacio), Mex. 25 45N 103 28w
64 Gomoh, India 23 52N 86 10E
95 Gonaives, Haiti 19 20N 72 45w
73 Gonder, Ethiopia 12 40N 37 45E
74 Goniri, Nigeria 11 30N 12 15E
76 Good Hope, C of, S. Afr. 34 20s 18 30E
83 Goodooga, Australia 29 1s 147 28E
27 Goole, England 53 42N 0 53w
83 Goondiwindi, Australia 28 31s 150 25E
90 Goose, L., U.S.A. 42 0N 120 30w
89 Goose Bay, Canada 53 25N 60 30w
64 Gop, India 22 5N 69 50E
44 Goppingen, Germany 48 43N 9 38E
65 Gorakhpur, India 26 49N 83 30E
31 Gordon, Scotland 55 41N 2 32w
80 Gordon Downs, Australia 18 30s 129 35E
82 Gordonvale, Australia 17 5s 145 50E
73 Goré, Chad 8 0N 16 48E
73 Gore, Ethiopia 8 12N 35 32E
84 Gore, New Zealand 46 5N 168 55E
35 Goresbridge, Ireland 52 38 7 0w
42 Gorey, Jersey, Channel Is. 49 12N 2 2w
35 Gorey, Ireland 52 40N 6 18w
44 Gorinchem, Netherlands 51 50N 4 59E
23 Goring, England 50 50N 0 21w
40 Gorizia, Italy 45 58N 13 38E
52 Gorki (Gorkiy), U.S.S.R. 56 17N 44 0E
23 Gorleston, England 52 35N 1 44E
46 Görlitz, Germany 51 11N 15 0E
72 Gorlovka, U.S.S.R. 48 25N 37 58E
60 Gorno, Filinskoye, U.S.S.R.
     60 15N 70 3E
50 Gornyatski, U.S.S.R. 67 32N 64 15E
47 Gorodok, U.S.S.R. 49 46N 23 32E
68 Gorontalo, Indonesia 0 25N 123 5E
34 Gort, Ireland 53 4N 8 49w
46 Goryn, R., U.S.S.R. 52 0N 27 0E
65 Gosainthan, Mt., Tibet 28 20N 85 45E
45 Göschenen, Switzerland 46 41N 8 35E
83 Gosford, Australia 33 24s 151 10E
46 Goslar, Germany 51 57N 10 28E
40 Gospic, Yugoslavia 44 35N 15 20E
22 Gosport, England 50 48N 1 8w
49 Gota Can., Sweden 58 40N 14 10E
49 Göteborg, Sweden 57 20N 11 50E
49 Göteborg & Bohus, Co., Sweden
     58 15N 11 30E
46 Gotha, Germany 50 56N 10 42E
48 Gothenburg, see Göteborg
48 Gotland, I., Sweden 57 35N 18 30E
46 Gotska Sandon I., Swed. 58 24N 19 15E
45 Göttingen, Germany 51 33N 9 44E
47 Gottwaldov, Cz-slov. 49 15N 17 42E
73 Goubone, Chad 20 45N 17 5E
44 Gouda, Netherlands 52 1N 4 42E
88 Gouin Res., Canada 48 35N 74 40w
83 Goulburn, Australia 34 45s 149 40E
81 Goulburn Is., Australia 11 30s 133 35E
72 Goundam, Mali 16 25N 3 45w
72 Gourdon, France 44 42N 1 25E
72 Gourma-Rarous, Mali 16 55N 2 5w
72 Gournay, France 49 30N 1 45E
30 Gourock, Scotland 55 58N 4 49w
83 Gourock Ra., Australia 36 0s 149 30E
72 Gourselik, Niger 13 40N 10 40E
94 Gouville, France 49 7N 1 32w
35 Gower, Pen., Wales 51 35N 4 10w
35 Gowran, Ireland 52 38N 7 5w
99 Goya, Argentina 29 5 59 10w
73 Goz Regeb, Sudan 16 0N 35 58E
40 Gozo, I., Malta 36 2N 14 18E
76 Graaf Reinet, S. Africa 32 18s 24 37
72 Grabo, Ivory Coast 4 55N 7 25w

40 Gracac, Yugoslavia 44 20N 15 55E
95 Gracias à Dios, C., Nicaragua 15 0N 83 2W
98 Gradaús, Sa. dos, mts., Brazil 7 0s 50 0W
37 Grado, Spain 43 25N 6 10W
33 Graemsay I., Scotland 58 56N 3 17W
48 Graénalon, L., Iceland 64 10N 17 20W
83 Grafton, Australia 29 41s 153 0E
91 Grafton, U.S.A. 48 30N 97 25W
100 Graham Land, Antarc. 64 0s 65 0W
76 Grahamstown, S. Africa 33 20s 26 38E
43 Graian Alps, The Alps 45 30N 7 0E
35 Graiguenamanagh, Ire. 52 32N 6 58W
33 Grampian, Reg. Scotland 57 20N 2 50W
33 Grampians, mts., Scot. 56 42N 4 27W
99 Gran Chaco, S. America 24 0s 60 0W
40 Gran Sasso, Mt., Italy 42 30N 13 50E
94 Granada, Nicaragua 12 0N 86 0W
37 Granada, Spain 37 17N 3 37W
89 Granby, Canada 45 20N 72 43W
93 Grand L., Canada 46 0N 66 0W
90 Grand, R., S. Dakota, U.S.A. 45 45N 101 30W
72 Grand Bassam, Ivory Coast 5 10N 3 40W
94 Grand Bourg, Marie-Galante I. Fr. W. Indies 15 50N 61 20W
66 Grand Canal, China 35 0N 117 0E
90 Grand Canyon, U.S.A. 36 0N 113 40W
95 Grand Cayman I., W.I. 19 30N 81 15W
88 Grand Falls, Newf., Can. 49 0N 55 43W
88 Grand Forks, Canada 49 0N 118 30W
91 Grand Forks, U.S.A. 47 40N 97 5W
90 Grand Island, U.S.A. 41 0N 98 10W
90 Grand Junction, U.S.A. 39 2N 108 32W
72 Grand Lahou, Ivory Coast 5 6N 5 0W
88 Grand Rapids, Canada 53 0N 99 30W
92 Grand Rapids, U.S.A. 42 57N 85 38W
99 Grande, B., Argentina 51 0s 69 0W
88 Grande Prairie, Canada 55 18N 118 50W
94 Grande Terre, Guadeloupe, W.I. 16 25N 61 15W
45 Grandson, Switzerland 46 49N 6 39E
26 Grange-over-Sands, Eng. 54 12N 2 56W
31 Grangemouth, Scotland 56 1N 3 42W
27 Grangetown, England 54 40N 1 10W
90 Grangeville, U.S.A. 45 57N 116 12W
34 Graney, L. & R., Ire. 53 0N 8 40W
91 Granite City, U.S.A. 38 45N 90 0W
84 Granity, New Zealand 41 38s 171 50E
37 Granollers, Spain 41 40N 2 15E
27 Grantham, England 52 55N 0 38W
33 Grantown-on-Spey, Scot. 57 20N 3 37W
90 Grants, U.S.A. 35 10N 107 50W
90 Grants Pass, U.S.A. 42 28N 124 14W
31 Grantshouse, Scotland 55 53N 2 17W
42 Granville, France 48 52N 1 39W
98 Grao Mogol, Brazil 16 30s 42 27W
26 Grasmere, England 54 28N 3 2W
88 Gras, L. de, Canada 65 0N 118 5W
43 Grasse, France 43 43N 6 54W
45 Graubunden, Canton, Switz. 46 45N 9 30E
43 Graulhet, France 43 45N 2 0E
44 's Gravenhage, see The Hague, Neth.
92 Gravenhurst, Canada 44 56N 79 28W
23 Gravesend, England 51 25N 0 23E
43 Gray, France 47 25N 5 32E
26 Grayrigg, England 54 22N 2 40W
90 Grays Harbor, U.S.A. 47 0N 124 0W
23 Grays Thurrock, Eng. 51 28N 0 23E
42 Graz, Austria 47 2N 15 25E
91 Great Abaco, Bahamas 26 30N 77 20W
61 Great Anyui R., U.S.S.R. 67 0N 163 0E
83 Great Australian Basin, Australia 27 0s 145 0E
80 Great Australian Bight 33 29s 129 0E
84 Great Barrier I., N.Z. 36 8s 175 25E
82 Great Barrier Reef, Australia 19 0s 149 0E
88 Great Bear L. & R., Can. 66 0N 120 0W
90 Great Basin, U.S.A. 40 0N 116 30W
90 Great Bend, U.S.A. 38 16N 99 6W
32 Great Bernera Island, Scotland 58 15N 6 48W
34 Great Blasket I., Ireland 52 7N 10 33W
13 Great Britain, Europe 50 0 to 58 0N; 1 45E to 6 15W
76 Great Bushman Land, S. Africa 29 15s 19 30E
82 Great Divide, Australia 22 0s 145 45E
90 Great Falls, U.S.A. 47 30N 110 45W
95 Great Inagua I., Bahamas 21 0N 73 20W
64 Great Indian Desert (Thar Desert), Pakistan 28 0N 72 0E
76 Great Karroo, S. Africa 32 42s 22 20E
67 Great Khingan Mts., China 47 0N 120 0E
22 Great Malvern, England 52 7N 2 19W
75 Great Namaqualand, S.W. Africa 24 50s 17 50E
25 Great Orme's Hd., Wales 53 21N 3 52W
23 Great Ouse R., England 52 35N 0 21E
85 Great Plains, N. America 40 0N 104 0W
74 Great Ruaha, R., Tanzania 7 30s 35 0E
43 Great St. Bernard P., Italy 45 47N 7 10E
90 Great Salt L. & Desert, U.S.A. 41 0N 112 30W
80 Great Sandy Desert, Australia 20 50s 123 30E
26 Great Shunner Fell, mt., England 54 22N 2 16W

34 Great Skellig, I., Ire. 51 47N 10 32W
88 Great Slave L., & R., Can. 62 0N 113 0W
23 Great Stour R., England 51 14N 1 0E
35 Great Sugar Loaf, mt., Ire. 53 9N 6 10W
80 Great Victoria Desert, Australia 28 30s 129 0E
66 Great Wall of China 38 12N 109 0E
89 Great Whale R., Can. 55 10N 76 0W
26 Great Whernside, mt., England 54 10N 1 59W
23 Great Yarmouth, Eng. 52 40N 1 44E
95 Greater Antilles, W.I. 18 0N 76 0W
23 Greater London, Co., Eng. 51 25N 0 10W
26 Greater Manchester, Co., Eng. 53 30N 2 20W
68 Greater Sunda Is., Indon. 4 20s 112 0E
27 Greatham, England 54 39N 1 15W
37 Gredos, Sa. de, mts., Spain 40 17N 5 20W
41 Greece, Europe 39 0N 23 0E
90 Greeley, U.S.A. 40 29N 104 48W
92 Green B., U.S.A. 45 0N 87 30W
90 Green R., Utah, U.S.A. 39 30N 110 0W
91 Green Bay, U.S.A. 44 32N 88 0W
84 Green Island, N.Z. 45 50s 170 30E
100 Greenland (Dan.), N. Amer. 70 0N 40 0W
100 Greenland Sea 70 0N 5 0W
31 Greenlaw, Scotland 55 42N 2 29W
36 Greenisland, Ireland 54 43N 5 50W
30 Greenock, Scotland 55 57N 4 45W
91 Greensboro, N.C., U.S.A. 36 8N 79 54W
72 Greenville, Liberia 5 2N 9 3W
91 Greenville, Miss., U.S.A. 33 29N 91 3W
91 Greenville, S.C., U.S.A. 34 53N 82 30W
91 Greenville, Texas, U.S.A. 33 9N 96 13W
23 Greenwich, Greater London, England 51 28N 0 0
93 Greenwich, U.S.A. 41 3N 73 4W
91 Greenwood, Miss., U.S.A. 33 30N 90 9W
91 Greenwood, S.C., U.S.A. 34 14N 82 19W
83 Gregory, L., Australia 29 10s 139 20E
82 Gregory Ra., Australia 19 0s 143 15E
49 Greifswald, Germany 54 3N 13 19E
94 Grenada, I., W. Indies 12 12N 61 45W
43 Grenade, France 43 42N 1 15E
83 Grenadines, West Indies 12 30N 61 30W
83 Grenfell, Australia 33 48s 148 4E
43 Grenoble, France 45 12N 5 44E
94 Grenville, Grenada, W.I. 12 8N 61 36W
82 Grenville, C., Australia 12 0s 143 20E
31 Gretna, Scotland 55 0N 3 1W
31 Gretna Green, Scotland 55 0N 3 5W
44 Grevenmacher, Lux. 49 41N 6 25E
83 Grey Ra., Australia 28 0s 143 0E
84 Grey, R., New Zealand 42 50s 171 30E
84 Greymouth, N.Z. 42 20s 171 20E
35 Greystones, Ireland 53 8N 6 4W
84 Greytown, New Zealand 41 0s 175 30E
76 Greytown, S. Africa 29 8s 30 39E
83 Griffith, Australia 34 13s 145 46E
43 Grignan, France 44 25N 5 0E
74 Grimari, Central Africa 5 43N 20 0E
27 Grimsby, England 53 35N 0 4W
49 Grimstad, Norway 58 22N 8 35E
45 Grindelwald, Switzerland 46 38N 8 3E
76 Griqualand East, S. Afr. 30 40s 29 0E
76 Griqualand West, Dist., South Africa 28 30s 23 20E
43 Gris Nez, C., France 50 53N 1 32E
45 Grisons, Canton, Switz., see Graubunden
26 Grizebeck, England 54 16N 3 10W
26 Grodno, U.S.S.R. 53 40N 23 50E
46 Grodzisk, Poland 52 16N 16 36E
42 Groix, I. de, France 47 40N 3 30W
47 Grójec, Poland 51 52N 21 0E
44 Gronau, Germany 52 14N 7 0E
48 Grong, Norway 64 30N 12 20E
49 Groningen, Netherlands 53 15N 6 35E
76 Groot, R., S. Africa 33 10s 24 12E
76 Groot-Brakrivier, S. Afr. 34 0s 22 5E
81 Groote Eylandt, Austral. 14 0s 136 35E
75 Grootfontein, S.W. Africa 19 0s 18 12E
76 Grootvloer, L., S. Africa 29 50s 20 17E
46 Gross Glockner, mt., Austria 47 7N 13 0E
46 Grossenbrode, Germany 54 21N 11 4E
46 Grossenhain, Germany 51 20N 13 30E
40 Grosseto, Italy 42 46N 11 7E
62 Grozny, U.S.S.R. 43 10N 45 34E
49 Grudziadz, Poland 53 30N 18 50E
48 Grundarf, Iceland 64 55N 23 12W
32 Gruting Voe, Scotland 60 12N 1 32W
45 Gruyères, Switzerland 46 35N 7 5E
52 Gryazi, U.S.S.R. 52 23N 39 56E
45 Gstaad, Switzerland 46 27N 7 18E
65 Gua, India 22 18N 85 20E
81 Guad-i-Zireh, Afghan. 29 50N 62 30E
94 Guadalajara, Mexico 20 40N 103 17W
37 Guadalajara, Spain 40 39N 3 5W
81 Guadalcanal, I., Pac. Oc. 9 40s 160 0E
37 Guadalhorce, R., Spain 36 40N 4 20W
38 Guadalquivir, R., Spain 36 45N 6 25W
37 Guadalupe, Sa. de, mts., Spain 39 30N 5 30W
37 Guadarrama, Sa. de, mts., Spain 41 0N 4 0W
95 Guadeloupe, I., Fr. W.I. 16 25N 61 25W
37 Guadiana, R., Spain 37 10N 4 0W
37 Guadix, Spain 37 18N 3 10W
98 Guainia R., Colombia 2 30N 69 0W
95 Guajira, Pen., Colombia 12 10N 72 10W

99 Gualeguaychu, Arg. 32 50s 58 45W
5 Guam, I., Pacific Ocean 13 25N 144 50E
94 Guamuchil, Mexico 25 30N 108 0W
95 Guanajuato, Mexico 21 10N 101 0W
95 Guane, Cuba 22 15N 83 5W
95 Guantanamo, Cuba 20 0N 75 20W
98 Guapore, R., Brazil 13 30s 62 0W
99 Guaqui, Bolivia 16 25s 68 50W
37 Guarda, Portugal 40 30N 7 15W
71 Guardafui, C., see Ras Asir
94 Guatemala, Cent. Amer. 16 0N 91 0W
95 Guaviare, R., Colombia 3 50N 69 0W
98 Guayaquil, & G. Ecuador 2 7s 80 0W
94 Guaymas, Mexico 27 55N 111 0W
46 Gubin, Poland 51 56N 14 43E
49 Gudbrandsdal, val., Nor. 61 40N 9 30E
43 Guebwiller, France 47 55N 7 10E
72 Guéckedou, Guinea 8 40N 10 5W
89 Guelph, Canada 43 35N 80 20W
43 Guérande, France 47 20N 2 25W
43 Guéret, France 46 10N 1 54E
42 Guernica, Spain 43 25N 2 45W
42 Guernsey I., Channel Is. 49 30N 2 37W
45 Guestling, England 50 53N 0 40E
96 Guiana, Br., S. Amer., see Guyana
96 Guiana, French, S. Amer. 4 0N 53 0W
72 Guibes, S.W. Africa 26 42s 16 50E
72 Guiglo, Ivory Coast 6 45N 7 30W
23 Guildford, England 51 14N 0 33W
25 Guilsfield, Wales 52 42N 3 9W
70 Guinea, reg., W. Africa 7 0N 5 0E
72 Guinea-Bissau, W. Africa 12 0N 15 0W
72 Guingamp, France 48 33N 3 20W
44 Guiscard, France 49 40N 3 0E
43 Guise, France 49 55N 3 40E
64 Gujarat, st., India 23 0N 71 0E
64 Gujranwala, Pakistan 32 10N 74 21E
64 Gujrat, Pakistan 32 40N 74 3E
64 Gulbarga, India 17 12N 76 59E
80 Gulf Basin, Australia 15 20s 129 0E
86 Gulf Plain, U.S.A. 30 0N 90 0W
91 Gulfport, U.S.A. 30 29N 89 6W
83 Gulgong, Australia 32 11s 149 38E
60 Gulshat, U.S.S.R. 46 45N 74 20E
74 Gulu, Uganda 2 50N 32 22E
82 Gumlu, Australia 19 53s 147 41E
72 Gummi, Nigeria 12 4N 5 9E
64 Guna, India 24 40N 77 20E
63 Gunabad, Iran 34 12N 58 40E
83 Gundagai, Australia 35 5s 148 7E
67 Gunma, Pref., Japan 36 0N 138 0E
83 Gunnedah, Australia 31 0s 150 12E
90 Gunnison, R., U.S.A. 38 30N 107 30W
64 Guntur, India 16 15N 80 18E
64 Gupis, Kashmir 36 15N 73 20E
64 Gurdaspur, India 32 4N 75 30E
64 Gurgaon, India 28 27N 76 58E
98 Gurgueia, R., Brazil 9 0s 44 0W
51 Gurnard's Head, Eng. 50 12N 5 37W
51 Gürün, Turkey 38 40N 37 20E
98 Gurupi, R., Brazil 2 30s 46 40W
72 Gusau, Nigeria 12 18N 6 31E
52 Gusev, U.S.S.R. 54 35N 22 20E
46 Güstrow, Germany 53 50N 12 12E
72 Guthulungra, Australia 19 52s 147 50E
94 Gutierrez, Mexico 16 45N 94 20W
96 Guyana, S. Amer. 5 0N 58 0W
43 Guyenne, Prov., France 44 40N 1 0E
83 Guyra, Australia 30 22s 151 31E
64 Gwa, Burma 17 35N 94 25E
64 Gwadar, Pakistan 25 10N 62 18E
64 Gwalior, India 26 18N 78 18E
64 Gwatar, Iran 25 8N 61 20E
25 Gwaun-Cae-Gurwen, Wales 51 46N 3 51W
36 Gweebarra B., Ireland 54 53N 8 30W
76 Gwelo, Rhodesia 19 28s 29 40E
25 Gwent, Co., Wales 51 45N 2 55W
83 Gwydir, R., Australia 29 30s 149 0E
25 Gwynedd, Co., Wales 53 0N 4 0W
65 Gyangtse, Tibet 28 54N 89 36E
62 Gyda Pen., U.S.S.R. 70 0N 78 0E
83 Gympie, Australia 26 10s 152 40E
47 Gyöngyös, Hungary 47 50N 20 10E
47 Györ, Hungary 47 40N 17 39E
88 Gypsumville, Canada 51 53N 98 35W

H

32 Haa, The, Scotland 60 20N 1 0W
48 Haápamäkj, Finland 62 17N 24 33E
48 Haarlem, Netherlands 52 23N 4 37E
64 Hab Nadi Chauki, Pakistan 24 55N 66 50E
67 Hachinohe, Japan 40 28N 141 30E
67 Hachioji, Japan 35 30N 139 30E
23 Hackney, Greater London, England 51 32N 0 2W
31 Haddington, Scotland 55 57N 2 47W
62 Hadera, Israel 32 27N 34 55E
62 Hadhramaut, Dist., Arabia 16 30N 49 30E
23 Hadleigh, England 52 3N 0 57E
23 Hadlow, England 51 12N 0 20E
23 Hadrian's Wall, England 55 0N 2 25W
67 Haeju, Korea 38 5N 125 30E
64 Hafizabad, Pakistan 32 10N 73 35E
65 Haflong, India 25 0N 93 0E

48 Hafnarfjördur, Iceland 64 5N 21 58W
73 Hagar Banga, Sudan 10 40N 22 45E
44 Hagen, Germany 51 21N 7 29E
92 Hagerstown, U.S.A. 39 40N 77 37W
49 Hagfors, Sweden 60 2N 13 34E
67 Hagi, Japan 34 36N 131 28E
34 Hags Hd., Ireland 52 57N 9 29W
42 Hague, C. de la, France 49 45N 2 0W
44 Hague, The, Netherlands 52 5N 4 18E
43 Haguenau, France 48 50N 7 50E
62 Haifa, Israel 32 50N 35 0E
62 Hail, Saudi Arabia 27 49N 42 42E
67 Hailar, China 49 17N 119 50E
89 Haileybury, Canada 47 30N 79 57W
23 Hailsham, England 50 52N 0 16E
67 Hailun, China 47 17N 127 10E
48 Hailuoto I., Finland 65 0N 24 45E
66 Hainan I. & Str., China 19 0N 109 30E
43 Hainaut, Prov., Belgium 50 32N 4 0E
66 Haiphong, Vietnam 20 57N 106 45E
95 Haiti, Hispaniola 19 0N 74 0W
47 Hajdúböszörmény, Hung. 47 42N 21 30E
47 Hajnówka, Poland 52 45N 23 32E
64 Hala, Pakistan 25 45N 68 20E
46 Halberstadt, Germany 51 53N 11 2E
49 Halden, Norway 59 9N 11 23E
64 Haldwani, India 29 15N 79 25E
51 Haleb, Syria, see Aleppo
22 Halesowen, England 52 27N 2 3W
89 Halifax, Canada 44 45N 63 0W
27 Halifax, England 53 44N 1 52W
82 Halifax B., Australia 18 50s 147 0E
33 Halkirk, Scotland 58 30N 3 30W
49 Halland, Co., Sweden 57 10N 12 30E
46 Halle, Belgium 50 44N 4 14E
46 Halle, Germany 51 30N 11 59E
49 Hallefors, Sweden 59 46N 14 36E
100 Hallet, Antarctica 71 30s 170 0E
100 Halley Bay, Antarctica 72 30s 25 0W
49 Hallingdal, val., Nor. 60 40N 8 50E
48 Hallnas, Sweden 64 18N 19 40E
80 Hall's Creek, Australia 18 18s 127 33E
69 Halmahera, I., Indonesia 1 0N 128 0E
49 Halmstad, Sweden 56 42N 12 47E
49 Halq el Oued, Tunisia 36 58N 10 16E
49 Hals, Denmark 57 0N 10 18E
49 Halsingborg, Sweden 56 3N 12 41E
23 Halstead, England 51 57N 0 39E
27 Haltwhistle, England 54 59N 2 28W
64 Halvad, India 23 1N 71 3E
44 Ham, France 49 44N 3 3E
67 Hamada, Japan 34 58N 132 5E
67 Hamamatsu, Japan 34 45N 137 50E
49 Hamar, Norway 60 50N 11 5E
48 Hamaröy, Norway 68 6N 15 35E
64 Hambantota, Sri Lanka 6 10N 81 10E
22 Hambledon, England 50 56N 1 4W
27 Hambleton Hills, Eng. 54 15N 1 15W
49 Hamburg, Germany 53 35N 9 58E
49 Häme, Co., Finland 61 30N 24 30E
49 Hameenlinna, Finland 61 0N 24 30E
44 Hameln, Germany 52 9N 9 22E
80 Hamersley Ra., Australia 22 10s 118 0E
83 Hamilton, Australia 37 45s 142 0E
84 Hamilton, N.Z. 37 47s 175 17E
89 Hamilton, Canada 43 14N 80 0W
84 Hamilton, Bermuda 32 15N 64 46W
92 Hamilton, Ohio, U.S.A. 39 23N 84 30W
31 Hamilton, Scotland 55 46N 4 3W
44 Hamm, Germany 51 40N 7 49E
62 Hammam, Saudi Arabia 25 10N 46 50E
48 Hammerfest, Norway 70 45N 23 37E
23 Hammersmith, Greater London, England 51 30N 0 11W
92 Hammond, U.S.A. 41 40N 87 30W
84 Hampden, New Zealand 45 18s 170 52E
22 Hampshire, Co., England 51 8N 1 0W
22 Hampshire Downs, Eng. 51 15N 1 0W
73 Hamrat esh Sheikh, Sudan 14 45N 27 40E
40 Hamrun, Malta 35 55N 14 27E
64 Hamun-el-Helmand, L., Afghanistan 31 15N 61 15E
41 Han Pijesak, Yugoslavia 44 0N 19 0E
67 Hanamaki, Japan 39 25N 140 30E
45 Hanau, Germany 50 10N 8 50E
66 Hanchung, China 32 57N 107 7E
74 Handeni, Tanzania 5 20s 38 0E
90 Hanford, U.S.A. 36 18N 119 37W
66 Hangchow, & B., China 29 55N 120 15E
49 Hanko, Finland 59 49N 22 55E
66 Hanku, China 39 15N 117 40E
88 Hanna, Canada 51 35N 112 0W
66 Hanoi, Vietnam 20 57N 105 55E
44 Hanover, Germany 52 25N 9 45E
99 Hanover I., Chile 50 30s 75 30W
66 Hansi, India 29 5N 75 55E
66 Hantan, China 36 40N 114 30E
66 Hanyang, China 30 30N 114 0E
48 Haparanda, Finland 65 58N 24 3E
64 Hapur, India 28 45N 77 45E
62 Haql, Saudi Arabia 29 10N 35 3E
66 Har Us Nuur, L., Mongolia 48 0N 92 10E
66 Harbin, China 45 40N 126 40E
89 Harbour Grace, Canada 47 40N 53 22W
44 Harburg, Germany 53 27N 9 58E
82 Harcourt, Australia 24 17s 149 55E
49 Hardanger Fd., Norway 60 10N 6 5E
44 Harderwijk, Netherlands 52 21N 5 38E
64 Hardoi, India 27 30N 80 5E
64 Hardwar, India 30 0N 78 9E

44 Harelbeke, Belgium 50 50N 3 20E
43 Harfleur, France 49 30N 0 10E
64 Hari Rud, R., Afghan. 34 25N 64 20E
23 Haringey, Gr. London, Eng. 51 33N 0 15E
65 Haringhata, R., Bangla. 22 0N 90 0E
25 Harlech, Wales 52 50N 4 7W
44 Harlingen, Netherlands 53 11N 5 26E
91 Harlingen, U.S.A. 26 14N 97 45W
23 Harlow, England 51 47N 0 8E
48 Harnösand, Sweden 62 37N 17 55E
32 Haroldswick, Scotland 60 47N 0 50W
43 Harpenden, England 51 49N 0 21W
51 Harran, Turkey 36 58N 39 3E
32 Harris, & Sd., Scotland 57 56N 7 0W
91 Harrisburg, Pa., U.S.A. 40 22N 76 48W
27 Harrogate, England 54 0N 1 33W
48 Harstad, Norway 68 48N 16 28E
76 Hartbees, R., S. Africa 28 45s 20 48E
92 Hartford, Conn., U.S.A. 41 49N 72 45W
31 Harthill, Scotland 55 52N 3 45W
24 Hartland Pt., England 51 2N 4 31W
27 Hartlepool, England 54 42N 1 11W
31 Hartley, England 55 5N 1 27W
76 Hartley, Rhodesia 18 8s 30 10E
76 Harts, R., S. Africa 26 50s 25 30E
22 Harwell, England 51 32N 1 16W
23 Harwich, England 51 57N 1 18E
64 Haryana, st., India 29 0N 76 00E
44 Harz Mts., Germany 51 45N 10 40E
63 Hasa, Dist., Arabia 26 0N 49 0E
63 Hasbaiya, Lebanon 33 25N 35 41E
23 Haslemere, England 51 5N 0 41W
26 Haslingden, England 53 43N 2 19W
64 Hassan, India 13 4N 76 8E
44 Hasselt, Belgium 50 56N 5 21E
72 Hassi El Gassi, Algeria 30 40N 6 0E
72 Hassi Inifel, Algeria 29 50N 3 28E
72 Hassi Messaoud, Algeria 32 10N 6 10E
72 Hassi R'Mel, Algeria 32 20N 3 30E
23 Hastings, England 50 52N 0 35E
84 Hastings, New Zealand 39 44s 176 53E
90 Hastings, Neb., U.S.A. 40 30N 98 30W
83 Hastings Ra., Australia 31 0s 152 0E
23 Hatfield, England 51 46N 0 11W
24 Hatherleigh, England 50 49N 4 4W
64 Hathras, India 27 40N 78 35E
65 Hatia, Bangladesh 22 30N 91 5E
62 Hatsoi Ashdod, Israel 31 36N 34 42E
91 Hatteras, C., U.S.A. 35 15N 75 20W
91 Hattiesburg, U.S.A. 31 20N 89 19W
47 Hatvan, Hungary 47 40N 19 45E
49 Haugesund, Norway 59 25N 5 13E
84 Hauraki G., N.Z. 36 30s 175 5E
62 Havrun, Wadi, Iraq 33 30N 41 30E
43 Haut-Rhin, Dépt., France 48 0N 7 20E
42 Haute-Corse, Dépt., Fr. 42 15N 9 5E
42 Haute-Garonne, Dépt., Fr. 43 30N 1 10E
42 Haute-Loire, Dépt., Fr. 45 20N 3 50E
42 Haute-Marne, Dépt., Fr. 48 18N 5 7E
42 Haute-Saône, Dépt., Fr. 47 45N 6 10E
42 Haute-Savoie, Dépt., Fr. 46 4N 6 38E
42 Haute-Vienne, Dépt., Fr. 45 58N 1 12E
42 Hautes-Alpes, Dépt., Fr. 44 40N 6 40E
42 Hauts-de-Seine, Dépt., Fr. 49 0N 2 10E
42 Hautes-Pyrénées, Dépt., Fr. 43 12N 0 12E
44 Hautmont, France 50 13N 3 55E
38 Hauts Plateau, Algeria 35 0N 2 0E
95 Havana, Cuba 23 0N 82 30W
23 Havant, England 50 51N 0 59W
46 Havel, R., Germany 52 40N 12 15E
44 Havelange, Belgium 50 23N 5 15E
84 Havelock, New Zealand 41 18s 173 46E
24 Haverfordwest, Wales 51 49N 4 58W
23 Haverhill, England 52 6N 0 27E
93 Haverhill, U.S.A. 42 50N 71 2W
23 Havering, Greater London, England 51 33N 0 15E
90 Havre, U.S.A. 48 35N 109 40W
90 Hawaii, st., U.S.A. 21 0N 158 0W
90 Hawaiian Is., Pac. Oc. 21 0N 158 0W
24 Hawarden, Wales 53 11N 2 59W
84 Hawea, L., New Zealand 44 30s 169 8E
84 Hawera, New Zealand 39 36s 174 30E
26 Hawes Water, L., England 54 31N 2 48W
31 Hawick, Scotland 55 25N 2 48W
84 Hawke, B., N.Z. 39 15s 177 30E
84 Hawker, Australia 31 53s 138 25E
84 Hawke's Bay Dist., N.Z. 39 25s 176 35E
89 Hawkesbury, Ont., Can. 45 35N 74 48W
90 Hawthorne, U.S.A. 38 30N 118 50W
83 Hay, Australia 34 37s 144 45E
25 Hay, Wales 52 4N 3 9W
81 Hay, R., Australia 23 10s 137 0E
42 Hayange, France 49 20N 6 0E
26 Haydon Bridge, England 54 58N 2 14W
24 Hayle, England 50 11N 5 26W
90 Hays, U.S.A. 38 55N 99 23W
23 Hayward's Heath, Eng. 51 0N 0 5W
65 Hazaribagh, India 23 58N 85 26E
88 Hazelton, Canada 55 23N 127 45W
92 Hazleton, U.S.A. 40 59N 76 0W
22 Headington, England 51 46N 1 1W
83 Healesville, Australia 37 35s 145 33E
27 Heanor, England 53 1N 1 22W
11 Heard I., Indian Ocean 53 0s 74 0E
90 Hearst, Canada 49 40N 83 25W
23 Heathfield, England 50 58N 0 16E
26 Hebden Bridge, Eng. 53 45N 2 0W
83 Hebel, Australia 28 59s 147 59E
32 Hebrides, Inner, Scot. 56 40N 6 50W

32 Hebrides, Outer, Scot. 57 40N 7 0W
89 Hebron, Canada 58 10N 62 50W
63 Hebron, Jordan 31 32N 35 5E
48 Hede, Sweden 62 23N 13 43E
49 Hedemora, Sweden 60 18N 15 58E
84 Hedgehope, N.Z. 46 12s 168 34E
49 Hedmark, Co., Norway 61 45N 11 0E
22 Hednesford, England 52 43N 2 0W
44 Heemstede, Netherlands 52 19N 4 37E
44 Heerenveen, Netherlands 52 58N 5 55E
44 Heerlen, Netherlands 50 53N 5 58E
73 Heiban, Sudan 11 13N 30 27E
45 Heidelberg, Germany 49 26N 8 46E
76 Heidelburg, S. Africa 34 5s 20 50E
45 Heidenheim, Germany 48 41N 10 8E
76 Heilbron, S. Africa 27 28s 27 55E
45 Heilbronn, Germany 49 5N 9 19E
67 Heilungkiang, Prov., China
    45 0N 130 0E
49 Heinola, Finland 61 13N 26 10E
65 Heinze Is., Burma 14 20N 97 45E
62 Hejaz, dist., Saudi Arabia 25 30N 38 30E
48 Hekla Torfa Jökull, Ice. 64 0N 19 30W
90 Helena, Mont., U.S.A. 46 40N 111 55W
30 Helensburgh, Scotland 56 1N 4 43W
84 Helensville, New Zealand 36 39s 174 28E
48 Helgeland, Dist., Norway
    66 0N 13 5E
46 Heligoland I., & B., Ger. 54 11N 7 52E
41 Hellespont, see Dardanelles
23 Hellifield, England 54 1N 2 14W
37 Hellin, Spain 38 30N 1 40W
64 Helville, Madagascar 13 20s 48 12E
64 Helmand Rud R., Afghan. 30 25N 63 0E
44 Helmond, Netherlands 51 30N 5 41E
33 Helmsdale, & R., Scot. 58 7N 3 39W
27 Helmsley, England 54 14N 1 3W
41 Helsingfors, see Helsinki
49 Helsingör, Denmark 56 2N 12 35E
49 Helsinki (Helsingfors), Fin.
    60 13N 24 55E
24 Helston, England 50 6N 5 17W
22 Helvellyn, mt., England 54 30N 3 0W
73 Helwân, Egypt 29 50N 31 20E
23 Hemel Hempstead, Eng. 51 45N 0 28W
49 Hemse, Sweden 57 14N 18 21E
24 Hemsworth, England 53 37N 1 21W
24 Hemyock, England 50 55N 3 14W
23 Henares, R., Spain 41 0N 2 50W
42 Hendaye, France 43 22N 1 50W
92 Henderson, Ken., U.S.A. 37 50N 87 30W
91 Henderson, N.C., U.S.A.
    36 17N 78 25W
32 Henderson, Scotland 57 42N 5 47W
83 Hendon, Australia 28 2s 151 55E
67 Hengchun, Taiwan 22 0N 120 40E
44 Hengelo, Netherlands 52 17N 6 48E
67 Hengoed, Wales 51 39N 3 14W
66 Hengyang, China 26 30N 111 58W
44 Hénin-Lietard, France 50 25N 2 58E
23 Henley, England 51 31N 0 54W
23 Henlow, England 52 2N 0 18W
86 Henrietta Maria, C., Can. 55 0N 82 38W
66 Hentiyn Nuruu, mt., Mongolia
    49 0N 108 0E
83 Henty, Australia 35 32s 147 2E
65 Henzada, Burma 17 39N 95 37E
64 Herat, Afghanistan 34 28N 62 3E
64 Herat, Prov., Afghan. 34 0N 63 0E
42 Hérault, Dépt., France 43 37N 2 57E
82 Herberton, Australia 17 28s 145 25E
34 Herbertstown, Ireland 52 32N 8 29W
83 Hercegnovi, Y-slav. 42 25N 18 30E
40 Hercegovina, Province, Yugoslavia
    43 30N 17 45E
48 Herdhubreid, Mt., Ice. 65 10N 16 21W
22 Hereford, Eng. 52 4N 2 42W
22 Hereford & Worcester, Co., England
    52 15N 2 25W
44 Herentals, Belgium 51 11N 4 51E
46 Herford, Germany 52 8N 8 40E
76 Herisau, Switzerland 47 24N 9 18E
76 Hermanus, S. Africa 34 15s 19 10E
84 Hermidale, Australia 31 28s 146 54E
84 Hermitage, N.Z. 43 45s 170 7E
63 Hermon, Mt., Syria-Leb. 33 25N 35 50E
47 Hernad, R., Hungary 48 30N 21 5E
23 Herne Bay, England 51 22N 1 9E
49 Herning, Denmark 56 8N 9 0E
89 Heron Bay, Can. 48 50N 86 10W
37 Herrera, Spain 39 12N 5 2W
49 Herstal, Belgium 50 38N 5 35E
23 Herstmonceux, Eng. 50 53 0 21E
23 Hertford, & Co., Eng. 51 48N 0 4W
44 s'Hertogenbosch, Neth. 51 42N 5 18E
63 Herzliya, Israel 32 10N 34 50E
46 Hesse, Land, Germany 50 27N 9 10E
27 Hessle, England 53 44N 0 26w
27 Hetton-le-Hole, England 54 49N 1 26W
27 Hexham, England 54 58N 2 0W
23 Heybridge, England 51 44N 0 42E
26 Heysham, England 54 4N 2 54W
83 Heywood, Australia 38 12s 141 36E
24 Heywood, England 53 34N 2 19W
94 Hidalgo del Parral, Mexico
    27 0N 105 40W
72 Hierro I., Canary Is. 27 45N 17 58W
26 High Pike, mt., England 54 42N 3 4W
47 High Tatra, mts., Cz-slov. 49 0N 20 0E
24 High Willhays, England 50 41N 4 1W
23 High Wycombe, Eng. 51 38N 0 45W
23 Higham Ferrers, England 52 18N 0 35W
32 Highland, Reg., Scotland 57 30N 5 0W
22 Highley, England 52 25N 2 23W
27 Highworth, England 51 38N 1 44W
67 Hikone, Japan 35 7N 136 20E
84 Hikurangi, N.Z. 35 42s 174 17E
46 Hildesheim, Germany 52 10N 9 58E
23 Hilgay, England 52 33N 0 24E
62 Hilla, Iraq 32 39N 44 30E
44 Hillegom, Netherlands 52 18N 4 34E
23 Hillingdon, Gr. London, Eng.
    51 34N 0 27W
91 Hillsboro, U.S.A. 32 0N 97 0W
36 Hillsborough, N. Ireland 54 28N 6 4E
94 Hillsborough, Carriacou, W.I.
    12 14N 61 12W
83 Hillston, Australia 33 29s 145 32E
36 Hilltown, N. Ireland 54 12N 6 9W
44 Hilversum, Netherlands 52 15N 5 10E
64 Himachal Pradesh, Prov., India
    31 30N 77 0E
65 Himalayas, mts., Asia 29 0N 82 0E
64 Himatnagar, India 23 37N 72 57E
67 Himeji, Japan 34 56N 134 48E
67 Himi, Japan 36 55N 137 0E
82 Hinchinbrook I., Australia
    18 21s 146 20E
22 Hinckley, England 52 33N 1 22W
74 Hinde Rapids, Zaïre 5 25s 27 3E
62 Hindian, R., Iran 30 20N 50 20E
26 Hindley, England 53 33N 2 35W
63 Hindu Kush, Afghanistan
    36 0N 71 30E
64 Hindubagh, Pakistan 30 55N 67 42E
64 Hindupur, India 13 45N 77 25E
88 Hines Cr., Canada 56 20N 118 40W
66 Hingan, China 25 55N 110 40E
66 Hingi, China 25 0N 105 8E
66 Hingol, R., Pakistan 27 30N 66 0E
64 Hingoli, India 19 50N 77 6E
64 Hinkley Pt., England 51 13N 3 7W
48 Hinnöy, I., Norway 68 40N 16 0E
67 Hino, C., Japan 35 25N 132 45E
37 Hinojosa, Spain 38 30N 5 15W
45 Hinterrhein, R., Switz. 46 35N 9 20E
92 Hinton, U.S.A. 37 40N 80 50W
67 Hirosaki, Japan 40 35N 140 30E
67 Hiroshima, & Pref., Japan
    34 30N 132 35E
43 Hirson, France 49 55N 4 3E
67 Hirwaun, Wales 51 43N 3 30W
63 Hisban, Jordan 31 48N 35 46E
95 Hispaniola, I., W.I. 17 30N 71 0W
64 Hissar, India 29 11N 75 41E
23 Hitchin, England 51 57N 0 17W
48 Hitra, I., Norway 63 30N 8 45E
49 Hjälmaren, L., Sweden 59 25N 15 50E
48 Hjeradsflói, Iceland 65 40N 14 0W
48 Hjeradsvötn, R., Iceland 65 40N 19 10W
49 Hjorring, Denmark 57 25N 10 0E
68 Ho-Chi-Minh City, Vietnam
    10 40N 106 37E
66 Hoa-Binh, Vietnam 21 0N 104 25E
83 Hobart, Australia 42 49s 147 6E
90 Hobbs, U.S.A. 32 43N 103 11W
44 Hoboken, Belgium 51 11N 4 21E
49 Hobro, Denmark 56 39N 9 46E
66 Hochih, China 24 45N 107 25E
45 Hochst, Germany 50 6N 8 32E
66 Hochwan, China 30 15N 105 50E
45 Hockenheim, Germany 49 20N 8 32E
62 Hodeida, Yemen 14 50N 42 55E
88 Hodgson, Canada 51 20N 97 40W
47 Hódmezövásárhely, Hungary
    46 28N 20 22E
44 Hoek van Holland, Netherlands
    52 0N 4 10E
46 Hof, Germany 50 20N 11 54E
48 Hof, Iceland 64 32N 14 35W
66 Hofei, China 31 50N 117 0E
76 Hofmeyr, S. Africa 31 35s 25 45E
48 Hofs Jökull, mt., Iceland 64 45N 19 0W
48 Hofsos, Iceland 65 52N 19 19W
67 Hofu, Japan 34 0N 131 30E
62 Hofuf, Saudi Arabia 25 20N 49 40E
72 Hoggar, mts., Algeria 23 0N 6 30E
27 Hog's Back, England 51 13N 0 40W
27 Hogsthorpe, England 53 13N 0 19E
66 Hohsien, China 24 35N 111 20E
66 Hoihow (Haikow), China 20 0N 110 10E
74 Hoima, Uganda 1 25N 31 25E
67 Hokang, China 47 36N 130 49E
84 Hokitika, New Zealand 42 44s 171 2E
67 Hokkaido, I., & Pref., Japan
    43 30N 143 0E
66 Hokow, China 22 55N 103 10E
23 Holbeach & Marsh, Eng. 52 48N 0 1E
83 Holbrook, Australia 35 42s 147 15E
27 Holderness, Dist., Eng. 53 48N 0 5W
90 Holdrege, U.S.A. 40 30N 99 21W
95 Holguin, Cuba 20 50N 76 20W
82 Hollams Bird I., S.W. Afr. 24 35s 14 30E
44 Holland, N., Prov., Neth. 52 29N 4 47E
44 Holland, S., Prov., Neth. 52 5N 4 30E
82 Hollandia, see Jayapura
36 Hollymount, Ireland 53 39N 9 7W
36 Hollywood, Ireland 53 6N 6 36W
90 Hollywood, U.S.A. 34 10N 118 28W
48 Holmavik, Iceland 65 42N 21 43W
24 Holmfirth, England 53 34N 1 47W
48 Holmsund, Sweden 63 42N 20 20E
63 Holon, Israel 32 2N 34 47E
89 Hólsteinsborg, Greenland 67 0N 53 20W
24 Holsworthy, England 50 48N 4 21W
23 Holt, England 52 55N 1 6E
25 Holt, Wales 53 5N 2 54W
27 Holy I., England 55 41N 1 47W
30 Holy I., Scotland 55 31N 5 4W
25 Holy I., Wales 53 18N 4 38W
25 Holyhead, & B., Wales 53 20N 4 39W
25 Holywell, Wales 53 17N 3 15W
36 Holywood, N. Ireland 54 39N 5 50W
65 Homalin, Burma 25 0N 94 55E
72 Hombori, Mali 15 20N 1 38W
45 Homburg, Germany 49 18N 7 18E
89 Home, B., Canada 68 40N 67 0W
82 Home Hill, Australia 19 40s 147 20E
88 Homer, Alaska 59 40N 151 35W
82 Homestead, Australia 20 20s 145 40E
62 Homs, Syria 34 55N 36 43E
76 Hondeklipbaai, S. Africa 30 22s 17 18E
94 Honduras, & G. of, Central America
    15 0N 86 0E
49 Hönefoss, Norway 60 10N 10 10E
43 Honfleur, France 49 24N 0 12E
66 Hong Kong, China 22 20N 114 10E
24 Honiton, England 50 48N 3 12W
67 Honjo, Japan 39 28N 140 0E
90 Honolulu, Pac. Oc. 21 20N 158 0W
67 Honshu, I., Japan 36 0N 139 0E
90 Hood, Mt., U.S.A. 45 20N 121 0W
44 Hoogeveen Netherlands 52 45N 6 30E
44 Hoogezand, Netherlands
    53 11N 6 45E
82 Hook I., Australia 20 4s 149 0E
44 Hoorn, Netherlands 52 40N 5 4E
91 Hope, U.S.A. 33 43N 93 38W
100 Hope Bay, Antarctica 60 0s 57 0W
89 Hopedale, Canada 55 27N 60 22W
76 Hopefield, S. Africa 33 0s 18 22E
83 Hopetoun, Australia 35 48s 142 26E
80 Hopetoun, Australia 33 52s 120 0E
76 Hopetown, S. Africa 29 42s 24 10E
92 Hopkinsville, U.S.A. 36 55N 87 29W
90 Hoquiam, U.S.A. 47 0N 123 58W
62 Hor al Hammar, Iraq 30 50N 46 0E
49 Hordaland, Co., Norway 60 8N 6 20E
31 Horden, England 54 46N 1 18W
23 Horgen, Switzerland 47 16N 8 35E
23 Horley, England 51 11N 0 11W
23 Horn, Austria 48 40N 15 40E
48 Horn (North C.), Ice. 66 29N 22 27W
99 Horn, C., Chile 55 47s 67 0W
36 Horn Hd., Ireland 55 13N 7 57W
48 Horna, Fjord, Iceland 64 17N 15 10E
66 Hornavan L., Seden 66 30N 18 0E
27 Horncastle, England 53 12N 0 8W
22 Horndean, England 50 55N 1 0W
92 Hornell, U.S.A. 42 20N 77 44W
83 Hornsby, Australia 33 36s 151 2E
27 Hornsea, England 53 54N 0 9E
35 Horseleap, Ireland 53 24N 7 34W
49 Horsens, Denmark 55 53N 9 45E
83 Horsforth, England 53 51N 1 38W
23 Horsham, England 51 3N 0 20W
83 Horsham, Australia 36 42s 142 13E
23 Horsham St. Faith, England
    52 41N 1 15E
49 Hörten, Norway 59 25N 10 27E
26 Horton-in-Ribblesdale, England
    54 10N 2 19W
88 Horton, R., Canada 69 0N 124 0W
26 Horwich, England 53 36N 2 33W
64 Hoshangabad, India 22 50N 77 58E
64 Hoshiarpur, India 31 45N 75 58E
64 Hospet, India 15 10N 76 15E
34 Hospital, Ireland 52 28N 8 28W
37 Hospitalet, Spain 41 22N 2 4E
99 Hoste, I., Argentina 55 30s 70 0W
91 Hot Springs, U.S.A. 34 25N 93 2W
48 Hoting, Sweden 64 4N 16 20E
76 Houffalize, Belgium 50 8N 5 48E
27 Houghton-le-Spring, Eng. 54 51N 1 28W
84 Houhora, New Zealand 34 49s 173 9E
93 Houlton, U.S.A. 46 15N 68 0W
91 Houma, U.S.A. 29 41N 90 43W
31 Hourn, L., Scotland 57 7N 5 35W
23 Hounslow, England 51 28N 0 23W
91 Houston, U.S.A. 29 45N 95 27W
76 Houtbaai, S. Africa 34 3s 18 27E
76 Houtkraal, S. Africa 30 30s 24 0E
66 Hovd, (Jargalant), Mongolia
    48 0N 91 30E
23 Hove, England 50 49N 0 13W
83 Howard, Australia 25 18s 152 35E
27 Howden, England 53 46N 0 52W
83 Howe, C., Australia 37 30s 149 58E
33 Howe of the Mearns, Scotland
    56 50N 2 30W
76 Howick, S. Africa 29 30s 30 12E
82 Howick Group, Australia 14 20s 145 30E
65 Howrah, India 22 40N 88 15E
35 Howth, & Hd., Ireland 53 23N 6 4W
33 Hoy, I. & Sd., Scotland 58 50N 3 19W
49 Höyanger, Norway 61 25N 6 5E
47 Hradec Králové, Cz-slov.
    50 15N 15 52E
48 Hruta Fjord, Iceland 65 30N 21 7W
65 Hsenwi, Burma 23 19N 98 0E
66 Hsiao Khingan Shan, Mts., China
    50 0N 128 0E
66 Hsi-liao, R., China 43 0N 122 0E
66 Hsuchang, China 34 0N 115 0E
66 Hualien, Taiwan 23 55N 121 55E
98 Huallaga, R., Peru 8 30s 76 10W
98 Huancavelica, Peru 12 50s 75 0W
98 Huancayo, Peru 12 5s 75 0W
98 Huascaran, Mt., Peru 8 45s 77 30W
99 Huasco, Chile 28 20s 71 15W
94 Huatabampo, Mexico 26 50N 109 40W
64 Hubli, India 15 20N 75 2E
67 Huchow, China 30 46N 120 10E
27 Huddersfield, England 53 38N 1 47W
49 Hudiksvall, Sweden 61 47N 17 5E
93 Hudson, & R., U.S.A. 42 0N 74 0W
89 Hudson B., Canada 59 0N 86 0W
89 Hudson Str., Canada 62 0N 70 0W
68 Hué, Vietnam 16 33N 107 40E
37 Huelva, Spain 37 16N 6 59W
37 Huesca, Spain 42 9N 0 25W
82 Hughenden, Australia 20 58s 144 5E
66 Huhehot, China 40 50N 111 20E
98 Huila, Mt., Colombia 3 0N 76 5W
94 Huixtla, Mexico 15 15N 92 45W
65 Hukawng, Valley, Burma
    26 30N 96 0E
63 Hula, L., Israel 33 4N 35 38E
88 Hull, Canada 45 30N 75 48W
27 Hull, & R., England 53 45N 0 20W
44 Hulst, Netherlands 51 17N 4 4E
67 Hulun, China, see Hailar
27 Humber, R., England 53 35N 0 20W
27 Humberside, Co., Eng. 53 50N 0 30W
88 Humboldt, Canada 52 25N 105 12W
90 Humboldt, R., U.S.A. 41 0N 117 30W
83 Hume, L., Australia 36 5s 147 30E
48 Huna Flói, Iceland 65 50N 20 50W
66 Hunan, Prov., China 27 0N 111 30E
66 Hunchun, China 43 0N 130 12E
47 Hunedoara, Rumania 45 44N 22 53E
47 Hungary, Europe 47 12N 19 10E
22 Hungerford, England 51 25N 1 30W
66 Hungkiang, China 27 5N 109 20E
66 Hungnam, Korea 39 55N 127 45E
66 Hungshui, R., China 23 50N 108 0E
67 Hungtze Hu., L., China
    33 20N 118 30E
46 Hunmanby, England 54 11N 0 19W
46 Hunsrück, Mts., Germany 50 0N 7 20E
67 Hunstanton, England 52 57N 0 29E
83 Hunter I., Australia 40 30s 144 46E
30 Hunterston, Scotland 55 45N 4 53W
84 Hunterville, N.Z. 39 56s 175 31E
23 Huntingdon, England 52 20N 0 12W
92 Huntington, Ind., U.S.A.
    40 55N 85 28W
91 Huntington, W. Va., U.S.A.
    38 21N 82 37W
84 Huntly, New Zealand 37 30s 175 8E
33 Huntly, Scotland 57 27N 2 47W
92 Huntsville, Canada 45 23N 79 13W
91 Huntsville, Alabama, U.S.A.
    34 44N 86 17W
91 Huntsville, Texas, U.S.A.
    30 44N 95 35W
83 Huonville, Australia 43 2s 147 0E
66 Hupei, prov., China 31 30N 113 0E
62 Hurghada, Egypt 27 15N 33 50E
30 Hurlford, Scotland 55 35N 4 29W
92 Huron, L., N. America 45 0N 82 30W
90 Huron, U.S.A. 44 25N 98 18W
23 Hurstpierpoint, England 50 56N 0 11W
48 Husavik, Iceland 66 3N 17 13W
49 Huskvarna, Sweden 57 50N 14 19E
90 Hutchinson, U.S.A. 38 0N 99 0W
45 Huttwil, Switzerland 47 7N 7 50E
44 Huy, Belgium 50 30N 5 16E
27 Huyton, England 53 25N 2 52W
44 Hvammr, Iceland 65 10N 21 50W
48 Hvammsfjord, Iceland 65 5N 22 30W
40 Hvar, I., Yugoslavia 43 10N 16 42E
48 Hvitá, R., Iceland 64 40N 21 30W
48 Hvitavatn, L., Iceland 64 35N 19 50W
67 Hwai-ho, R., China 33 0N 116 0E
67 Hwainan, China 32 40N 117 30E
67 Hwaiyang, mts., China 31 30N 115 0E
66 Hwang-ho, R., China 39 0N 107 0E
66 Hwangshih, China 30 15N 115 0E
66 Hweitseh, China 26 50N 103 0E
66 Hyargas Nuur, Mongolia
    49 0N 93 30E
26 Hyde, England 53 27N 2 5W
64 Hyderabad, India 17 25N 78 35E
64 Hyderabad, Pak. 25 20N 68 30E
43 Hyères, & Is., France 43 8N 6 6E
91 Hyndman, Pk., U.S.A. 44 0N 114 0W
67 Hyogo, Pref., Japan 35 0N 135 0E
23 Hythe, Kent, England 51 4N 1 4E
49 Hyvinkaa, Finland 60 38N 25 0E

I
47 Iar Connaught, Dist., Ire. 53 18N 9 20W
47 Iasi, Rumania 47 10N 27 37E
73 Ibadan, Nigeria 7 40N 3 50E
95 Ibagué, Colombia 4 30N 75 25W
67 Ibaraki, Pref., Japan 36 20N 140 20E
72 Ibarra, Ecuador 0 23N 78 15W
72 Ibi, Nigeria 8 7N 9 56E
98 Ibiapaba, Sa. da, mts., Brazil
    4 0s 41 0W
99 Ibicuy, Argentina 33 40s 59 10W
37 Ibiza, I. & Tn., Spain 39 0N 1 30E
22 Ibstock, England 52 42N 1 23W
98 Icá, R., Brazil 2 55s 67 58W
98 Ica, Peru 14 5s 75 30W
48 Iceland, Atlantic Oc. 65 0N 17 30W
66 Ichang, China 30 59N 111 23E
64 Ichchapuram, India 19 5N 84 40E
67 Ichinohe, Japan 40 8N 141 18E
41 Ida, Mt., Turkey 39 40N 27 15E
90 Idaho, st., U.S.A. 44 0N 115 50W
90 Idaho Falls, U.S.A. 43 30N 112 2W
45 Idar-Oberstein, Germany 49 43N 7 17E
73 Idd el Ghanam, Sudan 11 30N 24 25E
73 Idehan, Erg, Des., Libya 27 30N 12 0E
73 Idehan Marzuq, Dunes, Libya
    24 50N 13 51E
72 Idelès, Algeria 23 58N 5 58E
73 Idfu, Egypt 24 57N 32 50E
41 Idhi, Mt., Crete 35 15N 24 50E
41 Idhra, I., Greece 37 20N 23 25E
74 Idi Amin Dada, L., Uganda-Zaïre
    0 20s 29 35E
74 Idiofa, Zaïre 5 0s 19 45E
27 Idle, R., England 53 28N 0 58W
32 Idmiston, England 51 8N 1 43W
23 Idsworth, England 50 56N 0 56W
40 Ierzu, Italy 39 42N 9 35E
75 Ifanadiana, Madagascar 21 19s 47 50E
72 Ife, Nigeria 7 30N 4 31E
72 Iferouane, Niger 19 6N 8 30E
72 Ifni, Morocco 29 15N 10 0W
61 Igarka, U.S.S.R. 67 25N 87 20E
48 Igbetti, Nigeria 8 44N 4 8E
49 Iggesund, Sweden 61 43N 17 6E
40 Iglesias, Sardinia, Italy 39 21N 8 33E
94 Ignace, Canada 49 30N 91 40W
94 Iguala, Mexico 18 30N 99 15W
99 Iguape, Brazil 24 50s 47 45W
99 Iguassu, R. & Falls, Brazil
    25 30s 54 30W
99 Iguatú, Brazil 6 8s 39 15W
74 Iguéla, Gabon 2 5s 9 16E
48 Ii, & R., Finland 65 15N 25 30E
48 Iisalmi, Finland 63 35N 27 12E
72 Ijebu Ode, Nigeria 7 0N 3 58E
44 Ijmuiden, Netherlands 52 28N 4 35E
44 Ijsselmeer, Netherlands 52 45N 5 15E
41 Ikaria, I., Greece 37 35N 26 10E
67 Ikeda, Japan 34 0N 133 56E
67 Ilagan, Philippines 17 0N 121 58E
99 Ilapel, Chile 31 30s 71 0W
41 Ilawa, Poland 53 40N 19 31E
43 Ile de France, Prov., Fr. 49 0N 2 30E
43 Ile Rousse, France 42 35N 8 50E
74 Ilebo (Port Francqui), Zaïre 4 17s 20 47E
60 Ilek, R., U.S.S.R. 51 0N 55 15E
24 Ilfracombe, England 51 13N 4 8W
82 Ilfracombe, Australia 23 30s 144 28E
99 Ilhéus, Brazil 14 44s 39 18W
66 Ili, R., Sinkiang, China 43 20N 81 0E
66 Ili, R., U.S.S.R. 44 10N 77 25E
60 Ilich, U.S.S.R. 41 0N 68 20E
41 Iliodhromia I., Greece 39 10N 23 45E
72 Ilizi, Algeria 26 37N 8 54E
22 Ilkeston, England 52 59N 1 18W
26 Ilkley, England 53 55N 1 50W
42 Ille-et-Vilaine, Dépt., Fr. 48 22N 1 55W
45 Iller, R., Germany 47 48N 10 7E
98 Illmani, Mt., Bolivia 16 20s 67 40W
92 Illinois, st., & R., U.S.A. 40 15N 90 0W
61 Ilmen, L., U.S.S.R. 58 20N 31 28E
24 Ilminster, England 50 55N 2 56W
67 Iloilo, Philippines 10 40N 122 38E
72 Ilorin, Nigeria 8 30N 4 23E
50 Imandra, L., U.S.S.R. 67 40N 33 0E
62 Imabari, Japan 34 4N 133 0E
45 Immenstadt, Germany 47 33N 10 14E
27 Immingham, England 53 39N 0 13W
40 Imola, Italy 44 20N 11 40E
74 Impfondo, Congo (Fr.) 1 35N 18 10E
65 Imphal, India 24 15N 94 0E
41 Imroz, I., see Gökçeada
72 In Belbel, Algeria 27 55N 1 12E
72 In Gall, Niger 16 58N 6 57E
72 In Salah, see Ain Salah
67 Ina, Japan 35 56N 138 0E
84 Inangahua Junc., N.Z. 41 50s 171 52E
48 Inari, L., Finland 69 0N 28 0E
26 Ince, England 53 32N 2 38W
31 Ince, C., Turkey 42 2N 35 0E
31 Inchcape Rock, Scotland 56 26N 2 24W
67 Inchinomiya, Japan 35 20N 136 40E
67 Inchon, Korea 37 30N 126 30E
31 Inchture, Scotland 56 26N 3 8W
75 Incomati, R., Mozam. 25 13s 32 26E
30 Indaal, L., Scotland 55 44N 6 20W
48 Indals, R., Sweden 62 40N 16 50E
65 Indaw, Burma 24 10N 96 10E
88 Indian Head, Canada 50 32N 103 35W
5 Indian Ocean 10 0s 70 0E
91 Indian River, & Inlet, U.S.A.
    28 40N 80 30W
64–65 India, Asia 22 0N 78 0E
92 Indiana, st., U.S.A. 40 0N 86 0W
91 Indianapolis, U.S.A. 39 48N 86 15W
61 Indigirka, R., U.S.S.R. 69 10N 147 20E
68 Indonesia, S.E. Asia 0 0 110 0E
64 Indore, India 22 42N 75 53E
64 Indravati, R., India 19 12N 81 30E
42 Indre, Dépt., France 47 2N 1 33E
42 Indre-et-Loire, Dépt., Fr. 47 12N 0 43E
64 Indus, R. & Delta, Pak. 24 30N 65 30E
76 Indwe, S. Africa 31 28s 27 24E
51 Inebolu, Turkey 41 58N 33 58E
74 Ingende, Zaïre 0 12s 18 57E
82 Ingeniero Jacobacci 22 20s 146 0E
26 Ingleborough, Mt. Eng. 54 10N 2 35W
83 Inglewood, Australia 28 30s 151 2E
84 Inglewood, New Zealand 39 9s 174 14E
48 Ingólfshodi, Iceland 63 48N 16 40W
46 Ingolstadt, Germany 48 47N 11 20E
93 Ingonish, Canada 46 42N 60 25W
75 Inhambane, Mozambique 24 0s 35 45E

13

75 Inhamingo, Mozambique 18 25s 35 0e
75 Inharrime, Mozambique 24 25n 35 1e
36 Inishfree, Bay, Ireland 55 4n 8 20w
35 Inishkea, Is., Ireland 54 7n 10 13w
34 Inishmaan, I., Ireland 53 5n 9 35w
34 Inishmore I., Ireland 53 8n 9 45w
35 Inishturk I., Ireland 53 43n 10 8w
35 Inistioge, Ireland 52 30n 7 5w
83 Injune, Australia 25 48s 148 30e
65 Inle Lake, Burma 20 30n 96 55e
46 Inn, R., Austria-Ger. 47 16n 11 0e
30 Innellan, Scotland 55 54n 4 58w
32 Inner Hebrides, Scotland 56 40n 6 50w
66 Inner Mongolia, Autonomous Reg.,
   China 42 0n 111 0e
32 Inner Sd., Scotland 57 30n 5 55w
31 Innerleithen, Scotland 55 37n 3 6w
45 Innertkirchen, Switzerland 46 43n 8 16e
35 Inniscrone, Ireland 54 13n 9 5w
88 Innisfail, Canada 52 0n 114 0w
82 Innisfail, Australia 17 32s 146 5e
34 Innishannon, Ireland 51 46n 8 40w
45 Innsbruck, Austria 47 12n 11 20e
74 Inongo, Zaïre 1 50s 18 22e
47 Inowroclaw, Poland 52 56n 18 20e
33 Insch, Scotland 57 20n 2 39w
65 Insein, Burma 16 45n 95 30e
45 Interlaken, Switzerland 46 42n 7 53e
88 Inuvik, Canada 68 2n 135 30w
36 Inver, & B., Ireland 54 40n 8 16w
33 Inverallochy, Scotland 57 40n 1 56w
30 Inveraray, Scotland 56 14n 5 4w
33 Inverbervie, Scotland 56 50n 2 17w
84 Invercargill, N.Z. 46 28s 168 28e
83 Inverell, Australia 29 50s 151 0e
33 Invergordon, Scotland 57 42n 4 10w
31 Invergowrie, Scotland 56 29n 3 5w
31 Inverkeilor, Scotland 56 38n 2 33w
31 Inverkeithing, Scotland 56 2n 3 24w
93 Inverness, Canada 46 20n 60 15w
33 Inverness, Scotland 57 28n 4 12w
32 Invershiel, Scotland 57 13n 5 25w
33 Inverurie, Scotland 57 17n 2 22w
80 Investigator Group, Australia
   33 42s 134 25e
83 Investigator Str., Austral. 35 30s 137 0e
60 Inya, U.S.S.R. 50 40n 86 55e
75 Inyanga, Rhodesia 18 12s 32 40e
41 Ioannina, Greece 39 40n 20 52e
30 Iona I., Scotland 56 20n 6 30w
41 Ionian Is. & S., Greece 38 40n 20 0e
41 Ios I., Greece 36 42n 25 20e
91 Iowa, st., U.S.A. 42 15n 93 30w
91 Iowa City, U.S.A. 41 45n 91 40w
66 Ipin, China 29 15n 104 0e
68 Ipoh, Malaya 4 32n 101 0e
74 Ippy, Central Africa 6 5n 21 7e
23 Ipswich, England 52 4n 1 10e
83 Ipswich, Australia 27 38s 152 45e
98 Iquique, Chile 20 20s 70 5w
98 Iquitos, Peru 3 48s 73 12w
41 Iraklion (Candia), Crete 35 20n 25 10e
62 Iran (Persia), Asia 33 50n 54 0e
94 Irapuato, Mexico 20 50n 101 28w
62 Iraq, S.W. Asia 33 30n 45 0e
95 Irazu, Vol., Costa Rica 10 0n 83 43w
63 Irbid, Jordan 32 34n 35 50e
95 Ireland I., Bermudas 32 21n 64 52w
29 Ireland, Europe 53 0n 8 0w
29 Ireland, N., British Isles 54 40n 6 50w
61 Iret, U.S.S.R. 60 5n 154 5e
74 Iringa, Tanzania 7 50s 35 30e
94 Iriona, Honduras 16 0n 84 58w
18 Irish Sea, British Isles 53 50n 5 0w
61 Irkineyeva, U.S.S.R. 58 30n 97 0e
61 Irkutsk, U.S.S.R. 52 20n 104 0e
24 Irlam, England 53 26n 2 27w
83 Iron Baron, Australia 33 0s 137 0e
47 Iron Gate, Rum.-Y-slav. 44 43n 22 25e
83 Iron Knob, Australia 32 41s 137 0e
91 Iron Mt., U.S.A. 45 54n 88 0w
62 Ironbridge, England 52 38n 2 27w
65 Irrawaddy, R. & Delta, Burma
   16 0n 95 0e
61 Irthing, R., England 55 0n 2 37w
23 Irthlingborough, England 52 20n 0 37w
60 Irtysh, R., U.S.S.R. 59 0n 69 30e
37 Irun, Spain 43 20n 1 50w
30 Irvine, Scotland 55 37n 4 39w
36 Irvinestown, N. Ireland 54 28n 7 40w
83 Irymple, Australia 34 4s 142 1e
48 Isa Fjord, Iceland 66 10n 23 0w
48 Isafjördur, Iceland 66 10n 23 15w
74 Isangi, Zaïre 0 50n 24 10e
46 Isar, R., Germany 48 40n 12 30e
45 Ischia, I., Italy 40 46n 13 54e
43 Iseo, Italy 45 39n 10 2e
42 Isère, Dépt., France 45 25n 5 40e
60 Ishim, R., U.S.S.R. 56 15n 69 30e
67 Ishinomaki, Japan 38 26n 141 18e
64 Ishkuman, Kashmir 36 40n 73 45e
91 Ishpeming, U.S.A. 46 30n 87 40w
74 Isiolo, Kenya 0 19n 37 39e
76 Isiping Beach, S. Africa 30 0s 30 55e
74 Isiro (Paulis), Zaïre 2 53n 27 58e
61 Isitskoye, U.S.S.R. 60 55n 125 10e
51 Iskenderun & G., Turkey 36 48n 36 17e
33 Iskur R., Bulgaria 43 0n 24 0e
64 Islamabad, Pakistan 33 40n 73 20e
36 Island Magee, Pen., N. Ire. 54 50n 5 45w
30 Islay, I. & Sd., Scotland
   55 45n 6 15w
27 Isle of Axholme, England 53 33n 0 50w
26 Isle of Man, Br. Isles 54 10n 4 35w
95 Isle of Pines, Cuba 21 45n 82 50w

22 Isle of Purbeck, England 50 38n 2 0w
30 Isle of Whithorn, Scot. 54 42n 4 23w
22 Isle of Wight, Co., Eng. 50 40n 1 20w
92 Isle Royale, U.S.A. 48 0n 88 40w
73 Isma'iliya, Egypt 31 0n 32 0e
73 Isna, Egypt 25 12n 32 30e
51 Isnik Gölü, L., Turkey 40 30n 30 0e
74 Isoka, Zambia 10 10s 32 42e
62 Isparta, Turkey 37 30n 31 5e
63 Israel, S.W. Asia 32 0n 35 0e
43 Issoudun, France 47 0n 2 0e
60 Issyk Kul, L., U.S.S.R. 42 50n 77 30e
51 Istanbul, Turkey 41 1n 28 56e
40 Istra, Dist., Y-slav. 45 18n 13 50e
99 Itabira, Brazil 19 30s 43 10w
99 Itacoatiara, Brazil 3 0s 58 20w
40 Italy, Europe 42 0n 13 0e
22 Itchen, R., England 51 0n 1 20w
41 Ithaca, U.S.A. 42 28n 76 28w
41 Ithaki, Greece 38 25n 20 43e
67 Iturup I., U.S.S.R. 45 0n 148 0e
99 Ivai, R., Brazil 23 30s 53 20w
48 Ivalo, & R., Finland 68 38 27 35e
83 Ivanhoe, Australia 32 55s 144 20e
52 Ivanovo, U.S.S.R. 57 5n 41 0e
89 Ivigtut, Greenland 61 0n 47 30w
37 Iviza, & I., see Ibiza
72 Ivory Coast, Africa 7 0n 5 0w
43 Ivrea, Italy 45 30n 7 50e
43 Ivry, France 48 55n 1 30e
67 Iwakuni, Japan 34 10n 132 10e
67 Iwanuma, Japan 38 7n 140 58e
67 Iwate, Pref., Japan 39 30n 140 20e
76 Ixopo, S. Africa 30 10s 30 5e
44 Izegem, Belgium 50 55n 3 13e
50 Izhevsk, U.S.S.R. 56 50n 53 0e
47 Izmail, U.S.S.R. 45 21n 28 40e
41 Izmir, & G., Turkey 38 21n 27 8e
51 Izmit, Turkey 40 45n 29 50e
51 Izr'a, Syria 32 52n 36 15e
67 Izumo, Japan 35 25n 133 0e

J

62 Jabal At Tuwaiq, mts., Saudi Arabia
   22 30n 46 0e
62 Jabal Shammar, Mts., Saudi Arabia
   27 30n 42 30e
64 Jabalpur, India 23 10n 80 0e
41 Jablanica, mts., Albania 41 20n 20 30e
46 Jablonec, Cz-slov. 50 43n 15 10e
62 Jabrin, Saudi Arabia 23 10n 48 32e
62 Jaca, Spain 42 35n 0 32w
99 Jachal, Argentina 30 5s 69 10w
83 Jackson, Australia 26 46n 149 35e
84 Jackson B., N.Z. 43 58s 168 40e
92 Jackson, Mich., U.S.A. 42 15n 84 29w
91 Jackson, Miss., U.S.A.
   32 20n 90 13w
91 Jackson, Tenn., U.S.A. 35 36n 88 45w
84 Jacksons, New Zealand 42 46s 171 33e
91 Jacksonville Fla., U.S.A.
   30 28n 81 40w
91 Jacksonville, Ill., U.S.A. 39 44n 90 16w
95 Jacmel, Haiti 18 15n 72 35w
64 Jacobabad, Pakistan 28 20n 68 27e
63 Jacob's Well, Jordan 32 12n 35 17e
64 Jacuí, R., Brazil 30 0s 52 0w
73 Jado, Libya 32 0n 12 0e
37 Jadotville, see Likasi
37 Jaén, Spain 37 48n 3 43w
63 Jaffa, see Tel Aviv-Jaffa
64 Jaffna, Sri Lanka 9 45n 80 0e
64 Jagdalpur, India 19 1n 82 1e
76 Jagersfontein, S. Africa 29 40s 25 28e
73 Jaghbub, Libya 29 42n 24 38e
64 Jagraon, India 30 40n 75 40e
62 Jahrum, Iran 28 27n 53 30e
68 Jailolo Passage, Indonesia
   0 30n 129 20e
64 Jaipur, India 27 0n 75 50e
72 Jajere, Nigeria 11 58n 10 25e
68 Jakarta, Indonesia 6 9s 106 49e
94 Jalapa Enriquez, Mexico 19 32n 96 55w
64 Jalgaon, India 20 57n 76 30e
64 Jalna, India 19 45n 75 50e
37 Jalon, R., Spain 41 26n 1 35w
64 Jalpaiguri, India 26 15n 88 30e
95 Jamaica, I., West Indies 18 15n 77 30w
65 Jamalpur, India 25 20n 86 30e
68 Jambi, Indonesia 1 40s 103 35e
89 James, B., Canada 53 30n 81 0w
90 James, R., S. Dak., U.S.A.
   43 40n 97 40w
83 James Ras., Australia 24 10s 132 40e
83 Jamestown, Australia 33 11s 138 30e
90 Jamestown, North Dakota, U.S.A.
   46 58n 98 38w
92 Jamestown, N.Y., U.S.A. 42 8n 79 17w
64 Jamkhandi, India 16 30n 75 5e
64 Jammu, India 32 50n 74 58e
64 Jammu and Kashmir, Asia 34 0n 77 0e
64 Jamnagar, India 22 32n 70 5e
64 Jamshedpur, India 22 50n 86 10e
48 Jämtland, Co., Sweden 62 45n 14 30e
100 Jan Mayen I., Arctic Oc. 71 0n 8 0w
64 Jandola, Pakistan 33 30n 71 57e
83 Jandowae, Australia 26 40s 151 2e
91 Janesville, U.S.A. 42 48n 88 59w
63 Janin, Jordan 32 28n 35 18e
99 Januaria, Brazil 15 30s 44 30w
64 Jaora, India 23 42n 75 5e
67 Japan, E. Asia 36 0n 138 0e
67 Japan Sea, E. Asia 40 0n 134 30e
37 Jarama, R., Spain 40 50n 3 30w
63 Jarash, Jordan 32 17n 35 54e

62 Jarir, Wadi, Si. Arabia 24 10n 42 0e
47 Jaroslaw, Poland 50 0n 22 40e
27 Jarrow, England 54 59n 1 30w
65 Jarwa, India 27 52n 82 36e
62 Jask, Iran 25 52n 57 50e
47 Jaslo, Poland 49 45n 21 30e
47 Jaszbereny, Hungary 47 37n 19 58e
37 Jativa, Spain 39 1n 0 32w
98 Jauja, Peru 11 45s 75 25w
65 Jaunpur, India 25 42n 82 55e
68 Java I., Indonesia 7 0s 110 0e
68 Java Sea, Indonesia 5 0s 111 30e
68 Jayapura, Indonesia 2 28s 140 38e
65 Jaynagar, India 26 43n 86 9e
62 Jeb Aneiza, Mt., Iraq 32 10n 39 20e
73 Jebel Abyad, Plat. of, Sudan
   17 30n 28 40e
63 Jebel 'Ajlun, mts., Jordan 32 20n 35 50e
63 Jebel el Leja, Syria 33 17n 36 5e
62 Jebel Ibrahim, mt., Si. Arabia
   20 26n 41 15e
63 Jebel Sanmini, mt., Lebanon
   33 56n 35 5e
31 Jedburgh, Scotland 55 29n 2 32w
47 Jedrzejów, Poland 50 35n 20 15e
91 Jefferson City, U.S.A. 38 40n 92 18w
91 Jeffersonville, U.S.A. 38 22n 85 49w
72 Jega, Nigeria 12 15n 4 23e
46 Jelenia Góra, Poland 50 50n 15 45e
49 Jelgava, U.S.S.R. 56 39n 23 45e
44 Jemeppe, Belgium 50 37n 5 29e
46 Jena, Germany 51 0n 11 30e
74 Jennette I., U.S.S.R. 77 25n 157 20e
91 Jennings, U.S.A. 30 15n 92 45w
83 Jeparit, Australia 36 10s 142 5e
64 Jericho, Australia 23 38s 146 6e
63 Jericho, Jordan 31 51n 35 28e
83 Jerilderie, Australia 35 20s 145 40e
93 Jersey City, U.S.A. 40 50n 74 10w
42 Jersey I., Channel Is. 49 17n 2 10w
63 Jerusalem, Israel 31 47n 35 15e
68 Jesselton, see Kota Kinabalu
65 Jessore, Bangladesh 23 12n 89 10e
44 Jette, Belgium 50 52n 4 18e
65 Jeypore, India 18 45n 82 32e
63 Jezziné, Lebanon 33 33n 35 34e
64 Jhal Jhao, Pakistan 26 20n 65 30e
64 Jhalawar, India 24 40n 76 10e
64 Jhang Maghiana, Pak. 31 8n 72 15e
64 Jhansi, India 25 40n 78 49e
65 Jharsuguda, India 21 50n 84 5e
64 Jhelum, & R., Pak. 32 58n 73 45e
65 Jiachan, China 31 40n 81 5e
62 Jidda, Saudi Arabia 21 30n 39 0e
64 Jihlava, & R., Cz-slov. 49 21n 15 38e
94 Jimenez, Mexico 27 10n 104 55w
73 Jima, Ethiopia 7 50n 37 0e
73 Jindabyne, Australia 36 30s 148 35e
74 Jinja, Uganda 0 30n 33 15e
99 Joao Pessôa, Brazil 7 12s 35 0w
42 Jobourg, France 49 49n 1 54w
64 Jodhpur, India 26 10n 73 0e
50 Joensuu, Finland 62 40n 29 49e
47 Joeuf, France 49 12n 6 0e
76 Johannesburg, S. Africa 26 15s 28 4e
33 John o'Groats, Scotland 58 38n 3 5w
91 Johnston City, U.S.A. 36 29n 82 20w
74 Johnston Falls, see Mambilima
30 Johnstone. Scotland 55 50n 4 30w
35 Johnstown, Ireland 52 46n 7 34w
92 Johnstown, U.S.A. 40 20n 78 52w
68 Johor Baharu, Malaya 1 35n 103 40e
43 Joigny, France 48 0n 3 25e
48 Jokkmokk, Sweden 66 32n 19 56e
64 Joilet, U.S.A. 41 30n 88 0w
89 Joliette, Canada 46 1n 73 40w
68 Jolo I., Philippines 6 3n 121 3e
68 Jonesboro, U.S.A. 35 50n 90 45w
49 Jönköping, Sweden 57 48n 14 12e
88 Jonquière, Canada 48 27n 71 10w
91 Joplin, U.S.A. 36 58n 94 30w
63 Jordan, R., Jordan-Israel 32 15n 35 32e
62 Jordan, S.W. Asia 32 0n 37 0e
65 Jorhat, India 26 42n 94 15e
48 Jörn, Sweden 65 8n 20 0e
72 Jos, Nigeria 9 53n 8 51e
80 Joseph Bonaparte G., Australia
   13 45s 129 0e
49 Jötunheimen, Mts., Nor. 61 35n 8 20e
63 Jouaïya, Lebanon 33 14n 35 20e
63 Joub Jennine, Lebanon 33 38n 35 48e
88 Juan de Fuca Str., North America
   48 30n 124 30w
75 Juan de Nova I., Madagascar
   17 10s 43 45e
99 Juan Fernandez, I., Pacific Ocean
   33 15s 79 0w
99 Juazeiro, Brazil 9 30s 40 30w
73 Juba, Sudan 5 0n 31 35e
70 Juba, R., East Africa 1 45n 42 42e
72 Juby, C., Morocco 27 50n 13 45w
37 Júcar, R., Spain 40 5n 2 10w
94 Juchitan, Mexico 16 30n 95 15w
74 Judaea, Wilderness of, Jordan
   31 25n 35 18e
63 Judaean Hills, Jordan 31 45n 35 10e
66 Juikin, China 26 5n 115 25e
99 Juiz de Fora, Brazil 21 55s 43 0w
99 Jujuy, Argentina 24 5s 65 30w
82 Julia Creek, Australia 20 40s 141 55e
46 Julian Alps, Y-slav. 46 10n 13 50e
89 Julianehaab Greenland 60 40n 45 40w
44 Jülich, Germany 50 56n 6 20e

64 Jullundur, India 31 20n 75 40e
62 Jumaima, Saudi Arabia 29 40n 43 37e
44 Jumet, Belgium 50 28n 4 27e
64 Jumna, R., see Yamuna
64 Junagadh, India 21 34n 70 30e
91 Junction City, U.S.A. 39 5n 96 58w
82 Jundah, Australia 24 56s 143 5e
88 Juneau, Alaska 58 13n 134 0w
83 Junee, Australia 34 54s 147 36e
45 Jungfrau, mt., Switz. 46 30n 7 50e
99 Junin, Argentina 34 25s 60 50w
42 Jura, Dépt., France 46 46n 5 40e
30 Jura, I. & Sd., Scotland 55 57n 5 55w
43 Jura Mts., France-Switz. 46 40n 6 5e
80 Jurien Bay, Australia 30 20s 115 0e
98 Juruá, R., Brazil 6 0s 68 0w
43 Jussey, France 47 50n 5 55e
73 J'Uweinat, mt., Egypt 22 40n 25 0e
49 Jylland (Jutland), Den. 56 10n 9 0e
48 Jyvaskyla, Finland 62 12n 25 47e

K

64 K2 Mt., Kashmir 36 0n 77 0e
68 Kabaena, I., Indonesia 5 15s 122 0e
72 Kabala, Sierra Leone 9 38n 11 37w
74 Kabale, Uganda 1 11s 30 0e
74 Kabalo, Zaïre 6 0s 27 0e
74 Kabambare, Zaïre 4 40s 27 44e
51 Kabardino-Balkar, A.S.S.R., U.S.S.R.
   43 30n 43 30e
74 Kabarega Falls, Uganda 2 24n 31 55e
74 Kabinda, Zaïre 6 3s 24 20e
75 Kabompo, R., Zambia 13 30s 24 30e
74 Kabongo, Zaïre 7 18s 25 40e
62 Kabra, Australia 23 25s 150 25e
64 Kabul, & R., Afghanistan 34 30n 69 13e
75 Kabwe, Zambia 13 39s 28 38e
60 Kachiry, U.S.S.R. 53 20n 75 55e
72 Kaddi, Nigeria 13 40n 5 40e
83 Kadina, Australia 33 58s 137 48e
52 Kadiyevka, U.S.S.R. 48 17n 38 17e
73 Kadugli, Sudan 11 0n 29 45e
72 Kaele, Cameroon 10 15n 14 15e
73 Kaesong, Korea 38 0n 126 40e
72 Kafakumba, Zaïre 9 40s 23 40e
51 Kafan, U.S.S.R. 39 10n 46 15e
72 Kafanchan, Nigeria 9 49n 8 20e
63 Kafr Kanna, Israel 32 45n 35 20e
75 Kafue, R., Zambia 15 45s 28 25e
74 Kafulwe, Zambia 9 0s 29 10e
60 Kagan, U.S.S.R. 39 50n 64 30e
47 Kagul, U.S.S.R. 45 50n 28 15e
67 Kagoshima, & Pref., Japan
   31 48n 130 40e
74 Kahama, Tanzania 3 50s 32 25e
83 Kahmoomulga, Austral. 25 58s 145 51e
72 Kaiama, Nigeria 9 36n 4 1e
84 Kaiapoi, New Zealand 43 24s 172 40e
98 Kaieteur Falls Fs., Guyana
   5 5n 59 0w
66 Kaifeng, China 34 45n 114 40e
84 Kaikohe, New Zealand 35 25s 173 49e
84 Kaikoura, & Ra., N.Z. 42 23s 173 43e
84 Kailas Ra., Tibet 31 0n 82 0e
84 Kaimanawa Mts., N.Z. 39 0s 176 15e
84 Kaipara Hr., N.Z. 36 22s 174 10e
47 Kaiserslautern, Germany 49 29n 7 46e
84 Kaitaia, New Zealand 35 7s 173 17e
84 Kaitangata, N.Z. 46 18s 170 10e
92 Kajaani, Finland 64 15n 27 45e
82 Kajabbi, Australia 20 0s 140 0e
73 Kajo Kaji, Sudan 3 58n 31 40e
84 Kakanui, Mts., N.Z. 45 15s 170 35e
64 Kakhovka Res., U.S.S.R. 46 30n 33 50e
64 Kalabagh, Pakistan 30 1n 71 28e
41 Kalábaka, Greece 39 40n 21 35e
75 Kalabo, Zambia 14 58s 22 33e
52 Kalach, U.S.S.R. 50 30n 41 10e
65 Kaladan, R., Burma 21 15n 93 0e
75 Kalahari, des., Africa 23 0s 22 0e
51 Kalakan, U.S.S.R. 55 20n 116 55e
41 Kalamata, Greece 37 2n 22 7e
92 Kalamazoo, U.S.A. 42 15n 85 35w
92 Kalamazoo, R., U.S.A. 42 35n 86 0w
63 Kalat, Pakistan 29 5n 66 32e
73 Kalbuh, Wadi, Oman 22 0n 57 50e
74 Kalemie (Albertville), Zaïre 5 55s 29 9e
65 Kalewa, Burma 23 5n 94 20e
48 Kalfafellsstadur, Iceland 64 11n 15 45w
66 Kalgan, China 40 50n 114 50e
80 Kalgoorlie, Australia 30 40s 121 28e
52 Kaliakra, C., Bulgaria 43 23n 28 26e
74 Kalima, Zaïre 2 38s 26 37e
68 Kalimantan, prov., Indonesia
   0 30s 115 0e
52 Kalinin, U.S.S.R. 56 47n 35 55e
51 Kalinina, U.S.S.R. 60 0n 108 10e
49 Kaliningrad, U.S.S.R. 54 42n 20 30e
90 Kalispell, U.S.A. 48 18n 114 27w
47 Kalisz, Poland 51 48n 18 5e
48 Kaliua, Tanzania 5 0s 31 48e
48 Kalix, R., Sweden 67 30n 21 15e
53 Kallia, Jordan 31 46n 35 29e
51 Kallsjön, L., Sweden 63 35n 13 10e
49 Kalmar, & Co., Sweden 56 42n 16 20e
51 Kalmyk, A.S.S.R., U.S.S.R.
   46 30n 45 30e
64 Kalmykovo, U.S.S.R. 49 0n 51 50e
47 Kalocsa, Hungary 46 31n 18 58e
75 Kalomo, Zambia 16 54s 26 30e
46 Kalovy Vary, Cz-slov. 50 15n 12 55e
65 Kalutara, Sri Lanka 6 35n 80 0e

52 Kalyazin, U.S.S.R. 57 18n 37 45e
50 Kama, R., U.S.S.R. 60 0n 56 0e
67 Kamaishi, Japan 39 20n 142 0e
62 Kamaran I., Red Sea 15 28n 42 30e
61 Kamchatka, Pen., U.S.S.R. 56 0n 160
60 Kamen, U.S.S.R. 53 50n 81 30e
51 Kamenets-Podolski, U.S.S.R.
   48 45n 26 10e
47 Kamenka Bugskaya, Pol. 50 8n 24 1
60 Kamensk-Uralskiy, U.S.S.R.
   56 30n 62 50e
52 Kamensk Shakhtinskiy, U.S.S.R.
   48 23n 40 20e
61 Kamenskoye, U.S.S.R. 62 40n 165 0
30 Kames, Scotland 55 54n 5 15w
74 Kamina, Zaïre 8 40s 25 0e
88 Kamloops, Canada 50 40n 120 20w
44 Kamp Lintfort, Ger. 51 30n 6 38e
74 Kampala, Uganda 0 20n 32 30e
44 Kampen, Netherlands 52 34n 5 54e
68 Kampot, Cambodia 10 30n 104 0e
88 Kamsack, Canada 51 40n 102 0w
52 Kamyshin, U.S.S.R. 50 10n 45 30e
67 Kanagawa, Pref., Japan
   35 25n 139 20e
74 Kananga (Luluabourg), Zaïre
   5 55s 22 18e
50 Kanash, U.S.S.R. 55 48n 47 32e
67 Kanazawa, Japan 36 40n 136 48e
65 Kanchenjunga, Mt., Nepal
   27 45n 88 15e
66 Kanchow, China 25 50n 114 45e
74 Kanda Kanda, Zaïre 6 55s 23 33e
64 Kandahar, Afghanistan 31 42n 65 40e
64 Kandahar, Prov., Afghan 31 0n 65 0e
50 Kandalaksha, U.S.S.R. 67 3n 32 30e
64 Kandalu, Afghanistan 29 55n 63 20e
64 Kandavu I., Fiji Is. 19 0s 178 15e
45 Kandersteg, Switzerland 46 28n 7 40e
72 Kandi, Benin 11 15n 3 5e
64 Kandla, India 23 0n 70 7e
83 Kandos, Australia 32 55s 150 0e
65 Kandy, Sri Lanka 7 20n 80 35e
83 Kangaroo I., Australia 35 45s 137 15e
74 Kango, Gabon 0 11n 10 5e
61 Kangotovo, U.S.S.R. 63 30n 87 40e
89 Kaniapiskau, R., Can. 56 20n 68 40w
92 Kankakee, U.S.A. 41 7n 87 50w
72 Kankan, Guinea 10 27n 9 15w
65 Kanker, India 20 10n 81 40e
66 Kan-kiang, R., China 27 0n 115 0e
72 Kannod, India 22 45n 76 40e
72 Kano, Nigeria 11 58n 8 20e
80 Kanowna, Australia 30 30s 121 37e
64 Kanpur, India 26 30n 80 23e
90 Kansas, st., & R., U.S.A.
   38 30n 98 30w
91 Kansas City, U.S.A. 39 4n 94 37w
66 Kansen, China 37 45n 92 35e
61 Kansk, U.S.S.R. 56 20n 95 30e
66 Kansu, Prov., China 39 0n 105 0e
66 Kantse, China 31 30n 100 25e
34 Kanturk, Ireland 52 11n 8 52w
75 Kanye, Botswana 24 58s 25 25e
75 Kaoko Otavi, S.W. Afr. 18 12s 13 45e
72 Kaolack, Sénégal 14 10n 15 47w
74 Kapanga, Zaïre 8 15s 22 32e
47 Kapchagai, U.S.S.R. 44 10n 77 25e
46 Kapela, Mts., Y-slav. 44 40n 15 40e
84 Kapiti I., New Zealand
   40 45s 174 55e
47 Kaposvár, Hungary 46 25n 17 40e
68 Kapuas, R., Indon. 0 5s 110 30e
83 Kapunda, Australia 34 20s 138 57e
80 Kapuni, New Zealand 39 30s 174 5e
92 Kapuskasing, Canada 49 25n 82 25w
60 Kara, U.S.S.R. 69 15n 65 26e
60 Kara Bogaz Gol., U.S.S.R.
   41 30n 53 30e
60 Kara-Kalpak, A.S.S.R., U.S.S.R.
   42 0n 60 0e
60 Kara Kum, Des., U.S.S.R.
   39 40n 60 0e
60 Kara Sea, U.S.S.R. 75 0n 62 0e
64 Karachi, Pakistan 25 0n 67 0e
60 Karaganda, U.S.S.R. 49 50n 73 10e
64 Karaikal, India 10 55n 79 50e
64 Karaikkudi, India 10 0n 78 45e
64 Karakoram Ra. & P., India
   35 0n 78 0e
51 Karaköse (Agri), Turkey 39 45n 43 0e
84 Karamea Bight, N.Z. 41 40s 172 0e
76 Karasburg, S.W. Africa 28 0s 18 44e
60 Karasino, U.S.S.R. 66 50n 86 50e
60 Karauzyak, U.S.S.R. 43 35n 59 25e
62 Karbala, Iraq 32 47n 44 2e
47 Karcag, Hungary 47 20n 21 0e
41 Karditsa, Greece 39 20n 21 55e
49 Kardla, U.S.S.R. 58 58n 22 46e
73 Kareima, Sudan 18 35n 31 50e
50 Karelian A.S.S.R., U.S.S.R.
   64 0n 34 0e
74 Karema, Tanzania 6 45s 30 30e
60 Kargat, U.S.S.R. 55 20n 80 30e
75 Kariba Gorge & Lake, Africa
   16 30s 27 15e
68 Karimata Str., Indonesia 2 0s 109 0e
64 Karimnagar, India 18 28n 79 5e
60 Karkaralinsk, U.S.S.R. 49 27n 75 37e
82 Karkar I., Papua N.G. 4 40s 146 0e
62 Karkheh, R., Iran 33 0n 47 30e
51 Karkinitsk, Gulf of, U.S.S.R.
   46 0n 33 0e

Karkur, Israel 32 28N 35 0E
Karl Marx Stadt (Chemnitz), Germany 50 49N 12 50E
Karlovac, Yugoslavia 45 26N 15 34E
Karlsborg, Sweden 58 30N 14 29E
Karlskroga, Sweden 59 21N 14 26E
Karlskrona, Sweden 56 13N 15 37E
Karlshamn, Sweden 56 17N 14 50E
Karlsruhe, Germany 49 3N 8 26E
Karlstad, Sweden 59 21N 13 20E
Karnai, India 29 35N 76 58E
Karnaphuli Reservoir, Bangladesh 22 40N 92 20E
Karnataka, st., India 14 0N 76 0E
Karnobat, Bulgaria 42 40N 27 0E
Karoonda, Australia 35 0s 140 5E
Karonga, Malawi 9 57s 33 55E
Karora, Sudan 17 44N 38 15E
Karpathos I., Greece 35 47N 27 10E
Karpinsk, U.S.S.R. 59 45N 59 45E
Karram R., India 32 45N 71 0E
Karreeberge, S. Africa 30 50s 22 0E
Kars, Turkey 40 36N 43 0E
Karsakpay, U.S.S.R. 47 55N 66 50E
Karshi, U.S.S.R. 39 5N 65 50E
Karst, Plat., Yugoslavia 45 35N 14 0E
Karshi, U.S.S.R. 39 5N 65 50E
Karsun, U.S.S.R. 54 10N 47 15E
Kartaly, U.S.S.R. 53 15N 60 50E
Karun, U.S.S.R. 54 10N 47 15E
Karungu, Tanzania 0 45s 34 10E
Karur, India 10 55N 78 5E
Karwar, India 14 55N 74 13E
Kasai, R., Zaïre 4 0s 19 30E
Kasama, Zambia 10 10s 31 12E
Kasanga, Tanzania 8 23s 31 12E
Kasangulu, Zaïre 4 15s 15 25E
Kasempa, Zambia 13 15s 25 43E
Kashan, Iran 34 5N 51 30E
Kashgar, China 39 30N 76 10E
Kashing, China 30 50N 120 45E
Kashmir & Jammu, st., Asia 34 45N 76 0E
Kasimov, U.S.S.R. 54 58N 41 28E
Kaskinen (Kaskö), Finland 62 22N 21 13E
Kaslo, Canada 49 58N 117 0w
Kasongo, Zaïre 4 18s 26 40E
Kasongo-Lunda, Zaïre 6 32s 16 59E
Kassal, Germany 51 22N 9 30E
Kassala, Sudan 15 35N 36 27E
Kastamonu, Turkey 41 35N 34 2E
Kastoria, Greece 40 31N 21 18E
Kasulu, Tanzania 4 29s 30 7E
Katamatite, Australia 36 5s 145 40E
Katanga, reg., see Shaba
Katangi, India 21 56N 79 50E
Katanning, Australia 33 40s 117 32E
Katesbridge, Ireland 54 18N 6 8w
Katha, Burma 24 16N 96 13E
Katherine, Australia 14 30s 132 15E
Kathgotlam, India. see Haldwani
Katihar, India 25 40N 87 40E
Katmandu, Nepal 27 58N 85 23E
Katombora, Zambia 18 0s 25 30E
Katoomba (Blue Mountains), Australia 33 42s 150 18E
Katowice, Poland 50 18N 19 2E
Katrine, L., Scotland 56 15N 4 30w
Katrineholm, Sweden 59 3N 16 12E
Katsina, Nigeria 13 0N 7 35E
Katsuura, Japan 35 10N 140 20E
Kattegat, Europe 56 50N 11 15E
Katwijk-aan-Zee, Neth. 52 12N 4 25E
Katylyktakh, U.S.S.R. 68 55N 134 10E
Kauai, I., Hawaiian Is. 22 0N 159 40w
Kauliranta, Finland 66 28N 23 46E
Kaunas, U.S.S.R. 54 54N 23 54E
Kaura Namoda, Nigeria 12 40N 6 30E
Kautokeino, Norway 69 0N 23 8E
Kaválla, Greece 41 0N 24 4E
Kavieng, Papua N.G. 3 0s 151 0E
Kawagoe, Japan 36 0N 139 30E
Kawardha, India 21 58N 81 15E
Kawasaki, Japan 35 40N 139 35E
Kawerau, New Zealand 38 5s 176 50E
Kawhia Hr., New Zealand 38 5s 174 40E
Kawthoolei, state, Burma 18 0N 97 0E
Kayah, State, Burma 19 0N 97 30E
Kayes, Mali 14 15N 11 27w
Kayseri, Turkey 38 52N 35 30E
Kazache, U.S.S.R. 70 50N 137 0E
Kazakhstan, S.S.R., U.S.S.R. 49 0N 70 0E
Kazan, U.S.S.R. 55 48N 49 0E
Kazanluk, Bulgaria 42 39N 25 27E
Kazanskaya, U.S.S.R. 49 33N 41 25E
Kazatin, U.S.S.R. 49 45N 28 35E
Kazerun, Iran 29 30N 51 40E
Kazbek Mt., U.S.S.R. 42 48N 44 29E
Kazym R., U.S.S.R. 63 30N 69 2E
Ke-Macina Mali 14 5N 5 20w
Kea, I., Greece 37 36N 24 22E
Keady, N. Ireland 54 15N 6 41w
Keal, Loch na, Scotland 56 29N 6 5w
Kebnekaise, Mt., Sweden 68 0N 18 30E
Kediri, Indonesia 7 44s 112 5E
Kedougou, Sénégal 12 35N 12 10w
Keele, England 53 2N 2 17w
Keeling (Chilung), China 25 10N 121 45E
Keene, U.S.A. 42 58N 72 16w
Keetmanshoop, S.W. Africa 26 30s 18 5E
Keewatin, Terr., Canada 63 20N 88 30w

Kefallinia (Cephalonia), I., Greece 38 15N 20 33E
Kefar Sava, Israel 32 10N 34 55E
Keffi, Nigeria 8 58N 7 47E
Keflavik, Iceland 64 2N 22 35w
Kehl, Germany 48 34N 7 50E
Keighley, England 53 52N 1 54w
Keimoes, S. Africa 28 40s 20 55E
Keith, Scotland 57 33N 2 57w
Kelang, Malaya 3 0N 101 35E
Kelkit R., Turkey 40 9N 38 0E
Kellas, Scotland 57 33N 3 24w
Kellé, Congo (Fr.) 0 7s 14 20E
Kellé, Niger 14 18N 10 10E
Kellerberrin, Australia 31 34N 117 42E
Kellogg, U.S.A. 47 37N 116 13w
Kells, Ireland 52 33N 7 18w
Kells, see Ceannus Mor
Kells, N. Ireland 54 49N 6 14w
Kelowna, Canada 49 56N 119 26w
Kelsale, England 52 15N 1 30E
Kelsall, England 53 14N 2 44w
Kelso, New Zealand 45 53s 169 16E
Kelso, Scotland 55 37N 2 27w
Keluang, Malaya 1 50N 103 30E
Kelvedon, England 51 50N 0 43E
Kem, & R., U.S.S.R. 65 0N 34 40E
Kemerovo, U.S.S.R. 55 35N 86 7E
Kemi & R., Finland 65 48N 24 43E
Kemijärvi, Finland 66 42N 27 30E
Kemnay, Scotland 57 14N 2 28w
Kempsey, Australia 31 5N 152 53E
Kempston, England 52 7N 0 30w
Kempten, Germany 47 45N 10 20E
Kenali, Indonesia 4 0s 122 35E
Kenema, Sierra Leone 7 55N 11 13w
Keng Tawng, Burma 20 50N 98 25E
Keng Tung, Burma 21 0N 99 30E
Kenhardt, S. Africa 29 28s 21 6E
Kenilworth, England 52 21N 1 34w
Kenitra, Morocco 34 15N 6 40w
Kenmare, & R., Ireland 51 53N 9 35w
Kenmore, R., U.S.A. 45 0N 69 50w
Kennedy, C., (C. Canaveral), U.S.A. 28 3N 80 31E
Kennewick, U.S.A. 46 12N 119 8w
Keno Hill, Canada 64 0N 135 40w
Kenogami, R., Canada 50 0N 85 0w
Kenora, Canada 49 48N 94 20w
Kenosha, U.S.A. 42 40N 87 49w
Kent, Co., England 51 10N 0 45E
Kentisbeare, England 50 51N 3 18w
Kentucky, R., U.S.A. 37 30N 83 30w
Kentucky, st., U.S.A. 37 20N 85 0w
Kentville, Canada 45 6N 64 29w
Kenya, Africa 0 30s 38 30E
Kenya, Mt., Kenya 0 12s 37 30E
Keokuk, U.S.A. 40 27N 91 28w
Kerala, st., India 11 0N 77 0E
Kerang, Australia 35 47s 143 59E
Kerch, & Str., U.S.S.R. 45 12N 36 35E
Kerem Maharal, Israel 32 39N 35 0E
Kerguelen I., Indian Oc. 49 30s 69 40E
Kericho, Kenya 0 24s 35 14E
Kerinci, mt., Indonesia 1 35s 100 40E
Kerkenna I., Tunisia 34 48N 11 12E
Kerki, U.S.S.R. 37 50N 65 25E
Kérkira I. (Corfu), Gr. 39 30N 19 50E
Kermadec Is., Pacific Oc. 31 0s 178 0w
Kerman, Iran 30 15N 57 0E
Kermanshah, Iran 34 18N 47 5E
Kerme G., Turkey 36 55N 27 45E
Kerrera, I., Scotland 56 24N 5 32w
Kerrobert, Canada 52 0N 109 10w
Kerry, Co., Ireland 52 5N 9 30w
Kerry Hd., Ireland 52 20N 9 55E
Kerry, Wales 52 30N 3 15w
Kesh, N. Ireland 54 31N 7 43w
Keski Suomen, Co., Finland 63 0N 25 15E
Keswick, England 54 36N 3 7w
Ket, R., U.S.S.R. 58 50N 85 0E
Keta, Ghana 5 49N 1 0E
Ketapang, Indonesia 1 55s 110 0E
Ketrzyn, Poland 54 5N 21 21E
Kettering, England 52 25N 0 42w
Kettlewell, England 54 8N 2 2w
Kewanee, U.S.A. 41 17N 89 56w
Keweenaw, B., U.S.A. 47 0N 88 0w
Keweenaw Pen., U.S.A. 47 0N 88 0w
Key, L., Ireland 54 0N 8 15w
Key West, U.S.A. 24 40N 82 45w
Keynsham, England 51 25N 2 30w
Kezhma, U.S.S.R. 59 15N 100 57E
Kfar Ata, Israel 32 48N 35 7E
Khabarovsk, U.S.S.R. 48 20N 135 5E
Khaibar, Saudi Arabia 26 2N 39 28E
Khairagarh, India 21 15N 81 0E
Khairpur, & Prov., Pakistan 27 32N 68 45E
Khalkis, Greece 38 25N 23 40E
Khalmer-Sede, U.S.S.R. 67 25N 78 50E
Khalmer Yu, U.S.S.R. 68 0N 65 10E
Khamba Dzong, Tibet, China 28 25N 88 30E
Khamis Mushait, Si. Arabia 18 15N 42 45E
Khanda, India 15 25N 74 30E
Khanaqin, Iraq 34 30N 45 25E
Khandwa, India 21 59N 76 25E

Khanewal, Pakistan 30 25N 71 55E
Khangai, Mts., Mongolia 47 0N 99 0E
Khania, Crete 35 30N 24 0E
Khanpur, Pakistan 28 35N 70 30E
Khanu, Iran 28 0N 57 45E
Khara Usu Nur, see Har Us Nuur
Kharagpur, India 22 20N 87 20E
Kharda, India 18 40N 75 40E
Khargon, India 21 45N 75 35E
Kharkov, U.S.S.R. 49 50N 36 15E
Khartoum, Sudan 15 40N 32 52E
Khash, Afghanistan 31 28N 62 40E
Khash Desert, Afghan. 31 45N 62 30E
Khashm el Girba, Sudan 14 52N 35 30E
Khaskovo, Bulgaria 41 56N 25 30E
Khatanga, U.S.S.R. 72 0N 102 40E
Khatyn, U.S.S.R. 62 10N 174 55E
Khed Brahma, India 24 7N 73 5E
Khemis Miliana (Affreville), Algeria 36 14N 2 20E
Khenchela, Algeria 35 25N 7 12E
Khenifra, Morocco 32 58N 5 46w
Kherson, U.S.S.R. 46 47N 32 43E
Kheta R., U.S.S.R. 71 0N 97 0E
Khetinsiring, Tibet, China 33 0N 91 40E
Khilok, U.S.S.R. 51 30N 110 50E
Khingan Mts., China 47 0N 119 30E
Khios, Greece 38 20N 26 0E
Khirgiz Nur, see Hyargas Nuur
Khirsan R., Iran 31 15N 51 10E
Khiuma I., U.S.S.R. 59 0N 22 30E
Khiva, U.S.S.R. 41 27N 60 10E
Khoi, Iran 38 39N 45 0E
Khojak P., Afghanistan 30 57N 66 40E
Khonu, U.S.S.R. 66 36N 143 10E
Khor Dhahiya, South Yemen 18 50N 51 35E
Khora Sfakion, Crete 35 15N 24 10E
Khorog, U.S.S.R. 37 50N 71 50E
Khotan, China 37 8N 79 57E
Khotin, U.S.S.R. 48 31N 26 27E
Khouribga, Morocco 32 58N 6 50w
Khulna, Bangladesh 22 45N 89 34E
Khurramabad, Iran 36 37N 51 12E
Khush, Afghanistan 32 55N 62 10E
Khushab, Pakistan 32 25N 72 20E
Khushniye, Syria 33 0N 35 49E
Khust, U.S.S.R. 48 10N 23 18E
Khyber P., Pak. Afghan. 34 0N 71 15E
Kialing, R., China 33 0N 103 30E
Kiama, Australia 34 38s 150 58E
Kiamusze, China 46 20N 130 40E
Kian, China 27 0N 114 50E
Kiangling, China 30 25N 112 20E
Kiang-si, Prov., China 27 45N 115 30E
Kiangsu, Prov., China 33 0N 120 0E
Kiaohsien, China 36 5N 120 40E
Kibombo, Zaïre 3 54s 25 54E
Kibworth Beauchamp, England 52 33N 0 59w
Kicking Horse P., Can. 51 30N 116 10w
Kidderminster, England 52 23N 2 15w
Kidlington, England 51 49N 1 18w
Kidsgrove, England 53 6N 2 15w
Kidwelly, Wales 51 45N 4 17w
Kiel, B. & Can., Ger. 54 18N 10 5E
Kielce, Poland 50 52N 20 38E
Kielder, England 55 14N 2 35w
Kiev, U.S.S.R. 50 24N 30 28E
Kiffa, Mauritania 16 48N 11 15w
Kigali, Rwanda 1 58s 30 0E
Kigoma, Tanzania 4 49s 29 45E
Kikiang, China 29 0N 106 10E
Kikinda, Yugoslavia 45 47N 20 31E
Kikladhes (Cyclades) Arch., Greece 37 30N 25 15E
Kikori, Papua N.G. 7 45s 144 10E
Kikwit, Zaïre 4 50s 18 45E
Kilauea, Mt., Hawaii, I. 19 40N 155 30w
Kilbeggan, Ireland 53 21N 7 30w
Kilbirnie, Scotland 55 45N 4 42w
Kilbrannan Sd., Scot. 55 40N 5 23w
Kilbrittain, Ireland 51 40N 8 42w
Kilcock, Ireland 53 24N 6 40w
Kilcoe, Ireland 51 33N 9 26w
Kilconnell, Ireland 53 20N 8 25w
Kilcoy, Australia 27 0s 152 28E
Kilcreggan, Scotland 56 0N 4 50w
Kilcullen, Ireland 53 8N 6 45w
Kildare, & Co., Ireland 53 9N 6 54w
Kildonan & Strath, Scot. 58 10N 3 50w
Kildorrery, Ireland 52 14N 8 26w
Kilfenora, Ireland 53 0N 9 13w
Kilfinan, Scotland 55 57N 5 19w
Kilfinnane, Ireland 52 21N 8 30w
Kilgarvan, Ireland 51 54N 9 30w
Kilimanjaro, Mt., Tanzania 3 0s 37 0E
Kilindini, Kenya 4 10s 39 40E
Kiliya, U.S.S.R. 45 28N 29 16E
Kilkea, Ireland 52 57N 6 50w
Kilkee, Ireland 52 40N 9 37w
Kilkelly, Ireland 53 53N 8 50w
Kilkenny, & Co., Ireland 52 39N 7 13w
Kilkhampton, England 50 53N 4 30w
Kilkieran B., Ireland 53 18N 9 45w
Kilkis, Israel 32 38N 35 33E
Kilkis, Ireland 52 49N 8 45w
Kill, Kildare, Ireland 53 16N 6 36w
Killadysert, Ireland 52 42N 9 7w
Killala, & B., Ireland 54 11N 9 13w
Killaloe, Ireland 52 48N 8 28w
Killard Pt., N. Ireland 54 19N 5 32w
Killarney, Australia 28 27s 152 1E

Killarney, Ireland 52 4N 9 30w
Killary Hr., Ireland 53 35N 9 57w
Killeagh, Ireland 51 56N 8 0w
Killeigh, Ireland 53 13N 7 26w
Killenaula, Ireland 52 35N 7 40w
Killeshandra, Ireland 54 0N 7 30w
Killiecrankie P., Scot. 56 43N 3 44w
Killimor, Ireland 53 9N 8 17w
Killin, Scotland 56 27N 4 20w
Killini, Mt., Greece 37 57N 22 31E
Killinghall, England 54 1N 1 33w
Killorglin, Ireland 52 6N 9 48w
Killough, N. Ireland 54 16N 5 40w
Killucan, Ireland 53 30N 7 10w
Killurin, Ireland 52 20N 6 34w
Killybegs, Ireland 54 36N 8 30w
Killyleagh, N. Ireland 54 24N 5 40w
Kilmacolm, Scotland 55 54N 4 39w
Kilmacthomas, Ireland 52 12N 7 28w
Kilmaganny, Ireland 52 26N 7 20w
Kilmallock, Ireland 52 27N 8 11w
Kilmarnock, Scotland 55 37N 4 29w
Kilmaurs, Scotland 55 37N 4 33w
Kilmeedy, Ireland 52 25N 8 55w
Kilmelford, Scotland 56 16N 5 30w
Kilmihill, Ireland 52 44N 9 10w
Kilmore, Australia 37 20s 144 55E
Kilmore, Ireland 52 12N 6 35w
Kilmuir, Scotland 57 44N 4 7w
Kilmurry, Ireland 52 47N 9 30w
Kilnaleck, Ireland 53 52N 7 20w
Kilninver, Scotland 56 20N 5 30w
Kilosa, Tanzania 6 40s 37 2E
Kilrea, N. Ireland 54 48N 6 34w
Kilrenny, Scotland 56 15N 2 40w
Kilronan, Ireland 53 8N 9 40w
Kilsheelan, Ireland 52 23N 7 37w
Kilsyth, Scotland 55 58N 4 3w
Kiltamagh, Ireland 53 51N 9 0w
Kiltealy, Ireland 52 34N 6 45w
Kilwa, Zaïre 9 15s 28 15E
Kilwa Kisiwani, Tanzania 8 58s 39 12E
Kilwa Kivinje, Tanzania 8 45s 39 15E
Kilwinning, Scotland 55 40N 4 42w
Kilworth, Ireland 52 10N 8 15w
Kilworth, Mts., Ireland 52 14N 8 15w
Kimba, Australia 33 14s 136 22E
Kimberley, S. Africa 28 42s 24 59E
Kinabalu, Mt., Malaysia 5 55N 116 45E
Kinbrace, Scotland 58 16N 3 56w
Kincardine, Canada 44 8N 81 38w
Kincardine, Scotland 57 51N 4 21w
Kindia, Guinea 10 0N 12 52w
Kindu-Port Empain, Zaïre 3 0s 25 25E
Kineshma, U.S.S.R. 57 30N 42 0E
Kineton, England 52 10N 1 30w
King I., Australia 39 55s 144 0E
King Sd., Australia 16 30s 123 15E
King Frederick VI Coast, Greenland 63 0N 43 0w
King George Is., Canada 57 30N 80 0w
King George V Falls, Fs. Guyana 3 0N 58 0w
King Leopold Ra., Australia 17 0s 125 30E
King William I., Canada 69 0N 97 0w
King William's Town, S. Africa 32 50s 27 17E
Kingairloch, Dist., Scot. 56 37N 5 30w
Kingaroy, Australia 26 35s 151 38E
Kinghorn, Scotland 56 4N 3 10w
Kingisepp, U.S.S.R. 58 15N 22 15E
Kingman, U.S.A. 35 15N 114 10w
King's Lynn, England 52 45N 0 24E
Kings, R., Ireland 52 33N 7 20w
Kingsbury, England 52 33N 1 41w
Kingscote, Australia 35 40s 137 45E
Kingston, Canada 44 23N 76 47w
Kingston, England 51 23N 0 17w
Kingston, Jamaica 18 0N 76 47w
Kingston, New Zealand 45 15s 168 47E
Kingston, U.S.A. 41 55N 74 0w
Kingston-upon-Hull, see Hull
Kingston South East, Australia 36 50s 139 52E
Kingstown, St. Vincent, W.I. 13 10N 61 15w
Kingsville, U.S.A. 27 30N 97 55w
Kingswood, England 51 26N 2 30w
Kingtehchen, China 28 45N 118 50E
Kington, England 52 12N 3 2w
Kingussie, Scotland 57 5N 4 4w
Kinitty, Ireland 53 6N 7 44w
Kingyang, China 36 10N 107 35E
Kinhwa, China 28 55N 119 30E
Kinkala, Congo (Fr.) 4 18s 14 48E
Kinleith, New Zealand 38 25s 176 0E
Kinloch, Scotland 57 0N 6 18w
Kinloch, Sutherland, Scotland 58 17N 4 50w
Kinloch Rannoch, Scot. 56 41N 4 12w
Kinloss, Scotland 57 38N 3 37w
Kinlough, Ireland 54 27N 8 10w
Kinnegad, Ireland 53 28N 7 8w
Kinneret, Israel 32 44N 35 33E
Kinneret, L., (Sea of Galilee) Israel 32 50N 35 25E
Kinross, Scot. 56 12N 3 25w
Kinsale, & Hr., Ireland 51 43N 8 31w
Kinsale, Old Head of, Ireland 51 37N 8 32w
Kinsha, R., see Yangtze R.

Kinshasa (Leopoldville), Zaïre 4 0s 15 30E
Kinston, U.S.A. 35 15N 77 34w
Kintaravay, Scotland 58 4N 6 42w
Kintore, Scotland 57 14N 2 20w
Kintyre, Mull of, Scot. 55 17N 5 48w
Kintyre, Pen. & Dist., Scotland 55 35N 5 35w
Kinvara, Ireland 53 5N 8 46w
Kioga, L., see Kyoga, L., Uganda
Kiparissia & G., Greece 37 15N 21 32E
Kippure, Mt., Ireland 53 10N 6 15w
Kipushi, Zaïre 11 55s 27 20E
Kircubbin, N. Ireland 54 30N 5 33w
Kirensk, U.S.S.R. 57 55N 108 30E
Kirgiz Steppe, U.S.S.R. 50 0N 70 0E
Kirgizia, S.S.R., U.S.S.R. 42 0N 75 0E
Kirillov, U.S.S.R. 59 28N 38 10E
Kirin. China 43 50N 127 2E
Kirin, Prov., China 44 20N 128 0E
Kirkagaç, Turkey 39 0N 27 45E
Kirkburton, England 53 36N 1 42w
Kirkby, England 53 29N 2 54w
Kirkby-in-Ashfield, Eng. 53 6N 1 15w
Kirkby Lonsdale, England 54 12N 2 38w
Kirkby Moorside, Eng. 54 17N 0 55w
Kirkby Stephen, Eng. 54 27N 2 23w
Kirkcaldy, Scotland 56 8N 3 9w
Kirkcolm, Scotland 54 59N 5 4w
Kirkconnel, Scotland 55 23N 4 0w
Kirkcowan, Scotland 54 53N 4 38w
Kirkcudbright, Scotland 54 49N 4 3w
Kirkenes, Norway 69 40N 30 1E
Kirkham, Lancs., Eng. 53 48N 2 54w
Kirkintilloch, Scotland 55 56N 4 9w
Kirkjubaejar, Iceland 63 50N 18 1w
Kirkland Lake, Canada 48 15N 80 0w
Kirklareli, Turkey 41 45N 27 15E
Kirkliston, Scotland 55 55N 3 27w
Kirkmichael, Scotland 56 43N 3 31w
Kirksville, U.S.A. 40 10N 92 40w
Kirkuk, Iraq 35 30N 44 21E
Kirkwall, Scotland 58 59N 2 57w
Kirkwood, S. Africa 33 20s 25 25E
Kirov, U.S.S.R. 58 38N 49 30E
Kirovabad, U.S.S.R. 40 48N 46 35E
Kirovgrad, U.S.S.R. 57 30N 60 0E
Kirovograd, U.S.S.R. 48 35N 32 20E
Kirovsk, U.S.S.R. 67 48N 33 50E
Kirriemuir, Scotland 56 40N 3 0w
Kirsanov, U.S.S.R. 52 40N 42 35E
Kirsehir, Turkey 39 20N 34 0E
Kirtling, England 52 11N 0 29E
Kirton, England 52 56N 0 3w
Kiruna, Sweden 67 50N 20 5E
Kirundu, Zaïre 0 50s 25 40E
Kisangani (Stanleyville), Zaïre 0 40N 25 18E
Kiseiba, Egypt 22 30N 30 0E
Kiselevsk, U.S.S.R. 54 10N 86 35E
Kishinev, U.S.S.R. 47 2N 28 52E
Kishtwar, India 33 25N 75 57E
Kisii, Kenya 0 42s 34 44E
Kisiju, Tanzania 7 15s 39 28E
Kiskörös, Hungary 46 40N 19 20E
Kiskunhalas, Hungary 46 28N 19 21E
Kissidougou, Guinea 9 0N 10 0w
Kisumu, Kenya 0 2s 34 57E
Kiswe, Syria 33 23N 36 14E
Kita, Mali 13 5N 9 25w
Kitab, U.S.S.R. 39 5N 66 55E
Kitakami, R., Japan 39 30N 141 8E
Kitakyushu, Japan 33 25N 130 45E
Kitale, Kenya 1 0N 35 5E
Kitchener, Canada 43 30N 80 41w
Kitega, Burundi 3 28s 29 59E
Kitenen, R., Finland 67 45N 26 40E
Kithira, Greece 36 10N 22 57E
Kithira, I., Greece 37 27N 24 28E
Kithnos, I., Greece 37 27N 24 28E
Kitimat, Canada 54 5N 128 30w
Kitui, Kenya 1 10s 38 0E
Kitwe, Zambia 12 55s 28 10E
Kitzingen, Germany 49 40N 10 7E
Kiukiang, China 29 45N 116 0E
Kiukuan, China 39 50N 98 15E
Kivalo, mts., Finland 66 10N 26 3E
Kivu, L., Zaïre 2 0s 29 5E
Kizel, U.S.S.R. 59 0N 57 0E
Kizil, R., Turkey 40 30N 34 15E
Kizil Kiva, U.S.S.R. 40 20N 72 25E
Kizyl Arvat, U.S.S.R. 38 55N 56 30E
Kizlyar, U.S.S.R. 43 52N 46 45E
Kjolen, Mts., Europe 66 0N 13 0E
Kladno, Czechoslovakia 50 13N 14 2E
Klagenfurt, Austria 46 39N 14 19E
Klaipeda, U.S.S.R. 55 52N 21 15E
Klamath Falls, U.S.A. 42 15N 121 46w
Klamath, R., U.S.A. 41 30N 123 10w
Klar, R., Sweden 60 45N 13 0E
Klatovy, Cz-slov. 49 20N 13 10E
Klawer, S. Africa 31 44s 18 36E
Klerksdorp, Transvaal 26 45s 27 11E
Klerwe, Germany 51 48N 6 9E
Klin, U.S.S.R. 56 30N 36 45E
Klipplaat, S. Africa 33 0s 24 22E
Klodzko, Poland 50 28N 16 35E
Klondike, Canada 64 5N 139 0w
Klosters, Switzerland 46 54N 9 50E
Klouto, Togo 7 0N 0 59E
Kluchevskaya, U.S.S.R. 55 45N 160 27E
Knaresborough, England 54 1N 1 27w

34 Knockhoy, Mt., Ireland 51 49N 9 27w
44 Knokke, Belgium 51 20N 3 17E
27 Knottingley, England 53 42N 1 15w
22 Knowle, England 52 24N 1 43w
100 Knox Coast, Antarctica 68 0s 108 0E
91 Knoxville, U.S.A. 35 50N 83 55w
32 Knoydart, Dist., Scot. 57 4N 5 35w
26 Knutsford, England 53 19N 2 23w
40 Kobarid, Yugoslavia 46 15N 13 30E
66 Kobdo, Mongolia, see Hovd
67 Kobe, Japan 34 45N 135 12E
44 Koblenz, Germany 50 24N 7 32E
41 Kocane, Yugoslavia 41 55N 22 20E
40 Kocevje, Yugoslavia 45 40N 14 50E
61 Kocheya, U.S.S.R. 52 30N 120 27E
67 Kochi, & Pref., Japan 33 35N 133 40E
88 Kodiak, I., Alaska 57 0N 153 0w
73 Kodok (Fashoda), Sudan 9 57N 32 3E
76 Koes, S.W. Africa 26 1s 19 8E
76 Koffiefontein, S. Africa 29 23s 25 0E
72 Koforidua, Ghana 6 19N 0 15w
67 Kofu, Japan 35 38N 138 30E
67 Kogota, Japan 38 30N 141 5E
63 Koh-i-Sangan Mt., Afghan 33 30N 64 59E
64 Kohat, Pakistan 33 30N 71 33E
60 Kokand, U.S.S.R. 41 0N 71 0E
60 Kokchetov, U.S.S.R. 53 25N 69 30E
49 Kokemaen Is., Finland 61 16N 21 0E
60 Kokiu, China 23 30N 102 55E
48 Kokkola (Gamlakarleby), Finland 63 56N 23 0E
60 Koko Nor., L., China 37 0N 100 0E
65 Koko Shili, Mts., China 35 40N 90 0E
61 Kokoiva, U.S.S.R. 71 40N 144 40E
76 Kokstad, S. Africa 30 32s 29 29E
67 Kokura, Japan 33 45N 131 0s
50 Kola, U.S.S.R. 68 50N 32 35E
50 Kola, B. & Pen., U.S.S.R. 69 0N 35 0E
64 Kolar, India 13 10N 78 5E
64 Kolar Goldfields, India 12 55N 78 15E
64 Kolayat, India 27 50N 72 50E
72 Kolda, Sénégal 12 55N 14 50w
49 Kolding, Denmark 55 30N 9 24E
74 Kole, Zaïre 3 16s 22 42E
64 Kolhapur, India 16 40N 74 15E
61 Kolin, Czechoslovakia 50 2N 15 16E
46 Kolobrzeg, Poland 54 10N 15 32E
52 Kolomna, U.S.S.R. 55 10N 38 50E
51 Kolomyya, U.S.S.R. 48 30N 25 5E
60 Kolpashevo, U.S.S.R. 58 30N 83 5E
74 Kolwezi, Zaïre 10 50s 25 20E
55 Kolyma Plain, U.S.S.R. 68 0N 155 0E
61 Kolyma R., U.S.S.R. 65 0N 152 0E
73 Kôm Ombo (Nasser City), Egypt 24 30N 32 57E
61 Komandorskiye Is., U.S.S.R. 55 0N 167 0E
47 Komarno, Cz-slov. 47 49N 18 5E
47 Komati, R., Swaziland 26 0s 31 30E
76 Komatipoort, S. Africa 25 30s 31 50E
76 Komatsu, Japan 36 25N 136 30E
50 Komi, A.S.S.R., U.S.S.R. 62 0N 55 0E
52 Kommunist (Voroshilovsk), U.S.S.R. 48 28N 38 40E
41 Komotini, Greece 41 6N 25 32E
76 Kompasberg, mt., S. Africa 31 45s 24 35E
68 Kompong Cham, Cambodia 12 0N 105 30E
68 Kompong Som (Sinanoukville), Cambodia 10 35N 103 35E
61 Komsomolsk, U.S.S.R. 50 9N 136 0E
100 Komsomolskaya, Antarctica 74 30s 97 0E
74 Konam Dzong, China 29 5N 92 55E
74 Kondoa, Tanzania 5 0s 36 0E
74 Kondrashevo, U.S.S.R. 57 25N 98 30E
73 Konduga, Nigeria 11 35N 13 26E
66 Kongmoon, China 22 41N 113 5E
74 Kongolo, Zaïre 5 15s 26 55E
49 Kongsberg, Norway 59 41N 9 38E
49 Kongsvinger, Norway 60 15N 12 0E
41 Konjic, Yugoslavia 43 42N 18 0E
52 Konotop, U.S.S.R. 51 20N 33 10E
46 Konskie, Poland 51 16N 20 22E
52 Konstantinovka, U.S.S.R. 48 33N 37 45E
45 Konstanz, Germany 47 41N 9 10E
72 Kontagora, Nigeria 10 30N 5 32E
51 Konya, Turkey 38 0N 32 35E
74 Konza, Kenya 1 35s 37 0E
83 Koondrook, Australia 35 32s 144 5E
83 Koonawarra, Australia 34 0s 148 47E
90 Kootenay L. & R., Can. 49 30N 116 43w
41 Kopaonik, Plat., Y-slav. 43 17N 21 0E
41 Koper, Yugoslavia 45 55N 13 50E
49 Kopervik, Norway 59 16N 5 18E
49 Koping, Sweden 59 30N 16 0E
49 Kopeysk, U.S.S.R. 55 0N 61 50E
49 Kopparberg, & Co., Sweden 59 55 15 0E
41 Kora Sfakion, Crete 35 17N 24 9E
68 Korat, Thailand, see Nakhon Ratchasima
41 Korce, Albania 40 37N 20 50E
41 Korcula, I., Y-slav 42 55N 16 50E
61 Korda, U.S.S.R. 55 20N 104 25E
67 Korea North, Asia 40 0N 127 0E
67 Korea South, Asia 36 0N 128 0E
67 Korea, B., Korea 39 30N 124 0E
47 Korets, U.S.S.R. 50 30N 27 5E
72 Koro, Ivory Coast 8 40N 7 30w

84 Koro Sea, Fiji Islands (Inset)
83 Koroit, Australia 38 27s 142 24E
61 Korsakov, U.S.S.R. 46 50N 142 50E
49 Korsör, Denmark 55 19N 11 8E
49 Korsze, Poland 54 10N 21 3E
73 Korti, Sudan 18 2N 31 40E
44 Kortrijk, Belgium 50 51N 3 20E
61 Koryak, Ra., U.S.S.R. 62 0N 170 0E
41 Kos, I., Greece 36 40N 27 10E
51 Koschagyl, U.S.S.R. 46 45N 58 45E
46 Koscian, Poland 52 2N 16 40E
41 Kosciusko, Mt., Austral. 36 25s 148 12E
76 Kosi, L., S. Africa 26 45s 32 45E
62 Kosti, Sudan 13 7N 32 38E
57 Kostroma, U.S.S.R. 57 52N 41 0E
46 Kostrzyn, Poland 52 24N 14 38E
46 Koszalin, Poland 54 12N 16 8E
64 Kota. India 25 20N 75 50E
68 Kota Baharu, Malaya 6 10N 102 22E
68 Kota Kinabalu (Jesselton), Malaysia 5 50 116 13E
68 Kotabaru, Indonesia 3 20s 116 20E
63 Kotcha R., Afghanistan 36 5N 70 0E
68 Kotelnich, U.S.S.R. 58 20N 48 12E
61 Kotelny I., U.S.S.R. 75 10N 140 0E
49 Kotka, Finland 60 27N 27 8E
50 Kotlas, U.S.S.R. 61 13N 46 40E
41 Kotor, Yugoslavia 42 18N 18 47E
47 Kotovsk, U.S.S.R. 52 45N 29 35E
64 Kotri, Pakistan 25 28N 68 15E
64 Kottagudem, India 17 30N 80 40E
64 Kottayam, India 9 30N 76 30E
64 Kotturu, India 14 45N 76 10E
73 Kouga, Chad 9 59N 21 30E
74 Koula Moutou, Gabon 1 10s 12 30E
82 Koulikoro, Mali 13 0N 7 42w
82 Koumala, Australia 21 38s 149 15E
76 Kounradski, U.S.S.R. 47 15N 75 5E
73 Kousseri, Cam. 12 0N 14 55E
50 Kovel, U.S.S.R. 51 18N 24 39E
66 Kovrov, U.S.S.R. 56 25N 41 19E
66 Kowloon, Hong Kong 22 7N 114 15E
64 Kozani, Greece 40 13N 21 58E
47 Kozhikode, see Calicut
55 Kozhva, U.S.S.R. 65 0N 56 50E
47 Kozienice, Poland 51 32N 21 30E
72 Kpandu, Ghana 6 58N 0 16E
47 Kra, Isthmus of, Thail. 10 25N 99 20E
48 Kragero, Norway 58 55N 9 22E
41 Kragujevac, Yugoslavia 44 2N 20 55E
68 Krakatau, Indonesia 6 10s 105 30E
47 Krakow, Poland 50 7N 19 56E
41 Kraljevo, see Rankovicevo, Yugoslavia
52 Kramatorsk, U.S.S.R. 48 45N 37 35E
48 Kramfors, Sweden 63 10N 18 0E
48 Krangede Falls, Sweden 63 10N 16 8E
47 Krásnik, Poland 51 0N 22 5E
51 Krasnodar, U.S.S.R. 45 1N 39 0E
50 Krasnokamsk, U.S.S.R. 58 5N 55 48E
50 Krasnoturinsk, U.S.S.R. 59 45N 60 5E
51 Krasnovodsk, U.S.S.R. 40 5N 53 5E
61 Krasnoyarsk, U.S.S.R. 56 20N 92 50E
68 Kratie, Cambodia 12 30N 106 4E
44 Krefeld, Germany 51 22N 6 34E
40 Kremen, Mt., Yugoslavia 44 28N 15 55E
52 Kremenchug, U.S.S.R. 49 10N 33 30E
47 Kremenets, U.S.S.R. 50 8N 25 43E
61 Krestovski, U.S.S.R. 71 50N 101 40E
74 Kribi, Cameroon 3 0N 10 0E
65 Krishna .R., India 16 20N 76 30E
49 Krishnagar India 23 25N 88 30E
49 Kristiansand, Norway 58 7N 7 59E
49 Kristianstad, & Co., Sweden 56 6N 14 7E
49 Kristiansund, Norway 63 9N 7 45E
48 Kristiinankaupunki (Kristinestad), Finland 62 18N 21 25E
48 Kristinehamn, Sweden 59 20N 14 8E
52 Krivoy Rog, U.S.S.R. 47 58N 33 20E
74 Krokodil, R., S. Africa 25 30s 31 20E
49 Kronoberg, Co., Sweden 56 45N 14 30E
50 Kronshtadt, I., U.S.S.R. 60 2N 30 39E
61 Kropotkin, U.S.S.R. 58 50N 115 10E
47 Krosno, Poland 49 35N 21 55E
46 Krotoszyn, Poland 51 41N 17 19E
76 Krugersdorp, Transvaal 26 10s 27 45E
41 Krusevac, Yugoslavia 43 35N 21 21E
72 Ksar el Kebir, Morocco 35 0N 5 57w
72 Ksar es Souk, Morocco 31 58N 4 28w
68 Kuala Lipis, Malaya 4 5N 102 10E
68 Kuala Lumpur, Malaya 3 10N 101 40E
68 Kuala Selangor, Malaya 3 25N 101 20E
68 Kuala Terengganu, Malaya 5 20N 103 15E
68 Kualakapuas, Indonesia 3 0s 114 30E
68 Kuantan, Malaya 3 49N 103 20E
51 Kuba, U.S.S.R. 41 22N 48 21E
51 Kuban, R., U.S.S.R. 45 12N 40 0E
66 Kucha, China 41 40N 82 52E
64 Kuda, India 23 10N 71 15E
48 Kudafljot, Iceland 63 30N 18 15w
46 Kudus, Indonesia 6 48s 111 0E
73 Kufra Oasis, Libya 25 0N 23 0E
63 Kufrinja, Jordan 32 18N 35 60E
46 Kufstein, Austria 47 30N 12 10E
62 Kuh-i-Bul, Mt., Iran 30 35N 53 20E

63 Kuh-i-Lalehzar, mt., Iran 29 30N 57 20E
63 Kuh-i-Taftan, mt., Iran 28 55N 61 0E
73 Kukawa Nigeria 12 58N 13 30E
64 Kulasekharapatnam India 8 20N 78 3E
49 Kuldiga, U.S.S.R. 57 0N 22 0E
43 Kulmbach, Germany 50 5N 11 30E
60 Kulunda, U.S.S.R. 52 45N 79 20E
83 Kulwin, Victoria 35 0s 142 46E
60 Kulyab, U.S.S.R. 38 0N 69 50E
67 Kuma Tekei, U.S.S.R. 43 15N 79 18E
51 Kuma, R., U.S.S.R. 44 45N 44 30E
67 Kumamoto, & Pref., Japan 32 40N 130 45E
67 Kumano B., Japan 33 50N 136 30E
41 Kumanovo, Yugoslavia 42 9N 21 42E
84 Kumara, New Zealand 42 37s 171 12E
72 Kumasi, Ghana 6 40N 1 35w
50 Kumertau, U.S.S.R. 52 10N 56 15E
72 Kumo, Nigeria 10 1N 11 12E
61 Kunar, & Prov., Afghan. 34 30N 71 3E
61 Kunashir I., U.S.S.R. 44 0N 146 0E
64 Kunch, India 26 0N 79 8E
49 Kunda, U.S.S.R. 59 31N 26 35E
66 Kungho, China 36 25N 100 25E
66 Kungsbacka, Sweden 57 30N 12 7E
50 Kungur, U.S.S.R. 57 24N 56 45E
65 Kunlong, Burma 23 30N 98 45E
66 Kunlun Shan, mts., Asia 36 0N 90 0E
66 Kunming, China 25 3N 102 40E
67 Kunsan, Korea 36 0N 126 35E
67 Kuntsevo, U.S.S.R. 55 35N 37 30E
82 Kunwarara, Australia 22 55s 150 7E
66 Kunyang, China 24 50N 102 15E
48 Kuopio, Finland 62 59N 27 35E
94 Kupa, R., Yugoslavia 45 30N 15 10E
52 Kupyansk, U.S.S.R. 49 50N 37 45E
51 Kura, R., U.S.S.R. 41 40N 47 0E
82 Kuranda, Australia 16 48s 145 35E
51 Kurdistan, Dist., Turkey 37 30N 43 30E
51 Kure, Japan 34 15N 132 40E
61 Kurgen, U.S.S.R. 64 5N 172 50E
63 Kuria Muria Islands, Arabian Sea 17 23N 56 0E
61 Kuril Is., U.S.S.R. 45 0N 150 0E
76 Kurla, China 41 58N 86 10E
52 Kurlovskiy, U.S.S.R. 55 26N 40 40E
73 Kurmuk, Sudan 10 30N 34 22E
64 Kurnool, India 15 50N 78 0E
84 Kurow, New Zealand 44 40s 170 30E
83 Kurri Kurri, N.S.W. 32 53s 151 22E
52 Kursk, U.S.S.R. 51 51N 36 5E
41 Kursumlija, Yugoslavia 43 20N 21 16E
76 Kuruman, & R., S. Africa 27 8s 23 20E
64 Kurume, Japan 33 20N 130 27E
64 Kurunegala, Sri Lanka 6 52N 80 4E
62 Kurusku, Egypt 22 40N 32 12E
51 Kurya, U.S.S.R. 61 10N 108 10E
60 Kushevat, U.S.S.R. 65 15N 65 55E
76 Kushiro, Japan 43 0N 144 25E
64 Kushk, Afghanistan 35 15N 62 15E
60 Kushka, Afghanistan 35 15N 62 15E
60 Kushka, U.S.S.R. 33 35N 62 20E
88 Kushkokwim R., Alaska 61 0N 158 0w
60 Kushtia, Bangladesh 23 50N 89 5E
60 Kustanai, U.S.S.R. 53 25N 63 45E
62 Kut al Imara, Iraq 32 37N 45 40E
51 Kutahya, Turkey 39 30N 30 2E
51 Kutaisi, U.S.S.R. 42 10N 42 58E
68 Kutaraja, Indonesia, see Banda Aceh
64 Kutch, Rann of, India 24 0N 70 0E
46 Kutno, Poland 52 18N 19 20E
62 Kuwait, Asia 29 0N 47 30E
61 Kuwana, Japan 35 0N 136 43E
50 Kuybyshev, U.S.S.R. 53 2N 50 0E
61 Kuyumba, U.S.S.R. 61 0N 97 5E
52 Kuznetsk, U.S.S.R. 53 13N 46 29E
40 Kvarnevic B., Yugoslavia 44 50N 14 30E
74 Kwamouth, Zaïre 3 9s 16 20E
66 Kwanan, China 30 45N 106 0E
66 Kwanghua, China 31 45N 112 10E
66 Kwangju, Korea 35 10N 127 0E
66 Kwangsi-Chuang, Autonomous Reg., China 24 0N 107 30E
66 Kwangtung, China 23 30N 101 20E
66 Kweichow, Prov., China 26 30N 107 0E
66 Kweilin, China 25 12N 110 10E
66 Kweiping, China 23 25N 109 15E
66 Kwei-yang, China 26 30N 106 35E
49 Kwidzyn, Poland 53 45N 18 58E
80 Kwinana, Australia 32 20s 115 50E
83 Kyabram, Australia 36 19s 145 4E
65 Kyakhta, U.S.S.R. 50 30N 106 25E
65 Kyaring Tso, L., Tibet 31 10N 88 15E
65 Kyaukpyu, Burma 19 28N 93 40E
32 Kyle, Dist., Scotland 55 27N 4 27w
33 Kyle of Durness, Scot. 58 35N 4 49w
32 Kyle of Lochalsh, Scot. 57 20N 5 50w
33 Kyle of Tongue, Scotland 58 33N 4 24w
30 Kyles of Bute, Scotland 55 55N 5 10w
44 Kyllburg, Germany 50 2N 6 34E
83 Kyneton, Australia 37 20s 144 30E
74 Kyoga, L., Uganda 1 30N 33 20E
83 Kyogle, Australia 28 37s 152 44E
65 Kyonpyaw, Burma 17 15N 95 0E
67 Kyoto & Pref., Japan 35 0N 135 30E
51 Kystatym, U.S.S.R. 67 0N 123 0E
61 Kytalyktakh, U.S.S.R. 65 30N 123 30E
66 Kyulyunken, U.S.S.R. 64 10N 137 0E
65 Kyunhla, Burma 23 25N 95 15E
67 Kyushu I., Japan 32 30N 131 0E

41 Kyustendil, Bulgaria 42 2s 22 40E
83 Kywong, N.S.W. 34 59s 146 52E
60 Kyzyl Kum Des., U.S.S.R. 42 10N 66 0E
60 Kyzyl Orda, U.S.S.R. 44 56N 65 30E
60 Kyzyl Rabat, U.S.S.R. 37 50N 74 50E

L

37 La Alcarria, Dist., Spain 40 30N 2 10w
95 La Blanquilla, W.I. 12 0N 64 35w
72 La Calle, Algeria 36 55N 8 33E
44 La Capelle, France 49 59N 3 52E
37 La Carolina, Spain 38 17N 3 38w
45 La Chaux de Fonds, Switz. 47 7N 6 50E
94 La Ceiba, Honduras 15 45N 86 50w
43 La Charité, France 47 16N 3 2E
50 La Chorrera, Panama Canal (Inset)
72 La Ciotat, France 43 10N 5 32E
37 La Coruna, Spain 43 20N 8 28w
92 La Crosse, U.S.A. 43 49N 91 13w
37 La Estrada, Spain 42 43N 8 28w
92 La Fayette, U.S.A. 40 24N 86 45w
42 La Ferté Mace, France 48 38N 0 20w
42 La Flèche, France 47 42N 0 5E
90 La Grande, U.S.A. 45 22N 118 7w
91 La Grange, U.S.A. 33 3N 85 1w
90 La Junta, U.S.A. 38 3N 103 35w
44 La Louvière, Belgium 50 29N 4 12E
37 La Mancha, Dist., Spain 39 10N 2 50w
43 La Mure, France 45 0N 5 30E
94 La Oroya, Peru 11 42s 75 57w
95 La Palma, Panama 8 15N 78 2w
37 La Palma, Spain 37 20N 6 35w
98 La Paz, Bolivia 16 30s 68 0w
94 La Paz, & B., Mexico 24 5N 110 14w
67 La Pérouse Str., Japan 45 30N 142 0E
99 La Plata, Argentina 35 0s 57 50w
99 La Quiàca, Argentina 22 15s 65 45w
42 La Réole, France 44 38N 0 2w
99 La Rioja, Argentina 29 20s 66 50w
42 La Roche-sur-Yon, France 46 41N 1 26w
42 La Rochelle, France 46 10N 1 10w
37 La Roda, Spain 39 15N 2 12w
95 La Romana, Dom. Rep. 18 30N 68 55w
88 La Ronge, L., Canada 55 10N 105 15w
37 La Sagra, Mt., Spain 38 0N 2 35w
37 La Salle, U.S.A. 41 25N 89 5w
99 La Serena, Chile 29 55s 71 25w
43 La Seyne, France 43 0N 5 50E
40 La Spezia, Italy 44 9N 9 47E
42 La Tremblade, France 45 42N 1 10w
93 La Tuque, Canada 47 30N 72 57w
95 La Vega, Dominican Rep. 19 10N 70 35w
34 Labasheeda, Ireland 52 37N 9 15w
46 Labe (Elbe), R., Czechoslovakia 50 0N 15 30E
72 Labé, Guinea 11 24N 12 16w
68 Labrador, dist., Canada 55 50N 60 30w
68 Labuan, I., Sabah 5 22N 115 19E
68 Lac la Biche, Canada 54 45N 111 50w
55 Laccadive Is., see Lakshadweep Is.
93 Lachine, U.S.A. 45 30N 73 40w
83 Lachlan, R., N.S.W. 33 46s 145 0E
93 Lachute, Canada 45 42N 74 25w
34 Lackagh Hills, Ireland 54 14N 8 0w
88 Lacombe, Canada 52 30N 113 50w
93 Laconia, U.S.A. 43 32N 71 30w
64 Ladakh, Ra., India 34 0N 77 30E
62 Ladis, Iran 29 0N 61 15E
50 Ladoga, L., U.S.S.R. 61 30N 31 0E
76 Lady Grey, S. Africa 30 45s 27 12E
88 Ladysmith, Canada 49 0N 124 0w
76 Ladysmith, Natal 28 33s 29 50E
82 Lae, Papua N.G. 6 50s 146 50E
49 Laeso, I., Denmark 57 17N 11 0E
91 Lafayette, La., U.S.A. 30 16N 92 3w
72 Lafia, Nigeria 8 34N 8 30E
72 Lafiagi, Nigeria 8 54N 5 25E
48 Lagan, R., N. Ireland 54 29N 6 10w
48 Lagar Fliot, R., Iceland 65 10N 14 40w
48 Lagen, R., Norway 61 9N 10 25E
33 Laggan, Scotland 57 3N 4 48w
33 Laggan L., Scotland 56 56N 4 30w
72 Laghouat, Algeria 33 50N 2 49E
36 Laghy, Ireland 54 37N 8 7w
99 Lagoa dos Patos, Brazil 31 15s 51 0w
72 Lagos, Nigeria 6 20N 3 20E
72 Lagos, Portugal 37 7N 8 42w
94 Laguna de la Madre, Mexico 24 55N 97 30w
94 Laguna de Terminos, Mexico 18 30N 91 30w
91 Laguna Madre, U.S.A. 26 30N 97 0w
68 Lahat, Sumatra 3 40s 103 35E
63 Lahej, South Yemen 13 5N 44 50E
46 Lahn, R., Germany 50 38N 8 20E
49 Laholm, Sweden 56 30N 13 2E
64 Lahore, Pakistan 31 30N 74 23E
50 Lahti, Finland 60 59N 25 42E
73 Lai (Béhagle), Chad 9 25N 16 30E
84 Laidley, Australia 27 35s 152 6E
43 Laigle, France 48 45N 0 40E
62 Laila, Saudi Arabia 22 25N 46 27E
76 Laingsburg, S. Africa 33 6s 20 59E
33 Lairg, Scotland 58 1N 4 24w
83 Lake Cargelligo, Austral. 33 15s 146 22E
91 Lake Charles, U.S.A. 30 15N 93 7w

91 Lake City, U.S.A. 30 14N 93 10w
89 Lake of the Woods, L., Can. 49 30N 94 30w
91 Lakeland, U.S.A. 28 4N 81 59w
23 Lakenheath, England 52 25N 0 30E
83 Lakes Entrance, Victoria 38 0s 147
65 Lakhimpur, India 27 55N 80 55E
64 Lakhpat, India 23 48N 68 40E
48 Laki, Mt., Iceland 64 10N 18 10w
63 Lakkish, R., Israel 31 40N 34 42E
41 Lakonia, G. of, Greece 36 30N 22 4
72 Lakota, Ivory Coast 5 50N 5 30w
48 Lakse Fjord, Norway 70 40N 27 0E
55 Lakshadweep Is., Ind. Oc. 13 0N 72
74 Lalibala, Ethiopia 12 8N 39 10E
37 Lalin, Spain 42 40N 8 12w
64 Lalitpur, India 24 45N 78 28E
65 Lamaing, Burma 15 30N 97 50E
74 Lambarene, Gabon 0 50s 10 2E
35 Lambay I., Ireland 53 30N 6 2w
23 Lambeth, Greater London, Englan 51 26N 0 5w
22 Lambourn, England 51 33N 1 30w
72 Lame, Nigeria 10 25N 9 20E
37 Lamego, Portugal 41 0N 7 50w
94 Lamentin, Martinique 1. 14 37N 61
44 Lammel, Belgium 51 15N 5 10E
31 Lammermuir, Dist., Scot. 55 50N 2
31 Lammermuir Hills, Scotland 55 50N 2 40w
65 Lampang, Thailand 18 15N 99 35E
40 Lampedusa, I., Italy 35 32N 12 38E
25 Lampeter, Wales 52 8N 4 4w
65 Lamphun, Thailand 18 40N 99 5E
67 Lan Yu, I., Taiwan 22 0N 121 30E
90 Lanai, I., Hawaii, U.S.A. 20 50N 157 0w
29 Lanark, Scotland 55 40N 3 47w
28 Lancashire, Co., England 53 30N 2 45w
26 Lancaster, England 54 3N 2 48w
91 Lancaster, Ohio, U.S.A. 39 44N 82
92 Lancaster, Pa., U.S.A. 40 8N 76 18w
89 Lancaster Sd., Canada 74 0N 84 0w
27 Lanchester, England 54 50N 1 44w
66 Lanchow, China 36 0N 104 0E
40 Lanciano, Italy 42 15N 14 22E
23 Lancing, England 50 49N 0 19w
92 Lancing, U.S.A. 42 40N 84 30w
74 Lândana, Angola 5 11s 12 5E
45 Landau, Germany 49 11N 8 7E
45 Landeck, Austria 47 6N 10 37E
44 Landen, Belgium 50 45N 5 5E
44 Landerneau, France 48 30N 4 20w
42 Landes, Dépt., France 44 5N 0 40w
64 Landi Muhamed Amin Khan, Afghanistan 30 20N 61 30E
45 Landquart, Switzerland 46 57N 9 32
44 Landrecies, France 50 7N 3 42E
24 Land's End, England 50 4N 5 43w
45 Landsberg, Germany 48 4N 10 53E
46 Landshut, Germany 48 33N 12 10E
49 Landskrona, Sweden 56 0N 12 57E
36 Lanesborough, Ireland 53 40N 8 0w
48 Lang Jökull, Mts., Ice. 64 35N 20 30
43 Langanes, C., Iceland 66 27N 15 30
43 Langeac, France 45 5N 3 30E
76 Langeberge, mts., S. Africa 34 0s 21 0E
44 Langenthal, Switz. 47 11N 7 50E
31 Langholm, Scotland 55 9N 3 0w
45 Langnau, Switzerland 46 57N 7 48E
42 Langon, France 44 35N 0 20w
43 Langres, & Plat., France 47 54N 5 2
68 Langsa, Indonesia 4 30N 97 48E
26 Langstrothdale Chase, England 54 14N 2 13w
23 Langtoft, England 52 42N 0 19w
43 Languedoc, Prov., France 43 50N 3 30E
42 Lannion, France 48 41N 3 22w
92 Lansing, U.S.A. 42 42N 84 31w
65 Lantsien, China 32 2N 96 5E
72 Lanzarote I., Canary Is. 29 0N 13 35
40 Lanzo, Italy 45 20N 7 40E
68 Laoag, Philippines 18 25N 120 40E
29 Laois, Co., Ireland 52 57N 7 20w
43 Laon, France 49 35N 3 35E
70 Laos, S.E. Asia 18 0N 105 0E
48 Lapi, Co., Finland 67 0N 27 0E
13 Lappland, N. Europe 68 30N 25 0E
61 Laptev Sea, U.S.S.R. 76 0N 125 0E
73 Laqiya Arba'in, Sudan 19 50N 28 18
40 L'Aquila, Italy 42 20N 13 24E
62 L'Ar, Iran 27 48N 54 2E
72 Larache, Morocco 35 10N 6 5w
90 Laramie, & Ra., U.S.A. 41 22N 105 3
31 Larbert, Scotland 56 2N 3 50w
94 Laredo, U.S.A. 27 30N 99 28w
44 Laren, Netherlands 52 16N 5 12E
32 Largs, Scotland 55 50N 4 50w
41 Lárisa, Greece 39 38N 22 26E
64 Larkana, Pakistan 27 30N 68 0E
31 Larkhall, Scotland 55 44N 3 57w
51 Larnaca, Cyprus 34 58N 33 33E
36 Larne & L., N. Ireland 54 50N 5 48
42 Laruns, France 43 0N 0 30w
48 Larvik, Norway 59 7N 10 3E
60 Laryak, U.S.S.R. 61 20N 80 3E
90 Las Cruces, U.S.A. 32 25N 106 47w
72 Las Palmas, Canary Is. 28 0N 15 35w
94 Las Tres Marias, Is., Mexico 21 25N 106 20w
90 Las Vegas, Nevada, U.S.A. 36 12N 115 12w

Las Vegas, N. Mexico, U.S.A.
  35 35N 105 20w
23 Lashio, Burma 22 58N 97 58E
31 Lasswade, Scotland 55 53N 3 8w
23 Lastoursville, Gabon 0 48s 12 59E
29 Lastovo I., Yugoslavia 42 47N 16 53E
44 Latacunga, Ecuador 0 45s 78 30w
45 Latakia, Syria 35 27N 35 58E
Latheron, Scotland 58 17N 3 22w
Latium, Prov., Italy 42 0N 12 20E
Latrobe, Tasmania 41 5s 146 40E
Latur, India 18 35N 76 42E
Latvia, U.S.S.R. 56 50N 24 0E
Lau or Eastern Group, Fiji 17 0s 178 0w
Lauder & Dale, Scotland 55 43N 2 44w
Lauenberg, Germany 53 22N 10 34E
Laugharne, Wales 51 47N 4 28w
Launceston, Australia 41 24s 147 5E
Launceston, England 50 39N 4 22w
Launglon Bok Is. (S. Moscos Is.),
  Burma 13 50N 97 50E
Laura, Australia 15 45s 144 0E
Laurel, U.S.A. 31 45N 89 0w
Laurencekirk, Scotland 56 50N 2 28w
Lausanne, Switzerland 46 31N 6 39E
Lausitz (Lusatian), mts., Cz-slov.
  50 40N 15 0E
Laut I., Indonesia 3 30s 116 15E
Lauterbrunnen, Switz. 46 36N 7 54E
Laval, France 48 4N 0 46w
Lavaur, France 43 40N 1 50E
Lavendon, England 52 11N 0 39w
Laverton, Australia 28 36s 122 27E
Lavrion, Greece 37 41N 24 2E
Lawng Pit, Mts., Burma 26 15N 98 15E
Lawra, Ghana 10 39N 2 51w
Lawrence, Kan., U.S.A. 38 59N 95 16w
Lawrence, Mass., U.S.A.
  42 46N 71 2w
Lawrence, N.Z. 46 0s 169 45E
Lawton, U.S.A. 34 35N 98 30w
Laxey, I. of Man, Eng. 54 15N 4 23w
Laytown, Ireland 53 40N 6 15w
Le Blanc, France 46 40N 1 3E
Le Cateau, France 50 8N 3 30E
Le Chesne, France 49 31N 4 6E
Le Creusot, France 46 52N 4 25E
Le François, Martinique, Fr. W.I.
  14 35N 60 55w
Le Havre, France 49 30N 0 5E
Le Kef, Tunisia 36 12N 8 47E
Le Locle, Switzerland 47 3N 6 44E
Le Marinel, Zaïre 10 25s 25 26E
Le Maire Str., Arg. 55 0s 65 0w
Le Mans, France 48 0N 0 15E
Le Moule, Guadeloupe I.
  16 17N 61 22w
Le Puy, France 45 3N 3 53E
Le Quesnoy, France 50 15N 3 37E
Le Touquet, France 50 20N 1 45E
Le Verdon, France 45 33N 1 5w
Le Vigan, France 44 0N 3 32E
Lea, R., England 51 38N 0 1w
Leadenham, England 53 13N 0 33w
Leadgate, England 54 52N 1 48w
Leadhills, Scotland 55 27N 3 48w
Lealui, Zambia 15 10s 23 0E
Leamington, England 52 17N 1 32w
Leane, L., Ireland 52 0N 9 30w
Learmonth, Australia 22 30s 114 10E
Leatherhead, England 51 18N 0 20w
Leavenworth, U.S.A. 39 16N 94 59w
Lebanon, Mo., U.S.A. 37 43N 93 44w
Lebanon, Tenn., U.S.A.
  36 13N 86 15w
Lebanon Mts., Lebanon
  33 45N 35 45E
Lebanon, S.W. Asia 33 30N 35 40E
Lebrija, Spain 36 50N 6 2w
Lebu, Chile 37 47s 73 45w
Lecce, Italy 40 11N 18 12E
Lecco, Italy 45 51N 9 24E
Lech, R., Germany 47 45N 10 45E
Lectoure, France 43 55N 0 32E
Leczyca, Poland 52 2N 19 30E
Ledberg, Belgium 51 3N 3 40E
Ledesma, Spain 41 0N 6 0w
Leduc, Canada 53 20N 113 30w
Lee, England 50 47N 1 11w
Lee, R., Ireland 51 54N 8 50w
Leeds, Yorkshire, Eng. 53 49N 1 33w
Leek, England 53 6N 2 2w
Leeton, Australia 34 23s 146 28E
Leeuwarden, Neth. 53 13N 5 48E
Leeuwin, C., Australia 34 21s 115 2E
Leeward Is., West Indies 17 0N 64 0w
Legaspi, Philippines 13 10N 123 46E
Leghorn (Livorno), Italy 43 34N 10 20E
Legnica, Poland 51 12N 16 10E
Leh, India 34 10N 77 50E
Lehinch, Ireland 52 56N 9 20w
Leicester, & Co., Eng. 52 37N 1 6w
Leichhardt R., Austral. 20 46s 147 40E
Leiden, Netherlands 52 10N 4 30E
Leie, R., Belgium 51 0N 3 30E
Leigh, Lancs., England 53 30N 2 31w
Leigh, Worcs., England 52 10N 2 21w
Leigh Creek, Australia 30 25s 138 20E
Leighton Buzzard, Eng. 51 55N 0 38w
Leine, R., Germany 52 35N 9 40E
Leinster, Prov., Ireland 52 55N 6 55w
Leipzig, Germany 51 20N 12 21E
Leiria, Portugal 39 46N 8 50w

23 Leiston, England 52 13N 1 35E
31 Leith, Scotland 55 59N 3 10w
23 Leith Hill, England 51 10N 0 23w
31 Leitholm, Scotland 55 42N 2 16w
29 Leitrim, & Co., Ireland 54 0N 8 3w
44 Lek, R., Netherlands 51 56N 4 50E
44 Lelystad, Netherlands 52 32N 5 28E
45 Leman (Geneva), L., Switz.
  46 28N 6 30E
44 Lemmer, Netherlands 52 49N 5 42E
49 Lemvig, Denmark 56 33N 8 20E
61 Lena R., U.S.S.R. 64 30N 127 0E
23 Lenadoon Pt., Ireland 54 19N 9 3w
30 Lendalfoot, Scotland 55 12N 4 55w
60 Leninabad, U.S.S.R. 40 10N 69 50E
51 Leninakan, U.S.S.R. 41 0N 43 40E
50 Leningrad, U.S.S.R. 59 55N 30 25E
52 Leninsk, U.S.S.R. 48 40N 45 15E
60 Leninsk Kuznetskiy, U.S.S.R.
  55 15N 86 15E
60 Leninogorsk, U.S.S.R. 50 30N 83 45E
45 Lenk, Switzerland 46 28N 7 27E
51 Lenkoran, Azerbaijan 38 46N 48 50E
30 Lennox Hills, Scotland 56 2N 4 15w
30 Lennoxtown, Scotland 55 58N 4 14w
44 Lens, France 50 27N 2 49E
40 Lentini, Italy 37 20N 15 0E
72 Léo, Volta 11 3N 2 2w
22 Leoben, Austria 47 22N 15 4E
22 Leominster, England 52 14N 2 44w
94 León, Mexico 21 5N 101 50w
94 León, Nicaragua 12 20N 86 51w
37 Leon, & Prov., Spain 42 35N 5 35w
91 Leongatha, Victoria 39 0s 146 0E
80 Leonora, Australia 28 49s 121 19E
74 Léopoldville, see Kinshasa
50 Lepel, U.S.S.R. 54 45N 28 30E
61 Lepikha, U.S.S.R. 64 45N 126 55E
94 Lerdo, Mexico 25 35N 103 35w
72 Lere, Nigeria 10 22N 8 31E
37 Lerida, Spain 41 38N 0 38E
32 Lerwick, Scotland 60 9N 1 10w
43 Les Andelys, France 49 18N 1 30E
95 Les Cayes, Haiti 18 0N 74 0w
42 Les Landes, Dist., France
  44 20N 1 5w
42 Les Pieux, France 49 30N 1 50w
42 Les Sables d'Olonne, Fr. 46 34N 1 50w
31 Lesbury, England 55 25N 1 37w
41 Leskovac, Yugoslavia 42 55N 21 59E
31 Leslie, Scotland 56 12N 3 12w
30 Lesmahagow, Scotland 55 38N 3 55w
76 Lesotho, Africa 29 0s 28 0E
61 Lesozavodsk, U.S.S.R. 45 25N 133 30E
95 Lesser Antilles, W. Indies
  14 0N 61 30w
88 Lesser Slave L., Canada 55 30N 115 30w
68 Lesser Sunda Is., see Nusa Tenggara
44 Lessines, Belgium 50 43N 3 50E
41 Lésvos I., Greece 39 20N 26 34E
46 Leszno, Poland 51 53N 16 37E
76 Letaba, S. Africa 23 45s 31 40E
23 Letchworth, England 51 58N 0 13w
88 Lethbridge, Canada 49 45N 112 48w
68 Lèti Is., East Indies 8 0s 128 0E
98 Leticia, Colombia 4 0s 70 0w
65 Letpadan, Burma 17 45N 96 0E
36 Letterkenny, Ireland 54 57N 7 43w
31 Leuchars, Scotland 56 23N 2 53w
45 Leuk, Switzerland 46 20N 7 38E
45 Leukerbad, Switzerland 46 22N 7 38E
44 Leuven, Belgium 50 53N 4 42E
44 Leuze, Belgium 50 37N 3 36E
52 Lev Tolstoy, U.S.S.R. 53 13N 39 27E
48 Levanger, Norway 63 47N 11 35E
43 Levanto, Italy 44 10N 9 35E
30 Leven, L., Argyll, Scot. 56 40N 5 5w
31 Leven, L., Kinross, Scot. 56 10N 3 25w
80 Lévêque, C., Australia 16 15s 122 55E
44 Leverkusen, Germany 51 2N 6 59E
84 Levin, New Zealand 40 35s 175 15E
89 Levis, Canada 46 45N 71 15w
41 Lévka Ori, Mt., Crete 35 20N 24 0E
41 Levkás I., Greece 38 40N 20 35E
84 Levuka, Fiji Is. 17 34s 179 0E
23 Lewes, England 50 52N 0 1E
32 Lewis, Butt of, Scotland 58 30N 6 16w
32 Lewis I., Scotland 58 10N 6 40w
90 Lewis Ra., U.S.A. 48 15N 114 0w
23 Lewisham, Greater London, England
  51 26N 0 5E
90 Lewiston, Idaho, U.S.A. 46 27N 117 2w
90 Lewistown, Mont., U.S.A.
  47 11N 109 30w
92 Lexington, U.S.A. 38 2N 84 37w
26 Leyland, England 53 41N 2 42w
68 Leyte I., Philippines 10 30N 125 0E
43 Lezignan, France 43 10N 2 50E
52 Lgov, U.S.S.R. 51 41N 35 17E
64 Lhasa, Tibet 29 42N 91 10E
67 Liaoning, prov., China 42 0N 125 0E
67 Liaotung, G. of, China 40 30N 120 30E
67 Liaotung, Pen., China 40 0N 122 40E
67 Liaoyüan, China 43 52N 123 28E
88 Liard, R., Canada 61 51N 122 30w
74 Libenge, Zaïre 3 40N 18 55E
46 Liberec, Cz-slov. 50 47N 15 7E
72 Liberia, W. Africa 6 30N 9 30w
68 Libreville, Gabon 0 25N 9 26E
73 Libya, N. Africa 27 0N 16 0E
73 Libyan Des., N. Africa 27 0N 27 0E
62 Libyan Plateau, Egypt 31 0N 26 0E
40 Licata, Italy 37 8N 13 58E
22 Lichfield, England 52 41N 1 49w
75 Lichinga, Mozambique 13 8s 35 30E

76 Lichtenburg, S. Africa 26 10s 26 18E
49 Lida, U.S.S.R. 53 53N 25 15E
46 Lidköping, Sweden 58 31N 13 14E
46 Liechtenstein, Europe 47 2N 10 0E
44 Liège, & Prov., Belgium 50 38N 5 30E
22 Lienz, Austria 46 50N 12 46E
49 Liepája, U.S.S.R. 56 30N 21 0E
44 Lier, Belgium 51 9N 4 34E
45 Liestal, Switzerland 47 29N 7 44E
35 Liffey, R., Ireland 53 20N 6 31w
40 Lifford, Ireland 54 49N 7 29w
40 Liguria, prov., Italy 44 20N 8 30E
40 Ligurian Sea, Medit. S. 43 20N 8 40E
65 Lihwa, China 30 5N 100 20E
74 Likasi (Jadotville), Zaïre 10 52s 26 47E
74 Likati, Zaïre 3 20N 24 0E
66 Likiang, China 26 50N 100 5E
49 Lille, France 50 38N 3 3E
49 Lille Bælt, Denmark 55 8N 10 0E
49 Lillehammer, Norway 61 10N 10 29E
22 Lilleshall, England 52 45N 2 22w
49 Lillesand, Norway 58 12N 8 23E
49 Lilleström, Norway 59 56N 11 7E
88 Lillooet, Canada 50 44N 122 0w
49 Lilongwe, Malawi 14 0s 33 40E
49 Lim Fjord, Denmark 56 38N 8 23E
98 Lima, Peru 12 0s 77 5w
92 Lima, U.S.A. 40 40N 84 5w
44 Limassol, Cyprus 34 20N 33 0E
36 Limavady, N. Ireland 55 3N 6 56w
44 Limbourg, Prov., Belg. 51 0N 5 30E
44 Limburg, Germany 50 25N 8 5E
44 Limburg, Prov., Neth. 51 15N 6 0E
29 Limerick, & Co., Ireland 52 40N 8 37w
34 Limerick Junction, Ire. 52 30N 8 12w
41 Limnos, I., Greece 39 50N 25 10E
43 Limoges, France 45 51N 1 15E
95 Limón, Costa Rica 10 0N 83 2w
43 Limousin, Prov., France 45 35N 1 30E
43 Limoux, France 43 0N 2 15E
75 Limpopo, R., Mozam. 25 10s 33 30E
23 Limpsfield, England 51 15N 0 1E
74 Limuru, Kenya 1 6s 36 38E
94 Linares, Chile 36 0s 71 35w
94 Linares, Mexico 24 50N 99 20w
38 Linares, Spain 38 10N 3 42w
28 Lincoln, & Co., England 53 16N 0 33w
84 Lincoln, New Zealand 43 37s 172 30E
91 Lincoln, Neb., U.S.A. 40 55N 96 46w
27 Lincolnshire Wolds, Eng.
  53 30N 0 20w
45 Lindau, Germany 47 33N 9 40E
43 Lindesnes, C., Norway 57 58N 7 3E
92 Lindsay, Canada 44 28N 78 53w
44 Lingen, Germany 52 36N 7 19E
68 Lingfield, England 51 11N 0 1w
68 Lingga, Arch., E. Indies 0 0 104 37E
72 Linguéré, Senegal 15 25N 15 5w
67 Lini, China 35 10N 118 30E
31 Linköping, Sweden 58 24N 15 35E
25 Linlithgow, Scotland 55 58N 3 38w
25 Linney Head, Wales 51 37N 5 4w
66 Linnhe, L., Scotland 56 36N 5 25w
66 Linsia, China 35 40N 102 30E
23 Linslade, England 51 55N 0 40w
45 Linth, R., Switzerland 47 0N 9 0E
51 Liston, Cambs., England 52 6N 0 19E
66 Lintsing, China 36 55N 116 0E
43 Lions, G. of France 43 0N 4 0E
52 Lipari Is., Italy 38 40N 15 7E
52 Lipetsk, U.S.S.R. 52 45N 39 45E
46 Lipno, Poland 52 50N 19 15E
44 Lippe, R., Germany 51 40N 7 20E
37 Liria, Spain 39 35N 0 35w
74 Lisala, Zaïre 2 15N 21 37E
32 Lisbellaw, N. Ireland 54 20N 7 32w
36 Lisbon, Portugal 38 43N 9 10w
32 Lisburn, N. Ireland 54 31N 6 9w
34 Liscannor, & B., Ireland 52 55N 9 27w
34 Liscarroll, Ireland 52 15N 8 44w
34 Lisdoonvarna, Ireland 53 2N 9 18w
24 Liskeard, England 50 28N 4 26w
82 Lismore, Australia 28 47s 153 20E
34 Lismore, Ireland 52 8N 7 58w
34 Lisnaskea, N. Ireland 54 15N 7 28w
23 Liss, England 51 3N 0 53w
44 Lisse, Netherlands 52 17N 4 33E
34 Listowel, Ireland 52 28N 9 28w
66 Litang, China 23 25N 108 10E
26 Litherland, England 53 29N 3 0w
92 Lithgow, Australia 33 30s 150 14E
41 Lithinon, C., Crete 35 0N 24 45E
49 Lithuania, S.S.R., U.S.S.R.
  55 35N 24 0E
46 Litomerice, Cz-slov. 50 33N 14 10E
91 Little Abaco I., Bahamas
  26 51N 77 45w
100 Little America, Antarc. 79 0s 164 0w
76 Little Bushman Ld., S. Africa
  29 0s 18 30E
46 Little Carpathians, mts.,
  Czechoslovakia 48 30N 17 20E
92 Little Current, Canada 45 58N 81 59w
76 Little Karroo, S. Africa 33 44s 22 0E
67 Little Khinyan, mts., China
  48 0N 128 0E
32 Little Minch, Scotland 57 37N 6 50w
90 Little Missouri R., U.S.A. 46 0N 104 0w
64 Little Rann, India 23 25N 71 25E
91 Little Rock, U.S.A. 34 30N 92 25w
43 Little St. Bernard, Mt., Fr. 45 40N 6 47E

26 Littleborough, England 53 38N 2 8w
23 Littlehampton, England 50 48N 0 32w
23 Littleport, England 52 27N 0 18E
66 Liuchow, China 24 21N 109 5E
75 Liuwa Plain, Zambia 14 30s 22 35E
83 Liverpool, Australia 33 59s 150 52E
89 Liverpool, Canada 44 0N 65 0w
26 Liverpool, England 53 25N 3 0w
83 Liverpool Ra. & Pl., Australia
  31 40s 150 30E
90 Livingston, U.S.A. 45 43N 110 41w
75 Livingstone, Zambia 17 48s 25 58E
74 Livingstonia, Malawi 10 33s 34 5E
40 Livorno, see Leghorn
99 Livramento, Brazil 30 50s 55 30w
74 Liwale, Tanzania 9 45s 38 0E
24 Lixnaw, Ireland 52 24N 9 38w
24 Lizard Pt., England 49 58N 5 11w
46 Ljubljana, Yugoslavia 46 4N 14 50E
48 Ljungan, R., Sweden 62 30N 14 0E
49 Ljungby, Sweden 56 55N 13 56E
49 Ljusdal, Sweden 61 50N 16 5E
49 Ljusna, Sweden 61 16N 17 12E
49 Ljusnan, R., Sweden 62 0N 15 20E
25 Llanaelhaiarn, Wales 52 59N 4 24w
25 Llanafan-fawr, Wales 52 12N 3 29w
25 Llanarth, Wales 52 12N 4 19w
25 Llanarthney, Wales 51 51N 4 9w
25 Llanberis, Wales 53 6N 4 4w
25 Llanddewi-Brefi, Wales 52 11N 3 57w
25 Llandeilo, Wales 51 53N 3 59w
25 Llandogo, Wales 51 43N 2 42E
25 Llandovery, Wales 51 59N 3 48w
25 Llandrillo, Wales 52 56N 3 27w
25 Llandrindod Wells, Wales 52 15N 3 23w
25 Llandudno, Wales 53 20N 3 51w
25 Llandygwydd, Wales 52 3N 4 33w
25 Llandyrnog, Wales 53 10N 3 19w
25 Llandyssul, Wales 52 3N 4 20w
25 Llanelli, Wales 51 41N 4 8w
37 Llanes, Spain 43 25N 4 50w
25 Llanfaelog, Wales 53 13N 4 29w
25 Llanfair Caereinion, Wales
  52 39N 3 20w
25 Llanfairfechan, Wales 53 15N 3 58w
25 Llangefni, Wales 53 15N 4 20w
25 Llangelynin, Wales 52 39N 4 7w
25 Llangennech, Wales 51 41N 4 10w
25 Llangollen, Wales 52 58N 3 11w
25 Llanharan, Wales 51 32N 3 28w
25 Llanidloes, Wales 52 26N 3 32w
25 Llanllyfni, Wales 53 2N 4 8w
25 Llannor, Wales 52 55N 4 25w
90 Llano Estacado (Staked Plains)
  U.S.A. 33 30N 103 0w
25 Llanon, Wales 52 17N 4 9w
96 Llanos, Regs., Columbia & Ven.
  5 0N 67 0w
99 Llanquihue, L., Chile 41 2s 72 55w
25 Llanrhidian, Wales 51 36N 4 11w
25 Llanrwst, Wales 53 9N 3 48w
25 Llanstephan, Wales 51 46N 4 24w
25 Llantrisant, Wales 51 32N 3 25w
25 Llantwit-Major, Wales 51 24N 3 29w
25 Llanwenog, Wales 52 6N 4 11w
25 Llanystymdwy, Wales 52 56N 4 17w
25 Llethr, Mt., Wales 52 47N 3 58w
25 Lleyn Penin, Wales 52 55N 4 35w
88 Lloydminster, Canada 53 20N 110 3w
99 Llullaillaco, Mt., Chile
  24 40s 68 30w
31 Loanhead, Scotland 55 53N 3 10w
76 Lobatse, Botswana 25 15s 25 30E
75 Lobito, Angola 12 0s 13 0E
45 Lobos, Is., Peru 6 15s 81 0w
32 Locarno, Switzerland 46 11N 8 48E
32 Lochaber, Dist., Scotland 57 0N 5 0w
30 Lochaline, Scotland 56 32N 5 47w
30 Lochans, Scotland 54 52N 5 1w
32 Lochcarron, Scotland 57 25N 5 30w
44 Lochem, Netherlands 52 10N 6 26w
43 Loches, France 47 10N 1 0E
31 Lochgelly, Scotland 56 7N 3 18w
30 Lochgilphead, Scotland 56 5N 5 25w
30 Lochgoilhead, Scotland 56 10N 4 54w
32 Lochinver, Scotland 58 9N 5 15w
31 Lochmaben, Scotland 55 8N 3 27w
33 Lochnagar, Mt., Scotland 56 56N 3 15w
30 Lochranza, Scotland 55 42N 5 18w
30 Lochwinnoch, Scotland 55 47N 4 39w
33 Lochy, L., & R., Scot. 56 57N 4 55w
92 Loch Haven, U.S.A. 41 7N 77 33w
31 Lockerbie, Scotland 55 7N 3 21w
83 Lockhart, Australia 35 10s 146 48E
91 Lockport, U.S.A. 43 10N 78 35w
63 Lod (Lydda), Israel 31 57N 34 54E
43 Lodi, Italy 45 20N 9 32E
74 Lodja, Zaïre 3 28s 23 28E
74 Lodwar, Kenya 2 58N 35 25E
46 Lódz, Poland 51 45N 19 27E
76 Loeriesfontein, S. Africa 30 56s 19 28E
48 Lofoten Is., Norway 68 30N 15 0E
23 Loftus, England 54 33N 0 52w
90 Logan, U.S.A. 41 42N 111 47w
86 Logan, Mt., Yukon, Canada
  60 48N 138 40w
92 Logansport, U.S.A. 40 48N 86 20w
74 Loge, R., Angola 7 35s 14 15E
37 Logrono, Spain 42 25N 2 21w
65 Lohardaga, India 23 25N 84 45E
62 Loheia, Yemen 15 45N 42 40E
66 Loho, China 33 30N 114 0E
45 Lohr, Germany 49 59N 9 33E

65 Loikaw, Burma 19 43N 97 20E
42 Loimaa, Finland 60 51N 22 53E
42 Loir-et-Cher, Dépt., Fr. 47 33N 1 50E
43 Loire, R., France 47 40N 2 30E
42 Loire-Atlant., Dépt., Fr. 47 32N 1 48w
42 Loiret, Dépt. France 48 5N 2 20E
98 Loja, Ecuador 4 0s 79 16w
37 Loja, Spain 37 10N 4 15w
44 Lokeren, Belgium 51 6N 3 59E
74 Lokitaung, Kenya 4 18N 35 48E
48 Lokka Res., Finland 68 0N 27 30E
48 Løkken, Norway 63 8N 9 45E
72 Lokoja, Nigeria 7 48N 6 43E
72 Lokolama, Zaïre 2 10s 19 50E
49 Lolland, Denmark 54 50N 11 30E
65 Lolungchung, China 30 45N 96 10E
41 Lom, Bulgaria 43 48N 23 2E
40 Lombardy, Prov., Italy 45 22N 9 50E
68 Lomblen I., Indonesia 8 30s 123 32E
68 Lombok, I., Indonesia 8 35s 116 20E
72 Lome, Togo 6 8N 1 0E
74 Lomela & R., Zaïre 2 5s 23 52E
74 Lomié, Cameroon 3 13N 13 38E
30 Lomond, L., Scotland 56 8N 4 38w
89 London, Canada 43 0N 81 21w
23 London, Greater, Eng. 51 30N 0 5w
36 Londonderry, & Co., N. Ireland
  55 0N 7 18w
99 Londrina, Brazil 23 30s 50 45w
91 Long Bay, U.S.A. 33 30N 78 30w
90 Long Beach, Calif., U.S.A.
  33 50N 118 6w
22 Long Eaton, England 52 53N 1 15w
26 Long I., U.S.A. 40 50N 73 0w
30 Long, L., Scotland 56 5N 4 52w
66 Long Mt., Wales 52 39N 3 3w
23 Long Melford, England 52 5N 0 44E
23 Long Mynd, mt., Eng. 52 30N 2 56w
23 Long Sutton, England 52 47N 0 9E
68 Long Xuyen, Vietnam 10 19N 105 25E
32 Longa I., Scotland 57 45N 5 50w
65 Longdam, China 28 15N 98 15E
83 Longford, Australia 41 47s 147 4E
36 Longford, & Co., Ireland
  53 44N 7 46w
31 Longforgan, Scotland 56 28N 3 8w
89 Longlac, Canada 49 45N 86 25w
65 Longling, China 24 35N 98 35E
90 Longmont, U.S.A. 40 14N 105 10w
82 Longreach, Australia 23 29s 144 13E
26 Longridge, England 53 50N 2 37w
26 Longside, England 53 30N 2 48w
26 Longton (Lancs.), Eng. 53 43N 2 48w
26 Longton (Staffs.), England
  53 0N 2 8w
26 Longtown, Cumb., Eng. 55 0N 2 58w
44 Longuyon, France 49 27N 5 35E
91 Longview, U.S.A. 32 28N 94 29w
43 Lons le Saunier, France 46 42N 5 31E
48 Lönsdal, Norway 66 45N 15 30E
34 Loop Hd., Ireland 52 34N 9 56w
66 Lop Nor, L., China 40 0N 90 0E
74 Lopez, C., Gabon 0 47s 8 40E
65 Lora, R., Afghanistan 30 0N 67 15E
91 Lorain, U.S.A. 41 29N 82 5w
64 Loralai, Pakistan 30 25N 68 30E
37 Lorca, Spain 37 40N 1 41w
81 Lord Howe I., Pac. Oc. 31 0s 159 0E
82 Lorengau, Papua N.G. 2 0s 147 0E
40 Loreto, Italy 43 26N 13 40E
42 Lorient, France 47 45N 3 22w
30 Lorn, Firth of, Scot. 56 20N 5 40w
83 Lorne, Australia 38 35s 144 0E
44 Lorrach, Germany 47 37N 7 38E
42 Lorraine, reg., France 48 58N 6 0E
99 Los Andes, Chile 32 42s 70 25w
94 Los Angeles, Chile 37 42s 72 20w
90 Los Angeles, U.S.A. 33 40N 118 22w
94 Los Mochis, Mexico 25 50N 109 0w
61 Loshkalakh, U.S.S.R. 62 40N 147 5E
40 Losinj, I., Yugoslavia 44 55N 14 45E
32 Lossiemouth, Scotland 57 44N 3 16w
42 Lot, Dépt., France 44 52N 1 48E
42 Lot, R., France 44 30N 1 45E
99 Lota, Chile 37 15s 73 20w
73 Lotagipi Swamp, Sudan & Kenya
  4 28N 35 0E
42 Lot-et-Garonne, Dépt., Fr. 44 33N 0 22E
30 Lothian, Reg., Scotland 55 50N 3 0w
74 Loto, Zaïre 2 18s 23 0E
45 Lötschberg Tunnel, Switz. 46 25N 7 40E
48 Loudéac, France 48 11N 2 47w
72 Louga, Senegal 15 38N 16 7w
22 Loughborough, England 52 45N 1 12w
36 Loughbrickland, N. Ire. 54 19N 6 19w
25 Loughor, Wales 51 40N 4 5w
34 Loughrea, Ireland 53 14N 8 35w
36 Loughros More B., Ireland
  54 47N 8 34w
37 Loulé, Portugal 37 8N 8 0w
76 Louis Trichardt, S. Africa 25 5s 29 50E
82 Louisiade Arch., Papua N.G.
  10 0s 153 0E
91 Louisiana, U.S.A. 31 0N 92 0w
92 Louisville, U.S.A. 38 16N 85 48w
43 Lourdes, France 43 15N 0 3w
75 Lourenço Marques, see Maputo
27 Louth, England 53 24N 0 2w
34 Louth, & Co., Ireland 53 56N 6 31w
44 Louvain, see Leuven
43 Louviers, France 49 15N 1 10E
43 Lovere, Italy 45 50N 10 5E

49 Loviisa, Finland 60 25N 26 20E
93 Lowell, U.S.A. 42 44N 71 15W
46 Lower Austria, prov., Austria 48 0N 16 0E
94 Lower California, Mex. 28 0N 113 30W
84 Lower Hutt, N.Z. 41 10s 174 55E
46 Lower Saxony, Länd, Ger. 52 45N 9 0E
61 Lr. Tunguska, R., U.S.S.R. 64 0N 98 0E
23 Lowestoft, England 52 29N 1 47E
23 Lowicz, Poland 52 3N 19 59E
31 Lowther Hills, Scotland 55 20N 3 40W
83 Loxton, Australia 34 28s 140 31E
78 Loyalty Is., Pac. Oc. 20 20s 168 0E
66 Loyang, China 34 55N 112 15E
43 Lozère, Dépt., France 44 28N 3 30E
74 Luacano, Angola 11 15s 21 40E
74 Luanda, Angola 8 58s 13 9E
66 Luang Prabang, Laos 19 52N 101 50E
75 Luangwa, R., Zambia 12 0s 32 28E
75 Luanshya, Zambia 13 8s 28 25E
74 Luashi, Zaïre 11 3s 23 38E
74 Luau, Angola 10 39s 22 14E
75 Lubango, Angola 15 0s 13 30E
98 Lubbock, U.S.A. 33 37N 101 50W
46 Lübeck, & B., Germany 53 52N 10 41E
47 Lublin, Poland 51 18N 22 32E
75 Lubumbashi (Elisabethville), Zaïre 11 30s 27 31E
35 Lucan, Ireland 53 21N 6 27W
88 Lucania, Mt., Alaska 61 10N 140 20W
40 Lucca, Italy 43 52N 10 35E
30 Luce B., Scotland 54 45N 4 45W
94 Lucea, Jamaica 18 25N 78 10W
62 Lucena, Philippines 14 0N 121 35E
37 Lucena, Spain 37 28N 4 28W
47 Luzenéc, Cz-slov. 48 18N 19 42E
66 Luchow, China 29 5N 105 0E
75 Lucira, Angola 14 0s 12 35E
46 Luckenwalde, Germany 52 15N 13 10E
65 Lucknow, India 26 57N 80 59E
42 Luçon, France 46 30N 1 10W
75 Lüderitz, S.W. Africa 26 40s 15 19E
64 Ludhiana, India 30 53N 76 2E
91 Ludington, U.S.A. 43 55N 86 29W
22 Ludlow, England 52 22N 2 42W
45 Ludvika, Sweden 60 15N 15 5E
45 Ludwigsburg, Germany 48 53N 9 11E
45 Ludwigshafen, Germany 49 30N 8 27E
74 Luebo, Zaïre 5 10s 21 24E
75 Luena, Angola 11 45s 19 58E
74 Lufira, R., Zaïre 9 20s 27 0E
91 Lufkin, U.S.A. 31 17N 94 46W
45 Lugano, Switzerland 46 1N 8 48E
45 Lugano, L. di., Switz. 46 2N 8 57E
75 Lugansk, see Voroshilovgrad
75 Lugenda, R., Mozam. 12 30s 36 20E
35 Lugnaquillia, Mt., Ire. 52 57N 6 25W
37 Lugo, Spain 43 2N 7 34W
47 Lugoj, Rumania 45 38N 21 57E
61 Lugovoi, U.S.S.R. 43 10N 72 50E
22 Lugwardine, England 52 4N 2 38W
33 Luichart, L., Scotland 57 38N 4 44W
66 Luichow Pen., China 20 40N 110 0E
30 Luing, I., Scotland 56 15N 5 40W
45 Luino, Italy 45 59N 8 43E
74 Luisa, Zaïre 7 40s 22 30E
75 Lukanga Swamp, Zambia 14 30s 27 50E
74 Lukenie, R., Zaïre 3 0s 18 30E
74 Lukolela, Zaïre 1 30s 17 8E
47 Lukow, Poland 51 58N 22 22E
45 Lule, Zaïre, see Kananga
48 Lulea, Sweden 65 33N 22 8E
66 Luliang Mts., China 37 30N 111 0E
74 Lulonga, R., Zaïre 1 0N 18 40E
74 Lulua, R., Zaïre 6 20s 22 40E
74 Luluabourg, see Kananga
75 Lumai, Angola 13 20s 21 25E
75 Lumbala, Angola 14 12s 21 20E
32 Lumphanan, Scotland 57 8N 2 41W
84 Lumsden, N.Z. 45 41s 168 29E
84 Lund, Sweden 55 44N 13 6E
75 Lundazi, Zambia 12 30s 33 20E
34 Lundy, I., Bristol Chan. 51 11N 4 40W
26 Lune, R., England 54 10N 2 40W
46 Lüneburg, Germany 53 13N 10 22E
44 Lunel, France 43 40N 4 5E
93 Lunenburg, Canada 44 25N 64 32W
42 Luneville, France 48 39N 6 30E
48 Lungholt, Iceland 63 30N 18 5W
67 Lungkow, China 37 38N 120 25E
65 Lungleh, India 22 55N 92 45E
74 Luofu, Zaïre 0 1N 29 15E
74 Luqa, Malta 35 50N 14 27E
43 Lure, France 47 40N 6 30E
36 Lurgan (Craigavon), N. Ireland 54 28N 6 20W
75 Lusaka, Zambia 15 3s 28 20E
74 Lusambo, Zaïre 4 55s 23 20E
74 Lushoto, Tanzania 4 50s 38 10E
35 Lusk, Ireland 53 32N 6 10W
30 Luss, Scotland 56 6N 4 38W
67 Lü-ta (Dairen-Port Arthur), China 39 0N 121 33E
23 Luton, England 51 52N 0 25W
47 Lutsk, U.S.S.R. 50 50N 25 15E
22 Lutterworth, England 52 27N 1 14W
74 Luwingu, Zambia 10 15s 30 2E
44 Luxembourg, Prov., Belg. 49 58N 5 30E
44 Luxembourg, Lux. 49 37N 6 8E
44 Luxembourg, Europe 49 45N 6 20E
73 Luxor, Egypt 25 41N 32 38E
42 Luz, France 42 50N 0 2W
45 Luzern, & Cn., Switz. 47 3N 8 18E
46 Luzické Hory (Lusatian Mts.), Cz-slov., see Lausitz mts.

68 Luzon, I., Philippines 16 30N 121 0E
47 Lvov, U.S.S.R. 49 51N 24 0E
61 Lyakhov Is., U.S.S.R. 73 30N 143 0E
33 Lybster, Scotland 58 18N 3 16W
51 Lycian Taurus, Mts., Tur. 37 0N 30 30E
23 Lydd, England 50 56N 0 54E
63 Lydda, see Lod
76 Lydenburg, S. Africa 25 0s 30 27E
24 Lydford, England 50 38N 4 7W
84 Lyell, & Ra., N.Z. 41 46s 172 4E
24 Lyme Bay, England 50 38N 2 55W
24 Lyme Regis, England 50 43N 2 57W
22 Lymington, England 50 47N 1 34W
23 Lymm, England 53 23N 2 30W
47 Lyna, R., Poland 54 17N 21 0E
72 Lynchburg, U.S.A. 37 28N 79 12W
22 Lyndhurst, England 50 51N 1 36W
83 Lynd Ra., Australia 25 35s 149 20E
22 Lyneham, England 51 30N 1 57W
24 Lynmouth, England 51 14N 3 50W
72 Lynn, U.S.A. 42 30N 71 0W
43 Lyonnais, Prov., France 45 50N 4 20E
43 Lyons, France 45 47N 4 50E
26 Lytham, England 53 45N 2 58W
84 Lyttelton, New Zealand 43 38s 172 46E
52 Lyubertsy, U.S.S.R. 55 41N 37 54E

M

66 Ma, R., see Hwang
62 Ma'an, Jordan 30 15N 35 37E
49 Maarianhamina, Finland 60 12N 20 0E
44 Maas, R., Netherlands 51 48N 5 30E
44 Maaseik, Belgium 51 7N 5 47E
44 Maastricht, Netherlands 50 52N 5 42E
73 Maatin-es-Sarra, Libya 22 0N 22 0E
74 Mabirou, Congo (Fr.) 1 10s 15 48E
27 Mablethorpe, England 53 21N 0 14E
91 McAlester, U.S.A. 34 58N 95 50W
66 Macao, & Port. Terr., China 22 15N 113 35E
98 Macapá, Brazil 0 5N 52 0W
26 Macclesfield, England 53 16N 2 8W
86 McClure Str., Can. 74 20N 120 0W
91 McComb, U.S.A. 31 30N 90 27W
80 Macdonald, L., Australia 23 30s 128 40E
80 Macdonnell Ranges, Australia 23 30s 133 0E
88 Macdougall L., Canada 66 20N 98 30W
33 Macduff, Scotland 57 41N 2 29W
41 Macedonia, Prov., Greece 40 45N 23 0E
41 Macedonia, Yugoslavia 41 30N 21 30E
98 Maceio, Brazil 9 30s 35 40W
72 Macenta, Guinea 8 35N 9 20W
40 Macerata, Italy 43 18N 13 33E
34 Macgillacuddy's Reeks, Mts., Ireland 52 0N 9 48W
98 Machala, Ecuador 3 10s 79 59W
30 Machars, The, dist., Scot. 54 45N 4 30W
61 Machevna, U.S.S.R. 61 5N 172 0E
93 Machias, U.S.A. 44 45N 67 30W
65 Machilipatnam, India 16 12N 81 12E
*72 Macius Nguema Biyoga, I., W. Africa 3 25N 8 45E
82 Macintyre, R., Australia 28 32s 150 25E
82 Mackay, Australia 21 6s 149 14E
80 Mackay, L., Australia 23 0s 131 0E
92 McKeesport, U.S.A. 40 22N 79 41W
88 Mackenzie, Terr., Can. 64 30N 115 0W
88 Mackenzie Mts., Canada 64 0N 130 0W
82 Mackenzie R., Australia 23 30s 148 45E
88 Mackenzie R., Canada 62 0N 122 0W
83 Macksville, Australia 30 40s 152 56E
83 Maclean, Australia 29 29s 153 15E
83 Macleay R., Australia 30 56s 153 0E
88 McLennan, Canada 55 50N 117 0W
100 McMurdo, & Sd., Antarctica 78 0s 166 0E
88 McMurray, Canada 56 35N 111 30W
90 McPherson, U.S.A. 38 25N 97 45w
83 McPherson Ra., Australia 28 20s 153 0E
43 Mâcon, France 46 21N 4 48E
91 Macon, U.S.A. 32 40N 83 28W
75 Macondo, Angola 12 40s 23 48E
83 Macquarie, Hr., Austral. 42 25 145 10E
100 Macquarie, I., S. Ocean 54 0s 159 0E
81 Macquarie, R., Australia 27 0s 136 0E
63 Madaba, Jordan 31 42N 35 48E
73 Madagali, Nigeria 10 56N 13 33E
74 Madagascar I., Africa 19 0s 46 0E
73 Madama, Niger 21 35N 13 50E
82 Madang, Papua N.G. 5 15s 145 46E
72 Madaoua, Niger 14 5N 6 27E
65 Madaripur, Bangladesh 23 10N 90 10E
40 Maddalena I., Italy 41 20N 9 22E
94 Madden L., Panama 9 15N 79 35W
32 Maddy, L., Scotland 57 36N 7 6W
72 Madeira, I.. Atlant. Oc. 32 40N 17 20W
98 Madeira, R., Brazil 6 0s 61 0W
94 Madera, Mexico 29 15N 107 55W
64 Madhya Pradesh, st., India 22 0N 78 0E
62 Madinat al Shaab, S. Yemen 13 0N 44 0E
74 Madingou, Congo (Fr.) 4 10s 13 33E
92 Madison, Wis., U.S.A. 43 15N 89 30W
64 Madiun, Indonesia 7 27s 111 30E
64 Madras, India 13 2N 80 22E
64 Madre, Sa., mts., Mex. 25 0N 106 0W
68 Madre, Sa., mts., Phil. 17 30N 122 0E
99 Madre de Dios, I., Chile 50 30s 75 30W
37 Madrid, Spain 40 27N 3 42W
68 Madura, I., Indonesia 7 0s 114 0E
64 Madurai, India 9 50N 78 5E
65 Mae Hong Son, Thailand 19 25N 98 5E
* Renamed Bioko

25 Maesteg, Wales 51 36N 3 40W
75 Maevatanana, Madag. 16 57s 46 50E
83 Maffra, Australia 38 4s 147 0E
63 Mafraq, Jordan 32 21N 36 12E
74 Magadi, Kenya 1 40s 36 20E
98 Magangue, Colombia 9 15N 74 50W
72 Magburaka, Sierra Leone 8 41N 11 45W
98 Magdalena, R., Colombia 9 0N 74 40W
46 Magdeburg, Germany 52 8N 11 35E
68 Magelang, Indonesia 7 45s 110 20E
99 Magellan's Str., Chile 52 20s 69 0W
45 Maggia, R., Switzerland 46 17N 8 40E
45 Maggiore, L., Italy 46 0N 8 40E
36 Maghera, N. Ireland 54 51N 6 40W
36 Magherafelt, N. Ireland 54 45N 6 38W
60 Magnitogorsk, U.S.S.R. 53 20N 59 0E
93 Magog, Canada 45 20N 72 6W
64 Maguires' Bridge, N. Ire. 54 18N 7 28W
64 Mahabaleshwar, India 17 58N 73 50E
68 Mahakam, R., Indonesia 0 25N 116 30E
73 Mahalapye, Botswana 23 0s 26 48E
73 Mahalla el Kubra, Egypt 31 10N 31 0E
64 Mahanadi, R., India 20 30N 84 30E
73 Mahdia, Tunisia 35 30N 11 2E
84 Maheno, New Zealand 45 8s 170 50E
82 Mahia Pen., N.Z. 39 12s 177 53E
74 Mai-Ndombe, L., Zaïre 2 0s 18 30E
62 Maidan-i-Naftan, Iran 32 0N 49 27E
23 Maidenhead, England 51 31N 0 42W
23 Maidstone, England 51 15N 0 32E
72 Maiduguri, Nigeria 12 0N 13 5E
65 Maijdi, Bangladesh 22 45N 91 25E
65 Maikala, Ra., India 21 50N 81 0E
65 Maimana, Afghanistan 35 55N 64 35E
45 Main, R., Germany 49 50N 9 30E
42 Maine, Prov., France 48 10N 0 0
91 Maine, st., U.S.A. 45 0N 68 30W
42 Maine-et-Loire, Dépt., France 47 17N 0 23W
33 Mainland, I., Orkneys, Scotland 59 0N 3 0W
32 Mainland, I., Shetlands, Scotland 60 15N 1 20W
43 Maintenon, France 48 35N 1 38E
75 Maintirano, Madag. 18 3s 44 5E
45 Mainz, Germany 50 0N 8 13E
99 Maipo Vol., Chile 34 0s 70 0W
83 Maitland, Australia 32 49s 151 38E
67 Maizuru, Japan 35 25N 135 25E
64 Majene, Indonesia 3 29s 119 4E
62 Majma'a, Saudi Arabia 25 52N 45 28E
37 Majorca, I., see Mallorca
72 Majunga, Madag. 15 40s 46 25E
72 Maka-Koulibentane, Sénégal 13 40N 14 13W
75 Makarikari Salt Pan, Botswana 20 45s 26 20E
68 Makasar, see Ujung Pandang
68 Makasar, Str. of, Indonesia 3 0s 117 0E
51 Makat, U.S.S.R. 47 40N 53 25E
72 Makeni, Sierra Leone 8 56N 12 5W
52 Makeyevka, U.S.S.R. 48 0N 38 0E
51 Makhachkala, U.S.S.R. 42 58N 47 40E
66 Makhai, China 38 30N 93 40E
47 Makó, Hungary 46 16N 20 27E
74 Makokou, Gabon 0 35N 12 55E
61 Makorovo, U.S.S.R. 57 30N 107 40E
64 Makrai, India 22 2N 77 0E
63 Makran, dist., Iran 26 0N 60 30E
64 Makran Coast Ra., Pakistan 25 30N 64 0E
60 Maksimoyarskoye, U.S.S.R. 58 50N 87 5E
64 Malabar Coast, India 12 0N 75 25E
68 Malacca, Str. of, Malaya 4 0N 100 0E
37 Maladetta, Mt., Spain 42 40N 0 30E
37 Malaga, Spain 36 46N 4 47W
75 Malagasy Rep., Africa 19 0s 46 0E
35 Malahide, Ireland 53 27N 6 10W
64 Malakal, Sudan 9 37N 31 45E
64 Malakand, Pakistan 34 30N 72 0E
68 Malaku (Moluccas), Is., Indonesia 2 0s 127 30E
51 Malamyzh, U.S.S.R. 50 0N 136 50E
68 Malang, Indonesia 8 0s 112 34E
*74 Malanje, Angola 9 30s 16 17E
51 Mälaren L., Sweden 59 30N 16 50E
51 Malatya, Turkey 38 37N 38 35E
74 Malawi, E. Africa 13 0s 33 40E
75 Malawi, L., see Nyasa L.
68 Malay Pen., S.E. Asia 4 30N 102 0E
†68 Malaya, st., S.E. Asia 4 0N 103 0E
68 Malaysia, S.E. Asia 4 0N 110 0E
51 Malazgirt, Turkey 39 13N 42 30E
82 Malbon, Australia 21 5s 140 17E
47 Malbork, Poland 54 3N 19 10E
80 Malcolm, Australia 28 58s 121 30E
44 Maldegem, Belgium 51 12N 3 28E
44 Maldive Is., Indian Ocean 5 0N 73 0E
23 Maldon, England 51 43N 0 41E
65 Malegaon, India 20 35N 74 25E
48 Malgomaj, L., Sweden 64 45N 16 5E
73 Malha, Sudan 15 8N 26 10E
23 Malham Tarn, England 54 6N 2 11W
37 Malhão, Sa. do, mts., Port. 37 25N 8 0W
90 Mali, West Africa 18 0N 1 0W
65 Mali, R., Burma 26 30N 97 50E
36 Malin Hd., & Pen., Ire. 55 23N 7 22W
66 Malipo, China 23 25N 104 45E
* Renamed Malanga

32 Mallaig, Scotland 57 0N 5 48W
73 Maljawi, Egypt 27 44N 30 44E
37 Mallorca I., Balearic Is., Spain 39 30N 3 0E
34 Mallow, Ireland 52 9N 8 38W
25 Malltraeth B., Wales 53 7N 4 25W
48 Malmberget, Sweden 67 13N 20 32E
44 Malmédy, Belgium 50 26N 6 2E
22 Malmesbury, England 15 36N 2 6W
45 Malmö, Sweden 55 38N 12 57E
49 Malmöhus, Co., Sweden 55 45N 13 15E
40 Malta, I., Medit. Sea 35 54N 14 28E
27 Malton, England 54 10N 0 45W
64 Malvan, India 16 0N 73 30E
61 Maly I., U.S.S.R. 74 20N 140 30E
73 Mambilima Falls, Zambia 10 45s 28 45E
43 Mamers, France 48 20N 0 20E
72 Mamfe, Cameroon 5 59N 9 40E
98 Mamore, R., Bolivia 16 30s 63 20W
72 Mamou, Guinea 10 15N 12 0W
26 Man, I. of, British Isles 54 10N 4 35W
51 Man-Na, Burma 23 52N 97 20E
37 Manacor, Mallorca, Spain 39 37N 3 46E
68 Manado, Indonesia 1 35N 124 50E
98 Managua, Nicaragua 12 0N 86 20W
75 Manakara, Madagascar 22 5s 48 5E
75 Manakha, Yemen 15 2N 43 50E
82 Manam I., Papua N.G. 4 10s 145 0E
75 Mananjary, Madagascar 21 10s 48 28E
75 Manantenina, Madags. 24 6s 47 20E
84 Manapouri, New Zealand 45 30s 167 33E
62 Manasarowar L., China 30 40N 81 20E
66 Manass, China 44 20N 86 20E
98 Manaus, Brazil 3 0s 60 10W
42 Manche, Dépt., France 48 57N 1 20W
26 Manchester, England 53 28N 2 15W
93 Manchester, U.S.A. 43 0N 71 22W
66 Manchouli, China 49 40N 117 0E
67 Manchuria, reg., China 44 30N 126 0E
55 Manchurian Plain, China 45 0N 125 0E
75 Manda, Tanzania 10 37s 34 52E
75 Mandabé, Madagascar 21 0s 44 55E
49 Mandal, Norway 58 0N 7 22E
65 Mandalay, Burma 22 0N 96 12E
41 Mandalya, G., Turkey 37 15N 27 15E
60 Mandar, G., Indonesia 3 30s 119 30E
64 Mandi, India 31 40N 76 55E
65 Mandla, India 22 45N 80 26E
64 Mandya, India 12 30N 76 50E
62 Manfalut, Egypt 27 20N 31 0E
40 Manfredonia, G. of, Italy 41 39N 15 54E
47 Mangalia, Rumania 43 50N 28 37E
64 Mangalore, India 12 58N 75 0E
84 Mangaweka, N.Z. 39 47s 175 43E
34 Mangerton, Mt. Ireland 51 57N 9 29W
68 Manggar, Indonesia 3 0s 108 15E
65 Mangin Ra., Burma 24 15N 95 45E
75 Mangoche (Fort Johnston), Malawi 14 25s 35 16E
60 Mangole, I. Indonesia 1 45s 126 0E
60 Mangyshlak, Pen., U.S.S.R. 43 40N 52 30E
91 Manhattan, U.S.A. 39 20N 96 40w
65 Mani, Tibet, China 34 45N 87 10E
89 Manicouagan R., Can. 50 25N 68 32W
68 Manila, Philippines 14 30N 121 12E
83 Manila Bay, Phil. 14 20N 120 30E
83 Manilla, Australia 30 45s 150 36E
64 Manipur, st., India 24 44N 94 0E
41 Manisa, Turkey 38 38N 27 24E
92 Manistee, U.S.A. 44 19N 86 15W
88 Manitoba, L. & Prov., Canada 51 0N 98 55W
91 Manitowoc, U.S.A. 44 10N 87 42w
98 Manizales, Columbia 5 30N 75 56W
72 Mankono, Ivory Coast 8 10N 6 10W
92 Mankato, U.S.A. 44 10N 94 0w
75 Mankoya, Zambia 14 58s 24 57E
35 Manly, Australia 33 48s 151 17E
83 Manna Hill, Australia 32 29s 140 0E
64 Mannar, & G., Sri Lanka 9 0N 79 49E
45 Mannheim, Germany 49 32N 8 32E
23 Manningtree, England 51 56N 1 3E
83 Mannum, Australia 34 57s 139 12E
75 Manombo, Madagascar 22 55s 43 30E
74 Manono, Zaïre 7 19s 27 23E
36 Manorhamilton, Ireland 54 19N 8 10W
44 Manosque, France 43 50N 5 45E
37 Manresa, Spain 41 46N 1 51E
74 Mansa, Zambia 11 7s 28 54E
89 Mansel I., Canada 62 10N 80 0W
83 Mansfield, Australia 37 4s 146 5E
27 Mansfield, England 53 9N 1 12W
92 Mansfield, U.S.A. 40 45N 82 38W
27 Mansfield Woodhouse, England 53 12N 1 11W
98 Manta, Ecuador 1 0s 80 40W
43 Mantes, France 49 0N 1 42E
64 Manthani, India 18 40N 79 35E
98 Mantiqueira, Se. da, mts., Brazil 22 0s 44 30W
45 Mänttä, Finland 61 59N 24 32E
40 Mantua, Italy 45 8N 10 47E
84 Manukau, N.Z. 37 0s 174 40E
82 Manurewa, N.Z. 37 0s 174 54E
82 Manyara, L., Tanzania 3 40s 35 50E
51 Manych-Gudila L., U.S.S.R. 46 17N 42 55E
75 Manyoni, Tanzania 5 55s 35 0E
64 Manzai, Pakistan 32 25N 70 12E
37 Manzanares, Spain 39 0N 3 22W
94 Manzanillo, Cuba 20 25N 77 10w
94 Manzanillo, Mexico 19 12N 104 12W

76 Manzini, Swaziland 26 30s 31 20E
73 Mao, Chad 14 45N 15 50E
75 Maputo, Mozambique 25 59s 32 42E
62 Maqna, Saudi Arabia 28 30N 35 0E
74 Maquela do Zombo, Ang. 6 2s 15 2E
99 Maquinchao, Argentina 41 0s 68 30W
33 Mar, Dist., Scotland 57 8N 2 55W
99 Mar, Sa. do, mts., Brazil 25 30s 49 0W
99 Mar Chiquita, L., Arg. 30 30s 62 40W
99 Mar del Plata, Argentina 38 0s 57 30W
98 Maraca, I., Brazil 2 10N 50 20W
98 Maracaby Fall, Fs., Brazil 0 10s 66 50W
98 Maracaibo & L., of, Venezuela 10 37N 71 40W
98 Maracay, Venezuela 10 15N 67 35W
51 Maragheh, Iran 37 25N 46 10E
98 Marajo, I., Brazil 1 0s 49 30W
74 Maralal, Kenya 1 0N 36 38E
80 Maralinga, Australia 30 13s 131 30E
75 Marandellas, Rhodesia 18 5s 31 35E
98 Maranhao, st., Brazil 5 0s 44 30W
83 Maranoa, R., Australia 27 40s 148 0E
98 Maranón, R. Peru 4 40s 75 30W
51 Maras, Turkey 37 50N 36 58E
82 Marathon, Australia 20 51s 143 32E
41 Marathon, Greece 38 10N 23 55E
37 Marbella, Spain 36 33N 4 53W
80 Marble Bar, Australia 21 5s 119 43E
43 Marburg, Germany 50 45N 8 50E
23 March, England 52 32N 0 6E
44 Marche, Belgium 50 14N 5 21E
43 Marche, Prov., France 46 10N 1 40E
37 Marchena, Spain 37 23N 5 27W
40 Marches, Prov., Italy 43 20N 13 20E
44 Marchin, Belgium 50 26N 5 12E
64 Mardan, Pakistan 34 20N 72 0E
51 Mardin, Turkey 37 20N 41 0E
82 Mareeba, Australia 17 0s 145 27E
42 Marennes, France 45 50N 1 5W
47 Marfleet, England 53 45N 0 15W
25 Margam, Wales 51 34N 3 44W
94 Margarita, Panama Canal Zone (Ins) 9 20N 79 55W
98 Margarita, I., Venezuela 11 0N 64 0W
23 Margate, England 51 23N 1 25E
76 Margate, S. Africa 30 50s 30 15E
50 Mari, A.S.S.R., U.S.S.R. 56 30N 48 0E
83 Maria I., Australia 42 39s 147 57E
84 Maria van Diemen, C., N.Z. 34 29s 172 36E
5 Mariana Is., Pac. Oc. 18 0N 146 0E
90 Marias, R., U.S.A. 48 30N 111 30W
40 Maribor, Yugoslavia 46 15N 15 40E
89 Maricourt, Canada 61 30N 72 0W
94 Marie Galante I., W.I. 16 0N 61 15W
44 Mariembourg, Belgium 50 6N 4 31E
92 Marietta, U.S.A. 39 28N 81 28W
60 Mariinsk, U.S.S.R. 56 10N 87 20E
98 Marilia, Brazil 22 0s 50 0W
37 Marin, Spain 42 28N 8 46W
92 Marinette, U.S.A. 45 3N 87 38W
92 Marion, Ind., U.S.A. 40 35N 85 37w
92 Marion, Ohio, U.S.A. 40 33N 83 10E
43 Maritime Alps, France 44 10N 6 52E
41 Maritsa, R., Bulgaria 42 10N 24 20E
44 Marken, Netherlands 52 27N 5 6E
22 Market Bosworth, Eng. 52 37N 1 24W
23 Market Drayton, Eng. 52 55N 2 30W
27 Market Rasen, England 53 23N 0 21W
27 Market Weighton, Eng. 53 52N 0 40W
100 Markham, Mt., Antarc. 82 0s 160 0E
31 Markinch, Scotland 56 12N 3 8W
50 Marks, U.S.S.R. 51 43N 46 45E
44 Marl, Germany 51 39N 7 7E
80 Marlborough, Australia 22 46s 149 52E
22 Marlborough, England 51 25s 1 43w
84 Marlborough, dist., N.Z. 41 46s 173 33E
44 Marle, France 49 43N 3 47E
23 Marlow, England 51 35N 0 46W
64 Marmagao, India 15 25N 73 45E
43 Marmande, France 44 30N 0 10E
41 Marmara, Sea of, Turkey 40 40N 28 0E
40 Marmolada, Mt., Italy 46 29N 11 55E
42 Marne, Dépt., France 49 12N 4 5E
43 Marne, R., France 48 30N 5 0E
75 Maroantsetra, Madagascar 15 28s 49 44E
98 Maroni, R., S. America 5 50N 54 0W
83 Maroochydore, Australia 26 35s 153 5E
83 Maroona, Australia 37 30s 142 57E
74 Maroua, Cameroon 10 50N 14 20E
75 Marovoay, Madagascar 16 10s 46 35E
76 Marquard, S. Africa 28 35s 27 30E
92 Marquette, U.S.A. 46 30N 87 27w
83 Marree, Australia 29 35s 137 55E
75 Marromeu, Mozambique 18 8s 35 45E
75 Marrupa, Mozambique 13 5s 37 40E
73 Marsa Brega, Libya 30 30s 19 40E
73 Marsa Susa, Libya 32 45N 21 48E
74 Marsabit, Kenya 2 10N 38 0E
42 Marseilles, France 43 21N 5 22E
91 Marsh I., U.S.A. 29 40N 91 50w
72 Marshall, Liberia 6 8N 10 22W
91 Marshall, Mo., U.S.A. 39 11N 93 16E
4 Marshall Is., Pac. Oc. 9 30N 167 0E
91 Marshalltown, U.S.A. 42 5N 93 0W
92 Marshfield, U.S.A. 44 47N 90 10W
25 Marske by the Sea, Eng. 54 35N 1 0W
49 Marstrand, Sweden 57 53N 11 35E
65 Martaban, & G., Burma 16 42N 97 45E
73 Marte, Nigeria 12 23N 13 46E
44 Martelange, Belgium 49 50N 5 44E

† Renamed Peninsular Malaysia

Martha's Vineyard, I., U.S.A. 41 27N 70 43W
Martigny, Switzerland 46 7N 7 5E
Martigues, France 43 20N 5 2E
Martinique, I., Fr. W.I. 14 40N 61 0W
Marton, N.Z. 40 5S 175 14E
Martos, Spain 37 44N 3 58W
Marvejols, France 44 35N 3 15E
Marwar, India 25 40N 73 30E
Mary, U.S.S.R. 37 40N 61 43E
Mary Kathleen, Austral. 20 40S 139 55E
Maryborough, Queens., Australia 25 32S 152 30E
Maryborough, Victoria, Australia 37 0S 143 48E
Maryland, st., U.S.A. 39 30N 77 0W
Maryport, England 54 43N 3 31W
Marywell, Scotland 56 35N 2 31W
Marzuq, Libya 25 50N 13 50E
Masada, Israel 31 20N 35 19E
Masaka, Uganda 0 20S 31 48E
Masasi, Tanzania 11 0S 39 0E
Masbate, I., Phil. 12 15N 123 30E
Mascara, Algeria 35 28N 0 2E
Maseru, Lesotho 29 35S 27 20E
Mashhad, Iran 36 15N 59 30E
Mashike, Japan 43 48N 141 20E
Mashkel, R., Iran 27 7N 63 0E
Mashki Chah, Pakistan 29 0N 62 25
Masi Manimba, Zaïre 4 40S 18 5E
Masillon, U.S.A. 40 52N 81 28W
Masindi, Uganda 1 40N 31 40E
Masira, G., Oman 20 0N 58 0E
Mask, L., Ireland 53 36N 9 20W
Massa, Italy 44 1N 10 12E
Massachusetts, st., U.S.A. 42 20N 72 0
Massenya, Chad 11 45N 16 25E
Massif Central, mts., Fr. 44 50N 3 0E
Massinga, Mozambique 23 15S 35 22E
Masterton, N.Z. 40 51S 175 41E
Mastuj, Pakistan 36 20N 72 35E
Mastung, Pakistan 29 50N 66 42E
Masuda, Japan 34 48N 131 58E
Masurian Lakes, Poland 53 45N 21 40E
Mata da Corda, Sa. da, mts., Brazil 17 30S 45 30W
Matadi, Zaïre 5 55S 13 13E
Matagalpa, Nicaragua 13 5N 85 36W
Matagami, L., Canada 49 50N 77 35W
Matale, Sri Lanka 7 37N 80 40E
Matam, Sénégal 15 34N 13 17W
Matamoros, Mex. 25 50N 97 27W
Matane, Canada 48 48N 67 37W
Matanzas, Cuba 23 0N 80 40W
Matara, Sri Lanka 5 58N 80 30E
Mataram, Indonesia 8 35S 116 18E
Mataró, Spain 41 37N 2 30E
Matehuala, Mexico 23 50N 100 39W
Matera, Italy 40 40N 16 38E
Mathura, India 27 39N 77 48E
Matlock, England 53 9N 1 32W
Mato Grosso, plateau & st., Brazil 15 0S 56 0W
Matopo, S. Africa 20 0S 30 0E
Matozinhos, Portugal 41 15N 8 42W
Matrah, Oman 23 31N 58 27E
Matsang, R., Tibet, China 29 30N 89 0E
Matsue, Japan 35 28N 133 5E
Matsumoto, Japan 36 8N 138 0E
Matsuyama, Japan 33 56N 132 56E
Mattagami, R., Canada 49 40N 81 40W
Mattancheri, India 9 50N 76 15E
Matterhorn, mt., Switz. 45 58N 7 30E
Mattoon, U.S.A. 39 28N 88 27W
Matun, Afghanistan 33 15N 69 55E
Maturín, Venezuela 9 42N 63 18W
Matylka, U.S.S.R. 63 55N 82 0E
Maubeuge, France 50 18N 3 58E
Mauganj, India 24 50N 81 55E
Maughold Hd., I. of Man 54 18N 4 20W
Maui I., Hawaiian Is. 21 0N 156 30W
Mauléon, France 43 15N 1 0W
Maumturk Mts., Ireland 53 33N 9 35W
Maun, Botswana 20 0S 23 30E
Maunmagan Is., Burma 14 10N 97 45E
Maures, Mts., France 43 20N 6 30E
Mauritania, Africa 20 0N 10 0W
Mauritius, I., Indian Oc. 20 20S 57 10E
Maushij, Yemen 13 44N 43 17E
Mawson, Antarctica 67 0S 62 0E
Maxesibeni, S. Africa 30 50S 29 20E
May, C., U.S.A. 38 58N 75 0W
May, I. of, Scotland 56 1N 2 41W
May Pen., Jamaica 17 55N 77 12W
Maya, R., U.S.S.R. 58 20N 135 0E
Mayaguana I., Bahamas 22 12N 73 0W
Mayagüez, Puerto Rico 18 10N 67 0W
Maybole, Scotland 55 21N 4 41W
Mayenne, Dépt., France 48 17N 0 40W
Maykop, U.S.S.R. 44 38N 40 11E
Maynooth, Ireland 53 23N 6 35W
Mayo, Co., Ireland 53 46N 9 0W
Maysville, Ky., U.S.A. 38 40N 83 45W
Mayum La, pass, Tibet, China 30 20N 82 20E
Mazabuka, Zambia 15 50S 27 45E
Mazamet, France 43 30N 2 20E
Mazar-i-Sharif, Afghan. 36 50N 67 0E
Mazarrón, Spain 37 39N 1 17W
Mazaruni, R., Guyana 6 0N 60 0W
Mazatlan, Mexico 23 30N 106 20W
Mbabane, Swaziland 26 30S 31 30E
Mbaiki, Central Africa 4 0N 18 0E

Mbala, Zambia 8 49S 31 20E
Mbale, Uganda 1 10N 34 0E
Mbalmayo, Cameroon 3 33N 11 33E
Mbandaka (Coquilhatville), Zaïre 0 3S 18 20E
Mbanza Ngungu, Zaïre 5 12S 14 53E
Mbuji-Mayi, Zaïre 6 10S 23 29E
Mdina, Malta 35 54N 14 22E
Mead, L., U.S.A. 36 10N 114 20W
Meadville, U.S.A. 41 39N 80 7W
Meath, Co., Ireland 53 37N 6 35W
Meaux, France 48 59N 2 52E
Mecca, Saudi Arabia 21 20N 40 13E
Mechelen, Belgium 51 2N 4 29E
Mecheria, Algeria 33 35N 0 15W
Medan, Indonesia 3 45N 98 45E
Médéa, Algeria 36 12N 2 50E
Medellín, Colombia 6 10N 75 40W
Médenine, Tunisia 33 15N 10 50E
Mederdra, Mauritania 17 0N 15 35W
Medford, U.S.A. 42 25N 123 0W
Medias, Rumania 46 5N 24 21E
Medicine Front Ra., U.S.A. 41 0N 105 40W
Medicine Hat, Canada 50 0N 110 30W
Medina, Saudi Arabia 24 20N 39 55E
Medina, Spain 41 18N 4 52W
Medina Sidonia, Spain 36 30N 5 58W
Médoc, Dist., France 45 15N 1 0W
Medveditsa, R., U.S.S.R. 50 20N 44 0E
Medvezhi Is., U.S.S.R. 71 0N 161 0E
Medway, R., England 51 13N 0 25E
Meekatharra, Australia 26 30S 118 27E
Meerut, India 29 0N 77 45E
Mega, Ethiopia 3 57N 38 30E
Megantic, Canada 45 30N 70 42W
Megara, Greece 38 0N 23 20E
Meghalaya, st., India 25 30N 91 0E
Megiddo, Israel 32 37N 35 9E
Megiste (Kastellórizon), Greece 36 8N 29 35E
Mehadia, Rumania 44 55N 22 22E
Meheisa, Sudan 19 37N 33 30E
Mehsana, India 23 39N 72 26E
Mehun, France 47 15N 2 12E
Meiktila, Burma 20 56N 95 58E
Meiningen, Germany 50 35N 10 25E
Meiringen, Switzerland 46 45N 8 10E
Meissen, Germany 51 11N 13 23E
Meiyganga, Cameroon 6 20N 14 10E
Mejillones, Chile 23 15S 70 32W
Mekambo, Gabon 1 1N 13 50E
Mekele, Ethiopia 13 30N 39 20E
Mekhtah, Pakistan 30 30N 69 15E
Meknes, Morocco 34 0N 5 25W
Mekong, R., S.E. Asia 16 30N 104 50E
Melagiri Hills, India 12 25N 77 30E
Melaka, Malaya 2 20N 102 12E
Melbourne, Australia 37 45S 144 50E
Melekess, U.S.S.R. 54 20N 49 30E
Melfi, Chad 11 0N 17 59E
Melfort, Canada 53 0N 104 56W
Melilla, Morocco 35 17N 2 55W
Melitopol, U.S.S.R. 46 50N 35 20E
Melk, Austria 48 15N 15 20E
Melksham, England 51 22N 2 9W
Mellansel, Sweden 63 26N 18 12E
Mellerud, Sweden 58 40N 12 28E
Melmoth, S. Africa 28 35S 31 20E
Melo, Uruguay 32 15S 54 0W
Melrose, Australia 32 40S 146 58E
Melrose, Scotland 55 36N 2 45W
Melstadur, Iceland 65 20N 20 55W
Melton, England 52 6N 1 21E
Melton Mowbray, Eng. 52 45N 0 52W
Melun, France 48 35N 2 40E
Melut, Sudan 10 30N 32 20E
Melvaig, Scotland 57 48N 5 49W
Melvich, Scotland 58 34N 3 55W
Melville B., Australia 12 5S 136 45E
Melville, C., Australia 14 20S 144 50E
Melville, I., Australia 11 30S 131 0E
Melville, L., Canada 53 40N 59 0W
Melville Pen., Canada 67 40N 84 0W
Melvin, L., Ireland 54 27N 8 10W
Memmingen, Germany 47 59N 10 12E
Memphis, U.S.A. 35 10N 89 49W
Menai Bridge & Str., Wales 53 14N 4 10W
Ménaka, Mali 16 0N 2 10E
Menam, R., Thailand 15 0N 100 30E
Menasha, U.S.A. 44 18N 88 28W
Mende, France 44 33N 3 30E
Mendip Hills, England 51 17N 2 40W
Mendocino, C., U.S.A. 40 25N 124 25W
Mendong Gomba, Tibet, China 31 0N 85 15E
Mendoza, Argentina 32 45S 68 39W
Menemen, Turkey 38 18N 27 10E
Menfi, Italy 37 35N 12 55E
Menggala, Indonesia 4 25S 105 26E
Mengtsz, China 23 20N 103 45E
Menin, Belgium 50 48N 3 8E
Menindee, Australia 32 22S 142 22E
Meningie, Australia 35 38S 139 27E
Menkong, China 28 40N 98 15E
Menominee, U.S.A. 45 15N 87 37W
Menominee, R., U.S.A. 45 50N 88 12W
Menongue, Angola 14 45S 17 59E
Menorca I., Balearic Is., Spain 40 0N 4 0E
Mentawai Is., Indonesia 2 30S 99 30E

Menton, France 43 50N 7 30E
Menzel Temime, Tunisia 36 50N 11 0E
Menzies, Australia 29 42S 121 2E
Me'ona, Israel 33 1N 35 15E
Meppel, Netherlands 52 42N 6 12E
Merabéllou B., Greece 35 15N 25 50E
Merano, Italy 46 39N 11 12E
Mercara, India 12 40N 75 40E
Merced, U.S.A. 37 16N 120 26W
Mercedes, Argentina 29 15S 58 10W
Mercedes, Arg. 33 5S 65 21W
Mercedes, Uruguay 33 58S 58 5W
Mercer, New Zealand 37 15S 175 5E
Mercy C., Canada 65 0N 62 30W
Mere, England 51 6N 2 16W
Mérê, Central Africa 7 35N 23 0E
Mergui, Burma 12 30N 98 40E
Mérida, Mexico 20 55N 89 40W
Mérida, Spain 38 56N 6 26W
Mérida, Venezuela 8 30N 71 2W
Meriden, England 52 26N 1 38W
Meriden, U.S.A. 41 28N 72 54W
Merksem, Belgium 51 17N 4 25E
Merowe, Sudan 18 57N 32 15E
Merredin, Australia 31 29S 118 23E
Merrill, U.S.A. 45 16N 89 40W
Merriwa, Australia 32 10S 150 28E
Merriwagga, Australia 34 15S 145 43E
Merrygoen, Australia 31 55S 149 10E
Mersch, Luxembourg 49 44N 6 7E
Merse, The, Scotland 55 40N 2 25W
Merseburg, Germany 51 22N 12 0E
Mersey, R., England 53 20N 2 55W
Merseyside, Co., Eng. 53 25N 2 55W
Mersin, Turkey 36 52N 34 29E
Mersing, Malaya 2 30N 103 50E
Merthyr Tydfil, Wales 51 45N 3 22W
Mertola, Portugal 37 39N 7 39W
Merton, Greater London, England 51 23N 0 9W
Meru, Kenya 0 2N 37 35E
Merzig, Germany 49 27N 6 39E
Mesa, U.S.A. 33 25N 111 50W
Mesewa, Ethiopia 15 35N 39 25E
Meshra el Req, Sudan 8 25N 29 18E
Mesocco, Switzerland 46 24N 9 14E
Mesolongion, Greece 38 25N 21 25E
Mesopotamia, Dist., S.W. Asia 32 30N 45 0E
Messina, & Str., Italy 38 13N 15 33E
Messina, S. Africa 22 20S 30 0E
Messini, Greece 37 0N 22 0E
Mesta, R., Greece 41 10N 25 0E
Meta, R., Colombia 5 30N 70 0W
Methil, Scotland 56 11N 3 1W
Methven, N.Z. 43 37S 171 40E
Methven, Scotland 56 24N 3 36W
Metil, Mozambique 16 24S 39 0E
Mettur Dam, India 11 45N 77 45E
Metulla, Israel 33 17N 35 34E
Metz, France 49 10N 6 10E
Meurthe-et-Moselle, Dépt., France 48 53N 5 53E
Meuse, Dépt., France 49 3N 5 53E
Meuse, R., Fr., Belgium 50 29N 5 5E
Mevagissey, & B., Eng. 50 15N 4 40W
Mexborough, England 53 30N 1 17W
Mexiana, I., Brazil 0 0N 49 30W
Mexicali, México 32 40N 115 30W
Mexican Plat., Mexico 23 0N 104 0W
Mexico, Cent. Amer. 23 0N 102 0W
Mexico City, Mexico 19 25N 99 5W
Mexico, G. of, Central Am. 25 0N 90 0W
Mèze, France 43 30N 3 30E
Mezen, R., U.S.S.R. 64 34N 46 30E
Mezökövesd, Hungary 47 44N 20 35E
Mezötúr, Hungary 47 0N 20 45E
Mhow, India 22 25N 75 51E
Miami, Fla., U.S.A. 25 55N 80 23W
Miandrivazo, Madag. 19 40S 45 40E
Mianeh, Iran 37 27N 47 39E
Mianwali, Pakistan 32 33N 71 43E
Miarinarivo, Madag. 18 50S 46 58E
Miass, U.S.S.R. 55 0N 60 0E
Michigan City, U.S.A. 41 40N 86 58W
Michigan, L., N. America 44 0N 87 0W
Michigan, st., U.S.A. 45 0N 85 30W
Michikamau, L., Canada 54 0N 64 0W
Michipicoten, I., Canada 47 45N 86 0W
Michurinsk, U.S.S.R. 53 0N 40 30E
Mickle Fell, mt., Eng. 54 36N 2 18W
Mickleover, England 52 55N 1 32W
Mid Calder, Scotland 55 53N 3 23W
Middelburg, Netherlands 51 31N 3 37E
Middlesboro, U.S.A. 36 42N 83 40W
Middlesbrough, England 54 34N 1 16W
Middlesex, Belize 16 50N 88 40W
Middleton, England 52 43N 0 29E
Middleton Cheney, Eng. 52 5N 1 10W
Middleton-on-the-Wolds, England 53 50N 0 35W
Middletown, N.Y., U.S.A. 41 29N 74 28W
Middletown, Ohio, U.S.A. 39 30N 84 7W
Middlewich, England 53 12N 2 28W
Mid-Glamorgan, Co., Wales 51 40N 3 50W
Midland, Mich., U.S.A. 43 35N 84 15W
Midland, Texas, U.S.A. 32 0N 102 8W
Midland Junc., Austral. 31 40S 116 0E
Midleton, Ireland 51 54N 8 7W
Midnapore, India 22 18N 87 30E
Midsomer Norton, Eng. 51 17N 2 29W

Midway I., Pac. Oc. 28 0N 178 0W
Mie, Pref., Japan 34 20N 136 30E
Miedzyrzec, Poland 52 0N 22 45E
Mieres, Spain 43 16N 5 48W
Migdal, Israel 32 50N 35 30E
Mikinai, Greece 37 45N 22 45E
Mikindani, Tanzania 10 0S 40 0E
Mikkeli, Finland 61 43N 27 15E
Mikkeli, Co., Finland 62 0N 28 0E
Mikonos I., Greece 37 30N 25 25E
Mikura Shima, I., Japan 33 50N 139 30E
Milan, Italy 45 28N 9 10E
Milang, Australia 35 39S 139 0E
Milas, Turkey 37 20N 27 50E
Milazzo, Italy 38 14N 15 14E
Mildenhall, England 52 21N 0 29E
Mildura, Australia 34 13S 142 5E
Miles, Australia 26 35S 150 18E
Miles City, U.S.A. 46 30N 105 47W
Milford Haven, Wales 51 41N 5 9W
Milford-on-Sea, Eng. 50 44N 1 34W
Milford Sd., N.Z. 44 35S 167 50E
Milk R., N. America 49 0N 107 0W
Millau, France 44 8N 3 10E
Milledgeville, U.S.A. 33 0N 83 20W
Millicent, Australia 37 50S 140 25E
Millinocket, U.S.A. 45 44N 68 31W
Millmerran, Australia 27 52S 151 8E
Millom, England 54 12N 3 16W
Millport, Scotland 55 45N 4 55W
Millstreet, Ireland 52 3N 9 4W
Milltown, Ireland 52 10N 9 42W
Milnerton, S. Africa (Inset) 33 5S 18 29E
Milngavie, Scotland 55 57N 4 19W
Milos, I., Greece 36 40N 24 27E
Milparinka, Australia 29 46S 141 57E
Milton, New Zealand 46 8S 169 59E
Milton Keynes, England 52 3N 0 45W
Miltown Malbay, Ire. 52 53N 9 22W
Milverton, England 51 2N 3 15W
Milwaukee, U.S.A. 43 5N 88 5W
Mimitsu, Japan 32 55S 131 30E
Min Kiang, R., China 26 40N 117 30E
Mina al Ahmadi, Kuwait 29 0N 47 0E
Minab, Iran 27 7N 57 7E
Minas (Lavelleja), Uruguay 34 20S 54 48W
Minas Basin, Canada 45 14N 64 20W
Minas de Rio Tinto, Spain 37 45N 6 36W
Minas Gerais, st., Brazil 19 15S 45 0W
Minato, Japan 36 24N 140 38E
Minch, The, Scotland 58 10N 5 50W
Minchinhampton, Eng. 51 42N 2 10W
Mindanao, I., Philippines 8 0N 125 0E
Minden, Germany 52 18N 8 57E
Minden, U.S.A. 32 44N 93 19W
Mindoro, I., Philippines 12 40N 121 0E
Mine Hd., Ireland 52 0N 7 33W
Minehead, England 51 14N 3 30W
Mineral Wells, U.S.A. 32 50N 98 10W
Mingechaur Res., U.S.S.R. 40 45N 46 30E
Mingin, Burma 22 55N 94 30E
Minginish, Dist., Scot. 57 17N 6 15W
Mingulay I., Scotland 56 49N 7 35W
Minho & Prov., Port. 41 25N 8 20W
Minho, R., Spain 43 10N 7 30W
Minhow, see Foochow
Minneapolis, U.S.A. 45 0N 93 30W
Minnesota, st., U.S.A. 46 0N 94 30W
Minorca I., see Menorca
Minore, Australia 32 15S 148 25E
Minot, U.S.A. 48 15N 101 10W
Minsk, U.S.S.R. 54 0N 27 30E
Minsk Mazowiecki, Pol. 52 10N 21 30E
Minusinsk, U.S.S.R. 53 50N 92 15E
Minutang, India 28 20N 96 30E
Minwakh, South Yemen 15 59N 49 28E
Minya Konka, mt., China 30 0N 101 15E
Miquelon I., St. Pierre & Miquelon, North America 47 0N 56 30W
Mir, Niger 14 6N 11 58E
Miraflores, Panama Canal Zone (Inset)
Miraj, India 16 57N 74 46E
Miram Shah, Pakistan 33 0N 70 0E
Miranda, Portugal 41 33N 6 20W
Miranda, Spain 42 40N 2 53W
Mirande, France 43 30N 0 20E
Mirecourt, France 48 20N 6 5E
Mirfa, U.A.E. 24 0N 53 24E
Miri, Sarawak, Malaysia 4 30N 114 5E
Miriam Vale, Australia 24 20S 151 39E
Mirim, L., S. America 33 0S 53 0W
Mirny, Antarctica 66 30S 96 0E
Mirpur Khas, Pakistan 25 33N 68 0E
Mirzapur, India 25 8N 82 39E
Miscou, I., Canada 48 0N 64 32W
Mishan, China 45 30N 131 30E
Mishmar Aiyalon, Israel 31 57N 34 58E
Miskolc, Hungary 48 8N 20 46E
Misratah, Libya 32 20N 15 7E
Missinaibi, R., Canada 49 30N 83 15W
Mississippi, R., U.S.A. 35 0N 90 0W
Mississippi, st., U.S.A. 33 0N 89 30W
Mississippi Delta, U.S.A. 29 15N 90 30W
Missoula, U.S.A. 46 57N 113 58W
Missouri, R., U.S.A. 42 0N 98 30W
Missouri, st., U.S.A. 38 0N 92 30W
Mistassini, L., Canada 51 0N 73 35W
Misterton, England 50 51N 2 35W
Misti, Vol., Peru 16 0S 71 0W
Mistretta, Italy 38 0N 14 20E
Misumi, Japan 32 34N 130 32E
Misurata, Libya, see Misratah

Mitchel Troy, Wales 51 46N 2 45W
Mitchell, Australia 26 30S 147 58E
Mitchell, U.S.A. 43 45N 98 2W
Mitchell, R., Australia 16 0S 142 30E
Mitchelstown, Ireland 52 17N 8 15W
Mitilini, Greece 39 8N 26 36E
Mito, Japan 36 28N 140 26E
Mitsinjo, Madagascar 15 35S 45 45E
Mittagong, Australia 34 25S 150 25E
Mitú, Colombia 1 0N 70 0W
Mitumba Mts., Zaïre 7 0S 27 0E
Mitwaba, Zaïre 8 37S 27 20E
Mitzick, Gabon 0 45N 11 40E
Miyagi, Pref., Japan 38 15N 141 0E
Miyake Jima, Japan 34 0N 139 30E
Miyako, Japan 39 40N 141 45E
Milyakonojo, Japan 31 30N 131 0E
Miyasu, Japan 35 40N 135 8E
Miyazaki, & Pref., Japan 31 58N 131 30E
Mizdah, Libya 31 40N 13 13E
Mizen Hd., Ireland 51 27N 9 49W
Mizoram, st., India 23 20N 93 0E
Mjölby, Sweden 58 19N 15 4E
Mjosa L., & R., Norway 60 40N 11 0E
Mlada Boleslav, Cz-slov. 50 28N 15 0E
Mlanje, mt., Mozambique 16 0S 35 55E
Mlawa, Poland 53 6N 20 20E
Moanda, Gabon 1 5S 13 0E
Moate, Ireland 53 24N 7 42W
Moberley, U.S.A. 39 28N 92 27W
Mobile, U.S.A. 30 47N 88 0W
Mobutu Sese Seko, L., E. Africa 1 45N 31 0E
Mochudi, Botswana 24 25S 26 5E
Mocoa, Colombia 1 15N 76 45W
Modane, France 45 12N 6 30E
Modder, R., S. Africa 28 48S 26 15E
Modena, Italy 44 38N 10 54E
Modesto, U.S.A. 37 36N 120 58W
Modica, Italy 36 54N 14 50E
Moe, Australia 38 12S 146 19E
Moers, Germany 51 27N 6 39E
Moffat, Scotland 55 38N 3 25W
Mogadishu, Somali Republic 2 1N 45 25E
Mogador, see Essaouira
Mogami, R., Japan 38 50N 140 0E
Mogaung, Burma 25 26N 96 55E
Mogilev, U.S.S.R. 54 17N 30 30E
Mogilev-Podolski, U.S.S.R. 48 25N 27 50E
Mogincual, Mozambique 15 30S 40 22E
Mogocha, U.S.S.R. 53 40N 119 50E
Mogok, Burma 23 0N 96 30E
Mohacs, Hungary 45 59N 18 40E
Mohembo, Botswana 18 15S 21 43E
Moher Cliffs, Ireland 52 58N 9 28W
Moidart, L. & Dist., Scot. 56 50N 5 52W
Mointy, U.S.S.R. 47 40N 73 45E
Moira, N. Ireland 54 29N 6 14W
Moisäkula, U.S.S.R. 58 2S 25 12E
Moisie, Canada 50 17N 66 0W
Moissac, France 44 8N 1 0E
Moiyero R., U.S.S.R. 67 30N 104 0E
Mojave Desert, U.S.A. 35 0N 116 20W
Moji, Japan 33 56N 131 0E
Mokokchung, India 26 15N 94 25E
Mokpo, Korea 34 50N 126 30E
Mol, Belgium 51 11N 5 7E
Mold, Wales 53 10N 3 9W
Moldavia S.S.R., U.S.S.R. 47 40N 28 0E
Molde, Norway 62 45N 7 8E
Mole, R., England 51 18N 0 20W
Molepolole, Botswana 24 28S 25 28E
Molfetta, Italy 41 12N 16 40E
Moline, U.S.A. 41 30N 90 25W
Moliro, Zaïre 8 5S 30 30E
Molise, Reg., Italy 41 33N 14 30E
Mölndal, Sweden 57 35N 12 0E
Molokai, I., Hawaiian Is. (Inset)
Molong, Australia 33 0S 149 0E
Molucca Sea, Indonesia 4 0S 126 0E
Moluccas, Indonesia, see Maluku
Mombasa, Kenya 4 0S 39 40E
Momchilgrad, Bulgaria 41 33N 25 23E
Mompos, Colombia 9 15N 74 25W
Mön, I., Denmark 54 57N 12 23E
Mon, R., Burma 20 30N 94 30E
Monach Is., Scotland 57 31N 7 40W
Monaco, Europe 43 46N 7 23E
Monadhliath Mts., Scot. 57 8N 4 20W
Monaghan, & Co., Ire. 54 14N 6 58W
Monar, L. & Forest, Scot. 57 26N 5 4W
Monasterevan, Ireland 53 10N 7 7W
Monastir, Tunisia 35 40N 10 50E
Monavullagh, Mts., Ire. 52 10N 7 40W
Moncayo, Mt., Spain 41 47N 1 50W
Mönchen-Gladbach, Ger. 51 13N 6 26E
Monchique, Portugal 37 16N 8 40W
Monchique Sa. de, mts., Portugal 37 20S 8 40W
Monclova, Mexico 27 0N 101 20W
Moncton, Canada 46 10N 65 0W
Mondego, R., Portugal 40 30N 7 50W
Mondovi, Italy 44 25N 7 50E
Moneygall, Ireland 52 53N 7 58W
Monforte, Spain 42 30N 7 30W
Mong Pawk, Burma 22 0N 99 20E
Mong Ton, Burma 20 20N 98 40E
Mong Wa, Burma 21 25N 100 25E
Mong Kung, Burma 21 35N 97 35E
Mongalla, Sudan 5 10N 31 50E
Monger, L., Australia 29 10S 117 0E
Monghyr, India 25 20N 86 22E
Mongo, Chad 12 14N 18 43E

66 Mongolia, Asia 45 20N 105 30E
73 Mongororo, Chad 12 1N 22 28F
75 Mongu, Zambia 15 16s 23 3E
31 Monifieth, Scotland 56 29N 2 49W
34 Monivea, Ireland 53 28N 8 42W
74 Monkoto, Zaïre 1 30s 20 45E
22 Monmouth, Wales 51 48N 2 43W
22 Monmouth, Co., see Gwent
40 Monopoli, Italy 40 57N 17 18E
91 Monroe, La., U.S.A. 32 30N 92 1W
92 Monroe, Mich., U.S.A. 41 54N 83 27W
72 Monrovia, Liberia 6 15N 10 43W
44 Mons, Belgium 50 26N 3 58E
75 Mont Aux Sources, S. Africa 28 54s 28 50E
43 Mont Blanc, Fr. & Italy 45 52N 6 50E
43 Mont Cenis, mt., France 45 20N 7 5E
42 Mont de Marsan, France 43 58N 0 34W
43 Mont Dore, mt., France 45 32N 2 30E
43 Mont du Cantal, mt., Fr. 45 10N 2 20E
93 Mont Joli, Canada 48 35N 68 10N
93 Mont Laurier, Canada 46 35N 75 30W
43 Mont Mézenc, mt., Fr. 44 45N 4 35E
43 Mont St. Michel, France 48 40N 1 32W
37 Montalban, Spain 40 50N 0 48W
90 Montana, St., U.S.A. 47 0N 109 0W
43 Montargis, France 48 0N 2 40E
43 Montauban, France 44 1N 1 20E
43 Montbeliard, France 47 32N 6 48E
43 Montbrison, France 45 35N 4 0E
43 Montceau, France 46 40N 4 25E
44 Montcornet, France 49 42N 4 0E
43 Montdidier, France 49 40N 2 30E
40 Monte Argentario, mt., Italy 42 25N 11 10E
80 Monte Bello Is., Austral. 20 30s 115 30E
43 Monte Carlo, Monaco 43 46N 7 23E
99 Monte Caseros, Arg. 30 10s 57 50W
40 Monte Cimone, mt., Italy 44 10N 10 40
43 Monte Cinto, mt., France 42 20N 9 10E
40 Monte Rosa, Italy & Switz. 46 0N 8 0E
40 Monte S. Angelo, Italy 41 40N 16 0E
95 Montego Bay, Jamaica 18 30N 77 50W
43 Montélimar, France 44 34N 4 48E
94 Montemorelos, Mexico 25 8N 99 30W
40 Montenegro, Fed. Unit, Yugoslavia 42 52N 19 20E
43 Montereau, France 48 20N 3 0E
90 Monterey, U.S.A. 36 39N 121 45W
94 Monterrey, Mexico 25 42N 100 22W
98 Montes Claros, Brazil 16 30s 43 50W
37 Montes de Toledo, Spain 39 30N 4 30W
74 Monteverde, Angola 8 45N 16 45E
99 Montevideo, Uruguay 34 50s 56 15W
42 Montfort, France 48 10N 2 0W
91 Montgomery, U.S.A. 32 17N 86 20W
25 Montgomery, Wales 52 33N 3 9W
64 Montgomery, Pakistan, see Sahiwal
45 Monthey, Switzerland 46 15N 6 56E
45 Montigny les Metz, Fr. 49 6N 6 9E
37 Montijo, Portugal 38 40N 8 56W
37 Montilla, Spain 37 36N 4 40W
43 Montluçon, France 46 21N 2 37E
43 Montmédy, France 49 35N 5 25E
43 Montmorillon, France 46 23N 0 50E
82 Monto, Australia 24 58s 151 0E
43 Montoro, Spain 38 0N 4 30W
93 Montpelier, Ver., U.S.A. 44 15N 72 30W
43 Montpellier, France 43 40N 3 50E
93 Montreal, Canada 45 42N 73 50W
42 Montreuil, France 50 30N 1 48E
45 Montreux, Switzerland 46 27N 6 54E
31 Montrose, Scotland 56 43N 2 28W
90 Montrose, U.S.A. 38 30N 107 53W
95 Montserrat, I., W.I. 16 30N 62 0W
64 Monveda, Zaïre 3 0N 21 35E
65 Monywa, Burma 22 5N 95 8E
75 Monze, Zambia 16 23s 27 28E
64 Monze C., Pakistan 24 47N 66 37E
37 Monzon, Spain 41 53N 0 12E
35 Mooncoin, Ireland 52 18N 7 16W
35 Moone, Ireland 52 58N 6 49W
82 Moonie, R., Australia 28 0s 149 20E
83 Moonta, Australia 34 6s 137 32E
80 Moore, L., Australia 30 0s 117 30E
31 Moorfoot Hills, Scotland 55 45N 3 5W
91 Moorhead, U.S.A. 47 0N 96 42W
83 Mooroopna, Australia 36 30s 145 25E
93 Moosehead L., U.S.A. 45 45N 69 48W
88 Moosejaw, Canada 50 24N 105 25W
72 Mopti, Mali 14 34N 4 0W
64 Moradabad, India 28 50N 78 54E
74 Morafenobe, Madag. 17 50s 44 53E
75 Moramanga, Madag. 18 58s 48 15E
94 Morant Point, Jamaica 17 55N 76 10W
72 Morar, & L., Scotland 56 57N 5 40W
64 Moratuwa, Sri Lanka 6 45N 80 0E
41 Morava, R., Yugoslavia 44 10N 21 0E
46 Moravia, Dist., Cz-slov. 49 27N 16 55E
46 Moravian Hts., Cz-slov. 49 20N 15 20E
42 Morbihan, Dépt., France 47 55N 2 45W
42 Morcenx, France 44 0N 1 0W
88 Morden, Canada 49 12N 98 10W
52 Mordovian, A.S.S.R., U.S.S.R. 54 20N 44 30E
33 More L., Scotland 58 18N 4 50W
48 Möre and Romsdal, Co., Norway 62 30N 8 0E
26 Morecambe, & B., Eng. 54 5N 2 52W
83 Moree, Australia 29 25s 149 46E
45 Morel, Switzerland 46 23N 8 2E

94 Morelia, Mexico 19 48N 101 0W
82 Morella, Australia 23 0s 143 47E
37 Morena, Sa. de, mts., Spain 38 20N 4 40W
83 Moreton I., Austral. 27 0s 153 15E
43 Morez, France 46 32N 6 0E
82 Morgan, Australia 34 3s 139 40E
91 Morgantown, U.S.A. 39 43N 79 59W
45 Morges, Switzerland 46 31N 6 30E
67 Morioka, Japan 39 48N 141 8E
83 Morkalla, Australia 34 18s 141 4E
42 Morlaix, France 48 38N 3 51W
27 Morley, England 53 46N 1 36W
83 Mornington, Australia 38 15s 145 5E
36 Mornington, Ireland 53 42N 6 17W
82 Mornington I., Austral. 16 30s 139 20E
84 Moro G., Philippines 7 0N 123 0E
72 Morocco, N. Africa 32 0N 5 0W
74 Morogoro, Tanzania 7 0s 37 50E
75 Morombé, Madagascar 21 38s 43 27E
95 Moron, Cuba 21 0N 78 45W
37 Moron, Spain 37 5N 5 30W
74 Morondava, Madag. 20 25s 44 30E
74 Moroto, Uganda 2 50N 34 0E
27 Morpeth, England 55 10N 1 42W
51 Morphou, Cyprus 35 17N 32 56E
84 Morrinsville, N.Z. 37 38s 175 30E
91 Morristown, U.S.A. 36 25N 83 18W
52 Morshansk, U.S.S.R. 53 28N 41 48E
42 Mortagne, France 47 0N 1 0W
22 Mortimer's Cross, Eng. 52 15N 2 47W
83 Mortlake, Australia 38 4s 142 50E
83 Moruya, Australia 35 55s 150 2E
33 Morven, Mt., Scotland 58 12N 3 40W
80 Morwell, Australia 38 12s 146 8E
24 Morwenstow, England 50 53N 4 32W
90 Moscow, U.S.A. 46 47N 117 2W
52 Moscow, U.S.S.R. 55 50N 37 40E
42 Moselle Dépt., France 49 5N 6 45E
45 Moselle, R., W. Europe 50 10N 7 10E
90 Moses Lake, U.S.A. 41 5N 119 0W
84 Mosgiel, New Zealand 45 53s 177 21E
74 Moshi, Tanzania 3 10s 37 30E
48 Mosjöen, Norway 66 0N 13 15E
48 Moskenstraumen, Norway 67 45N 13 0E
52 Moskva, R., U.S.S.R. 55 45N 36 0E
95 Mosquito Coast, Nicaragua 13 0N 84 0W
49 Moss, Norway 59 26N 10 40E
83 Moss Vale, Australia 34 38s 150 29E
84 Mossburn, New Zealand 45 40s 168 15E
76 Mosselbaai, S. Africa 34 10s 22 9E
74 Mossendjo, Congo (Fr.) 2 55s 12 55E
83 Mossgiel, Australia 33 5s 144 33E
99 Mossoró, Brazil 5 0s 37 15W
75 Mossuril, Mozambique 14 57s 40 42E
46 Most, Czechoslovakia 50 31N 13 38E
41 Mostar, Yugoslavia 43 21N 17 46E
36 Mostrim, Ireland 53 42N 7 38W
47 Mosty, U.S.S.R. 53 30N 24 30E
25 Mostyn, England 53 18N 3 14W
62 Mosul, Iraq 36 5N 43 15E
34 Mota, Ethiopia 11 5N 37 50E
49 Motala, & Can., Sweden 58 30N 15 20E
31 Motherwell, Scotland 55 47N 4 0W
64 Motihari, India 26 45N 85 0E
41 Motril, Spain 36 45N 3 44W
41 Moudhros, Greece 39 53N 25 18E
45 Moudon, Switzerland 46 41N 6 49E
74 Mouila, Gabon 1 50s 11 0E
74 Mouka, Central Africa 7 18N 21 50E
43 Moulins, France 46 36N 3 20E
65 Moulmein, Burma 16 30N 97 52E
72 Moundou, Central Africa 8 40N 16 10E
90 Mount Adams, Mt., U.S.A. 46 12N 121 35W
83 Mount Barker, S. Australia 35 8s 138 52E
80 Mount Barker, W. Australia 34 40s 117 50E
34 Mount Bellew Bridge, Ire. 53 29N 8 27W
75 Mount Darwin, Rhodesia 16 30s 31 35E
82 Mount Douglas, Australia 21 35s 146 50E
83 Mount Gambier, Austral. 37 45s140 45E
80 Mount Goldsworthy, Australia 20 25s 119 39E
90 Mount Hood, Mt., U.S.A. 45 15N 121 40W
84 Mount Hope, Australia 32 48s 146 0E
82 Mount Isa, Australia 20 40s 139 30E
90 Mount Lassen, Mt., U.S.A. 40 32N 121 15W
64 Mount Lavinia, Sri Lanka 6 50N 79 50E
83 Mount Lofty Ras, Austral. 35 0s 139 30E
84 Mount Maunganui, N.Z. 37 35s 176 30E
82 Mount Morgan, Austral. 23 35s 150 28E
90 Mount Rainier, Mt., U.S.A. 46 48N 121 43W
90 Mount Shasta, Mt., U.S.A. 41 30N 122 1W
82 Mount Surprise, Austral. 18 10s 144 17E
90 Mount Taylor, Mt., U.S.A. 35 20N 107 35W
80 Mount Tom Price, Austral. 22 40s 118 9E
92 Mount Vernon, U.S.A. 38 22N 88 44W
80 Mount Whaleback, Australia 24 38s 113 33E
80 Mount Whitney, Mt., U.S.A. 36 35N 118 13W
24 Mount's B., England 50 4N 5 25W

25 Mountain Ash, Wales 51 42N 3 23W
36 Mountcharles, Ireland 54 38N 8 13W
35 Mountmellick, Ireland 53 8N 7 17W
35 Mountrath, Ireland 53 0N 7 29W
72 Mourdhia, Mali 14 35N 7 25W
36 Mourne Mts., N. Ireland 54 8N 6 2W
36 Mourne, R., N. Ireland 54 45N 7 24W
51 Mouscron, Belgium 50 45N 3 15E
73 Moussoro, Chad 13 48N 16 48E
42 Moutiers, France 45 30N 6 30E
35 Moville, Ireland 55 11N 7 2W
36 Moy, N. Ireland 54 27N 6 41W
75 Moyamba, Sierra Leone 8 15N 12 30W
34 Moylough, Ireland 53 29N 8 35W
98 Moyobamba, Peru 6 5s 77 5W
75 Mozambique, Africa 15 3s 40 43E
75 Mozambique, Port. prov., Africa 19 0s 35 0E
70 Mozambique Channel, Indian Ocean 18 0s 42 0E
74 Mpanda, Tanzania 6 22s 30 40E
75 Mpangwe, Zambia 14 8s 32 10E
74 Mpika, Zambia 11 54s 31 32E
74 Mpwapwa, Tanzania 6 30s 36 30E
75 Msaken, Tunisia 35 49N 10 33E
75 Msoro, Zambia 13 35s 32 0E
74 Mtwara, Tanzania 10 16s 40 10E
74 Muanda, Zaïre 6 0s 12 20E
'68 Muang Khon Kaen, Thailand 16 59N 102 40E
68 Muang Nakhon Sawan, Thailand 15 40N 100 5E
68 Muang Phetchabun, Thailand 16 30N 101 10E
66 Muang Phitsanulak, Thailand 16 45N 100 3E
68 Muang Ubon, Thailand 15 20N 104 55E
68 Muar, Malaya 2 0N 102 40E
68 Muaraenim, Indonesia 3 35s 103 50E
68 Muaratewe, Indonesia 0 55s 114 50E
63 Mubarraz, Saudi Arabia 25 29N 49 40E
74 Mubende, Uganda 0 40N 31 21E
65 Mubi, Nigeria 10 16N 13 17E
22 Much Wenlock, Eng. 52 35N 2 33W
32 Muck I., Scotland 56 49N 6 13W
83 Mudgee, Australia 32 33s 149 32E
36 Muff, Ireland 55 4N 7 16W
51 Mufulira, Zambia 12 40s 28 12E
51 Mugla, Turkey 37 15N 28 30E
65 Muglad, Sudan 11 10N 27 35E
65 Mugu, Nepal 29 50N 82 30E
73 Muhammad Qol, Sudan 20 58N 37 0E
46 Mühlhausen, Germany 51 14N 10 26E
35 Muine Bheag, Ireland 52 41N 6 48W
31 Muirdrum, Scotland 56 31N 2 40W
31 Muirhead, Scotland 55 45N 4 5W
76 Muizenberg, S. Africa 34 7s 18 27E
63 Mujib, Wadiel, Jordan 31 28N 35 45E
47 Mukachevo, U.S.S.R. 48 27N 22 45E
63 Mukalla, South Yemen 14 38N 49 0E
67 Mukden, see Shenyang
65 Muktinath, Nepal 28 37N 83 55E
64 Muktsar, India 30 40N 74 30E
46 Mulde, R., Germany 51 30N 12 38E
94 Muleje, Mexico 26 50N 112 15W
93 Mulgrave, Canada 45 40N 61 30W
37 Mulhacen, Mt., Spain 36 45N 2 47W
44 Mulheim, Germany 51 0N 7 4E
45 Mulhouse, France 47 46N 7 19E
65 Muli, China 28 20N 100 40E
30 Mull I., Scotland 56 28N 6 0W
30 Mull of Galloway, Scot. 54 37N 4 52W
30 Mull of Kintyre, Scot. 55 17N 5 48W
30 Mull of Oa, Scotland 55 35N 6 20W
36 Mullagh, Ireland 53 49N 6 58W
79 Mullagharerikh Mts., Ire. 52 18N 9 50W
64 Mullaitivu, Sri Lanka 9 15N 80 50E
32 Mullardoch, L., Scotland 57 20N 5 0W
79 Mullet Pen., Ireland 54 10N 10 4W
80 Mullewa, Australia 28 33s 115 28E
35 Mullinahone, Ireland 52 32N 7 30W
35 Mullinavat, Ireland 52 22N 7 10W
35 Mullingar, Ireland 53 31N 7 19W
83 Mullumbimby, Austral. 28 30s 153 10E
64 Multan, Pakistan 30 3N 71 30E
75 Mumbles, The, Wales 51 34N 3 50W
25 Mumbles Hd., Wales 51 34N 3 59W
75 Mumbwa, Zambia 15 0s 27 2E
68 Muna I., Indonesia 5 0s 122 35E
64 Munabao, India 25 45N 70 15E
92 Muncie, U.S.A. 40 15N 85 22W
46 Münden, Germany 51 25N 9 40E
82 Mungallala, R., Austral. 26 25s 147 34E
82 Mungana, Australia 17 8s 144 27E
82 Mungbere, Zaïre 2 35N 28 35E
83 Mungindi, Australia 28 55s 149 0E
75 Munhango, Angola 12 18s 18 35E
46 Munich, Germany 48 9N 11 30E
92 Munising, U.S.A. 46 25N 87 0W
44 Munsingen, Switzerland 46 54N 7 37E
46 Munster, Germany 51 58N 7 39E
44 Munster, Prov., Ireland 52 20N 8 40W
44 Munstereifel Germany 50 33N 6 47E
48 Muonio, Finland 68 20N 23 0E
62 Mupa, Angola 16 5s 15 50E
62 Muqainama, Si. Arabia 22 9N 48 51E
62 Mur, R., Cent., Europe 46 30N 16 30E
50 Murashi, U.S.S.R. 59 30N 49 0E
43 Murat, France 45 10N 9 5E
84 Murchison, New Zealand 41 45s 172 23E
74 Murchison Falls, see Kabarega
80 Murchison R., Austral. 27 35s 115 0E
80 Murchison R., Austral. 20 0s 135 0E
37 Murcia, Spain 38 0N 1 8W
37 Murcia, Prov., Spain 38 35N 1 50W

47 Mures, R., Rumania 46 0N 22 10E
43 Muret, France 43 26N 1 16E
64 Murghab, R., Afghan. 35 4N 64 5E
83 Murgon, Australia 26 5s 151 55E
46 Muritz, L., Germany 53 30N 12 25E
50 Murmansk, U.S.S.R. 69 0N 33 10E
52 Murom, U.S.S.R. 55 31N 42 4E
67 Muroran, Japan 42 20N 141 5E
83 Murray Bridge, Australia 35 2s 139 8E
93 Murray Hr., Canada 46 0N 62 32W
83 Murray, R., Australia 34 30s 141 40E
64 Murree, Pakistan 33 50N 73 25E
45 Murren, Switzerland 46 33N 7 58E
34 Murrough, Ireland 53 8N 9 17W
83 Murrumbidgee R., Australia 34 37s 144 30E
83 Murrumburrah, Austral. 34 35s 147 30E
83 Murrurundi, Australia 31 42s 150 51E
83 Murtoa, Australia 36 42s 142 28E
31 Murton, England 54 51N 1 22W
84 Murupara, New Zealand 38 25s 176 45E
65 Murwara, India 23 46N 80 28E
83 Murwillumbah, Austral. 28 21s 153 2E
73 Murzuq, Libya 25 53N 13 38E
46 Mürzzuschalg, Austria 47 5N 15 35E
62 Mus, Turkey 38 50N 41 28E
63 Musa Qala, Afghan. 32 23N 64 48E
41 Musala, Mt., Bulgaria 42 15N 23 35E
63 Musallim, Wadi, Oman 22 0N 56 30E
63 Muscat, Oman 23 40N 58 38E
63 Muscat & Oman, see Oman
78 Musgrave Ras., Austral. 26 10E 131 30E
91 Muskegon, U.S.A. 43 13N 86 10W
91 Muskegon, R., U.S.A. 43 25N 85 40W
91 Muskogee, U.S.A. 35 46N 95 32W
65 Musmar, Sudan 18 6N 35 40E
62 Musoma, Tanzania 1 31s 33 58E
90 Musselshell, R., U.S.A. 46 35N 108 30W
74 Mussooree, India 30 23N 78 10E
94 Mustique, I., W.I. 12 50N 61 10W
83 Muswellbrook, Australia 32 18s 151 0E
62 Mut, Egypt 25 27N 29 0E
67 Mutankiang, Manchuria 44 34N 129 45E
75 Mutana, Angola 16 40s 15 1E
74 Mutarai, U.S.S.R. 61 20N 100 55E
74 Mutshatsha, Zaïre 10 35s 24 20E
34 Mutton I., Ireland 52 50N 9 33W
82 Muttaburra, Australia 22 30s 144 30E
62 Muwaih, Saudi Arabia 22 35N 41 32E
74 Muxima, Angola 9 33s 13 52E
55 Muyun Kum, U.S.S.R. 47 0N 65 0E
64 Muzaffarabad, Kashmir 34 30N 73 25E
64 Muzaffarnagar, India 29 27N 77 40E
65 Muzaffarpur, India 26 15N 85 29E
63 Muzhi, U.S.S.R. 65 25N 64 40E
66 Muztagh, Mt., China 36 30N 87 22E
75 Mwanza, Tanzania 2 30s 33 1E
74 Mwaya, Tanzania 9 30s 33 58E
74 Mweka, Zaïre 4 12s 21 56E
74 Mwenga, Zaïre 3 7s 28 27E
74 Mweru, L., Zaïre 9 0s 28 50E
74 Mweru Marsh, Zambia 8 40s 29 40E
75 Mwinilunga, Zambia 11 43N 24 27E
74 My Tho, Vietnam 10 20N 106 48E
74 Myadhi, Gabon 1 16N 13 10E
65 Myanaungmya, Burma 16 27N 94 58E
41 Mycenae, Greece 37 45N 22 45E
65 Myingyan, Burma 21 35N 94 40E
65 Myitkyina, Burma 25 50N 97 15E
64 Mymensingh, Pakistan, see Nasirabad
25 Mynydd du, Wales 51 45N 3 45W
25 Mynydd Epynt, Mt., Wales 52 3N 3 30W
25 Mynydd Prescelly, Mt., Wales 51 56N 4 45W
48 Myrdals Jökull, Ice. 63 40N 19 0W
52 Mysore, India 12 18N 76 37E
52 Mytishchi, U.S.S.R. 55 54N 37 47E
48 Myvatn, Iceland 65 35N 16 55W

N

46 Naab, R., Germany 49 40N 12 10E
49 Naantali, Finland 60 32N 21 55E
46 Naaldwijk, Netherlands 52 0N 4 15E
63 Na'ar, Jordan 31 53N 35 50E
35 Naas, Ireland 53 14N 6 39W
76 Nababeep, S. Africa 29 35s 17 35E
65 Nabadwip, India 23 25N 88 20E
61 Naband, Iran 27 12N 52 38E
73 Nabeul, Tunisia 36 30N 10 40E
63 Nabulus, Jordan 32 13N 35 15E
75 Nacala, Mozambique 14 40s 40 40E
94 Nacaome, Honduras 13 40N 87 35W
74 Nachingwea, Tanzania 10 40N 37 15E
49 Nacka, Sweden 59 17N 18 14E
94 Nacozari, Mexico 30 30N 109 50W
64 Nadiad, India 22 41N 72 56E
47 Nadvornaya, U.S.S.R. 48 37N 24 30E
64 Nadym, & R., U.S.S.R. 65 30N 73 0E
72 Nafada, Nigeria 11 0N 11 20E
68 Naga, Philippines 13 37N 123 5E
65 Nagaland, st. India 26 0N 94 30E
34 Nagalle, Ethiopia 5 20N 39 30E
67 Nagano, & Pref., Japan 36 38N 138 0E
67 Nagaoka, Japan 37 30N 138 55E
64 Nagappattinam, India 10 40N 79 45E
64 Nagar Parkar, Pak. 24 30N 70 35E
67 Nagasaki, & Pref., Jap. 32 40N 129 48E
67 Nagato, Japan 34 19N 131 15E
65 Nagchu Dzong, Tibet, China 31 25N 91 57E
64 Nagercoil, India 8 12N 77 33E

34 Nagles mts., Ireland 52 3N 8 30E
67 Nagoya, Japan 35 17N 137 0E
64 Nagpur, India 21 5N 79 5E
47 Nagykörös, Hungary 46 55N 19 48E
67 Naha, Japan 26 10N 127 45E
63 Naharayim, Jordan 32 38N 35 34E
63 Nahariya, Israel 33 0N 35 6E
63 Nahr Bisri R., Lebanon 33 34N 35 25
63 Nahr ed Dâmour, R., Leb. 33 44N 35 35E
63 Nahr el-Litani, R., Leb. 33 20N 35 20
99 Nahuel Huapi L., Arg. 41 0s 71 40W
89 Nain, Canada 56 38N 62 0W
64 Nainpur, India 22 30N 80 10E
29 Nairn, Scotland 57 36N 3 51W
33 Nairn R., Scotland 57 25N 4 10W
74 Nairobi, Kenya 1 15s 36 49E
74 Naivasha, Kenya 0 50s 36 30E
67 Najin, Korea 42 10N 130 10E
67 Nakadori Shima, Japan 33 0N 129 5E
67 Nakamura, Japan 33 0N 133 0E
67 Nakatsu, Japan 33 40N 131 15E
51 Nakhichevan, & A.S.S.R., U.S.S.R. 39 20N 45 30E
68 Nakhodka, U.S.S.R. 42 50N 132 50E
68 Nakhon Ratchasima, Thailand 15 0N 105 40E
68 Nakhon Si Thammarat, Thailand 8 30N 100 6E
92 Nakina, Canada 50 8N 86 35W
62 Nakhl, Egypt 29 55N 33 43E
78 Nakop, S.W. Africa 28 15 20 1E
49 Nakskov, Denmark 54 45N 11 12E
74 Nakuru, Kenya 0 10s 36 0E
51 Nalchik, U.S.S.R. 43 24N 43 32E
64 Nalgonda, India 17 4N 79 8E
64 Nallamalai Hs., India 16 0N 79 0E
73 Nalut, Libya 31 55N 11 2E
65 Nam Dinh, Vietnam 20 20N 106 15E
66 Nam Tso L., Tibet 30 45N 90 30E
60 Namangan, U.S.S.R. 41 30N 71 45E
76 Namaqualand, Dist., S. Africa 29 45s 18 0E
83 Nambour, Australia 26 31s 152 50E
83 Nambucca Heads, Australia 30 45s 152 48E
66 Namcha Barwa, Mt., China 29 50N 95 10E
70 Namib Des., Namibia 24 0s 15 0E
75 Namibia (South West Africa), Africa 22 0s 17 30E
83 Namoi, R., Australia 30 20s 150 30E
91 Nampa, U.S.A. 43 32N 116 50W
48 Namsen, R., Norway 64 40N 12 45E
48 Namsos, Norway 64 25N 11 30E
65 Namtu, Burma 23 0N 97 25E
44 Namur, & Prov., Belgium 50 28N 4 52E
75 Namutoni, S.W. Africa 18 50s 17 0E
75 Namwala, Zambia 15 50s 26 12E
66 Nan Ling, mts., China 25 30N 112 30E
55 Nan Shan, mts., China 38 30N 98 0E
88 Nanaimo, Canada 49 7N 123 58W
83 Nanango, Australia 26 40s 152 1E
67 Nanao, Japan 37 0N 137 0E
66 Nanchang, China 28 22N 115 49E
66 Nanchung, China 31 0N 105 20E
43 Nancy, France 48 42N 6 10E
64 Nanda Devi, mt., India 30 45N 80 0E
65 Nander, India 19 10N 77 16E
84 Nandi, Viti Levu, Fiji 17 40s 177 20E
64 Nandurbar, India 21 20N 74 15E
64 Nanga Parbat, mt., India 35 10N 75 0E
64 Nangrahar Prov., Afghan. 35 0N 71 0E
66 Nanking, China 32 5N 118 55E
76 Nannine, Australia 26 50s 118 16E
66 Nanning, China 22 50N 107 8E
67 Nanping, China 26 45N 118 0E
42 Nantes, France 47 17N 1 34W
64 Nanticoke, U.S.A. 41 10N 76 0W
43 Nantua, France 46 10N 5 35E
93 Nantucket I., U.S.A. 41 5N 70 5W
66 Nantung, China 31 50N 120 55E
26 Nantwich, England 53 5s 2 31W
66 Nanyang, China 33 11N 112 37E
74 Nanyuki, Kenya 0 1N 37 3E
37 Náo, C., Spain 38 25N 0 15E
67 Naoetsu, Japan 37 6N 138 9E
90 Napa, U.S.A. 38 24N 122 1W
84 Napier, New Zealand 39 37s 176 52E
40 Naples (Napoli), Italy 40 53N 14 18E
67 Nara, & Pref., Japan 34 30N 135 40E
83 Naracoorte, Australia 36 55s 140 50E
83 Naradhan, Australia 33 38s 146 27E
65 Narasapur, India 16 50N 81 48E
65 Narayanganj, Bangla. 23 35N 90 30E
64 Narayanpet, India 16 50N 77 12E
25 Narberth, Wales 51 48N 4 45W
43 Narbonne, France 43 12N 3 1E
22 Narborough, England 52 34N 1 12W
40 Nardo, Italy 40 10N 18 0E
49 Narew, R., Poland 53 12N 21 50E
64 Narmada R., India 22 0N 75 15E
64 Narodnaya M., U.S.S.R. 65 5N 60 50E
83 Narooma, Austral. 36 14s 150 4E
83 Narrabri, Australia 30 25s 149 47E
83 Narrandera, Australia 34 46s 146 19E
80 Narrogin, Australia 32 58s 117 10E
83 Narromine, Australia 32 1s 148 8E
64 Narsinghpur, India 23 0N 79 6E
64 Narva, Estonia, U.S.S.R. 59 10N 28 10E
48 Narvik, Norway 68 27N 17 30E
50 Naryan-Mar, U.S.S.R. 68 0N 53 0E
60 Narymskoye, U.S.S.R. 49 15N 84 15E

Naryn, U.S.S.R. 41 30N 76 10E
Nasa, mt., Norway 66 32N 16 0E
Naseby, England 52 23N 1 0w
Nashua, U.S.A. 42 46N 71 30w
Nashville, U.S.A. 36 0N 86 50w
Nasik, India 20 0N 74 0E
Nasirabad, Bangladesh 24 50N 90 25E
Nasirabad, India 26 14N 74 44E
Nassar City, Egypt, *see* Kôm Ombo
Nassau, Bahamas 25 2N 77 25w
Nasir, Sudan 8 30N 33 2E
Nasser, L., Egypt 24 0N 32 40E
Nässjö, Sweden 57 38N 14 45E
Natal, Brazil 5 48s 35 20w
Natal Prov., S. Africa 28 40s 30 30E
Natashquan, & R., Can. 50 14N 61 46w
Natchez, U.S.A. 31 35N 91 20w
Natchitoches, U.S.A. 31 40N 93 3w
Natimuk, Australia 36 52s 142 0E
Natron, L., Tanzania 2 0s 36 0E
Naturaliste, C., Australia 33 35s 115 1E
Naumburg, Germany 51 10N 11 45E
Nauntawa, India 27 20N 83 25E
Naushahra, Pakistan 34 0N 72 0E
Naushki, U.S.S.R. 50 30N 106 0E
Navalcarnero, Spain 40 15N 4 0w
Navan, *see* An Uaimh
Navarino I., Chile 55 0s 67 30w
Navarra, Prov., Spain 43 0N 1 45w
Naver, L. & R., Scot. 58 18N 4 27w
Navojoa, Mexico 27 10N 109 25w
Navolok, U.S.S.R. 62 50N 40 0E
Nápaktos, Greece 38 23N 21 26E
Návplion, Greece 37 30N 22 50E
Navsari, India 20 58N 72 45E
Nawa, Syria 32 54N 36 3E
Nawabshah, Pakistan 26 20N 68 25E
Nawakot, Nepal 28 2N 83 55E
Nayakhon, U.S.S.R. 62 5N 159 0E
Naxos, I., Greece 37 5N 25 29E
Nazare, Brazil 12 52s 39 15w
Nazareth, Israel 32 42N 35 17E
Nazas, R., Mexico 25 30N 104 0w
Naze, The, England 51 52N 1 19E
Nazir Hat, Bangladesh 22 40N 91 50E
Ndalatando, Angola 9 12s 14 48E
Ndélé, Central Africa 8 30N 20 37E
Ndjamena, Chad 12 3N 15 3E
N'Djolé, Gabon 0 10s 10 45E
Ndola, Zambia 12 54s 28 35E
Neagh, L., N. Ireland 54 35N 6 25w
Neath, & R., Wales 51 40N 3 47w
Nebine, Cr., Australia 28 30s 146 50E
Nebit Dag., U.S.S.R. 39 50N 54 30E
Nebraska, st., U.S.A. 42 15N 100 30w
Nebraska City, U.S.A. 40 44N 95 55w
Neckar, R., Germany 48 37N 9 10E
Necochea, Argentina 38 30s 58 50w
Needles, The, England 50 40N 1 35w
Neemuch, India 24 25N 74 50E
Neepawa, Canada 50 19N 99 30w
Negaunee, U.S.A. 46 30N 87 32w
Negev, Israel 30 50N 35 0E
Negoiu, mt., Rumania 45 20N 25 0E
Negotin, Yugoslavia 44 15N 22 34E
Negrais, C., Burma 16 0N 94 18E
Negro R., Argentina 40 0s 64 0w
Negro R., Brazil 1 0s 63 0w
Negros, I., Philippines 10 0N 123 0E
Neh, Iran 31 30N 59 58E
Neikiang, China 29 45N 104 25E
Neilston, Scotland 55 47N 4 26w
Neisse, R., Pol.-Ger. 51 27N 14 59E
Neiva, Colombia 3 0N 75 25w
Nejd, reg., Si. Arabia 25 15N 45 0E
Nekemte, Ethiopia 9 4N 36 30E
Nekso, Denmark 55 4N 15 8E
Nelka, U.S.S.R. 57 50N 136 0E
Nellore, India 14 30N 80 1E
Nelma, U.S.S.R. 47 30N 139 0E
Nelson, Canada 49 25N 117 17w
Nelson, England 53 50N 2 14w
Nelson, New Zealand 41 18s 173 20E
Nelson, C., Australia 38 18s 141 40E
Nelson, Dist., N.Z. 41 20s 173 23E
Nelson, R., Canada 56 22N 95 0w
Nelspruit, S. Africa 25 29s 30 59E
Néma, Mauritania 16 30N 7 0w
Neman, R., U.S.S.R. 55 5N 23 0E
Nemours, Algeria, *see* Ghazaouet
Nemours, France 48 16N 2 40E
Nemui, U.S.S.R. 55 35N 136 0E
Nemuro, Japan 43 20N 145 30E
Nene, R., England 52 38N 0 50w
Nenagh, Ireland 52 53N 8 12w
Nepal, Asia 28 0N 83 40E
Nepalganj, Nepal 28 0N 81 30E
Nephi, U.S.A. 39 43N 111 50w
Nephin, mt., Ireland 54 0N 9 22w
Nephin Beg Ra., Ireland 54 0N 9 35w
Neretva, R., Y-slav. 43 10N 17 53E
Nerchinsk, U.S.S.R. 52 1N 116 25E
Nerchinski Zavod, U.S.S.R. 51 10N 119 35E
Nerva, Spain 37 43N 6 30w
Nes, Iceland 65 50N 17 18w
Nesle, France 49 45N 2 53E
Ness, L. & R., Scotland 57 15N 4 28w
Neston, England 53 17N 3 4w
Nesttun, Norway 60 17N 5 31E
Netanya, Israel 32 20N 34 51E
Netherdale, Australia 21 10s 148 33E
Netherlands, Europe 52 20N 6 0E
Nettleham, England 53 15N 0 28w

46 Neu Brandenburg, Ger. 53 35N 13 15E
45 Neuchâtel, & Cn., Switz. 47 0N 6 56E
45 Neuchâtel, Lac de, Switz. 46 55N 6 50E
44 Neufchâteau, Belgium 49 50N 5 26E
43 Neufchâtel, France 49 42N 1 30E
44 Neufchâtel sur Aisne, Fr. 49 27N 4 0E
46 Neumünster, Germany 54 5N 10 0E
45 Neunkirchen, Germany 49 20N 7 0E
99 Neuquen & R., Arg. 39 5s 68 0w
46 Neuruppin, Germany 52 52N 12 48E
44 Neuss, Germany 51 13N 6 39E
46 Neusiedler, L., of, Austria 47 58N 16 47E
45 Neustadt, Germany 47 53N 8 14E
46 Neustrelitz, Germany 53 19N 13 0E
44 Neuwied, Germany 50 27N 7 30E
91 Neva, U.S.A. 37 51N 94 28w
90 Nevada, U.S.A. 37 51N 94 28w
90 Nevada, st., U.S.A. 39 30N 118 0w
37 Nevada, Sa. de, mts., Spain 37 10N 3 20w
95 Nevada de Chita, Colombia 6 30N 72 0w
61 Nevelski mt., U.S.S.R. 50 0N 143 25E
43 Nevers, France 47 3N 3 12E
83 Nevertire, Australia 31 38s 147 50E
94 Nevis I., W. Indies 17 0N 62 30w
32 Nevis, L., Scotland 57 0N 5 45w
31 New Abbey, Scotland 54 58N 3 37w
91 New Albany, U.S.A. 38 20N 85 50w
98 New Amsterdam, Guyana 6 12N 57 30w
91 New Bedford, U.S.A. 41 30N 71 0w
35 New Birmingham, Ire. 52 36N 7 38w
90 New Braunfels, U.S.A. 29 40N 98 13w
26 New Brighton, England 53 27N 3 4w
84 New Brighton, N.Z. 43 29s 172 43E
93 New Britain, U.S.A. 41 35N 72 50w
82 New Britain. I., Papua N.G. 6 0s 150 0E
89 New Brunswick, Prov., Canada 46 30N 66 30w
81 New Caledonia, I., Pacific Ocean 21 15s 165 0E
37 New Castile, prov., Spain 40 5N 3 20w
92 New Castle, Ind. U.S.A. 41 2N 80 20w
30 New Cumnock, Scot. 55 24N 4 3w
83 New England Ra., Austral. 30 0s 152 0E
22 New Forest, England 50 52s 1 48w
31 New Galloway, Scotland 55 4N 4 9w
93 New Glasgow, Canada 45 35N 62 57w
78 New Guinea, I. E. Indies 5 0s 140 0E
91 New Hampshire, st., U.S.A. 43 20N 71 30w
82 New Hanover, I., Pacific Ocean 2 18s 150 0E
91 New Haven, U.S.A. 41 15N 72 58w
81 New Hebrides, Is., Pacific Ocean 16 0s 166 30E
91 New Iberia, U.S.A. 30 0N 91 46w
82 New Ireland, I., Papua N.G. 3 0s 152 0E
93 New Jersey, st., U.S.A. 39 50N 74 30w
93 New London, U.S.A. 41 20N 72 5w
30 New Luce, Scotland 54 56N 4 51w
90 New Mexico, st., U.S.A. 34 40N 106 0w
26 New Mills, England 53 22N 2 0w
30 New Milns, Scotland 55 36N 4 19w
83 New Norfolk, Australia 42 45s 146 59E
91 New Orleans, U.S.A. 30 0N 90 0w
84 New Plymouth, N.Z. 39 2s 174 5E
91 New Providence, Bahamas 25 0N 77 25w
25 New Quay, Wales 52 12N 4 22w
25 New Radnor, Wales 52 14N 3 9w
23 New Romney, England 50 59N 0 56E
35 New Ross, Ireland 52 25N 6 57w
27 New Rossington, England 53 30N 1 4w
61 New Siberian Is., U.S.S.R. 75 30N 140 0E
83 New South Wales, st., Australia 32 20s 147 0E
25 New Tredegar, Wales 51 43N 3 15w
91 New Ulm, U.S.A. 44 19N 94 35w
88 New Westminster, Can. 49 12N 122 50w
93 New York, & st., U.S.A. 40 45N 74 0w
84 New Zealand 40 0s 173 0E
74 Newala, Tanzania 11 0s 39 0E
27 Newark, England 53 5N 0 49w
93 Newark, Del., U.S.A. 39 45N 75 45w
93 Newark, N.J., U.S.A. 40 45N 74 0w
92 Newark, Ohio, U.S.A. 40 8N 82 30w
91 New Bern, U.S.A. 35 7N 77 4w
27 Newbiggin-by-the-Sea, England 55 12N 1 30w
31 Newbigging, Scotland 55 42N 3 33w
36 Newbliss, Ireland 54 9N 7 8w
35 Newbridge, *see* Droichead Nua
25 Newbridge-on-Wye, Wales 52 13N 3 26w
31 Newburgh, Scotland 56 21N 3 14w
93 Newburgh, U.S.A. 41 33N 74 0w
27 Newburn, England 54 58N 1 44w
22 Newbury, England 51 24N 1 19w
83 Newcastle, Australia 32 59s 151 49E
35 Newcastle, Ireland 53 5N 6 4w
36 Newcastle, N. Ireland 54 13N 5 54w
35 Newcastle Emlyn, Wales 52 4N 4 28w
80 Newcastle Waters, Australia 17 1s 133 42E
27 Newcastle-on-Tyne, Eng. 54 58N 1 36w
26 Newcastle-under-Lyme, England 53 1N 2 14w
80 Newdegate, Australia 33 0s 119 30w
22 Newent, England 51 56N 2 24w
* *Renamed Vanuatu*

89 Newfoundland, prov., Canada 49 0N 56 0w
23 Newham, Greater London, England 51 31N 0 3E
23 Newhaven, England 50 47N 0 3E
23 Newington, England 51 6N 1 8E
91 Newman, U.S.A. 33 32N 84 35w
23 Newmarket, England 52 15N 0 24E
34 Newmarket, Ireland 52 10N 9 0w
94 Newmarket, Jamaica 18 8N 77 53w
34 Newmarket-on-Fergus, Ireland 52 46N 8 54w
22 Newnham, England 51 48N 2 27w
22 Newport, Salop, Eng. 52 46N 2 23w
25 Newport, Monmouth, Wales 51 35N 3 0w
35 Newport, & B., Mayo, Ireland 53 53N 9 33w
34 Newport, Tipperary, Ire. 52 43N 8 24w
31 Newport, Scotland 56 57N 2 56w
91 Newport, Ark., U.S.A. 35 34N 91 17w
91 Newport, Ken., U.S.A. 39 3N 84 28w
93 Newport, R.I., U.S.A. 41 30N 71 19w
93 Newport, Vt. U.S.A. 44 47N 72 12w
91 Newport News, U.S.A. 37 6N 76 25w
23 Newport Pagnell, Eng. 52 5N 0 43w
24 Newquay, England 50 25N 5 6w
36 Newry, N. Ireland 54 10N 6 18w
91 Newton, Iowa, U.S.A. 41 43N 93 4w
91 Newton, Kansas, U.S.A. 38 6N 97 17w
24 Newton Abbot, England 50 32N 3 37w
30 Newton Aycliffe, England 54 36N 1 33w
30 Newton Stewart, Scot. 54 57N 4 28w
26 Newton-le-Willows, Eng. 53 27N 2 37w
33 Newtonhill, Scotland 57 1N 2 9w
31 Newtown, Scotland 55 34N 2 38w
25 Newtown, Wales 52 30N 3 22w
36 Newtown Forbes, Ireland 53 46N 7 50w
36 Newtown Hamilton, N. Ireland 54 12N 6 34w
36 Newtown Monasterboice, Ireland 53 46N 6 26w
36 Newtownabbey, Ireland 54 40N 5 55w
36 Newtownards, N. Ireland 54 36N 5 42w
36 Newtownbutler, N. Ireland 54 11N 7 21w
36 Newtowncunningham, Ireland 54 59N 7 31w
35 Newtownmountkennedy, Ireland 53 6N 6 6w
36 Newtownstewart, N. Ireland 54 43N 7 23w
75 Nezhin, Ukraine, U.S.S.R. 51 3N 32 5E
75 Ngami, Ll (Former), Botswana 20 35s 22 35E
73 Ngaoundere, Cameroon 7 23N 13 20E
84 Ngapara, New Zealand 44 57s 170 46E
66 Ngoring, Nor., L., China 35 0N 97 15E
74 Ngudu, Tanzania 3 25s 32 2E
73 Ngulmi, Niger 14 20N 13 20E
68 Nha Trang, Vietnam 12 15N 109 15E
83 Nhill, Australia 36 18s 141 40E
81 Nhulunbuy, Australia 12 18s 137 0E
92 Niagara Falls, N. America 43 12N 79 0w
72 Niamey, Niger 13 31N 2 20E
68 Nias, Is., East Indies 1 0N 97 20E
94 Nicaragua, & L., Central America 12 30N 85 0w
41 Nicastro, Italy 39 0N 16 18E
43 Nice, France 43 45N 7 17E
55 Nicobar Is., India 8 0N 93 20E
62 Nicosia, Cyprus 35 7N 33 2E
27 Nidd, R., England 54 2N 1 40w
46 Nienburg, Germany 52 38N 9 10E
76 Nieu Bethesda, S. Africa 31 55s 24 30E
44 Nieuwpoort, Belgium 51 9N 2 46E
42 Nièvre, Dépt., France 47 17N 3 40E
51 Nigde, Turkey 38 0N 34 40E
72 Niger, W. Africa 15 0N 9 0E
72 Niger, R., W. Africa 16 0N 0 20E
72 Niger Delta, Nigeria 4 0N 5 0E
72 Nigeria, W. Africa 9 30N 8 0E
33 Nigg, B., Scotland 57 42N 4 0w
84 Nightcaps, New Zealand 45 58s 168 3E
67 Niigata, & Pref., Japan 38 0N 139 5E
90 Niihau, Hawaii 21 45N 160 10w
44 Nijkerk, Netherlands 52 14N 5 29E
44 Nijmegen, Netherlands 51 50N 5 52E
67 Nikko, Japan 36 50N 139 30E
51 Nikolayev, U.S.S.R. 46 58N 32 7E
61 Nikolayevski, Siberia 53 30N 140 10E
52 Nikopol, U.S.S.R. 47 20N 34 20E
41 Niksic, Yugoslavia 42 47N 18 57E
73 Nile, R., N.E. Africa 27 20N 31 0E
73 Nile, prov., Sudan 20 0N 33 0E
43 Nîmes, France 43 51N 4 21E
83 Nimmitabel, Australia 36 42s 149 0E
83 Nindigully, Australia 28 27s 149 0E
67 Ningan, China 44 30N 129 45E
66 Ningpo, China 30 0N 121 40E
66 Ningsia, *see* Yinchwan
66 Ningsia Hui, Autonomous Region, China 37 0N 106 0E
66 Ningtsin, China 29 50N 98 25E
66 Ningtu, China 26 50N 115 30E
66 Ninove, Belgium 50 51N 4 2E
72 Nioro, Mali 15 30N 9 30w
42 Niort, France 46 20N 0 43w
88 Nipawin, Canada 53 20N 104 0w
89 Nipigon, & L., Canada 49 48N 88 20w
89 Nipigon, L., Canada 49 40N 88 30w
62 Niriz, Iran 29 15N 54 5E
65 Nirmali, India 26 25N 86 30E

41 Nis, Yugoslavia 43 17N 21 53E
99 Niterói, Brazil 22 52s 42 55w
31 Nith, R., Scotland 55 27N 3 58w
31 Nithsdale, Scotland 55 13N 3 45w
47 Nitra, Czechoslovakia 48 20N 18 4E
84 Niuafo'ou, I., Pacific Ocean (Inset)
44 Nivelles, Belgium 50 36N 4 20E
43 Nivernais, Prov., France 47 20N 3 25E
61 Nizamabad, India 18 45N 78 7E
61 Nizhne Kolymsk, U.S.S.R. 68 35N 160 55E
61 Nizhneudinsk, U.S.S.R. 55 0N 99 25E
50 Nizhniy Tagil, U.S.S.R. 57 45N 60 0E
72 Nkambe, Camer. 6 35N 10 40E
74 Nkhata Bay, Malawi 11 35s 34 20E
75 Nkhota Kota, Malawi 13 0s 34 20E
65 Nmai, mts., Burma 25 45N 98 0E
65 Noakhali, *see* Maijdi
67 Nobber, Ireland 53 49N 6 45w
67 Nobeoka, Japan 32 35N 131 40E
94 Nogales, Mexico 31 30N 111 0w
94 Nogales, U.S.A. 31 25N 111 0w
43 Nogent le Rotou, Fr. 48 20N 0 50E
32 Noginsk, U.S.S.R. 55 50N 38 28E
61 Noginsk, U.S.S.R. 64 30N 90 50E
61 Noirmoutier, I. de, Fr. 47 0N 2 17w
61 Nokhtuisk, U.S.S.R. 60 10N 117 15E
88 Nokomis, Canada 51 10N 105 10w
68 Nok Kundi, Pakistan 28 55N 62 55E
83 Noondoo, Australia 28 35s 148 25E
44 Noord Beveland I., Neth. 51 35N 3 45E
44 Noord Brabant, prov. Netherlands 51 40N 5 0E
44 Noord Holland, prov., Netherlands 52 30N 4 45E
76 Noordhoek, S. Africa 34 7s 18 25E
44 Noordoost Polder, Neth. 52 45N 5 45E
92 Noranda, Canada 48 20N 79 0w
42 Nord, Dépt., France 50 29N 3 20E
88 Nordegg, Canada 52 0N 116 47w
23 Nordelph, England 52 30N 0 18E
46 Norderney I., Germany 53 43N 7 12E
46 Nordhausen, Germany 51 30N 10 43E
44 Nordhorn, Germany 52 29N 7 3E
13 Nordkinn, C., Europe 71 3N 28 0E
48 Nordland, Co., Norway 66 30N 14 0E
61 Nordvik, U.S.S.R. 73 45N 110 57E
28 Norfolk, Co., England 52 42N 1 0E
91 Norfolk, Neb., U.S.A. 42 6N 97 28w
91 Norfolk, Va., U.S.A. 36 55N 76 12w
23 Norfolk Broads, Eng. 52 45N 1 30E
76 Norfolk I., Pacific Ocean 29 0s 167 55E
27 Norham, England 55 42N 2 10w
82 Norman R., Australia 19 20s 142 25E
82 Normanby, I., Papua N.G. 10 0s 151 0E
82 Normanby, R., Australia 15 0s 145 0E
42 Normandy, Prov., France 49 0N 0 0
82 Normanton, Australia 17 52s 140 58E
23 Normanton, England 53 42N 1 25w
48 Norrbotten, Co., Sweden 66 40N 20 0E
49 Nörresundby, Denmark 57 5N 9 52E
49 Norrköping, Sweden 58 39N 16 6E
80 Norseman, Australia 32 8s 121 45E
61 Norsk, U.S.S.R. 52 30N 130 5E
98 Norte, Sa. do, mts., Brazil 12 59s 59 0w
32 North Ballachulish, Scot. 56 42N 5 9w
30 North Battleford, Can. 52 48N 108 6w
89 North Bay, Canada 46 20N 79 30w
90 North Bend, U.S.A. 43 28N 124 15w
31 North Berwick, Scotland 56 3N 2 43w
68 North Bunguran Is., Indonesia 4 40N 108 0E
93 North C., Canada 47 0N 60 28w
84 North C., New Zealand 34 22s 173 1E
49 North C., Norway 71 0N 26 0E
91 North Carolina, st., U.S.A. 35 30N 79 0w
30 North Channel, U.K. 55 0N 5 30w
92 North Chan., U.S.A. 46 5N 83 0w
90 North Dakota, st., U.S.A. 47 30N 100 0w
22 North Dorset Downs, England 50 40N 2 30w
22 North Downs, England 51 18N 0 20E
13 North Dvina R., U.S.S.R. 62 30N 43 0E
65 North East Frontier Agency, *see* Arunachal Pradesh
33 North Esk R., Scotland 56 54N 2 45w
13 North European Plain 57 0N 26 0E
23 North Foreland, England 51 23N 1 28E
49 North Frisian Is., Ger. 55 0N 8 20E
84 North I., New Zealand 38 0s 176 0E
67 North Korea, st., Asia 40 0N 127 0E
65 North Moscos Is., *see* Heinze Is.
51 North Ossetian, A.S.S.R., U.S.S.R. 43 0N 44 10E
68 North Pageh, I., Indon. 3 0s 100 10E
24 North Petherton, Eng. 51 6N 3 0w
90 North Platte R., U.S.A. 42 30N 105 0w
31 North Queensferry, Scot. 56 1N 3 22w
46 North Rhine-Westphalia, Land, Germany 51 0N 7 0E
32 North Roe, dist., Scot. 60 35N 1 20w
33 North Ronaldsay, I., & Firth, Scotland 59 23N 2 30w
88 North Saskatchewan R. Canada 54 0N 112 30w
13 North Sea, Europe 56 0N 3 0E
27 North Somercotes, Eng. 53 26N 0 9E
34 North Sd., Ireland 53 10N 9 48w
31 North Sd., Scotland 59 17N 2 45w
84 North Taranaki Bight, New Zealand 38 50s 174 0E

92 North Tonawanda, U.S.A. 43 0N 78 50w
32 North Tolsta, Scotland 58 21N 6 14w .
48 North Tröndelag, Co., Norway 64 15N 12 0E
32 North Uist, I., Scotland 57 37N 7 20w
95 North Village, Bermuda 32 19N 64 47w
23 North Walsham, England 52 49N 1 24E
80 North-West C., Austral. 21 42s 114 10E
32 North-West Highlands, Scotland 57 30N 5 2w
89 North-West River, Can. 53 45N 60 10w
27 North Yorkshire, Co., Eng. 54 20N 1 0w
73 Northern Darfur, prov., Sudan 15 0N 25 0E
73 Northern Kassala, prov., Sudan 15 0N 30 0E
84 Northland, Dist., N.Z. 35 30s 174 0E
88 Northwest Terr.. Canada 65 0N 97 0w
27 North York Moors, Eng. 54 25N 0 50w
27 Northallerton, England 54 21N 1 27w
80 Northam, Australia 31 40s 116 40E
24 Northam, England 51 2N 4 13w
80 Northampton, Australia 28 24s 114 37E
28 Northampton, & Co., England 52 14N 0 54w
65 Northern Circars, India 17 30N 82 30E
36 Northern Ireland, U.K. 54 40N 6 50w
80 Northern Terr., Australia 19 30s 134 0E
23 Northfleet, England 51 27N 0 20E
22 Northleach, England 51 50N 1 51w
83 Northumberland, C., Australia 38 0s 140 30E
28 Northumberland, Co., England 55 13N 2 0w
82 Northumberland Is., Australia 21 45s 150 20E
93 Northumberland Str., Canada 46 20N 64 15w
26 Northwich, England 53 16N 2 32w
27 Norton, England 54 8N 0 47w
92 Norwalk, U.S.A. 41 6N 82 46w
48 Norway, Europe 65 30N 12 0E
16 Norwegian Sea 70 0N 0 2E
23 Norwich, England 52 38N 1 19E
67 Noshiro, & R., Japan 40 12N 140 0E
60 Nosok, U.S.S.R. 69 20N 82 20E
62 Nossi Bé, I., Madag. 13 25s 48 15E
75 Nossi Mitsio, Madag. 12 55s 48 20E
76 Nossob, R., Botswana 25 0s 20 20E
76 Notec, R., Europe 53 5N 17 10E
40 Noto, Sicily, Italy 36 59N 15 10E
28 Nottingham, & Co., Eng. 52 58N 1 8w
72 Nouadhibou (Port Etienne), Mauritania 21 0N 17 0w
76 Noupoort, South Africa 31 10s 24 57E
43 Nouzonville, France 49 49N 4 45E
74 Nova Chaves, Angola 10 20s 21 26E
74 Nova Sagres, Port. Timor 8 20s 127 30E
93 Nova Scotia, Prov., Can. 45 0N 64 0w
60 Novaya Lyalya, U.S.S.R. 59 0N 60 50E
60 Novaya Zemlya, Is., U.S.S.R. 75 0N 55 0E
47 Nové Zámky, Cz-slov. 48 2N 18 8E
50 Novgorod, U.S.S.R. 58 30N 31 10E
41 Novi Pazar, Yugoslavia 43 12N 20 28E
41 Novi Sad, Yugoslavia 45 17N 19 44E
60 Novo Kuznetsk, U.S.S.R. 53 30N 87 10E
74 Novo Redondo, Angola 11 3s 13 46E
52 Novocherkassk, U.S.S.R. 47 22N 40 8E
47 Novograd Volynsk, U.S.S.R. 50 6N 27 33E
60 Novokazalinsk, U.S.S.R. 45 50N 62 5E
52 Novokuybyshevsk, U.S.S.R. 53 10N 49 52E
60 Novokuznetsk, U.S.S.R. 54 0N 87 10E
100 Novolazarevskaya, Antarctica 70 45s 2 0E
52 Novomoskovsk, U.S.S.R. 54 5N 38 15E
51 Novorossiysk, U.S.S.R. 44 40N 37 50E
52 Novoshakhtinsk, U.S.S.R. 47 45N 39 55E
60 Novosibirsk, U.S.S.R. 55 10N 83 5E
60 Novouzensk, U.S.S.R. 50 30N 48 10E
40 Novska, Yugoslavia 45 22N 16 59E
60 Novy Port, U.S.S.R. 67 40N 73 20E
65 Nowgong, India 26 22N 92 40E
83 Nowra, Australia 34 51s 150 38E
51 Nowy Sacz, Poland 49 39N 20 42E
46 Nowy Tomysl, Poland 52 20N 16 5E
43 Noyon, France 49 35N 3 0E
75 Nsanje, Malawi 16 55s 35 15E
73 Nubian Des., Sudan 21 0N 33 0E
98 Nudo Coropuna, mt., Peru 16 0s 72 30w
88 Nueltin, L., Canada 59 40N 99 30w
94 Nueces, R., U.S.A. 28 40N 98 30w
94 Nueva Rosita, Mexico 28 0N 101 20w
94 Nuevo Laredo, Mexico 27 25N 99 35w
84 Nuhaka, New Zealand 39 0s 177 47E
62 Nukheila, Oasis, Sudan 19 7N 26 15E
84 Nuku'alofa, Tonga Is. 21 9s 175 14w
60 Nukus, U.S.S.R. 42 30N 60 0E
80 Nullarbor Plain, Austral. 30 40s 129 30E
73 Numan, Nigeria 9 29N 12 3E
67 Numata, Japan 36 45N 139 4E
67 Numazu, Japan 35 10N 138 50E
83 Numurkah, Australia 36 3s 145 30E
22 Nuneaton, England 52 31N 1 28w
31 Nunivak Is., Alaska 60 0N 166 0w
44 Nunspeet, Netherlands 52 22N 5 46E
40 Nuoro, Sardinia, Italy 40 20N 9 20E
83 Nuriootpa, Australia 34 27s 139 0E
* *Renamed Ngunza*

AIL

45 Nürnberg (Nuremberg), Germany 49 28N 11 7E
68 Nusa Tenggara, Prov., Indonesia 7 40s 118 0E
62 Nusaybin, Turkey 37 3N 41 10E
64 Nushki, Pakistan 29 35N 65 57E
76 Nuweveldberge, mts., S. Africa 32 10s 21 45E
80 Nuyts, Pt., Australia 35 1s 116 40E
80 Nyabing, Australia 33 30s 118 10E
74 Nyahanga, Tanzania 2 10s 33 32E
83 Nyah, Australia 35 8s 143 26E
73 Nyala, Sudan 12 2N 24 58E
65 Nyalam Dz., Tibet, China 28 10N 85 50E
73 Nyamlell, Sudan 9 0N 27 3E
74 Nyahururu, Kenya 0 2N 36 27E
75 Nyasa, L., E. Africa 12 0s 34 30E
74 Nyasaland, E. Africa, see Malawi
49 Nybro, Sweden 56 43N 15 55E
60 Nyda, U.S.S.R. 66 40N 73 28E
66 Nyenchen Tanghla, Ra., Asia 30 30N 90 0E
74 Nyeri, Kenya 0 34s 37 0E
47 Nyíregyháza, Hungary 47 47N 21 43E
49 Nyköbing, Denmark 54 51N 11 50E
49 Nylöping, Sweden 58 46N 17 0E
75 Nylstroom, S. Africa 24 40s 28 0E
83 Nymagee, Australia 32 7s 146 20E
49 Nynashamn, Sweden 58 55N 17 57E
83 Nyngan, Australia 31 39s 147 13E
45 Nyon, Switzerland 46 24N 6 15E
39 Nyons, France 44 20N 5 5E
47 Nysa, Poland 50 40N 17 22E
67 Nyudo, C., Japan 40 0N 139 30E
74 Nzega, Tanzania 4 12s 33 11E
72 Nzérékoré, Guinéa 7 46N 8 58W

O

31 Oa, Mull of, Scotland 55 35N 6 20W
22 Oadby, England 52 37N 1 7W
90 Oahu, Hawaii 21 30N 158 0W
83 Oakbank, Australia 32 58s 140 50E
22 Oakengates, England 52 42N 2 29W
83 Oakey, Australia 27 28s 151 33E
23 Oakham, England 52 40N 0 47W
90 Oakland, U.S.A. 37 55N 122 5W
84 Oamaru, New Zealand 45 1s 171 0E
100 Oasis, Antartica 77 0s 101 0E
94 Oaxaca, Mexico 17 15N 96 38W
60 Ob, G. of, U.S.S.R. 70 0N 73 0E
60 Ob, R., U.S.S.R. 62 40N 66 0E
92 Oba, Canada 48 50N 84 10W
84 Oban, New Zealand 46 55s 168 10E
30 Oban, Scotland 56 25N 5 27W
44 Oberhausen, Germany 51 28N 6 50E
83 Oberon, Australia 33 40s 149 50E
68 Obi Is., Indonesia 1 40s 128 0E
98 Obidos, Brazil 1 48s 55 37W
62 Obock, Djibouti 12 0N 43 15E
34 O'Briensbridge, Ireland 52 46N 8 30W
72 Obuasi, Ghana 6 17N 1 40W
98 Ocaña, Colombia 8 0N 73 35W
37 Ocaña, Spain 39 55N 3 30W
31 Ochil Hills, Scotland 56 15N 3 40W
61 October Revolution I., U.S.S.R. 79 30N 97 0E
62 Oda, Gebel, Sudan 20 15N 36 50E
48 Odadahraun, Iceland 65 10N 17 0W
49 Odda, Norway 60 3N 6 35E
49 Oddeyri, Iceland 65 40N 18 5W
76 Odendaalsrus, S. Africa 27 53s 26 45E
49 Odense, Denmark 55 22N 10 23E
49 Oder, R., Poland 53 3N 14 20E
90 Odessa, U.S.A. 31 50N 102 25W
51 Odessa, U.S.S.R. 46 37N 30 50E
72 Odienné, Ivory Coast 9 30N 7 15W
23 Odiham, England 51 16N 0 57W
47 Odorhei, Rumania 46 20N 25 20E
44 Odzak, Yugoslavia 45 3N 18 18E
75 Odzi, Rhodesia 19 0s 32 20E
40 Ofanto, R., Italy 41 0N 16 50E
45 Ofenpass, Switzerland 46 40N 10 20E
35 Offaly, Co., Ireland 53 10N 7 30W
44 Offenbach, Germany 50 7N 8 51E
45 Offenburg, Germany 48 28N 7 57E
45 Oftringen, Switzerland 47 20N 7 56E
67 Ogaki, Japan 35 25N 136 30E
72 Ogbomosho, Nigeria 8 5N 4 10E
90 Ogden, U.S.A. 41 22N 111 50W
91 Ogdensburg, U.S.A. 44 42N 75 20W
67 Oginohama, Japan 38 27N 141 30E
40 Oglio, R., Italy 46 0N 10 20E
82 Ogmore, Australia 22 37s 149 35E
25 Ogmore Vale, Wales 51 35N 3 32W
84 Ohakune, New Zealand 39 26s 175 25E
44 Ohey, Belgium 50 26N 5 8E
91 Ohio, R., U.S.A. 39 45N 81 30W
91 Ohio, st., U.S.A. 40 40N 82 30W
46 Ohre, R., Cz-slov. 50 10N 12 30E
44 Ohrid, Yugoslavia 41 10N 20 50E
76 Ohrigstad, S. Africa 24 30s 30 32E
35 Oilgate, Ireland 52 25N 6 30W
61 Oimyakon, U.S.S.R. 63 20N 143 5E
60 Oirot-Tura, U.S.S.R. 52 0N 86 3E
43 Oise, Dépt., France 49 35N 2 12E
43 Oise, R., France 49 20N 3 0E
44 Oisterwijk, Netherlands 51 35N 5 12E
67 Oita, & Pref., Japan 33 10N 131 50E
99 Ojos del Salado, mt., Arg. 27 0s 68 0W
64 Okahandja, S.W. Africa 22 0s 16 52E
84 Okarito, New Zealand 43 15s 170 10E
75 Okavango Swamp, Botswana 19 30s 23 0E

67 Okayama, & Pref., Japan 34 40N 133 6E
67 Okazaki, Japan 34 55N 137 10E
91 Okeechobee, L., U.S.A. 27 0N 80 50W
24 Okehampton, England 50 45N 4 0W
72 Okene, Nigeria 7 32N 6 11E
64 Okha, India 22 25N 69 0E
61 Okha, U.S.S.R. 53 40N 142 50E
61 Okhotsk, U.S.S.R. 59 25N 143 10E
61 Okhotsk, Sea of, U.S.S.R. 57 0N 149 0E
67 Oki Is., Japan 36 17N 133 10E
75 Okiep, S. Africa 29 41s 17 59E
67 Okinawa, I., Japan 26 30N 128 0E
90 Oklahoma City, U.S.A. 35 40N 97 20W
90 Oklahoma, st., U.S.A. 35 40N 97 0W
72 Okrika, Nigeria 4 47N 7 4E
51 Oktabrsk, U.S.S.R. 49 20N 57 15E
84 Okuru, New Zealand 43 55s 168 58E
48 Olafsvik, Iceland 64 52N 23 45W
49 Oland I., Sweden 56 50N 16 40E
83 Olary, Australia 32 8s 140 7E
99 Olavarria, Argentina 37 0s 60 20W
40 Olbia, Sardinia, Italy 40 55N 9 30E
37 Old Castile, Prov. Spain 42 0N 4 0W
36 Old Castle, Ireland 53 46N 7 10W
33 Old Deer, Scotland 57 30N 2 3W
35 Old Head of Kinsale, Ire., see Kinsale
30 Old Kilpatrick, Scotland 55 56N 4 34W
62 Old Sennar, Sudan 13 52N 33 32E
22 Oldbury, England 52 30N 1 59W
44 Oldenburg, Germany 53 10N 8 15E
26 Oldham, England 53 34N 2 7W
44 Oldenzaal, Netherlands 52 19N 6 55E
92 Olean, U.S.A. 42 7N 78 27W
61 Olekma, R., U.S.S.R. 57 30N 121 30E
33 Oldmeldrum, Scotland 57 20N 2 19W
61 Olekminsk, U.S.S.R. 60 40N 120 30E
61 Olenek, R., U.S.S.R. 72 30N 122 30E
47 Olésnica, Poland 51 13N 17 22E
60 Olga, U.S.S.R. 43 50N 135 20E
76 Olifants R., S. Africa 24 0s 31 25E
76 Olifantshoek, S. Africa 27 50s 22 55E
63 Olives, Mt. of Israel 31 47N 35 14E
27 Ollerton, England 53 12N 1 1W
27 Olney, England 52 0N 0 42W
46 Olomouc, Cz-slov. 49 35N 17 8E
42 Oloron, France 43 10N 0 40W
61 Olovyannaya, U.S.S.R. 50 55N 115 30E
49 Olsztyn, Poland 53 45N 20 30E
45 Olten, Switzerland 47 22N 7 54E
44 Olympia, Ruins of, Gr. 37 40N 21 39E
41 Olympia, U.S.A. 47 2N 122 50W
41 Olympus, Mt., Greece 40 2N 22 25E
86 Olympus, Mt., U.S.A. 47 8N 124 0W
36 Omagh, N. Ireland 54 35N 7 18W
91 Omaha, U.S.A. 41 28N 96 12W
62 Oman, G. of, S.W. Asia 24 30N 59 0E
68 Ombai Str., East Indies 8 15s 124 45E
22 Ombersley. England 52 17N 2 12W
74 Omboue, Gabon 1 35s 9 15E
40 Ombrone, R., Italy 42 40N 11 3E
73 Omdurman, Sudan 15 50N 32 45E
67 Ominato, Japan 41 25N 141 8E
44 Ommen, Netherlands 52 32N 6 26E
61 Omolon, R., U.S.S.R. 64 30N 161 0E
67 Omoto, Japan 39 57N 142 0E
66 Ompor, U.S.S.R. 49 50N 117 0E
60 Omsk, U.S.S.R. 55 0N 73 30E
47 Omul, Mt., Rumania 45 20N 25 20E
75 Omuramba Omatako, R., South-West Africa 20 0s 17 50E
67 Omuta, Japan 33 0N 130 26E
67 Ondangua, S.W. Africa 18 0s 16 0E
66 Ondörhaan, Mongolia 47 30N 110 15E
48 Ondverdarnes, Iceland 64 52N 24 0W
50 Onega, & G. of, & R., U.S.S.R. 60 40N 37 30E
84 Onehunga, New Zealand 36 58s 174 50E
61 Onekotan, I., U.S.S.R. 49 30N 154 30E
61 Onguren, U.S.S.R. 54 0N 108 0E
72 Onitsha, Nigeria 6 8N 6 55E
67 Onomichi, Japan 34 30N 133 5E
80 Onslow, Australia 21 44s 115 1E
91 Onslow Bay, U.S.A. 34 30N 77 0W
67 Ontake, Mt., Japan 35 57N 137 30E
90 Ontario, U.S.A. 43 50N 117 0W
92 Ontario, L., N. America 43 40N 78 0W
89 Ontario, Prov., Canada 50 0N 86 0W
80 Ontonagon, U.S.A. 46 58N 89 12W
80 Oodnadatta, Australia 27 30s 135 30E
80 Ooldea, Australia 30 30s 131 5E
44 Oosterhout, Netherlands 51 38N 4 51E
64 Ootacamund, India 11 30N 76 40E
80 Ootse, Botswana 25 0s 25 40E
74 Opala, Zaïre 1 13s 24 45E
61 Opanake, Sri Lanka 6 30N 80 35E
47 Opava, Czechoslovakia 49 57N 17 50E
80 Ophthalmia Ra., Austral. 23 14s 119 30E
49 Oporto, Portugal 41 10N 8 38W
84 Opotiki, New Zealand 38 0s 177 30E
49 Oppland, Dist., Norway 61 10N 10 0E
84 Opua, New Zealand 35 13s 174 0E
84 Opunake, New Zealand 39 27s 173 52E
64 Oqair, Saudi Arabia 25 45N 50 10E
63 Or Yehuda, Israel 32 1N 34 53E
48 Oraefa Jokull, mt., Ice. 64 10N 16 20W
47 Oradea, Rumania 47 2N 21 57E
64 Orai, India 26 3N 79 30E
72 Oran, Algeria 35 45N 0 38W
99 Oran, Argentina 23 5s 64 15W
83 Orange, Australia 33 13s 149 0E
43 Orange, France 44 10N 4 50E
91 Orange, U.S.A. 30 5N 93 47W
76 Orange, R.. S.W. Africa 28 40s 16 30E

76 Orange Free State, Prov., South Africa 28 20s 27 0E
91 Orangeburg, U.S.A. 33 30N 80 51W
84 Orangemouth, S.W. Afr. 23 38s 16 24E
92 Orangeville, Canada 43 58N 80 2W
44 Oranienburg, Germany 52 43N 13 14E
76 Oranjefontein, S. Africa 23 30s 27 30E
34 Oranmore, Ireland 53 16N 8 57W
40 Orbe, Switzerland 46 44N 6 30E
40 Orbetello, Italy 42 25N 11 5E
83 Orbost, Australia 37 40s 148 28E
44 Orchies, France 50 28N 3 14E
66 Ordos, Desert, China 39 30N 108 0E
51 Ordzhonikidze, U.S.S.R. 43 20N 44 30E
46 Ore Mts., Germany, see Erz Gebirge
49 Orebro, & Co., Sweden 59 20N 15 18E
90 Oregon, St., U.S.A. 43 45N 120 30W
52 Orekhovo-Zuyevo, U.S.S.R. 55 0N 39 2E
52 Orel, U.S.S.R. 53 3N 36 8E
50 Orenburg, U.S.S.R. 51 42N 55 7E
37 Orense, Spain 42 19N 7 53W
38 Orihuela, Spain 38 8N 0 58W
37 Origny Ste. Benoite, Fr. 49 50N 3 30E
98 Orinoco, Delta of, Ven. 9 0N 61 0W
98 Orinoco R., Venezuela 8 0N 64 50W
62 Orissa, Prov., India 21 0N 85 0E
40 Oristano, Italy 39 57N 8 39E
48 Orkanger, Norway 63 16N 9 57E
48 Orkla, R., Norway 63 0N 9 40E
33 Orkney, S. Africa 27 0s 26 35E
33 Orkneys Is., & Co., Scotland 59 5N 3 0W
100 Orkneys, South, Islands, Southern Ocean 61 0s 46 0W
91 Orlando, U.S.A. 28 30N 81 0W
43 Orléanais, Prov., France 47 50N 2 0E
43 Orléans, France 47 57N 1 53E
72 Orléansville, see El Asnam
64 Ormara, Pakistan 25 13N 64 37E
68 Ormoc, Philippines 11 5N 124 30E
26 Ormskirk, England 53 34N 2 53W
48 Ormond, N.Z. 38 30s 177 55E
42 Orne, Dépt., France 48 40N 0 5W
48 Örnsköldsvik, Sweden 63 18N 18 44E
40 Orosei, Italy 40 20N 9 40E
83 Orroroo, Australia 32 45s 137 30E
45 Orsières, Switzerland 46 2N 7 10E
50 Orsk, U.S.S.R. 51 8N 58 30E
47 Orsova, Rumania 44 42N 22 22E
45 Orta, L., Italy 45 48N 8 28E
37 Ortigueira, Spain 43 40N 7 50W
40 Ortles, Mt., Italy 46 19N 10 38E
26 Orton, England 54 28N 2 35W
40 Ortona, Italy 42 20N 14 22E
98 Oruro, Bolivia 17 50s 67 25W
40 Orvieto, Italy 42 43N 12 8E
23 Orwell, R., England 52 10N 1 0E
41 Oryakhovo, Bulgaria 43 43N 23 55E
91 Osage, R., U.S.A. 38 0N 94 0W
67 Osaka, & Pref., Japan 34 40N 135 39E
92 Oshawa, Canada 44 0N 78 50W
75 Oshikango, S.W. Africa 17 9s 16 10E
72 Oshogbo, Nigeria 7 5N 4 50E
74 Oshwe, Zaïre 3 10s 19 35E
41 Osijek, Yugoslavia 45 32N 18 42E
91 Osinino, U.S.S.R. 41 17N 148 57E
91 Oskaloosa, U.S.A. 41 17N 92 44W
84 Oskarshamn, Sweden 57 18N 16 23E
49 Oslo, Norway 59 54N 10 50E
49 Oslo Fjord, Norway 59 0N 10 30E
64 Osmanabad, India 18 6N 76 4E
51 Osmaniye, Turkey 37 7N 36 15E
44 Osnabrück, Germany 52 19N 8 2E
45 Osogna, Switzerland 46 18N 8 58E
94 Osorno, Chile 40 30s 73 0W
44 Oss, Netherlands 51 47N 5 32E
82 Ossa, Mt., Australia 41 47s 146 0E
27 Ossett, England 53 40N 1 35W
54 Oster Dal, R., Seden 61 30N 13 50E
49 Östergötland, Sweden 58 20N 15 30E
49 Östersund, Sweden 63 14N 14 40E
49 Östfold, Co., Norway 59 30N 11 0E
40 Ostia, Italy 41 40N 12 20E
47 Ostrava, Cz.slov. 49 55N 18 19E
49 Ostróda, Poland 53 40N 20 1E
47 Ostróg, U.S.S.R. 50 20N 26 30E
47 Ostroleka, Poland 53 21N 21 34E
47 Ostrów, Poland 51 40N 17 40E
47 Ostrów Mazowiecka, Pol. 52 48N 21 55E
47 Ostrowiec, Poland 51 0N 21 25E
67 Osumi Chan., see Van Diemen Str.), Japan 30 55N 131 0E
26 Oswaldtwistle, England 53 44N 2 27W
91 Oswego, U.S.A. 43 25N 76 33W
25 Oswestry, England 52 15N 3 5W
67 Ota, Japan 36 42N 140 30E
84 Otago, Dist., N.Z. 45 20s 169 50E
84 Otaki, New Zealand 40 38s 175 10E
67 Otaru, Japan 43 10N 141 0E
84 Otavi, S.W. Africa 19 35s 17 25E
67 Otley, England 53 56N 1 31W
84 Otorohanga, N.Z. 38 10s 175 12E
41 Otranto, & Str., Italy 40 11N 18 28E
67 Otsu, Japan 35 0N 136 0E
93 Ottawa, & R., Canada 45 20N 75 41W
91 Ottawa, U.S.A. 38 40N 95 20W
89 Ottawa Is., Canada 59 30N 81 0W
68 Otter, R., England 50 48N 3 15W
24 Ottery St. Mary, Eng. 50 45N 3 16W
91 Ottumwa, U.S.A. 41 5N 92 20W
72 Oturkpo, Nigeria 7 10N 8 15E

47 Otwock, Poland 52 10N 21 20E
91 Ouachita, Mts., U.S.A. 34 58N 94 20E
91 Ouachita, R., U.S.A. 32 30N 92 5W
72 Ouagadougou, Volta 12 25N 1 30W
73 Ouadda, Central Africa 8 15N 22 20E
72 Ouallene, Algeria 24 30N 1 20E
74 Ouanda Djalé, Central Africa 8 55N 22 53E
74 Ouango, Central Africa 4 19N 22 30E
72 Ouargla, Algeria 31 50N 5 20E
72 Ouarzazate, Morocco 31 0N 6 40W
74 Oubangi, R., Congo (Fr.) 1 0N 17 30E
44 Oudenaarde, Belgium 50 51N 3 37E
44 Oudensbock, Neth. 51 35N 4 30E
75 Oudtshoorn, S. Africa 33 32s 22 8E
74 Ouesso, Congo (Fr.) 1 40N 16 10E
72 Ouezzane, Morocco 34 51N 5 42W
44 Ougrée, Belgium 50 37N 5 30E
72 Ouidah, Benin 6 25N 2 0E
72 Oujeft, Mauritania 20 0N 13 0W
72 Ouled Djellal, Algeria 34 20N 6 30E
23 Oulton Broad, England 52 28N 1 44E
50 Oulu, Co., Finland 64 53N 25 23E
48 Oulu, L. & R., Finland 64 20N 27 15E
48 Ounas, R., Finland 67 45N 24 55E
23 Oundle, England 52 29N 0 27W
44 Our, R., Germany 50 3N 6 8E
98 Ouro Preto, Brazil 20 17s 43 48W
44 Ourthe, R., Belgium 50 15N 5 33W
23 Ousdale, Scotland 58 10N 3 34W
23 Ouse, Great, R., Cambs., England 52 21N 0 6E
21 Ouse, R., Sussex, Eng. 50 50N 0 5E
27 Ouse, R., Yorks., Eng. 54 0N 1 10W
32 Out Skerries, Scotland 60 25N 0 44W
32 Outer Hebrides, Scot. 57 40N 7 0W
83 Ouyen, Australia 35 0s 142 30E
99 Ovalle, Chile 30 35s 71 17W
75 Ovamboland, reg., S.W. Africa 17 40s 16 0E
37 Ovar, Portugal 40 50N 8 40W
33 Overbister, Scotland 59 16N 2 33W
44 Overijssel, Prov., Neth. 52 24N 6 33E
48 Övertornea, Sweden 66 25N 23 32E
37 Oviedo, Spain 43 25N 5 53W
84 Owaka, New Zealand 46 30s 169 48E
91 Owatonna, U.S.A. 44 8N 93 34W
92 Owen Sound, Canada 44 40N 81 0W
82 Owen Stanley Ra., Papua 9 0s 148 0E
91 Owensboro, U.S.A. 37 47N 87 7W
91 Owosso, U.S.A. 43 2N 84 12W
36 Ox Mts., see Slieve Gamph
49 Oxelösund, Sweden 58 43N 17 15E
22 Oxford, & Co., England 51 45N 1 15W
84 Oxford, New Zealand 43 20s 172 10E
83 Oxleys Pk., Australia 31 50s 150 20E
33 Oykel R., Scotland 57 58N 4 40W
72 Oyo, Nigeria 7 58N 3 59E
43 Oyonnax, France 46 15N 5 40E
82 Oyster B., Australia 42 10s 148 0E
68 Ozamiz, Philippines 8 10N 123 40E
91 Ozark Plateau, U.S.A. 37 0N 92 30W
91 Ozarks, L. of the, U.S.A. 38 0N 93 0W

P

65 Paan, China 29 55N 99 5E
76 Paarl, Cape Prov. 33 45s 18 59E
52 Paatsi, R., U.S.S.R. 68 55N 29 0E
64 Pab Hills, Pakistan 26 20N 64 45E
32 Pabbay I., & Sd., Scot. 57 47N 7 14W
65 Pabna, Bangladesh 24 0N 89 10E
95 Pacaraima, Sa., mts., Venezuela 4 0N 63 0W
98 Pacasmayo, Peru 7 28s 79 30W
64 Pachpadra, India 25 57N 72 0E
94 Pachuca, Mexico 20 13N 98 45W
4 Pacific Ocean 45 0s to 60 0N, 120 0E to 75 0W
68 Padang, Indonesia 1 5s 100 25E
46 Paderborn, Germany 51 47N 8 52E
26 Padiham, England 53 48N 2 20W
88 Padlei, Canada 62 10N 97 5W
24 Padstow, & B., England 50 32N 4 57W
40 Padua (Padova), Italy 45 23N 11 51E
91 Paducah, U.S.A. 37 1N 88 29W
84 Paeroa, New Zealand 37 18s 175 39E
46 Pag I., Yugoslavia 44 20N 15 0E
68 Pagadian, Philippines 7 55N 123 30E
71 Pagalu, I. Atlant. 1 35s 5 35E
90 Page, U.S.A. 37 0N 111 25W
84 Pago Pago, Samoa 14 5s 171 48W
68 Pahandut, Indonesia, see Palangkaraya
84 Pahiatua, New Zealand 40 27s 175 48E
62 Pahlevi, Iran 37 37N 49 8E
24 Paignton, England 50 26N 3 33W
49 Päijänne, L., Finland 61 40N 25 30E
42 Paimboeuf, France 47 20N 2 0W
42 Paimpol, France 48 42N 3 2W
30 Paisley, Scotland 55 51N 4 25W
22 Painswick, England 51 47N 2 11W
90 Painted Desert, U.S.A. 36 0N 111 10W
65 Paiyu, China 31 10N 98 45E
68 Pakanbaru, Indonesia 0 30N 101 35E
65 Pakhoi, China 21 30N 109 12E
62 Pakistan, Asia 30 0N 70 0E
65 Pakistan, West see Pakistan
65 Pakistan, East see Bangladesh
66 Pakokku, Burma 21 15N 95 6E
68 Pakse, Laos 15 5N 105 47E
64 Paktya, prov., Afghan. 33 0N 69 0E
64 Palam, India 19 0N 77 0E
37 Palamos, Spain 41 52N 3 13E

68 Palangkaraya (Pahandut), Indonesia 2 25s 114 0E
64 Palanpur, India 24 15N 72 30E
75 Palapye, Botswana 22 30s 27 28E
91 Palatka, U.S.A. 29 35N 81 42w
5 Palau Is., Pacific Ocean 7 20N 135 0E
5 Palawan, I., Philippines 9 30N 119 0E
49 Paldiski, U.S.S.R. 59 23N 24 9E
68 Paleleh, Indonesia 1 0N 122 0E
68 Palembang, Indonesia 3 0s 104 47E
37 Palencia, Spain 42 1N 4 35w
40 Palermo, Italy 38 8N 13 18E
63 Palestine, see Israel and Jordan
91 Palestine, U.S.A. 31 46N 95 40w
64 Palghat, India 11 N 76 59E
23 Palgrave, England 52 22N 1 6E
64 Pali, India 25 45N 73 10E
64 Palitana, India 21 48N 71 49E
64 Palk Bay, Sri Lanka 9 20N 80 0E
64 Palk Str., India 10 0N 80 0E
45 Pallanza, Italy 45 58N 8 35E
34 Pallaskenry, Ireland 52 38N 8 52W
82 Palm Is., Australia 18 45s 146 35E
37 Palma, Balearic Is., Spain 39 37N 2 4E
72 Palma, I., Canary Is. 28 50N 17 50W
40 Palmas, G. of, Italy 38 50N 8 25E
84 Palmerston, N.Z. 45 30s 170 45E
84 Palmerston North, N.Z. 40 18s 175 36E
40 Palmi, Italy 38 20N 15 55E
98 Palmira, Colombia 3 40N 76 20W
62 Palmyra, Syria 34 20N 37 55E
64 Palni Hs., India 10 30N 77 30E
51 Palo Seco, Trinidad 10 5N 61 32W
51 Palu, Turkey 38 37N 40 0E
43 Pamiers, France 43 5N 1 40E
55 Pamir, mts., Cent. Asia 37 0N 73 0E
90 Pampa, U.S.A. 35 32N 101 0w
98 Pampas, The, Argentina 36 20s 62 0w
37 Pampiona, Spain 42 48N 1 37w
95 Panama, & G., Panama 9 3N 79 30w
*95 Panama Canal Zone, Pan. 9 3N 79 45w
95 Panama, Cent. Amer. 9 0N 80 0w
91 Panama City, U.S.A. 30 13N 85 14w
41 Pancevo, Yugoslavia 44 52N 20 42E
64 Pandharpur, India 17 36N 75 24E
22 Pangbourne, England 51 29N 1 6w
68 Pangkal Pinang, Indon. 2 0s 106 8E
64 Pangon Tso, L., Tibet 33 50N 78 50E
65 Pangyang, Burma 22 10N 98 45E
64 Panjim, Goa, India 15 30N 73 45E
64 Panna, India 24 45N 80 15E
64 Pannani, India 10 40N 75 55E
40 Pantelleria, I., Italy 36 50N 12 0E
94 Panuco, R., Mexico 21 30N 98 30w
72 Panyam, Nigeria 9 27N 9 8E
66 Paoki, China 34 30N 106 50E
66 Pao-shan, China 25 16N 99 35E
66 Pao-ting, China 39 10N 115 47E
66 Paotow, China 40 45N 110 1E
73 Paoua, Central Africa 7 25N 16 30E
47 Pápa, Hungary 47 20N 17 30E
32 Papa Stour I., Scotland 60 19N 1 40w
33 Papa Stronsay, Scotland 59 9N 2 34w
33 Papa Westray I., Scot. 59 21N 2 54w
94 Papantla, Mexico 20 27N 97 15w
30 Paps of Jura, Scotland 55 55N 6 0w
82 Papua New Guinea 8 0s 145 0E
82 Papua, G. of, New Guinea 8 30s 145 0E
98 Para, st., Brazil 4 0s 52 30w
98 Pará, Brazil 1 20s 48 30w
68 Paracel Is., S. China Sea 16 30N 111 30E
98 Paragould, U.S.A. 36 5N 90 29w
98 Paraguaná, Pen. de, Ven. 12 0N 70 0w
99 Paraguari, Paraguay 25 30s 57 15w
99 Paraguay R., S. Amer. 23 0s 58 0w
97 Paraguay, S. Amer. 21 0s 60 0w
98 Paraíba, st., Brazil 7 12s 38 0w
49 Parainen, Finland 60 21N 22 17E
98 Parakou, Benin 9 30N 2 35E
98 Paramaribo, Surinam 5 45N 55 15w
61 Paramushir I., U.S.S.R. 50 10N 156 0E
99 Paraná, Argentina 32 0s 60 30w
99 Paraná R., Argentina 29 0s 59 30w
99 Parana, St., Brazil 24 30s 51 0w
99 Paranagua, Brazil 25 45s 48 30w
99 Paranaiba, R., Brazil 18 40s 48 30w
99 Paranapanema, R., Brazil 22 30s 52 0w
99 Paranpiacaba, Sa., mts., Brazil 24 30s 49 0w
83 Paratoo, Australia 32 45s 139 15E
43 Paray le Monial, France 46 25N 4 5E
64 Parbhani, India 19 30N 77 0E
46 Parchim, Germany 53 30N 11 50E
46 Pardubice, Cz-slov. 50 0N 15 45E
98 Parecis, Sa. dos, mts., Brazil 13 50s 59 0w
61 Paren, U.S.S.R. 62 30N 163 0E
93 Parent, Canada 47 50N 74 40w
95 Paria, G. of, S. America 10 15N 62 0w
95 Parintins, Brazil 2 30s 56 20w
43 Paris, France 48 52N 2 18E
91 Paris, U.S.A. 33 42N 95 34w
99 Park, Ra., U.S.A. 40 10N 106 30w
76 Park Rynie, S. Africa 30 20s 30 25E
83 Parkersburg, U.S.A. 39 18N 81 35w
83 Parkes, Australia 33 0s 148 6E
40 Parma, Italy 44 48N 10 3E
98 Parnaiba, Brazil 3 10s 41 40w
98 Parnaiba, R., Brazil 6 45s 44 0w
41 Parnassos, mt., Greece 38 30s 22 40E
49 Pärnus, U.S.S.R. 58 24N 24 37E
64 Paroo R., Afghan. 34 40N 63 0E
64 Paropamisus Ra., Afghan. 34 40N 63 0E
41 Paros, I., Greece 37 3N 25 10E

* Renamed Anzeli

* Returned to Panamanian Sovereignty

Parracombe, England 51 20N 3 50W
Parramatta, Australia 33 48s 151 0E
Parry Is. Arctic Ocean 78 30N 112 0w
Parsons, U.S.A., 37 18N 95 18w
Parthenay, France 46 40N 0 18w
Partry, Mts., Ireland 53 40N 9 24w
Paru, R., Brazil 1 0N 54 40w
Parvatipuram, India 18 56N 83 30E
Parwan, Prov., Afghan, 35 0N 69 0E
Pasadena, Calif., U.S.A. 34 0N 118 0w
Pasadena, Texas, U.S.A.
    29 42N 95 23w
Pas-de-Calais, Dépt., Fr. 50 27N 2 15E
Pascagoula, U.S.A. 30 30N 88 30w
Pasco, U.S.A., 46 16N 119 3w
Pasir Mas, Malaya 6 0N 102 0E
Pasni, Pakistan 25 15N 63 25E
Pass of Brander, Scot. 56 24N 5 8w
Pass of the Tarters, U.S.S.R.
    48 20N 24 50E
Passage E., Ireland 52 13N 6 59w
Passage W., Ireland 51 55N 8 26w
Passau, Germany 48 33N 13 21E
Passero, C., Sicily, Italy 36 41N 15 10E
Passo Fundo, Brazil 28 10s 52 25w
Pastaza, R., Ecuador 3 30s 76 30E
Pasto, Colombia 1 12N 77 25w
Pasvik R., U.S.S.R. 69 15N 29 30E
Patagonia, S. Argentina 45 0s 69 0w
Patan, India 23 56N 72 5E
Patcham, England 50 52N 0 9w
Patchewollock, Austral. 36 27s 142 0E
Patea, New Zealand 39 45s 174 28E
Pategi, Nigeria 8 50N 5 45E
Paterno, Italy 37 35N 14 50E
Paterson, U.S.A. 40 59N 74 10w
Pathfinder Res., U.S.A. 42 10N 105 50w
Patiala, India 30 22N 76 28E
Patmos, I., Greece 37 18N 26 35E
Patna, Bihar, India 25 40N 85 10E
Pátrai, Greece 38 15N 21 47E
Patrington, England 53 42N 0 1w
Patti, Italy 38 10N 14 55E
Patuakhali, Bangladesh 22 20N 90 15E
Pau, France 43 21N 0 23w
Pauk, Burma 21 25N 94 30E
Paulis, see Isiro
Paulistana, Brazil 8 0s 41 15w
Paulo Afonso Rapids, Brazil
    9 20s 37 40w
Paulpietersburg, S. Africa 27 25s 30 50E
Payia, Italy 45 11N 9 11E
Pavlodar, U.S.S.R. 52 25N 77 10E
Pavlograd, U.S.S.R. 48 40N 36 0E
Pavlovo, U.S.S.R. 56 0N 43 10E
Pavlovsk, U.S.S.R. 50 32N 40 7E
Pavlovskiy-Posad, U.S.S.R.
    55 47N 38 64E
Pawtucket, U.S.A. 41 55N 71 25w
Payakumbah, Indonesia 0 20s 100 40E
Payerne, Switzerland 46 50N 6 56E
Payette, U.S.A. 44 6N 116 55w
Payne, L., Canada 59 30N 74 30w
Paysandú, Uruguay 32 19s 58 0w
Payson, U.S.A. 34 23N 111 20w
Pazardzhik, Bulgaria 42 12N 24 19E
Peace, R., Canada 58 47N 114 0w
Peace River, Canada 56 0N 117 18w
Peak Hill, N.S.W., Australia
    32 36s 148 9E
Peak Hill, W.A., Australia
    25 42s 118 47E
Peak, The, England 53 25N 1 52w
Pearl City, Hawaii 21 15N 157 55w
Pec, Yugoslavia 42 41N 20 14E
Pechenga, U.S.S.R. 69 30N 31 25E
Pechora, G. of, U.S.S.R. 68 40N 54 0E
Pecos, & R., U.S.A. 31 25N 103 35w
Pécs, Hungary 46 4N 18 13E
Peebles, Scotland 55 39N 3 11w
Peekskill, U.S.A. 41 15N 73 57w
Peel, Isle of Man 54 13N 4 43w
Peel Fell, mt., England 55 19N 2 34w
Peel R., Australia 30 58s 150 30E
Peene, R., Germany 53 52N 13 40E
Pegasus B., New Zealand 43 13s 173 0E
Pegu, Burma 17 33N 96 25E
Pegu Yoma, mts., Burma 19 0N 96 0E
Pehan, China 49 10N 126 20E
Pei Kiang, China 24 10N 113 10E
Pekalongan, Indonesia 6 50s 109 45E
Pekin, U.S.A. 40 30N 89 43w
Peking, China 39 49N 116 20E
Peleaga, mt., Rumania 45 17N 22 58E
Pelly, R., Canada 62 20N 133 0w
Peloponnese, Pen., Greece 37 50N 22 0E
Pelotas, Brazil 31 45s 52 20w
Pelvoux, Mt., France 44 52N 6 10E
Pematang Siantar, Indon. 3 0N 99 1E
Pemba, Mozambique 13 0s 40 42E
Pemba I., Tanzania 5 0s 39 40E
Pemberton, Australia 34 28s 115 59E
Pembridge, England 52 13N 2 54w
Pembroke, Canada 45 40N 77 10w
Pembroke, Wales 51 41N 4 55w
Pembrey, Wales 51 42N 4 16w
Penalara, Mt., Spain 40 55N 3 50w
Penarth, Wales 51 27N 3 12w
Penas, G. de, Chile 47 30s 75 0w
Pencoed, Wales 51 31N 3 30w
Pend Oreille L., U.S.A. 47 20N 116 30w
Pendembu, Sierra Leone 8 6N 10 45w
Pendle Hill, Eng. 53 52N 2 20w
Pendleton, U.S.A. 45 42N 118 47w

Pendzhikent, U.S.S.R. 39 20N 67 30E
Pengpu, China 32 50N 117 50E
Penguin, Australia 41 4s 146 7E
Peniche, Portugal 39 20N 9 22w
Penicuik, Scotland 55 50N 3 11w
Penistone, England 53 32N 1 38w
Penki, China 41 15N 122 40E
Penmaenmawr, Wales 53 16N 3 56w
Penmarch, Pte. de ,Fr. 47 50N 4 30w
Penn Yan, U.S.A. 42 40N 77 0w
Penner R., India 14 40N 80 10E
Pennines, mts., England 54 20N 2 10w
Pennsylvania, st., U.S.A. 41 10N 77 30w
Penola, Australia 37 12s 140 51E
Penong, Australia 32 0s 133 0E
Penrith, Australia 33 48s 150 40E
Penrith, England 54 40N 2 47w
Penryn, England 50 10N 5 7w
Pensacola, U.S.A. 30 30N 87 15w
Pensacola Mts., Antarctica
    84 0s 45 0w
Penshurst, Australia 37 55s 142 56E
Penticton, Canada 49 30N 119 30w
Pentland, Australia 20 37s 145 27E
Pentland Firth, Scot. 58 41N 3 0w
Pentland Hills, Scotland 55 47N 3 35w
Penybont, Wales 52 16N 3 15w
Pen-y-ghent, mt., Eng. 54 8N 2 10w
Pen-y-groes, Wales 51 48N 4 3w
Penza, U.S.S.R. 53 8N 45 0E
Penzance, England 50 8N 5 33w
Penzhina G., U.S.S.R. 61 0N 163 0E
Penzhino, U.S.S.R. 63 50N 168 3E
Peoria, U.S.A. 40 40N 89 35w
Perdido, mt., Spain 42 45N 0 15w
Perekop, U.S.S.R. 46 0N 33 0E
Pereyaslav Khmelnitski, U.S.S.R.
    50 5N 31 27E
Pergamino, Argentina 33 45s 60 40w
Perigueux, France 45 16N 0 42E
Perija, Sa. de. mts., Colombia
    9 30N 73 3w
Perim I., Red Sea 12 40N 43 17E
Perm, U.S.S.R. 58 0N 55 15E
Pernambuco (Recife), Brazil
    8 20s 35 0w
Pernambuco, st., Brazil 8 0s 39 0w
Pernik, Bulgaria 42 37N 23 4E
Peronne, France 49 55N 2 55E
Perovo, U.S.S.R. 55 40N 37 45E
Perpignan, France 42 43N 2 55E
Perranporth, England 50 20N 5 9w
Perranzabuloe, England 50 18N 5 7w
Perryton, U.S.A. 36 25N 100 55w
Pershore, England 52 7N 2 4w
Persia, see Iran
Persian G., S.W. Asia 27 0N 51 0E
Perth, Australia 32 0s 115 50E
Perth, Canada 44 52N 76 28w
Perth, Scotland 56 24N 3 27w
Perth Amboy, U.S.A. 40 30N 74 25w
Peru, S. America 88 0s 75 0w
Perugia, Italy 43 8N 12 25E
Pervomaisk, U.S.S.R. 47 58N 31 0E
Pesaro, Italy 43 57N 12 55E
Pescara, Italy 42 30N 14 18E
Peshawar, Pakistan 34 3N 71 30E
Petah Tiqva, Israel 32 5N 34 52E
Petange, Luxembourg 49 33N 5 55E
Peter 1st, I., S. Ocean 69 0s 91 0w
Peterborough, Canada 44 21N 78 27w
Peterborough, Australia 32 58s 138 49E
Peterborough, England 52 35N 0 14w
Peterchurch, England 52 3N 2 58w
Peterculter, Scotland 57 7N 2 20w
Peterhead, Scotland 57 32N 1 47w
Peterlee, England 54 45N 1 18w
Petersburg, U.S.A. 37 13N 77 25w
Petersfield, England 51 0N 0 56w
Petitsikapau, L., Canada 54 40N 66 30w
Petlad, India 22 30N 72 40E
Peto, Mexico 20 3N 89 0w
Petone, New Zealand 41 5s 174 50E
Petoskey, U.S.A. 45 20N 84 58w
Petrich, Bulgaria 41 25N 23 12E
Petrolia, Canada 42 54N 82 5w
Petropavlovsk-Kamchatski, U.S.S.R.
    53 10N 158 30E
Petropolis, Brazil 22 30s 43 10w
Petrograd, see Zrenjanin
Petroseni, Rumania 45 30N 23 28E
Petrovaradin, Yugoslavia
    45 15N 19 58E
Petrovsk, U.S.S.R. 52 23N 45 18E
Petrovsk, U.S.S.R. 51 20N 108 50E
Petrozavodsk, U.S.S.R. 61 50N 34 25E
Petrusburg, S. Africa 29 0s 25 20E
Pettigo, Ireland 54 38N 7 50w
Petworth, England 50 59N 0 37w
Pevek, U.S.S.R. 69 35N 170 50E
Pewsey, Vale of, Eng. 51 20N 1 48w
Pézenas, France 43 28N 3 50E
Pfarers-Dorf, Switzerland 46 58N 9 28E
Pfäffikon, Switzerland 47 21N 8 48E
Pforzheim, Germany 48 50N 8 25E
Phagwara, India 31 10N 75 40E
Phalodi, India 27 5N 72 25E
Phan Rang, Vietnam 11 38N 109 4E
Phan Thiet, Vietnam 11 0N 108 9E
Phanom Dang Raek, mts., Thailand
    14 30N 104 0E
Phari, Tibet, China 27 53N 89 10E
Philadelphia, U.S.A. 39 55N 75 18w
Philippeville, see Skikda
Philippeville, Belgium 50 12N 4 33E

Philippi, L., Australia 24 20s 138 55E
Philippines, Asia 13 0N 123 0E
Philippolis, S. Africa 30 15s 25 16E
Philipstown, see Daingean
Philipstown, S. Africa 30 28s 24 28E
Phillip I., Australia 38 22s 145 18E
Phnom Penh, Cambodia 11 40N 105 0E
Phœnix, U.S.A. 33 45N 111 50w
Phœnix Is., Pacific Ocean 4 0s 171 0w
Phu Quoc, I., Vietnam 10 20N 104 0E
Piacenza, Italy 45 0N 9 40E
Pialba, Australia 25 18s 152 50E
Piatra Neamt, Rum. 46 59N 26 20E
Piaui, R., Brazil 7 55s 42 30w
Piaui, st., Brazil 6 30s 42 30w
Piaui, Sa. do, mts., Brazil 10 0s 43 0w
Piazza, Italy 37 20N 14 20E
Pic de Aneto, mt., Spain 42 35N 0 45E
Picardy, Prov., France 49 50N 3 0E
Picayune, U.S.A. 30 43N 89 43w
Pichilemu, Chile 34 20s 72 5w
Pickering, England 54 15N 0 45w
Pickering, Vale of, England 54 12N 0 45w
Pico Guina, mt., Spain 42 50N 6 45w
Picos de Europa, mts. Sp. 43 15N 5 0w
Picton, Australia 34 5s 150 38E
Picton, Canada 43 59N 77 0w
Picton, New Zealand 41 20s 174 1E
Pictou, Canada 45 45N 63 5w
Pidley, England 52 23N 0 4w
Pidurutalagala, mt., Sri Lanka
    7 0N 80 50E
Piedmont Plat., U.S.A. 34 0N 82 0w
Piedmont, Prov., Italy 45 0N 7 40E
Piedras Negras, Mex. 28 50N 100 35w
Pierre, U.S.A. 44 30N 100 15w
Pierrefontaine, France 47 14N 6 32E
Piet Retief, S. Africa 27 2s 30 52E
Pietermaritzburg, S. Africa
    29 38s 30 28E
Pietersburg, S. Africa 23 45s 29 30E
Pietrosul, mt., Rumania 47 36N 24 56E
Pietrosul, mt., Rumania 47 7N 25 13E
Pike's Pk., mt., U.S.A. 38 50N 105 0w
Piketberg, South Africa 32 54N 18 42E
Pila, Poland 53 10N 16 48E
Pilar, Chile 52 40s 75 0w
Pilbara, Australia 21 13s 118 21E
Pilcomayo, R., S. Amer. 22 30s 62 20w
Pilibhit, India 28 20N 79 58E
Pilica, R., Poland 51 20N 20 45E
Pilion, mt. Greece 39 23N 23 0E
Pilos, Greece 36 55N 21 45E
Pinang, I., Malaya 5 20N 100 12E
Pinar del Rio, Cuba 22 0N 84 30w
Pinczów, Poland 50 28N 20 45E
Pindiga, Nigeria 9 58N 10 53E
Pindus Mts., Greece 39 30N 21 30E
Pine Bluff, U.S.A. 34 5N 91 58w
Pine Creek, Australia 13 40s 131 37E
Pine Hill, Australia 23 42s 147 0E
Pinega, R., U.S.S.R. 63 48N 45 0E
Pinerolo, Italy 44 53N 7 23E
Pinetown, South Africa 29 48s 30 54E
Ping, R., Thailand 16 30N 99 40E
Pingliang, China 35 30N 106 50E
Pinhel, Portugal 41 46N 6 57w
Pinhoe, England 50 44N 3 28w
Pinios R., Greece 39 37N 22 23E
Pinnaroo, Australia 35 5s 141 0E
Pino Hachado P., Chile 38 45s 71 0w
Pionerskaya, Antarctica 69 30s 97 0E
Piotrków, Poland 51 25N 19 40E
Pipmuacan, L., Can. 49 40N 70 20w
Piqua, U.S.A. 40 10N 84 15w
Piraievs, Greece 37 58N 23 42E
Pirapora, Brazil 17 25s 44 50w
Pirgos, Greece 37 38N 21 32E
Pirin Pl., Bulgaria 41 40N 23 20E
Pirmasens, Germany 49 12N 7 36E
Pirot, Yugoslavia 43 10N 22 39E
Pirou, France 49 12N 1 31w
Pisa, Italy 43 42N 10 25E
Pisciotta, Italy 40 7N 15 12E
Pisco, Peru 13 55s 76 10w
Pisek, Czechoslovakia 49 20N 14 8E
Pisuerga, R., Spain 42 45N 4 20w
Pit, R., U.S.A. 41 30N 120 45w
Pita, Guinea 11 0N 12 15w
Pitcairn I., Pacific Ocean 24 55s 131 0w
Pitea & R., Sweden 65 24N 21 30E
Pitesti, Rumania 44 52N 24 5E
Pithapuram, India 17 0N 82 20E
Pittenweem, Scotland 56 12N 2 44w
Pittsburg, Kan., U.S.A. 37 30N 94 40w
Pittsburgh, Pa., U.S.A. 40 30N 79 52w
Pittsfield, U.S.A. 42 28N 73 0w
Pittsworth, Australia 27 41s 151 37E
Piura, Peru 5 20s 80 35w
Piz Bernina, Pk., Switz. 46 22N 9 55E
Pizzo, Italy 38 42N 16 10E
Placentia, & B., Newf. 47 14N 54 2w
Pladda I., Scotland 55 25N 5 7w
Plainview, U.S.A. 34 15N 101 44w
Plant City, U.S.A. 28 3N 82 15w
Plasencia, Spain 40 3N 6 6w
Plateau de Langres, Fr. 47 45N 5 30E
Plateau du Coteau du Missouri, U.S.A.
    47 0N 100 0w
Platte R., U.S.A. 41 0N 99 0w
Plauen, Germany 50 30N 12 7E
Plaza Huincal, Argentina 39 0s 69 0w
Pleiku, Vietnam 14 0N 108 15E
Plenty, Bay of, N.Z. 37 45s 177 0E

Plesetsk, U.S.S.R. 62 40N 40 10E
Plessisville, Canada 46 15N 71 48w
Pleven, Bulgaria 43 22N 24 41E
Plock, Poland 52 37N 19 40E
Plockton, Scotland 57 20N 5 39w
Ploësti, Rumania 44 58N 26 0E
Plovdiv, Bulgaria 42 7N 24 48E
Plumtree, Rhodesia 20 27s 27 55E
Plymouth, England 50 22N 4 10w
Plymouth, Montserrat. W.I.
    16 38N 62 5w
Plympton, England 50 23N 4 2w
Plymstock, England 50 22N 4 4w
Plynlimon, mt., Wales 52 29N 3 47w
Plzeñ, Czechoslovakia 49 48N 13 20E
Po, R., Italy 45 2N 9 20E
Pobedy Pk., Mt., U.S.S.R. 42 10N 79 57E
Pocatello, U.S.A. 43 10N 111 0w
Pocklington, England 53 56N 0 46w
Podkamennaya Tunguska, U.S.S.R.
    61 40N 90 5E
Podolsk, U.S.S.R. 55 20N 37 40E
Podor, Sénégal 16 30N 14 50w
Pofadder, South Africa 29 10s 19 22E
Point, C., S. Africa 34 22s 18 30E
Point Fortin, Trinidad 11 0N 61 50w
Point of Ayre, I. of Man
    54 25N 4 22w
Pointe Noire, Congo (Fr.) 4 48s 12 0E
Point Saline, ,Grenada, W.I.
    12 12N 61 40w
Poitiers, France 46 38N 0 20E
Poitou, Prov., France 46 40N 0 10w
Poix Terron, France 49 40N 4 38E
Pokaran, India 27 0N 71 50E
Pokataroo, Australia 29 34s 148 50E
Pola, Yugoslavia, see Pula
Poland, Europe 52 20N 20 0E
Polden Hills, England 51 5N 2 50w
Poli, Cameroon 8 34N 12 54E
Poligny, France 46 50N 5 40E
Polillo I., Philippines 14 50N 121 50E
Poliyiros, Greece 40 15N 23 10E
Pollachi, India 10 40N 77 0E
Polnovat, U.S.S.R. 63 50N 66 10E
Polotsk, U.S.S.R. 55 30N 28 42E
Poltava, U.S.S.R. 49 37N 34 30E
Polyarny, U.S.S.R. 69 0N 33 10E
Pombal, Portugal 39 55N 8 40w
Ponca City, U.S.A. 36 43N 97 13w
Ponce, Puerto Rico 18 7N 66 48w
Pondicherry, India 12 0N 79 50E
Pondoland, dist., S. Africa 31 10s 29 40E
Ponferrada, Spain 42 34N 6 35w
Pongola, R., S. Africa 27 28s 32 7E
Ponnyadaung, mts., Burma 20 0N 94 0E
Ponoi, & R., U.S.S.R. 67 0N 41 15E
Pons, France 45 35N 0 35w
Pont-à-Mousson, France 48 54N 6 0E
Pont-l'Abbé, France 47 50N 4 16w
Pont St. Esprit, France 44 18N 4 40E
Ponta Grossa, Brazil 25 0s 50 10w
Pontardawe, Wales 51 43N 3 51w
Pontarlier, France 46 52N 6 20E
Pontchartrain, L., U.S.A. 30 10N 90 10w
Pontedera, Italy 43 40N 10 40E
Pontefract, England 53 41N 1 20w
Pontevedra, Spain 42 29N 8 40w
Ponthierville (Ubundu), Zaïre
    0 22s 25 30E
Pontiac, U.S.A. 42 40N 83 20w
Pontianak, Indonesia 0 12s 109 29E
Pontine, Is., Italy 40 58N 13 0E
Pontine Mts., Turkey 40 30N 39 0E
Pontivy, France 48 5N 3 0w
Pontoise, France 49 3N 2 5E
Pontremoli, Italy 44 22N 9 50E
Pontresina, Switzerland 46 30N 9 53E
Pontypool, Wales 51 43N 3 1w
Pontypridd, Wales 51 36N 3 19w
Poole, England 50 43N 1 59w
Poolewe, Scotland 57 46N 5 36w
Poona, see Pune
Poopelloe, L., Australia 31 30s 144 0E
Poopó L., Bolivia 19 0s 67 0w
Popayan, Colombia 2 10N 76 45w
Poperinge, Belgium 50 51N 2 44E
Popigai, U.S.S.R. 72 55N 106 5E
Poplar Bluff, U.S.A. 36 45N 90 27w
Poplita, U.S.A. 30 0s 101 0w
Popocatepetl, Mt., Mex. 18 45N 99 40w
Popokabaka, Zaïre 5 40s 16 35E
Porbandar, India 21 37N 69 46E
Porcupine R., Alaska 67 0N 143 0w
Pori, Finland 61 30N 21 35E
Porjus, Sweden 67 0N 19 50E
Porkkala, Finland 60 15N 24 30E
Porlock Hill, England 51 12N 3 40w
Pornic, France 47 8N 2 5w
Poronaisk, U.S.S.R. 49 25N 142 57E
Porrentruy, Switzerland 47 25N 7 4E
Porreta P., Italy 44 0N 11 10E
Porsanger Fjord, Norway 70 45N 26 0E
Port Adelaide, Australia
    34 50s 138 42E
Port Alberni, Canada 49 20N 124 50w
Port Alfred, S. Africa 33 37s 26 58E
Port Alma, Australia 23 38s 150 53E
Port Antonio, Jamaica 18 12N 76 28w
Port Arthur, Australia 43 10s 147 40E
Port Arthur, see Thunder Bay
Port Arthur, U.S.A. 29 56N 94 5w
Port Askaig, Scotland 55 51N 6 6w
Port-au-Prince, Haiti 18 40N 72 20w

Port Augusta, Australia
    32 22s 137 49E
Port aux Basques, Can. 47 43N 59 20w
Port Bannatyne, Scotland 55 52N 5 5w
Port-Berge, Madagascar 15 38s 47 40E
Port Bou, Spain 42 25N 3 5E
Port Canning, Bangladesh
    22 25N 88 40E
Port Cartier, Canada 50 10N 66 50w
Port Chalmers, N.Z. 45 45s 170 40E
Port Charlotte, Scotland 55 44N 6 24w
Port de Bouc, France 43 23N 5 0E
Port de Paix, Haiti 19 50N 72 50w
Port Dickson, Malaya 2 43N 101 45E
Port Douglas, Australia 16 30s 145 30E
Port Elizabeth, Bequia I. 13 0N 61 15w
Port Elizabeth, S. Africa 33 58s 25 42E
Port Ellen, Scotland 55 37N 6 12w
Port Erin, Isle of Man 54 6N 4 47w
Port Étienne, see Nouadhibou
Port Fairy, Australia 38 18s 142 15E
Port Francqui, see Ilebo
Port Gentil, Gabon 0 47s 8 40E
Port Glasgow, Scotland 55 56N 4 41w
Port Harcourt, Nigeria 4 45N 7 20E
Port Hawkesbury, Can. 45 35N 64 40w
Port Hedland, Australia
    20 16s 118 36E
Port Hood, Canada 46 2N 61 30w
Port Huron, U.S.A. 42 59N 82 30w
Port Jackson, Australia 33 55s 151 12E
Port Kelang, Malaya 3 0N 101 20E
Port Kembla, Australia 34 29s 150 56E
Port Laoise, Ireland 53 3N 7 15w
Port Lavoca, U.S.A. 28 35N 96 50w
Port Lincoln, Austral. 34 40s 135 47E
Port Logan, Scotland 54 42N 4 57w
Port Louis, France 47 40N 3 0w
Port Macdonnell, Austral. 38 0s 140 39E
Port Macquarie, Australia 31 29s 153 0E
Port Moresby, Papua N.G.
    9 15s 147 12E
Port Nelson, Canada 57 2N 93 0w
Port Nolloth, S. Africa 29 12s 16 55E
Port of Spain, Trinidad 10 47N 61 23w
Portpatrick, Scotland 54 50N 5 8w
Port Phillip, B., Australia 38 17s 144 40E
Port Pirie, Australia 33 10s 138 0E
Port Radium, see Echo Bay
Port Safaga, Egypt 26 48N 34 0E
Port Said, Egypt 31 28N 32 6E
Port St. Louis, France 43 20N 4 50E
Port Shepstone, S. Africa
    30 45s 30 30E
Port Simpson, Canada 54 20N 130 28w
Port Stanley, Canada 42 40N 81 12w
Port Sudan, Sudan 19 40N 37 20E
Port Talbot, Wales 51 36N 3 48w
Port Vendres, France 42 30N 3 5E
Port Weld, Malaya 4 50N 100 38E
Portaferry, N. Ireland 54 23N 5 31w
Portage, U.S.A. 43 30N 89 28w
Portage la Prairie, Can. 50 0N 98 25w
Portalegre, Portugal 39 18N 7 27w
Portarlington, Ireland 53 10N 7 11w
Portbail, France 49 20N 1 42w
Portglenone, N. Ireland 54 52N 6 29w
Porthcawl, Wales 51 29N 3 42w
Porthmadog, Wales 52 54N 4 7w
Portishead, England 51 29N 2 47w
Portknockie, Scotland 57 42N 2 48w
Portland, N.S.W., Australia
    33 25s 150 0E
Portland, Vic., Austral. 38 13s 141 35E
Portland, Me., U.S.A. 43 42N 70 18w
Portland, Ore., U.S.A. 45 35N 122 37w
Portland B., Australia 38 29s 142 0E
Portland, Bill of, Eng. 50 30N 2 27w
Portland, I. of, England 50 33N 2 27w
Portland Pt., Jamaica 17 40N 77 0w
Portland Promontory, Canada
    58 40N 79 30w
Portmadoc, see Porthmadog
Portmagee, Ireland 51 53N 10 24w
Portmarnock, Ireland 53 26N 6 8w
Porto Alegre, Brazil 30 5s 51 10w
Porto Alexandre, Angola 16 0s 11 40E
Porto Empedocle, Italy 37 20N 13 25E
Porto Novo, Benin 6 27N 2 40E
Porto Santo I., Madeira 33 0N 16 40w
Porto Torres, Italy 40 51N 8 22E
Porto Velho, Brazil 8 50s 63 56w
Portoferraio, Italy 42 48N 10 20E
Portoscuso, Italy 39 10N 8 25E
Portoviejo, Ecuador 0 55s 80 30w
Portree, Scotland 57 25N 6 11w
Portroe, Ireland 52 53N 8 22w
Portrush, Ireland 55 13N 7 37w
Portskerra, Scotland 58 35N 3 55w
Portslade, England 50 51N 0 13w
Portsmouth, England 50 47N 1 7w
Portsmouth, N.H., U.S.A.
    43 15N 71 0w
Portsmouth, Ohio, U.S.A. 38 46N 83 5w
Portsmouth, Va., U.S.A. 36 48N 76 25w
Portsoy, Scotland 57 41N 2 40w
Porttipahta Res., Finland 68 10N 26 30E
Portugal, Europe 39 40N 8 0w
Portuguese E. Africa, see Mozambique
Portuguese Guinea, see Guinea-Bissau
Portumna, Ireland 53 7N 8 12w
Porvoo, Finland 60 30N 25 40E
Posadas, Argentina 27 30s 56 0w
Poste Maurice Cortier (Bidon 5),
    Algeria 22 20N 1 15E

76 Postmasburg, S. Africa 28 25s 23 1e
61 Potapovskoye, U.S.S.R. 68 40n 86 55e
40 Potenza, Italy 40 41n 15 50e
84 Poteriteri L., N.Z. 46 0s 166 0e
75 Potgietersrus, South Africa 24 10s 29 3e
51 Poti, U.S.S.R. 42 20n 41 30e
72 Potiskum, Nigeria 11 39n 11 2e
92 Potomac, R., U.S.A. 39 10n 77 20w
98 Potosi, Bolivia 19 45s 65 45w
66 Potow, China 38 20n 117 0e
46 Potsdam, Germany 52 19n 13 15e
23 Potters Bar, England 51 42n 0 11w
64 Pottuvil, Sri Lanka 6 55n 81 50e
35 Poulaphouca Falls. & Res., Ireland 53 7n 6 35w
26 Poulton-le-Fylde, Eng. 53 51n 2 59w
50 Povenets, U.S.S.R. 62 48n 35 0e
84 Poverty B., N.Z. 38 42s 178 0e
37 Póvoa de Varzim, Port. 41 28n 8 45w
90 Powder R., U.S.A. 45 20n 105 40w
90 Powell, L., U.S.A. 37 20n 110 35w
80 Powell Creek, Australia 18 0s 133 50
25 Powys, Co., Wales 52 20n 3 30w
66 Poyang, L., China 29 0n 116 25e
63 Poyarkova, U.S.S.R. 49 35n 128 45e
41 Pozarevac, Yugoslavia 44 39n 21 10e
92 Poznan, Poland 52 23n 16 57e
37 Pozoblanco, Spain 38 35n 5 1w
43 Prades, France 42 40n 2 28e
46 Praha, see Prague
41 Prahova, R., Rumania 45 0n 25 40e
85 Prairies, N. America 43 0n 97 0w
40 Prato, Italy 43 53n 11 7e
90 Pratt, U.S.A. 37 42n 98 46w
37 Pravia, Spain 43 30n 6 10w
99 Pre-Cordilleras, mts., Arg. 29 0s 68 0w
80 Premier Downs, Austral. 30 30s 126 30e
22 Prenzlau, Germany 53 18n 13 52e
65 Preparis I., & Chans., India 15 0n 93 40e
47 Prerov, Czechoslovakia 49 27n 17 4e
26 Prescot, England 53 26n 2 49w
93 Prescott, Canada 44 46n 75 32w
90 Prescott, U.S.A. 34 24n 112 30w
90 Presidio, U.S.A. 29 35n 104 20w
47 Presov, Czechoslovakia 49 1n 21 33e
93 Presque Isle, U.S.A. 46 35n 68 3w
25 Prestatyn, Wales 53 20n 3 24w
25 Presteigne, Wales 52 16n 3 1w
26 Preston, England 53 47n 2 43w
31 Preston, Scotland 55 48n 2 18w
90 Preston, U.S.A. 42 6n 111 50w
31 Prestonpans, Scotland 55 57n 2 59w
26 Prestwich, England 53 32n 2 17w
31 Prestwick, Scotland 55 30n 4 36w
76 Pretoria, S. Africa 25 36s 28 12e
71 Preveza, Greece 38 58n 20 46e
46 Pribram, Czechoslovakia 49 43n 14 0e
90 Price, U.S.A. 39 33n 110 46w
76 Prieska, S. Africa 29 40s 22 30e
41 Prilep, Yugoslavia 41 19n 21 34e
88 Prince Albert, Canada 53 15n 105 47w
88 Prince Albert Pen., Can. 71 0n 115 0w
89 Prince Charles I., Can. 67 0n 76 0w
93 Prince Edward I., Prov., Canada 46 30n 63 30w
71 Prince Edward Is., Ind. Oc. 45 30s 38 0e
88 Prince George, Canada 54 0n 123 0w
88 Prince of Wales I., Alaska 55 30n 132 30w
88 Prince of Wales I., Can. 73 0n 99 0w
88 Prince Rupert, Canada 54 20n 130 25w
23 Princes Risborough, England 51 43n 0 51w
94 Princes Town, Trinidad 10 15n 61 28w
82 Princess Charlotte B., Australia 14 0s 144 0e
92 Princeton, U.S.A. 37 14n 87 54w
24 Princetown, England 50 33n 4 0w
71 Principé I., West Africa 1 45n 7 20e
50 Pripyat R., U.S.S.R. 52 10n 27 10e
50 Pripyat Marshes, Poland 51 53n 27 5e
41 Pristina, Yugoslavia 42 39n 21 9e
43 Privas, France 44 46n 4 40e
41 Prizren, Yugoslavia 42 20n 20 46e
94 Progreso, Mexico 21 31n 89 37w
60 Prokopyevsk, U.S.S.R. 53 58n 86 30e
80 Prome, Burma 18 52n 95 25e
43 Propriano, Corsica, Fr. 41 44n 8 55e
82 Proserpine, Australia 20 27s 148 40e
46 Prostejov, Cz-slov. 49 5n 17 0e
82 Proston, Australia 26 2s 151 32e
43 Provence, Prov., France 43 55n 6 10e
93 Providence, U.S.A. 41 42n 71 23w
91 Providence Channels, Bahama 26 0n 78 0w
88 Provideniya, U.S.S.R. 64 25n 173 15w
43 Provins, France 48 37n 3 15e
90 Provo, U.S.A. 40 18n 111 36w
26 Prudhoe, England 54 57n 1 51w
88 Prudhoe Bay, Alaska 70 20n 149 40w
46 Pruszków, Poland 52 9n 20 49e
47 Prut, R., Rum.-U.S.S.R. 46 20n 28 32e
47 Przemysl, Poland 49 44n 22 49e
47 Przeworsk, Poland 50 5n 22 43e
47 Przhevalsk, U.S.S.R. 42 30n 78 30e
50 Pskov, U.S.S.R. 57 30n 28 30e
27 Pudsey, England 53 47n 1 41w
94 Puebla, Mexico 19 11n 98 15w
90 Pueblo, U.S.A. 38 18n 104 48w
37 Pueblonuevo, Spain 38 16n 5 16w
37 Puente Genil, Spain 37 24n 4 17w
66 Puerh, China 23 0n 100 53e
94 Puerto Barrios, Guat. 15 50n 88 35w

95 Puerto Berrio Colombia 6 30n 74 30w
95 Puerto Cabello, Ven. 10 22n 67 58w
95 Puerto Cabezas, Nicar. 14 5n 83 20w
94 Puerto Corte's, Honduras 15 50n 88 0w
72 Puerto de Cabras, Canary Is. 28 40n 13 30w
99 Puerto Deseado, Arg. 47 0s 68 0w
98 Puerto Esperanza, Brazil 19 25s 57 25w
99 Puerto Madryn, Arg. 43 0s 65 0w
98 Puerto Maldonado, Peru 12 25s 69 0w
99 Puerto Montt, Chile 41 22s 72 40w
94 Puerto Morelos, Mexico 21 0n 86 0w
95 Puerto Rico, I., W.I. 18 15n 66 30w
4 Puerto Rico Trough, Atlantic Ocean 20 0n 65 0w
98 Puerto Suarez, Bolivia 19 0s 57 45w
98 Puerto Wilches, Col. 7 25n 73 45w
50 Pugachev, U.S.S.R. 52 0n 48 50e
94 Puget Sd., U.S.A. 48 0n 122 30w
93 Puge-Théniers, France 44 0n 7 0e
37 Puigcerda, Spain 42 23n 1 53e
47 Pukekohe, New Zealand 37 12s 174 55e
40 Pula, Yugoslavia 44 53n 13 53e
98 Pulacayo, Bolivia 20 25s 66 40w
92 Pulaski, Va., U.S.A. 37 0n 80 54w
47 Pulawy, Poland 51 28n 22 0e
23 Pulham Market, England 52 25n 1 13e
64 Pulicat, L. of, India 13 45n 80 12e
92 Pullman, U.S.A. 46 45n 117 0w
47 Pultusk, Poland 52 43n 21 9e
98 Puna I., Ecuador 3 0s 80 20w
99 Puna d'Atacama, Plat., Argentina 25 0s 67 0w
66 Punakha, Bhutan 28 0n 89 15e
64 Punch, India 33 40n 74 12e
64 Pune, India 18 25n 73 57e
64 Punjab, Prov., India 31 45n 74 30e
64 Puno, Peru 15 50s 70 12w
99 Punta Arenas, Chile 53 6s 71 5w
94 Puntarenas, Costa Rica 9 58n 84 40w
60 Pur R., U.S.S.R. 65 30n 78 0e
22 Purbeck I., England 50 38n 2 0w
64 Puri, India 19 50n 85 57e
22 Purley, England 51 29n 1 4w
44 Purmerend, Netherlands 52 30n 4 56e
65 Purnea, India 26 0n 87 38e
65 Purulia, India 23 20n 86 15e
98 Puru, R., Brazil 7 40s 66 0w
67 Pusan, Korea 35 12n 129 0e
61 Pushchino, U.S.S.R. 54 25n 158 10e
51 Pushkino, U.S.S.R. 51 16n 47 9e
63 Putao (Fort Hertz), Burma 27 24n 97 28e
84 Putaruru, N.Z. 38 3s 175 46e
40 Putignano, Italy 40 50n 17 10e
64 Puttalam, Sri Lanka 8 1n 79 55e
44 Putten, Netherlands 52 17n 5 37e
98 Putumayo, R., Col. 2 15s 72 0w
42 Puy-de-Dôme, Dépt., Fr. 45 40n 2 52e
94 Puyallup, U.S.A. 47 12s 122 22w
25 Pwllheli, Wales 52 54n 4 26w
67 Pyongyang, N. Korea 39 0n 126 0e
41 Pyramid L., U.S.A. 38 47n 119 27w
37 Pyrenees, mts., Europe 42 30n 1 0e
42 Pyrénées Orientales, dépt., France 42 30n 2 30e

Q

63 Qabatiya, Jordan 32 25n 35 16e
62 Qadhima, Saudi Arabia 22 15n 39 15e
62 Qal' at el Mudawwara, Saudi Arabia 29 28n 36 3e
64 Qal'eh Shaharak, Afghan. 34 10n 64 20e
63 Qalqilyah, Jordan 32 10n 34 58e
76 Qamata, S. Africa 32 1s 27 30e
62 Qamr B., South Yemen 16 0n 52 30e
73 Qara, Egypt 29 38n 26 30e
63 Qasr Dabâ, Jordan 31 36n 36 2e
73 Qasr Farafra, Egypt 27 2n 28 0e
62 Qasr Umm Ramad, Saudi Arabia 23 10n 49 0e
63 Qatana, Syria 33 27n 36 5e
62 Qatar Sheikhdom, Arabia 25 30n 51 0e
62 Qatif, Saudi Arabia 26 30n 50 0e
62 Qatrana Sta., Jordan 31 12n 36 2e
62 Qattara Depression, Egypt 30 0n 28 0e
51 Qazvin, Iran 36 15n 50 0e
73 Qena, Egypt 26 10n 32 37e
64 Qila Safed, Pakistan 29 3n 61 27e
64 Qila Saifullah, Pakistan 30 45n 68 17e
63 Qiryat Gat, Israel 31 36n 34 46e
62 Qishm, & I., Iran 26 45n 56 0e
62 Qishn, South Yemen 15 30n 51 30e
62 Qizan, Saudi Arabia 16 58n 42 35e
51 Qizil Uzun, R., Iran 37 0n 48 0e
83 Quambatook, Australia 35 55s 143 45e
83 Quambone, Australia 30 56s 148 0e
83 Quan Long, Vietnam 7 10n 105 15e
83 Quandialla, Australia 34 2s 147 50e
68 Quang Ngai, Vietnam 15 2n 109 20e
68 Quang Tri, Vietnam 16 45n 107 7e
88 Quatsino, Canada 50 30n 127 40w
75 Que Que, Rhodesia 18 54s 29 45e
83 Queanbeyan, Australia 35 23s 149 17e
89 Quebec, & Prov., Can. 46 50n 71 30w
88 Queen Charlotte Is., Can. 53 0n 132 0w
88 Queen Charlotte Str., Can. 51 0n 128 0w
88 Queen Maud G., Can. 68 25n 101 30w
100 Queen Maud Land, Antarc. 74 0s 15 0e
26 Queensbury, England 53 46n 1 50w
83 Queenscliff, Australia 38 12s 144 35e
82 Queensland, st., Australia 24 0s 145 0e
83 Queenstown, Australia 41 1s 145 38e

76 Queenstown, S. Africa 31 55s 27 1e
74 Quela, Angola 9 10 16 56e
75 Quelimane, Mozambique 17 55s 36 58e
67 Quelpart, see Cheju Do. I.
94 Queretaro, Mexico 20 47n 100 12w
88 Quesnel, Canada 52 25n 122 30w
64 Quetta, Pakistan 30 7n 66 55e
68 Quezon City, Philippines 14 50n 120 35e
68 Qui Nhon, Vietnam 13 37n 109 10e
74 Quibaxi, Angola 8 24s 14 27e
98 Quibdo, Colombia 6 0n 76 50w
42 Quiberon, France 47 31n 3 7w
75 Quilengues, Angola 14 12s 14 12e
64 Quilon, India 9 0n 76 40e
83 Quilpie, Australia 26 33s 144 17e
34 Quilty, Ireland 52 50n 9 27w
42 Quimper, France 48 0n 4 7w
42 Quimperlé, France 47 52n 3 37w
34 Quin, Ireland 52 50n 8 52w
91 Quincy, Ill., U.S.A. 39 55n 91 23w
93 Quincy, Mass., U.S.A. 42 15n 71 0w
37 Quintanar, Spain 39 35n 3 5w
98 Quirindi, Australia 31 27s 150 38e
98 Quito, Ecuador 0 20s 78 45w
62 Qum, Iran 34 50n 50 50e
62 Qumisheh, see Shahriza, Iran
32 Quoich, L., Scotland 57 4n 5 20w
83 Quondong, Australia 33 0s 140 15e
82 Quorn, Australia 32 30s 137 55e
73 Quorn, Canada 49 30n 91 0w
66 Qurug Tagh, mts., China 41 30n 90 0e
73 Quseir, Egypt 26 8n 34 20e

R

49 Raahe, Finland 64 40n 24 30e
32 Ra'anana, Israel 32 10n 34 53e
32 Raasay I. & Sd., Scot. 57 25n 6 3w
82 Rabat, Malta 35 53n 14 22e
82 Rabat, Morocco 34 0n 6 42w
82 Rabaul, Papua N.G. 4 15s 152 12e
62 Rabigh Qasr, Si. Arabia 22 54n 39 1e
89 Race, C., Canada 46 40n 53 5w
91 Rachaya, Syria 33 30n 35 50e
72 Rachid, Mauritania 18 45n 11 45w
91 Rachna, U.S.A. 42 41n 87 49w
47 Radauti, Rumania 47 53n 25 48e
26 Radcliffe, Lancs., Eng. 53 35n 2 19w
27 Radcliffe, Notts., Eng. 52 57n 1 3w
47 Radekhov, U.S.S.R. 50 15n 24 40e
91 Radford, U.S.A. 37 8n 80 33w
22 Radley, England 51 42n 1 14w
47 Radnor Forest, Wales 52 19n 3 20w
47 Radom, Poland 51 24n 21 24e
47 Radomir, Bulgaria 42 37n 23 4e
47 Radomsko, Poland 51 5n 19 28e
24 Radstock, England 51 17n 2 25w
47 Radyr, Wales 51 32n 3 16w
88 Rae, Canada 62 45n 115 50w
64 Rae Bareli, India 26 20n 81 5e
89 Rae Isthmus, Canada 66 40n 87 30w
84 Raetihi, New Zealand 39 25s 175 20e
99 Rafaela, Argentina 31 10s 61 25w
73 Raga, Sudan 8 30n 25 45e
64 Ragama, Sri Lanka 7 0n 79 50e
82 Raglan, Australia 23 48s 150 45e
84 Raglan, New Zealand 37 55s 174 55e
40 Ragusa, Sicily 37 0n 14 48e
73 Rahad el Berdi, Sudan 11 20n 23 40e
63 Raichur, India 16 15n 77 24e
63 Raifoun, Syria 33 58n 35 33e
63 Raigarh, India 21 56n 83 25e
83 Railton, Australia 41 25s 146 25e
91 Rainier, Mt., U.S.A. 46 42n 121 40w
88 Rainy L., Canada 48 40n 93 0w
63 Raipipla, India 21 45n 73 30e
63 Raipur, India 21 16n 81 42e
65 Raj Nandgaon, India 21 0n 81 0e
68 Raja Ampat Arch., Indon. 1 0s 129 30e
65 Rajahmundry, I., India 16 0n 81 46e
64 Rajapalaiyim, India 9 20n 77 30e
64 Rajasthan, Prov., India 27 15n 73 0e
64 Rajgarh, India 24 7n 76 35e
64 Rajkot, India 22 15n 70 34e
65 Rajshahi, Bangladesh 24 30n 88 35e
64 Rakaia, & R., N.Z. 43 45s 172 1e
64 Rakaposhi, Kashmir 36 10n 74 0e
64 Rakvere, U.S.S.R. 59 20n 26 30e
91 Raleigh, U.S.A. 35 46n 78 43w
91 Raleigh Bay, U.S.A. 34 50n 76 0w
63 Ram Allah, Jordan 31 55n 35 11e
62 Ramadi, Iraq 33 26n 43 15e
64 Ramanathapuram (Ramnad), India 9 10n 78 57e
63 Ramishk, Iran 26 59n 58 47e
63 Ramla, Israel 31 55n 34 52e
64 Ramnad, see Ramanathapuram
47 Râmnicu Sârat, Rum. 45 26n 27 3e
47 Ramnicu Valcea, Rum. 45 6n 24 20e
73 Ramotswa, Botswana 24 50s 25 50e
64 Rampur, India 28 50n 79 10e
64 Rampur Hat, India 24 15n 87 45e
65 Ramree, I., Burma 19 10n 93 50e
26 Ramsbottom, England 53 38n 2 20w
23 Ramsey, England 51 55n 1 12e

26 Ramsey, & B., I. of Man 54 19n 4 24w
25 Ramsey I., Wales 51 51n 5 20w
23 Ramsgate, England 51 20n 1 26e
64 Ramtek, India 21 20n 79 15e
65 Ranaghat, India 23 5n 88 35e
90 Rancagua, Chile 34 18s 70 45w
65 Ranchi, India 23 29n 85 18e
90 Randall Res., U.S.A. 43 25n 99 30w
36 Randalstown, N. Ireland 54 45n 6 20w
49 Randers, Denmark 56 30n 10 0e
42 Ranea, & R., Sweden 65 52n 22 20e
84 Rangaunu B., N.Z. 34 51s 173 15e
65 Rangia, India 26 30n 91 20e
84 Rangiora, New Zealand 43 26s 172 37e
65 Rangoon, & R., Burma 16 55n 96 25e
65 Rangpur, Bangladesh 25 42n 89 22e
64 Ranibennur, India 14 40n 75 35e
65 Raniganj, India 23 27s 150 38e
64 Raniwara, India 24 50n 72 10e
83 Rankins Springs, Austral. 33 45s 146 12e
41 Rankovicévo (Kraljevo), Yugoslavia 43 43n 20 40e
64 Rann of Kutch, India 24 0n 70 0e
82 Rannes, Australia 24 6s 150 11e
30 Rannoch, L. & Dist., Scotland 56 41n 4 15w
30 Rannoch Moor, Scotland 56 37n 4 43w
75 Ranohiro, Madagascar 22 30s 45 25e
43 Rapallo, Italy 44 20n 9 18e
36 Raphoe, Ireland 54 52n 7 32w
90 Rapid City, U.S.A. 44 0n 103 20w
33 Rapness, Scotland 59 15n 2 51w
45 Rapperswil, Switzerland 47 15n 8 49e
51 Raqqa, Syria 36 2n 39 0e
62 Ras Abu Shagara, Egypt 21 0n 37 30e
63 Ras al Hadd. C., Oman 22 30n 59 48e
63 Ras al Madraka. C., Oman 19 0n 57 47e
71 Ras Asir, C., Somali Rep. 11 50n 51 12e
73 Ras Banas, C., Egypt 24 0n 35 45e
74 Ras Dashen, mt., Ethiopia 13 8n 37 45e
73 Ras el Milh, C., Egypt 31 55n 25 10e
73 Ras Hadarba, C., Sudan 22 0n 36 50e
73 Ras Lanuf, Libya 30 30n 18 30e
62 Ras Rakan, C., Tr. States 26 7n 51 20e
73 Rasa, Pt., Argentina 40 35s 62 0w
73 Rashad, Sudan 11 55n 31 0e
62 Rasht, Iran 37 18n 49 40e
74 Rat Is., Alaska 50 10n 177 30w
34 Ráth Luirc (Charleville), Ireland 52 21n 8 40w
35 Rathangan, Ireland 53 13n 7 0w
35 Rathcoole, Ireland 53 17n 6 29w
35 Rathcormac, Ireland 52 5n 8 19w
35 Rathdowney, Ireland 52 52n 7 36w
35 Rathdrum, Ireland 52 55n 6 13w
46 Rathenow, Germany 52 36n 12 22e
34 Rathkeale, Ireland 52 31n 8 57w
36 Rathlin I., N. Ireland 55 17n 6 12w
34 Rathmore, Kerry, Ireland 52 5n 9 12w
36 Rathmullen, Ireland 55 7n 7 32w
35 Rathnew, Ireland 53 0n 6 5w
35 Rathvilly, Ireland 52 54n 6 42w
45 Ratische Alpen, Switz. 46 50n 10 10e
35 Ratoath, Ireland 53 30n 6 27w
90 Raton, U.S.A. 36 57n 104 30w
31 Rattray, Scotland 56 36n 3 20w
33 Rattray Hd., Scotland 57 40n 1 53w
84 Raukumara Ra., N.Z. 38 0s 178 0e
49 Rauma, Finland 61 10n 21 20e
49 Raumo, see Rauma.
23 Raunds, England 52 20n 0 32w
63 Ravar, Iran 31 10n 56 50e
40 Ravenna, Italy 44 26n 12 14e
46 Ravensburg, Germany 47 48n 9 35e
82 Ravenshoe, Australia 17 45s 145 30e
83 Ravensthorpe, Australia 33 35s 120 7e
64 Ravi, R., Pakistan 31 0n 73 20e
64 Rawalpindi, Pakistan 33 40n 73 10e
80 Rawlinna, Australia 31 0s 125 25e
80 Rawlinson Ra., Australia 25 0s 129 0e
90 Rawlins, U.S.A. 41 50n 107 20w
99 Rawmarsh, England 53 27n 1 20w
26 Rawtenstall, England 53 42n 2 18w
73 Ray, C., Canada 47 42n 59 22w
65 Rayagada, India 19 5n 83 15e
62 Rayak, Lebanon 33 52n 36 0e
23 Rayleigh, England 51 36n 0 38e
88 Raymond, Canada 49 28n 112 42w
62 Raz, Pte. du, France 48 2n 4 47w
47 Razgrad, Bulgaria 43 33n 26 33e
42 Ré, I. de, France 46 16n 1 25w
23 Reading, England 51 27n 0 57w
90 Reading, U.S.A. 40 25n 75 46w
33 Reay, Scotland 58 33n 3 48w
73 Rebiana, Libya 24 12n 22 10e
98 Recife (Pernambuco), Brazil 8 5s 35 0w
90 Red Bluff, U.S.A. 40 15n 122 25w
88 Red Deer, Canada 52 14n 113 55w
88 Red Lake, Canada 51 10n 93 45w
91 Red Lake, U.S.A. 48 0n 95 0w
90 Red R., U.S.A. 31 30n 92 0w
66 Red R., Vietnam & China 22 10n 104 0e
70 Red Sea. Arabia-Africa 20 0n 39 0e
73 Red Sea, proy., Sudan 20 0n 35 0e
94 Red Tank, Panama Canal Zone (Inset).
47 Red Tower Pass, Rumania 45 38n 24 20e
25 Red Wharf B., Wales 53 18n 4 10w
23 Redbridge, Gr. London, Eng. 51 35n 0 7e

27 Redcar, England 54 38n 1 4w
83 Redcliffe, Australia 27 12s 153 0e
83 Redcliffs, Australia 34 12s 142 4e
90 Redding, U.S.A. 40 35n 122 25w
22 Redditch, England 52 18n 1 58w
27 Rede R., England 55 18n 2 20w
23 Redhill, England 51 14n 0 10w
90 Redlands, U.S.A. 34 2n 117 12w
42 Redon, France 47 40n 2 5w
37 Redondela, Spain 42 15n 8 35w
37 Redondo, Portugal 38 40n 7 35w
24 Redruth, England 50 14n 5 14w
33 Ree, L., Ireland 53 30n 7 57w
84 Reefton, New Zealand 42 1s 171 50
46 Regensburg, Germany 49 0n 12 5e
40 Reggio, Calabria, Italy 38 7n 15 41e
40 Reggio, Emilia Romagna, Italy 44 41n 10 39e
88 Regina, Canada 50 30n 104 37w
75 Rehoboth, S.W. Africa 23 18s 17 1e
63 Rehovot, Israel 31 55n 34 48e
46 Reichenbach, Germany 50 37n 12 1e
23 Reigate, England 51 13n 0 11w
43 Reims, France 49 15n 4 0e
88 Reindeer L., Canada 57 30n 102 28w
84 Rejnga C., New Zealand 34 28s 172
37 Reinosa, Spain 43 3n 4 11w
76 Reitz, S. Africa 27 50s 28 35e
61 Rekiniki, U.S.S.R. 60 50n 163 20e
68 Rembang, Indonesia 6 38s 111 15e
43 Remiremont, France 48 0n 6 35e
44 Remscheid, Germany 51 11n 7 12e
46 Rendsburg, Germany 54 19n 9 41e
29 Renfrew, Scot. 55 53n 4 23w
84 Rengat, Indonesia 0 30s 102 40e
47 Reni, U.S.S.R. 45 30n 28 19e
32 Renish Pt., Scotland 57 44n 6 59w
62 Renk, Sudan 11 50n 32 50e
44 Renkum, Netherlands 51 58n 5 43e
83 Renmark, Australia 34 9s 140 48e
42 Rennes, France 48 10n 1 41w
90 Reno, U.S.A. 39 35n 119 45w
40 Reno, R., Italy 44 34n 11 30e
22 Repton, England 52 50n 1 32w
90 Republican R., U.S.A. 40 10n 99 0w
37 Requena, Spain 39 34n 1 14w
99 Resistencia, Argentina 27 30s 59 0w
47 Resita, Rumania 45 18n 21 53e
84 Resolution I., N.Z. 45 35s 166 40e
32 Resolven, Wales 51 43n 3 42w
43 Rethel, France 49 30n 4 20e
71 Rethimnon, Crete, Greece 34 45n 24 3e
76 Retreat, S. Africa 34 5s 18 20e
71 Réunion I., Indian Ocean 21 15s 56 0e
37 Réus, Spain 41 9n 1 5e
45 Reutlingen, Germany 48 30n 9 15e
43 Revel, France 43 26n 2 0e
88 Revelstoke, Canada 50 59n 118 5w
86 Revilla Gigedo Is., Pacific Ocean 18 50n 111 0w
44 Revin, France 49 57n 4 39e
64 Rewa, India 24 35n 81 25e
64 Rewari, India 28 18n 76 43e
48 Reykjafjord, Iceland 66 0n 21 20w
48 Reykjahlid, Iceland 65 40n 16 55w
48 Reykjanæs, Iceland 63 50n 22 40w
48 Reykjavik, Iceland 64 10n 21 53w
80 Reynolds Ra., Australia 22 30s 133 0e
94 Reynosa, Mexico 26 0n 98 0w
51 Reza'iyeh, Iran 37 40n 45 5e
45 Rhätikon, mts., The Alps 46 50n 10 0e
25 Rhayader, Wales 52 18n 3 31w
46 Rheine, West Germany 52 17n 7 25e
44 Rheydt, Germany 51 12n 6 27e
44–45 Rhine (Rhein), R., Ger. 50 45n 7 1e
46 Rhineland Palatinate, Land, Germany 50 55n 6 50e
91 Rhinelander, U.S.A. 45 48n 89 27w
25 Rhondda, Wales 51 40n 3 29w
25 Rhône, Dept. & R., Fr. 45 58n 4 35e
25 Rhos-on-Sea, Wales 53 18n 3 46w
32 Rhoslanerchrugog, Wales 53 3n 3 4w
25 Rhuddlan, Wales 53 17n 3 28e
32 Rhu Coigach, Scotland 58 6n 5 27w
32 Rhuddlan, Wales 53 17n 3 28e
32 Rhum I., Scotland 57 0n 6 20w
25 Rhyl, Wales 53 20n 3 28w
25 Rhymney, Wales 51 45n 3 17w
31 Rhynie, Scotland 57 20n 2 50w
64 Riasi, Kashmir 33 10n 74 45e
37 Ribadéo, Spain 43 35n 7 0w
64 Ribat, Pakistan 29 50n 60 55e
37 Ribatejo, Prov., Portugal 39 10n 8 30w
26 Ribble, R., England 53 56n 2 20w
49 Ribe, Denmark 55 20n 8 43e
98 Ribeirao Preto, Brazil 21 15s 47 40w
44 Ribemont, France 49 48n 2 55e
43 Riberac, France 45 15n 0 15e
98 Riberalta, Bolivia 11 0s 66 0w
84 Riccarton, New Zealand 43 31s 172 2
88 Richibucto, Canada 46 39n 65 5w
90 Richland, U.S.A. 46 25n 119 30w
82 Richmond, Australia 20 45s 142 13e
23 Richmond, Greater London, England 51 27n 0 17w
27 Richmond, Yorks., Eng. 54 24n 1 43w
84 Richmond, New Zealand 41 20s 173 1
91 Richmond, Ind., U.S.A. 39 47n 85 0w

* Renamed Zimbabwe

Richmond, Ky., U.S.A. 37 45N 84 18w	
Richmond, Va., U.S.A. 37 30N 77 28w	
Richmond Ra., Australia 29 0s 152 45E	
Rickmansworth, England 51 40N 0 27w	
Ried, Austria 48 15N 13 30E	
Riesen Geb., mts., Poland 50 50N 16 0E	
Rietfontein, S. Africa 26 45s 20 0E	
Rieti, Italy 42 25N 12 50E	
Rifstangi, Iceland 66 32N 16 0w	
Rig Rig, Chad 14 15N 14 26E	
Riga, & G., U.S.S.R. 56 58N 24 12E	
Riihimaki, Finland 60 44N 24 45E	
Rijeka, Yugoslavia 45 1N 14 22E	
Rijn, R., Netherlands 52 5N 4 30E	
Rijssen, Netherlands 52 18N 6 31E	
Rijswijk, Netherlands 53 4N 3 20E	
Rima, China 28 25N 97 5E	
Rimini, Italy 44 2N 12 30E	
Rimouski, Canada 48 25N 68 30w	
Rineanna (Shannon Airport), Ireland 52 42N 8 57w	
Ringford, Scotland 54 55N 4 3w	
Ringkøbing, Denmark 56 15N 8 15E	
Ringvassøy I., Norway 69 53N 19 25E	
Ringville, Ireland 52 3N 7 37w	
Ringwood, England 50 50N 1 48w	
Rinia I., Greece 37 15N 25 20E	
Rio Claro, Brazil 22 20s 47 35w	
Rio Claro, Trinidad 10 12N 61 15w	
Rio Cuarto, Argentina 33 0s 64 0w	
Rio de Janeiro, & st., Brazil 22 5s 43 12w	
Rio de la Plata, S. Amer. 35 0s 57 0w	
Rio Gallegos, Arg. 51 40s 69 10w	
Rio Grande, New Mexico, U.S.A. 34 20N 106 48w	
Rio Grande, Mexico 29 0N 107 0w	
Rio Grande de Santiago, Mexico 22 0N 103 35w	
Rio Grande del Norte, Mexico 25 55N 97 12w	
Rio Grande do Norte, st., Brazil 5 30s 36 0w	
Rio Grande do Sul, & st., Brazil 32 0s 52 0w	
Riobamba, Ecuador 1 40s 78 48w	
Riohacha, Colombia 11 33N 72 45w	
Riom, France 45 52N 3 5E	
Riouw Arch., Indonesia 0 50N 104 50E	
Ripley, England 53 3N 1 24w	
Ripon, England 54 9N 1 32w	
Riq'ai, Saudi Arabia 29 0N 46 33E	
Risca, Wales 51 36N 3 6w	
Rishon le Zion, Israel 31 58N 34 47E	
Rishton, England 53 46N 2 26w	
Risör, Norway 58 43N 9 10E	
Riva, Italy 45 54N 10 52E	
Rivarolo, Italy 45 20N 7 45E	
River Cess, Liberia 5 30N 9 25w	
Rivera, Uruguay 31 0s 55 40w	
Riversdale, S. Africa 34 10s 21 35E	
Riverside, U.S.A. 33 55N 117 25w	
Riverton, Australia 34 0s 138 50E	
Riverton, Canada 51 5N 97 0w	
Riverton, New Zealand 46 20s 168 5E	
Riviera au Renard, Can. 49 5N 64 25w	
Riviera di Levante, Italy 44 23N 9 15E	
Riviera di Ponente, Italy 43 58N 8 0E	
Rivière du Loup, Can. 47 50N 69 27w	
Rivière Pilote, Martinique, W.I. 14 30N 60 50w	
Riyadh, Saudi Arabia 24 40N 46 50E	
Rize, Turkey 40 59N 40 30E	
Rizzuto, C., Italy 38 54N 17 5E	
Rjukan Fos., Norway 59 54N 8 40E	
Road Weedon, England 52 14N 1 6w	
Roanne, France 46 4N 4 2E	
Roanoke, R., U.S.A. 37 18N 80 1w	
Roaringwater B., Ireland 51 30N 9 30w	
Robert, Martinique, W.I. 14 40N 60 57w	
Robert Williams, Angola 12 40s 15 45E	
Robertson Ra., Australia 23 0s 121 0E	
Robertsport, Liberia 6 45N 11 26w	
Robertstown, Ireland 53 16N 6 50w	
Roberval, Canada 48 24N 72 20w	
Robin Hood's B., Eng. 54 25N 0 31w	
Robinson Ranges, Austral. 25 40s 119 0E	
Robson, Mt., Canada 53 15N 118 0w	
Roca, Cabo de, Portugal 38 46N 9 30w	
Rocamadour, France 44 46N 1 40E	
Rochdale, England 53 38N 2 9w	
Rochechouart, France 45 50N 0 45E	
Rochefort, Belgium 50 12N 5 15E	
Rochefort, France 45 57N 0 57w	
Rochester, England 51 22N 0 29E	
Rochester, Minn., U.S.A. 44 2N 92 29w	
Rochester, N.H., U.S.A. 43 18N 71 0w	
Rochester, N.Y., U.S.A. 43 12N 77 40w	
Rochford, England 51 36N 0 42E	
Rochfortbridge, Ireland 53 25N 7 19w	
Rock Island, U.S.A. 41 30N 90 32w	
Rock Springs, U.S.A. 41 38N 109 13w	
Rockall I., Atlantic Oc. 57 37N 13 42w	
Rockall Deep, Atlantic Ocean 56 45N 11 0w	
Rockcliffe, England 54 58N 3 0w	
Rockcorry, Ireland 54 7N 7 0w	
Rockford, U.S.A. 42 19N 89 8w	
Rockhampton, Australia 23 28s 150 31E	
Rockingham, & For., Eng. 52 30N 0 40w	
Rockland, U.S.A. 44 10N 69 10w	
Rocky Mount, U.S.A. 35 57N 75 2w	
Rocky Mts., N. America 40 0N 110 0w	
Roden, Netherlands 53 7N 6 20E	
Rodez, France 44 22N 2 39E	
*Renamed Caála	

Ródhos I., Greece 36 21N 28 77E	
Roding R., England 51 43N 0 16E	
Roebourne, Australia 20 43s 117 10E	
Roebuck B., Australia 18 10s 122 0E	
Roermonde, Netherlands 51 12N 6 0E	
Roes Welcome, Sd., Can. 65 0N 87 0w	
Roeselare, Belgium 50 57N 3 7E	
Rogaland, Co., Norway 59 0N 6 30E	
Rogliano, Corsica, France 42 55N 9 25E	
Rohri, Pakistan 27 47N 68 50E	
Rohtak, India 28 57N 76 30E	
Roisel, France 49 58N 3 6E	
Rojo, C., Mexico 21 30N 97 20w	
Rolla, U.S.A. 37 59N 91 46w	
Rollingstone, Australia 19 0s 146 15E	
Roma, Australia 26 32s 148 49E	
Roma, Sweden 57 32N 18 26E	
Romaine, R., Canada 51 40N 63 40w	
Roman, Rumania 46 50N 26 29E	
Roman, U.S.S.R. 60 25N 112 10E	
Romans, France 45 2N 5 0E	
Romanshorn, Switz. 47 35N 9 22E	
Rome, Italy 41 53N 12 33E	
Rome, Ga., U.S.A. 34 15N 85 8w	
Rome, N.Y., U.S.A. 43 15N 75 30w	
Romilly, France 48 30N 3 46E	
Romney Marsh, England 51 0N 0 54E	
Romont, Switzerland 46 42N 6 54E	
Romorantin, France 47 20N 1 45E	
Romsdal, val., Norway 62 30N 7 50E	
Romsey, England 50 59N 1 29w	
Rona, I., Scotland 57 33N 6 0w	
Ronay, I., Scotland 57 30N 7 10w	
Roncesvalles & P., Spain 43 1N 1 20w	
Ronda, Spain 36 48N 5 9w	
Rondane, Plat., Norway 61 66N 95 7E	
Rønne, Denmark 55 5N 14 41E	
Ronse, Belgium 50 44N 3 36E	
Roorkee, India 29 45N 78 20E	
Roosevelt I., Antarctica 80 0s 161 0E	
Roosky, Ireland 53 50N 7 47w	
Roper R., Australia 14 58s 134 0E	
Roquefort, France 44 1N 0 20w	
Roraima, mt., Venezuela 5 45N 62 0w	
Roraima, state, Brazil 2 30N 62 0w	
Røros, Norway 62 35N 11 22E	
Rorschach, Switzerland 47 29N 9 29E	
Rosario, Argentina 33 3s 60 40w	
Rosario, Mexico 23 0N 105 40w	
Rosario de la Frontera, Argentina 25 45s 65 0w	
Rosas, Spain 42 19N 3 10E	
Roscoff, France 48 40N 4 0w	
Roscommon, & Co., Ire. 53 38N 8 8w	
Roscrea, Ireland 52 58N 7 48w	
Roseau, Dominica, W.I. 15 15N 61 15w	
Rosebery, Australia 41 52s 145 38E	
Roseburg, U.S.A. 43 13N 123 20w	
Rosedale, Australia 24 38s 151 53E	
Rosehearty, Scotland 57 42N 2 8w	
Roseires, Sudan 11 50N 34 30E	
Rosemarkie, Scotland 57 35N 4 8w	
Rosenheim, Germany 47 55N 12 5E	
Rosetown, Canada 51 30N 108 10w	
Rosetta, Egypt 31 30N 30 25E	
Rosewood, Australia 27 38s 152 20E	
Röskilde, Denmark 55 39N 12 3E	
Roslavl, U.S.S.R. 53 57N 32 40E	
Ross on Wye, England 51 54N 2 34w	
Ross, New Zealand 42 55s 170 52E	
Ross Dependency, Antarctica 70 0s 170 0E	
Ross Ice Shelf, Antarc. 82 0s 175 0w	
Ross Sea, Antarctica 75 0s 178 0E	
Rossan Pt., Ireland 54 42N 8 49w	
Rosscarbery & B., Ireland 51 34N 9 1w	
Rosses Bay, Ireland 55 2N 8 30w	
Rosses Point, Ireland 54 17N 8 34w	
Rossland, Canada 49 5N 117 35w	
Rosslare & Hr., Ireland 52 15N 6 20w	
Rosso, Mauritania 16 40N 15 45w	
Rossosh, U.S.S.R. 50 17N 39 30E	
Rostherne, Canada 52 58N 106 10w	
Rostock, Germany 54 3N 12 7E	
Rostov, U.S.S.R. 47 12N 39 40E	
Rosvatn L., Norway 65 40N 14 0E	
Roswell, U.S.A. 33 28N 104 36w	
Rosyth, Scotland 56 2N 3 26w	
Rothbury & For., Eng. 55 19N 1 52w	
Rother, R., Kent, England 51 1N 0 37E	
Rotherham, England 53 26N 1 20w	
Rothes, Scotland 57 33N 3 13w	
Rothesay, Scotland 55 50N 5 3w	
Rothhaar, G., mt., Ger. 51 6N 8 10E	
Rothwell, Northants, England 52 25N 0 48w	
Rothwell, Yorks., Eng. 53 46N 1 29w	
Rotoroa, I., N.Z. 41 50s 172 39E	
Rotorua, & L., N.Z. 38 13s 176 20E	
Rotterdam, Netherlands 51 55N 4 30E	
Rottingdean, England 50 48N 0 3w	
Rottweil, Germany 48 12N 8 26E	
Rotuma I., Pacific Oc. 12 0s 177 0E	
Roubaix, France 50 42N 3 4E	
Rouen, France 49 28N 1 7E	
Rough Pt., Ireland 52 19N 10 0w	
Roundstone, Ireland 53 24N 9 55w	
Roundwood, Ireland 53 4N 6 14w	
Rousay, I., Scotland 59 9N 3 2w	
Roussillon, Dist., France 42 40N 2 40E	
Rouyn, Canada 48 6N 79 0w	
Rovaniemi, Finland 66 35N 25 40E	

Rovereto, Italy 45 53N 11 2E	
Rovigo, Italy 45 2N 11 41E	
Rovinj, Yugoslavia 45 18N 13 40E	
Rovno, U.S.S.R. 50 30N 26 22E	
Rowanburn, Scotland 55 5N 2 54w	
Roxas, Philippines 11 40N 122 45E	
Roxburgh, New Zealand 45 30s 169 27E	
Roxburgh, Scot. 55 34N 2 30w	
Royston, Herts., England 52 3N 0 1w	
Royton, Lancs., England 53 34N 2 7w	
Rozoy-sur-Serre, France 49 40N 4 8E	
Rtishchevo, U.S.S.R. 52 27N 43 50E	
Ruabon, Wales 52 59N 3 3w	
Ruahine Ra., N.Z. 39 45s 176 0E	
Rubery, England 52 21N 1 59w	
Rubha a' Mhail, C., Scot. 55 57N 6 7w	
Rubicone, R., Italy 44 9N 12 29E	
Rud-i-Khoran R., Iran 29 0N 56 30E	
Rudnichny, U.S.S.R. 59 40N 52 20E	
Rudok, Tibet, China 33 30N 79 40E	
Rudolf, L., see Turkana, L.	
Rudolstadt, Germany 50 45N 11 55E	
Ruffec, France 46 0N 0 18E	
Rufiji, R., Tanzania 8 0s 38 0E	
Rufisque, Sénégal 14 42N 17 8w	
Rugby, England 52 21N 1 17w	
Rugeley, England 52 45N 1 54w	
Rügen I., Germany 54 32N 13 30E	
Rühr, R., Germany 51 25N 8 0E	
Ruki R., Zaïre 0 10s 18 30E	
Rukwa, L., Tanzania 8 5s 33 0E	
Rum I., see Rhum	
Rum Jungle, Australia 13 20s 131 12E	
Rumania, Europe 45 40N 25 20E	
Rumbek, Sudan 6 50N 29 30E	
Runanga, New Zealand 42 25s 171 15E	
Runcorn, England 53 21N 2 44w	
Rungwa R., Tanzania 6 40s 33 50E	
Rupa, India 27 15N 92 25E	
Rupert, R., Canada 51 30N 78 40w	
Rusape, Rhodesia 18 32s 32 5E	
Rusé (Ruschuk), Bulgaria 43 53N 25 57E	
Rush, Ireland 53 31N 6 7w	
Rushden, England 52 17N 0 37w	
Russian S.F.S.R., Europe and Asia 58 0N 80 0E	
Russkaya Polyana, U.S.S.R. 54 5N 74 0E	
Rustenburg, S. Africa 25 34s 27 10E	
Rutba, Iraq 33 4N 40 15E	
Ruthenia, reg., U.S.S.R. 48 30N 23 40E	
Rutherglen, Scotland 55 48N 4 13w	
Ruthin, Wales 53 8N 3 18w	
Ruthven, Scotland 57 4N 4 2w	
Rutland, U.S.A. 43 47N 72 55w	
Rutshuru, Zaïre 1 0s 29 28E	
Ruurlo, Netherlands 52 5N 6 27E	
Ruwenzori, Mt., Uganda 0 40N 29 50E	
Ruzayevka, U.S.S.R. 54 10N 44 55E	
Ruzomberok, Cz. 49 12N 19 15E	
Rwanda, Africa 2 0s 30 0E	
Ryan, L., Scotland 55 0N 5 4w	
Ryazan, U.S.S.R. 54 35N 39 45E	
Ryazhsk, U.S.S.R. 53 43N 40 0E	
Rybache, U.S.S.R. 46 40N 81 20E	
Rybachi Pen., U.S.S.R. 69 40N 32 0E	
Rybinsk (Shcherbakov), U.S.S.R. 58 0N 38 51E	
Rybinsk Res., U.S.S.R. 58 30N 37 50E	
Ryde, England 50 44N 1 11w	
Rye, & B., England 50 58N 0 44E	
Ryhope, England 54 53N 1 21w	
Rylstone, Australia 32 40s 149 58E	
Rypin, Poland 53 0N 19 30E	
Ryukyu Is., Japan 26 30N 128 0E	
Rzhev, U.S.S.R. 56 20N 34 25E	

S

Saanen, Switzerland 46 29N 7 17E	
Saar, Land, Germany 49 38N 6 33E	
Saar (Sarre), R., Fr. & Germany 49 20N 6 45E	
Saarbrücken, Germany 49 19N 7 0E	
Saarburg, Germany 49 38N 6 33E	
Saarlouis, Germany 49 18N 6 44E	
Saas Fee, Switzerland 46 8N 7 56E	
Sabah, state, Malaysia 6 0N 117 0E	
Sabastiya, Jordan 32 16N 35 11E	
Sabha, Wadi, Saudi Arabia 23 50N 50 0E	
Sabinas, Mexico 27 40N 101 10w	
Sabinas Hidalgo, Mex. 26 25N 100 15w	
Sabine, Mts., Italy 42 20N 12 50E	
Sabine R., U.S.A. 31 40N 93 45w	
Sable, C., Canada 43 28N 65 60E	
Sable, C., U.S.A. 25 15N 81 5w	
Sable I., Canada 43 57N 60 00w	
Sabzawar, Iran 36 25N 57 55E	
Sabzawar, Afghanistan 33 2N 62 0E	
Säckingen, Germany 47 35N 7 55E	
Sacramento, & R., U.S.A. 38 37N 121 25w	
Sacramento Mts., U.S.A. 32 20N 105 0w	
Sacriston, England 54 49N 1 38w	
Sadaba, Spain 42 20N 1 15w	
Saddell, Scotland 55 31N 5 30w	
Saddle Hd., Ireland 54 0N 10 10w	
Sado, I., Japan 38 0N 138 15E	
Sadon, Burma 25 25N 97 50E	
Saffron Walden, England 52 1N 0 15E	
Safi, Morocco 32 15N 9 15w	
Saga, & Pref., Japan 33 18N 130 6E	

Sagaing, Burma 21 58N 95 56E	
Sagami B., Japan 35 0N 139 30E	
Sagar, India 23 50N 78 50E	
Sageston, Wales 51 41N 4 48w	
Saginaw, & B., U.S.A. 43 29N 84 0w	
Sagres, Portugal 37 1N 8 57w	
Sagua la Grande, Cuba, 22 58N 80 2w	
Saguenay, R., Canada 48 18N 70 0w	
Sagunto, Spain 39 42N 0 18w	
Sahagúna, Spain 42 20N 5 0w	
Sahah, Jordan 31 51N 36 0E	
Sahara Atlas, mts., Algeria 34 0N 3 0E	
Sahara, Des., N. Africa 20 0N 12 0E	
Saharanpur, India 29 57N 77 38E	
Sahiwal, Pakistan 30 48N 73 5E	
Saidabad, Iran 29 27N 55 48E	
Saidapet, India 13 0N 80 15E	
Sa'id Bundas, Sudan 8 24N 24 48E	
Saidu, Pakistan 34 50N 72 15E	
Saigon, see Ho-Chi-Minh City	
Saihut, South Yemen 15 25N 51 20E	
Saikhoa Ghat, India 27 50N 95 40E	
Saimaa, L., Finland 61 20N 28 0E	
St. Abb's, Scotland 55 54N 2 7w	
St. Abb's Hd., Scotland 55 55N 2 8w	
St. Affrique, France 43 58N 2 55E	
St. Agnes, & Hd., Eng. 50 19N 5 15w	
St. Albans, England 51 46N 0 20w	
St. Albans, U.S.A. 44 50N 73 0w	
St. Albans Hd., England 50 35N 2 4w	
St. Amand, France 50 26N 3 27E	
St. Amand-Montrond, France 46 40N 2 30E	
St. Amandsberg, Belgium 51 5N 3 42E	
St. André, France 44 0N 6 30E	
St. André, C., Madagascar 16 0s 44 25E	
St. Andrews, Scotland 56 20N 2 48w	
St. Anne, Channel Is. 49 44N 2 10w	
St. Annes, England 53 46N 3 4w	
St. Ann's, & B., Jamaica 18 10N 77 15w	
St. Arnaud, France 36 33s 143 15E	
St. Asaph, Wales 53 17N 3 26w	
St. Augustin, Canada 51 30N 58 30w	
St. Augustine, U.S.A. 29 58N 81 21w	
St. Austell, England 50 20N 4 48w	
St. Avold, France 49 6N 6 43E	
St. Barthélemy I., W.I. 17 56N 62 45w	
St. Bees & Hd., England 54 31N 3 39w	
St. Boniface, Canada 49 50N 97 0w	
St. Boswells, Scotland 55 34N 2 39w	
St. Brelade's, Jersey, Channel Is. 49 12N 2 13w	
St. Bride's B., Wales 51 48N 5 11w	
St. Brieuc, France 48 34N 2 45w	
St. Calais, France 47 55N 0 40E	
St. Catherine, Mt., Grenada, W.I. 12 13N 61 40w	
St. Catherine's Point, England 50 35N 1 19w	
St. Céré, France 44 50N 1 50E	
St. Clair L., Canada-U.S.A. 42 38N 82 30w	
St. Claude, France 46 22N 5 50E	
St. Cloud, U.S.A. 45 28N 94 10w	
St. Columb Major, Eng. 50 26N 4 56w	
St. Croix, I., W. Indies 17 45N 64 45w	
St. Cyrus, Scotland 56 47N 2 25w	
St. Davids & Hd., Wales 51 53N 5 16w	
St. David's I., Bermudas 32 23N 64 38w	
St. Dié, France 48 20N 7 0E	
St. Dizier, France 48 40N 5 8E	
St. Elias, Mt., Canada 60 40N 140 0w	
St. Étienne, France 45 27N 4 22E	
St. Eustatius I., W.I. 17 30N 63 30w	
St. Félicien, Canada 48 38N 72 30w	
St. Florent, France 42 40N 9 15E	
St. Flour, France 45 0N 3 10E	
St. Gallen, & Canton, Switzerland 47 26N 9 21E	
St. Gaudens, France 43 5N 0 45E	
St. George, Bermudas 32 25N 64 40w	
St. George, U.S.A. 37 10N 113 35w	
St. George's, Grenada, W.I. 12 5N 61 40w	
St. Georges, Belgium 50 36N 5 22E	
St. Germain, Yvelines France 48 52N 2 5E	
St. Germains, England 50 24N 4 19w	
St. Gilles, France 43 41N 4 26E	
St. Girons, France 43 0N 1 8E	
St. Govan's Hd., Wales 51 35N 4 56w	
St. Helena B., S. Africa 32 40s 18 0E	
St. Helena I., S. Atlan. Oc. 15 55s 5 44w	
St. Helens, Eng. 53 28N 2 43w	
St. Helens, U.S.A. 45 50N 122 52w	
St. Helier, Jersey 49 15N 2 8w	
St. Hippolyte, France 47 20N 6 50E	
St. Hubert, Belgium 50 2N 5 22E	
St. Hyacinthe, Canada 45 40N 73 0w	
St. Ingbert, Germany 49 16N 7 6E	
St. Ives, & B., Corn., Eng. 50 14N 5 30w	
St. Ives, Hunts., England 52 19N 0 4w	
St. Jean, France 45 20N 6 20E	
St. Jean de Luz, France 43 25N 1 40w	
St. Jean, L., Canada 48 39N 72 10w	
St. Jérôme, Canada 45 57N 74 0w	
St. John, N.B., Canada 45 16N 65 55w	
St. John, R., U.S.A. 46 42N 69 35w	
St. John's, Antigua, W.I. 17 0N 61 50w	
St. John's Newf'd., Can. 47 37N 52 40w	
St. Johnston, Ireland 54 56N 7 29w	
St. Joseph, U.S.A. 39 46N 94 50w	
St. Joseph, L., Canada 51 10N 90 50w	
St. Joseph R., U.S.A. 42 8N 85 30w	
St. Junien, France 45 50N 0 55E	

St. Just, England 50 7N 5 41w	
St. Kilda, I., Atlantic Oc. 57 50N 8 40w	
St. Kilda, N.Z. 45 53s 170 31E	
St. Kitts I., West Indies 17 20N 62 49w	
St. Lawrence, G. of, Can. 48 0N 62 0w	
St. Lawrence, R., Canada 49 0N 68 0w	
St. Leonards, England 50 51N 0 33E	
St. Lô, France 49 12N 1 5w	
St. Louis, Senegal 16 0N 16 27w	
St. Louis, U.S.A. 38 40N 90 20w	
St. Lucia, I. & Chan., Wind. Is., W. Indies 14 0N 61 0w	
St. Lucia, L., S. Africa 27 45s 32 30E	
St. Maarten I., Neth. W.I. 18 5N 63 0w	
St. Magnus B., Scotland 60 23N 1 35w	
St. Malo, France 48 42N 2 2w	
St. Marc, Haiti, W.I. 19 0N 72 50w	
St. Martin, Jersey, Channel Is. 49 15N 2 5w	
St. Martin, France 44 2N 7 15E	
St. Martin I., W.I. 18 15N 63 0w	
St. Mary Pk., Australia 31 30s 138 40E	
St. Mary's, Australia 41 30s 148 15E	
St. Mary's I., England 49 55N 6 18w	
St. Mathieu, Pte. de, Fr. 48 20N 4 50w	
St. Maur, France 48 44N 2 30E	
St. Maurice, Switzerland 46 14N 7 1E	
St. Mellons, England 51 31N 3 3w	
St. Michael's Mt., Eng. 50 7N 5 29w	
St. Monance, Scotland 56 12N 2 45w	
St. Moritz, Switzerland 46 30N 9 51E	
St. Nazaire, France 47 20N 2 13w	
St. Neots, England 52 13N 0 16w	
St. Niklaas, Belgium 51 10N 4 8E	
St. Omer, France 50 42N 2 12E	
St. Paul, France 42 50N 2 30E	
St. Paul, U.S.A. 44 58N 93 6w	
St. Paul's Bay, Malta 36 57N 14 24E	
St. Peter Port, Channel Is. 49 43N 2 30w	
St. Petersburg, U.S.A. 27 49N 82 44w	
St. Pierre and Miquelon, Fr. Overseas Terr., N. Amer. 46 49N 56 15w	
St. Polten, Austria 48 10N 15 38E	
St. Quentin, France 49 54N 3 13E	
St. Raphael, France 43 22N 6 50E	
St. Rémy, France 43 43N 4 50E	
St. Servan, France 48 40N 2 0w	
St. Sever, France 43 47N 0 40w	
St. Stephen, Canada 45 12N 67 18w	
St. Thomas, Canada 42 45N 81 20w	
St. Thomas, I., W. Indies 18 20N 65 0w	
St. Trond, Belgium 50 49N 5 11E	
St. Tropez, France 43 16N 6 35E	
St. Valéry-en-Caux, Fr. 49 52N 0 45E	
St. Valéry sur Somme, Fr. 50 10N 1 40E	
St. Vallier, France 45 12N 4 50E	
St. Vincent, C., Portugal 37 0N 9 0w	
St. Vincent, G. Australia 35 0s 138 0E	
St. Vincent I., W. Indies 13 17N 61 15w	
St. Vith, Belgium 50 17N 6 5E	
St. Yrieix, France 45 32N 1 15E	
Sainte Anne, Guadeloupe, Fr. W.I. 16 13N 61 23w	
Sainte Anne, Martinique, Fr. W.I. 14 25N 60 52w	
Sainte Marie, I., Madag. 16 55s 50 0E	
Sainte Marie, Martinique, Fr. W.I. 14 46N 61 0w	
Sainte Ménéhould, France 49 10N 4 52E	
Sainte Rose, Guadeloupe, W.I. 16 18N 61 40w	
Saintes, France 45 47N 0 40w	
Saintfield, N. Ireland 54 28N 5 50w	
Saintonge, Dist., France 45 30N 0 40w	
Sairang, India 23 50N 92 40E	
Saitama, Pref., Japan 36 20N 139 45E	
Saiun, South Yemen 15 52N 48 55E	
Sajama, Mt., Bolivia 17 30s 68 30w	
Sakai, Japan 34 30N 135 30E	
Sakashima Gunto, Is., Jap. 25 0N 124 0E	
Sakata, Japan 38 58N 139 56E	
Sakhalin, U.S.S.R. 52 0N 143 0E	
Sakskrivier, S. Africa 31 10s 20 28E	
Sala, Sweden 59 56N 16 30E	
Salado, R., Argentina 29 0s 63 0w	
Salaga, Ghana 8 35N 0 45w	
Salamanca, Spain 40 59N 5 40w	
Salamaua, Papua N.G. 7 10s 147 0E	
Salamis, Greece 37 58N 23 30E	
Salaverry, Peru 8 12s 79 0w	
Salayar, I., Indonesia 6 12s 120 25E	
Salbris, France 47 22N 2 8E	
Saldaña, Spain 42 30N 4 48w	
Sale, Australia 38 7s 147 0E	
Sale, England 53 26N 2 19w	
Salé, Morocco 33 29N 6 47w	
Salekhard, U.S.S.R. 66 30N 66 50E	
Salem, India 11 35N 78 0E	
Salem, Mass., U.S.A. 42 30N 71 0w	
Salem, Ore., U.S.A. 44 48N 123 0w	
Salerno, Italy 40 42N 14 50E	
Salford, England 53 29N 2 18w	
Salida, U.S.A. 38 25N 106 0w	
Salima, Malawi 13 50s 34 30E	
Salina, U.S.A. 38 50N 97 58w	
Salina Cruz, Mexico 16 25N 95 10w	
Salinas, U.S.A. 36 40N 121 42w	
Salinas Grandes, Arg. 29 15s 63 30w	
Salins, France 46 59N 5 50E	
Salisbury, Australia 34 45s 138 35E	
Salisbury, England 51 5N 1 47w	
Salisbury, Rhodesia 17 50s 31 2E	
Salisbury, Md., U.S.A. 38 25N 75 33w	
Salisbury, N.C., U.S.A. 35 42N 80 30w	

22 Salisbury Plain, England 51 14N 1 57w
62 Sallom, Sudan 19 22N 37 6E
90 Salmon, & R., U.S.A. 45 10N 113 50w
90 Salmon River Mts., U.S.A.
    44 45N 120 0w
49 Salo, Finland 60 22N 23 3E
43 Salo, Italy 45 40N 10 30E
43 Salon, France 43 40N 5 5E
* 22 Salop, Co., England 52 48N 2 50w
64 Salsette, I., India 18 30N 72 10E
51 Salsk, U.S.S.R. 46 10N 41 30E
43 Salsomaggiore, Italy 44 50N 10 0E
48 Salt Fd., Norway 67 10N 14 10E
90 Salt Fork R., Texas, U.S.A.
    33 15N 101 0w
90 Salt Lake City, U.S.A. 40 45N 111 50w
99 Salta, Argentina 24 47s 65 20w
24 Saltash, England 50 25N 4 12w
27 Saltburn, England 54 35N 0 58w
30 Saltcoats, Scotland 55 38N 4 47w
35 Saltee Is., Ireland 52 7N 6 35w
27 Saltergate, England 54 20N 0 40w
94 Saltillo, Mexico 25 28N 101 0w
99 Salto, Uruguay 31 25s 58 0w
98 Salto Augusto, Falls, Fs., Brazil
    8 30s 58 0w
90 Salton Sea, U.S.A. 33 20N 115 45w
72 Saltpond, Ghana 5 15N 1 3w
23 Saltwood, England 51 4N 1 5E
74 Salum, G. of, Egypt 31 30N 25 10E
65 Salur, India 18 36N 83 12E
40 Saluzzo, Italy 44 40N 7 30E
99 Salvador (Bahia), Brazil 12 50s 38 25w
94 Salvadore, C. Amer. 13 45N 88 50w
65 Salween, R., China-Burma
    19 30N 97 40E
46 Salzburg, & prov., Austria 47 46N 13 1E
46 Salzgitter, Germany 52 7N 10 19E
60 Sama, U.S.S.R. 60 25N 60 27E
61 Samagaltai, U.S.S.R. 51 40N 95 0E
63 Samar, Jordan 32 40N 35 47E
68 Samar, I., Philippines 11 30N 125 0E
82 Samarai, Papua N.G. 10 30s 151 0E
63 Samaria, Dist., Jordan 32 21N 35 30E
63 Samaria, Mts. of, Jordan 32 15N 35 15E
68 Samarinda, Indonesia 0 48s 117 18E
60 Samarkand, U.S.S.R. 39 45N 66 55E
62 Samarra, Iraq 34 30N 43 55E
62 Samawa, Iraq 31 15N 45 15E
65 Sambalpur, India 21 32N 83 59E
68 Sambas, Indonesia 1 30N 109 20E
75 Sambava, Madagascar 14 10s 50 3E
64 Sambhal, India 28 40N 78 35E
64 Sambhar, India 26 55N 74 45E
40 Sambiase, Italy 38 57N 16 16E
47 Sambor, U.S.S.R. 49 30N 23 15E
44 Sambre, R., Fr.-Belg. 50 20N 4 15E
74 Same, Tanzania 4 1s 37 45E
51 Samnan, Iran 35 31N 53 20E
41 Samos, I., Greece 37 41N 26 50E
41 Samothraki, I., Greece 40 28N 25 38E
68 Sampit, Indonesia 2 23s 113 0E
66 Samshui, China 23 15N 112 55E
51 Samsun, Turkey 41 20N 36 12E
68 Samut Songkhram, Thailand
    13 20N 100 0E
72 San Mali 13 15N 4 45w
95 San Andres, I., Colombia
    12 30N 81 35w
90 San Andres, Mts., U.S.A.
    33 0N 106 40w
94 San Andres Tuxtla, Mex. 18 25N 95 15w
90 San Angelo, U.S.A. 31 25N 100 28w
99 San Antonio Oeste, Arg. 40 40s 65 5w
99 San Antonio, Chile 33 30s 71 40w
90 San Antonio, U.S.A. 29 27N 98 32w
94 San Antonio, C., Cuba 21 58N 85 0w
91 San Antonio, R., U.S.A. 28 45N 97 30w
91 San Benito, U.S.A. 26 5N 97 45w
90 San Bernardino, U.S.A. 34 11N 117 25w
68 San Bernardino Str., Philippines
    12 30N 124 17E
91 San Blas, C., U.S.A. 29 40N 85 20w
68 San Carlos, Philippines 10 7N 124 20E
99 San Carlos de Bariloche, Argentina
    41 20N 71 0w
90 San Clemente I., U.S.A. 32 50N 118 30w
99 San Cristobal, Argentina 30 25s 61 10w
94 San Cristobal, Mexico 17 16N 92 32w
95 San Cristobal, Venezuela 7 30N 72 15w
78 San Cristobal, I., Solomon Is.
    11 0s 162 0E
90 San Diego, U.S.A. 32 45N 117 12w
99 San Felipe, Chile 32 40s 70 45w
95 San Felipe, Venezuela 10 10N 68 50w
37 San Feliu, Spain 41 45N 3 0E
94 San Fernando, Mexico 24 50N 98 2w
37 San Fernando, Spain 36 36N 6 14w
94 San Fernando, Trinidad 10 10N 61 28w
98 San Fernando, Venezuela 7 50N 67 30w
90 San Francisco, U.S.A. 37 47N 122 25w
95 San Francisco de Macoris, Dominican
    Republic 19 15N 70 5w
99 San Ignacio, Bolivia 16 10s 61 0w
90 San Joaquin, U.S.A. 37 0N 120 0w
94 San Jorge B., Mexico 31 0N 113 30w
99 San Jorge, G. de, Arg. 46 0s 66 30w
98 San José, Bolivia 18 0s 60 30w
95 San José, Costa Rica 9 50N 84 2w
68 San Jose, Philippines 10 45N 122 0E
90 San Jose, Cal., U.S.A. 37 20N 122 50w
99 San José, Uruguay 34 7s 57 0w
99 San Juan, Argentina 31 38s 68 38w
95 San Juan, Puerto Rico 18 27N 66 10w
90 San Juan Mts., U.S.A. 37 30N 107 0w

* *Renamed Shropshire*

99 San Julian, Argentina 49 20s 67 35w
99 San Lorenzo, Mt., Arg. 47 30s 72 0w
94 San Lucas, C., Mexico 23 0N 110 0w
99 San Luis, Argentina 33 24s 66 15w
90 San Luis Obispo, U.S.A.
    35 18N 120 38w
94 San Luis Potosi, Mex. 22 10N 100 37w
40 San Marino, Italy 43 58N 12 30E
90 San Mateo, U.S.A. 37 30N 122 15w
99 San Matias, G. de, Arg. 41 30s 64 0w
94 San Miguel, Salvador 13 25N 88 10w
99 San Nicolas, Argentina 33 20s 60 10w
94 San Pedro, Mexico 26 0N 102 58w
99 San Pedro, Paraguay 24 0s 57 10w
95 San Pedro de Macoris,
    Dominican Republic 18 30N 69 20w
94 San Pedro Sula, Honduras
    15 35N 88 0w
99 San Rafael, Argentina 34 30s 68 20w
40 San Remo, Italy 43 50N 7 50E
94 San Salvador, Salvador 13 59N 89 18w
95 San Salvador I., Bahama
    24 0N 74 30w
37 San Sebastian, Spain 43 20N 1 58w
40 San Severo, Italy 41 40N 15 20E
94 San Vicente, Salvador 13 45N 88 50w
37 San Vicente de la Barquera, Spain
    43 28N 4 30w
62 San'a, Yemen 15 25N 44 15E
63 Sanamein, Syria 33 5N 36 10E
68 Sanana, I., Indonesia 2 20s 126 0E
95 Sanchez, Dominican Republic
    19 10N 69 35w
43 Sancoins, France 46 50N 2 58E
95 Sancti Spiritus, Cuba 22 0N 78 0w
68 Sandakan, Malaysia 6 0N 118 12E
68 Sandalwood I., Indonesia 10 0s 120 0E
33 Sanday, I. & Sd., Orkneys, Scotland
    59 12N 2 30w
26 Sandbach, England 53 8N 2 23w
83 Sandgate, Australia 27 26s 152 57E
23 Sandgate, England 51 4N 1 7E
23 Sandhurst, England 51 21N 0 48w
49 Sandnes, Norway 58 50N 5 45E
74 Sandoa, Zaïre 9 48s 22 4E
47 Sandomierz, Poland 50 40N 21 42E
65 Sandoway, Burma 18 14N 94 30E
90 Sandpoint, U.S.A. 48 27N 116 35w
32 Sandray, Hebrides, Scot. 56 53N 7 30w
23 Sandringham, England 52 49N 0 30E
80 Sandstone, Australia 27 59s 119 25E
91 Sandusky, U.S.A. 41 25N 82 45w
49 Sandviken, Sweden 60 38N 16 58E
23 Sandwich, England 51 16N 1 22E
23 Sandy, England 52 8N 0 18w
82 Sandy, C., Australia 24 45s 152 30E
64 Sandy Desert, Pakistan 28 0N 65 0E
91 Sanford, U.S.A. 28 48N 81 27w
88 Sanford, Mt., Alaska 62 5N 143 30w
64 Sangamner, India 19 35N 74 10E
64 Sangatolon, U.S.S.R. 61 50N 149 30E
68 Sangihe Is., Indonesia 3 57N 125 14E
64 Sangli, India 16 55N 74 25E
74 Sangmelina, Cameroon 2 57N 12 1E
37 Sangonera, R., Spain 37 40N 2 0w
90 Sangre de Cristo Ra., U.S.A.
    37 30N 105 20w
94 Sangre Grande, Trinidad 10 36N 61 8w
74 Sangwa, Zaïre 5 30s 26 5E
37 Sankuru R., Zaïre 4 0s 21 0E
37 Sanlúcar la Mayor, Spain 36 46N 6 21w
37 Sanlúcar de Barrameda, Spain
    36 40N 6 28w
47 Sanok, Poland 49 35N 22 14E
31 Sanquhar, Scotland 55 22N 3 55w
72 Sansanné-Mango, Togo 10 28N 0 25E
94 Santa Ana, Salvador 14 0N 89 35w
90 Santa Ana, U.S.A. 33 40N 117 48w
90 Santa Barbara, U.S.A. 34 30N 119 40w
90 Santa Barbara I., U.S.A.
    33 15N 118 30w
90 Santa Blanca Pk., U.S.A.
    33 20N 105 45w
90 Santa Catalina I., U.S.A.
    33 10N 119 0w
99 Santa Catarina I., Brazil 27 45s 48 20w
95 Santa Clara, Cuba 22 30N 79 40w
95 Santa Clara, U.S.A. 37 22N 122 0w
98 Santa Cruz, Bolivia 17 50s 63 26w
72 Santa Cruz, Canary Is. 28 25N 16 19w
90 Santa Cruz, U.S.A. 36 57N 122 0w
78 Santa Cruz I., U.S.A. 34 5N 119 50w
81 Santa Cruz Is., Pac. Oc. 10 20s 168 0E
99 Santa Eugenia, Pt., Mex. 27 50N 115 5w
95 Santa Fé, Argentina 31 40s 60 45w
90 Santa Fe, U.S.A. 35 40N 105 50w
99 Santa Inés I., Chile 54 0s 73 0w
74 Santa Isabel, Equatorial Guinea
    3 45N 8 50E
99 Santa Maria, Brazil 29 30s 53 40w
99 Santa Maria, U.S.A. 34 50N 120 28w
41 Santa Maria di Leuca, C., Italy
    39 50N 18 23E
95 Santa Marta, Colombia 11 13N 74 12w
95 Santa Marta, Sa. Nevada de, mts.,
    Colombia 11 0N 73 0w
90 Santa Monica, U.S.A. 34 5N 118 31w
99 Santa Rosa, Argentina 36 35s 64 0w
94 Santa Rosa, Honduras 14 50N 88 45w
90 Santa Rosa, U.S.A. 38 25N 122 43w
94 Santa Rosalia, Mexico 27 10N 112 32w
66 Santai, China 31 20N 104 30E
40 Santander, Spain 43 28N 3 52w
98 Santarém, Brazil 3 12s 54 30w
37 Santarém, Portugal 39 17N 8 43w

91 Santee, R., U.S.A. 33 30N 80 15w
99 Santiago, Chile 33 35s 70 40w
95 Santiago, Dominican Republic
    19 25N 70 40w
37 Santiago, Spain 42 54N 8 31w
95 Santiago de Cuba, Cuba 20 5N 75 48w
99 Santiago del Estero, Arg. 27 45s 64 27w
74 Santo Antonio do Zaire, Angola
    5 50s 12 10E
98 Santo Antonio Falls, Brazil 9 0s 64 0w
95 Santo Domingo, Dominican Republic
    18 32N 69 50w
37 Santona, Spain 43 28N 3 29w
99 Santos, Brazil 24 0s 46 10w
67 Santuaho, China 26 50N 119 50E
74 Sanza Pombo, Angola 7 16s 15 5E
98 São Francisco R., Brazil 8 45s 40 0w
98 São Luiz (Maranhao), Brazil
    2 45s 44 10w
98 São Manuel R., Brazil 10 0s 55 35w
99 São Paulo, & st., Brazil 23 35s 46 30w
98 São Roque, C., Brazil 5 0s 35 0w
74 São Salvador do Congo, Angola
    6 30s 14 25E
99 São Sebastião I., Brazil 24 0s 45 30w
99 São Tomé, C., de, Brazil 22 0s 41 10w
43 Saône, R., France 46 10N 3 50E
42 Saône-et-Loire, Dept., Fr. 46 42N 4 25E
72 Sapele, Nigeria 5 50N 5 40E
67 Sapporo, Japan 43 1N 141 15E
73 Saqota, Ethiopia 12 30N 38 45E
41 Sar Planina, Mts., Y-slav. 42 0N 20 45E
63 Sarakhs, U.S.S.R. 36 35N 61 2E
65 Sarangarh, India 21 30N 82 57E
52 Saransk, U.S.S.R. 54 13N 45 5E
50 Sarapul, U.S.S.R. 56 35N 53 47E
91 Sarasota, U.S.A. 27 15N 82 29w
91 Saratoga Springs, U.S.A. 43 6N 73 50w
52 Saratov, U.S.S.R. 51 35N 45 59E
68 Saravane, Laos 15 35N 106 25E
68 Sarawak, St., Malaysia 2 40N 113 15E
65 Sarda, R., India 28 50N 80 30E
72 Sardalas, Libya 25 48N 10 40E
40 Sardinia, I., Italy 40 20N 9 5E
63 Sardarshahr, India 28 30N 74 30E
48 Sarektjakko, Mt., Nor. 67 30N 17 30E
50 Sarema, I., U.S.S.R. 58 30N 22 45E
45 Sargans, Switzerland 47 4N 9 30E
63 Sargodha, Pakistan 32 10N 72 35E
60 Sargumei, U.S.S.R. 45 20N 74 53E
82 Sarina, Australia 21 22s 149 13E
43 Sarlat, France 44 52N 1 10E
99 Sarmiento, Argentina 45 30s 69 0w
45 Sarnen, Switzerland 46 54N 8 14E
92 Sarnia, Canada 43 0N 82 30w
47 Sarny, U.S.S.R. 51 18N 26 40E
41 Saros, G. of, Turkey 41 37N 26 35E
49 Sarpsborg, Norway 59 16N 11 12E
43 Sarrebourg, France 48 44N 7 2E
43 Sartène, Corsica, France 41 38N 8 55E
43 Sarthe, Dépt., France 48 5N 0 3E
60 Sartynya, U.S.S.R. 63 25N 63 7E
63 Sarur, Oman 23 20N 58 7E
42 Sarzeau, France 47 30N 2 50w
65 Sasaram, India 24 56N 84 0E
67 Sasebo, Japan 33 6N 129 50E
64 Saser, Mt., Kashmir 35 0N 77 45E
88 Saskatchewan, Prov., Can. 54 0N 106 0w
88 Saskatchewan, R., Can. 53 20N 104 30w
88 Saskatoon, Canada 52 10N 106 38w
61 Saskylakh, U.S.S.R. 72 0N 114 40E
61 Sasnovka, U.S.S.R. 54 20N 109 50E
72 Sasovo, U.S.S.R. 54 41N 41 55E
72 Sassandra, & R., Ivory Coast
    5 0N 6 0w
40 Sassari, Italy 40 45N 8 35E
46 Sassnitz, Germany 54 33N 13 35E
47 Sasyk, L., U.S.S.R. 45 39N 29 12E
72 Satadougou, Mali 12 40N 11 25w
64 Satara, India 17 50N 74 0E
64 Satmala Hills, Andhra Pradesh, India
    19 30N 78 30E
64 Satmala Hills, Maharashtra, India
    20 20N 74 30E
64 Satna, India 24 40N 80 50E
47 Sátoraljaújhely, Hungary 48 25N 21 40E
64 Satpura Hills, India 22 0N 77 0E
47 Satu Mare, Hungary 47 50N 23 0E
48 Saudharkrókur, Iceland 65 45N 19 37w
62 Saudi Arabia, S.W. Asia 25 0N 45 0E
44 Sauer, R., Luxembourg 49 51N 6 17E
35 Saulieu, France 47 18N 2 35w
92 Sault Ste. Marie, Canada 46 35N 84 22w
84 Sault Ste. Marie, U.S.A. 46 30N 84 24w
42 Saumur, France 47 18N 0 10w
74 Saurimo, Angola 9 38s 20 23E
40 Sava, R., Yugoslavia 46 14N 14 20E
84 Savaii I., Samoa (Inset)
72 Savalou, Benin 8 0N 2 9E
95 Savanna la Mar., Jamaica 18 14N 78 6w
91 Savannah, & R., U.S.A. 32 0N 81 5w
68 Savannakhet, Laos 16 35N 105 0E
75 Save, R., Mozambique 21 16s 34 0E
51 Saveh, Iran 35 0N 50 10E
72 Savelugu, Ghana 9 38N 0 4w
43 Saverne, France 48 40N 7 15E
43 Savigliano, Italy 44 40N 7 40E
42 Savoie, Dépt., France 45 33N 6 20E
40 Savona, Italy 44 21N 8 32E
68 Sawah Lunto, Indon. 0 30s 100 48E
64 Sawai Madhopur, India 26 5N 76 22E
67 Sawara, Japan 35 58N 140 36E

90 Sawatch Ra., U.S.A. 38 30N 106 30w
23 Sawbridgeworth, Eng. 51 49N 0 10E
36 Sawel, Mt., N. Ireland 54 47N 7 2w
73 Sawknah, Libya 29 10N 16 0E
27 Selby, England 53 48N 1 5w
68 Sawu I., Indonesia 10 30s 122 0E
23 Saxmundham, England 52 13N 1 29E
72 Say, Niger 12 57N 2 25E
90 Sayan Mts., U.S.S.R. 54 0N 98 0E
63 Sayda (Sidon), Lebanon 33 33N 35 21E
66 Saynshand, Mongolia 45 0N 110 8E
92 Sayre, Pa., U.S.A. 41 57N 76 35w
41 Sazan, Albania 40 30N 19 20E
46 Sazava, R., Cz-slov. 49 42N 15 10E
64 Sazin, Kashmir 35 35N 73 25E
79 Scafell Pikes, England 54 28N 3 13w
27 Scalby & Ness, C., Eng. 54 18N 0 24w
32 Scalloway, Scotland 60 7N 1 22w
32 Scalpay I., Inner Hebrides 57 18N 6 0w
32 Scalpay I., Outer Hebrides, Scotland
    57 51N 6 40w
48 & 49 Scandinavia Europe 65 0N 15 0E
33 Scapa Flow, Scotland 58 53N 3 2w
30 Scarba I., Scotland 56 10N 5 42w
27 Scarborough, England 54 13N 0 25w
34 Scariff, Ireland 52 55N 8 30w
32 Scarp, I., Scotland 58 1N 7 8w
34 Scattery I., Ireland 52 38N 9 30w
45 Schaffhausen & Canton, Switzerland
    47 43N 8 38E
89 Schefferville, Canada 54 50N 66 55w
44 Schelde, R., Belgium 51 10N 4 15E
93 Schenectady, U.S.A. 42 47N 73 55w
44 Scheveningen, Neth. 52 7N 4 20E
44 Schiedam, Netherlands 51 55N 4 24E
31 Schiehallion, Scotland 56 39N 4 9w
44 Schiermonnikoog, Neth. 53 30N 6 15E
40 Schio, Italy 45 49N 11 21E
46 Schleswig, Germany 54 50N 9 30E
46 Schleswig Holstein, Länd, Germany
    54 30N 9 36E
45 Schmidt I., U.S.S.R. 81 0N 91 0E
45 Schorndorf, Germany 48 47N 9 32E
44 Schoten, Belgium 51 15N 4 30E
44 Schouwen, I., Neth. 51 41N 3 53E
45 Schramberg, Germany 48 17N 8 24E
92 Schreiber, Canada 48 50N 87 20w
45 Schwabischer Alb (Swabian Jura), mts.,
    Germany 48 30N 9 30E
45 Schwäbisch Gmünd, Germany
    48 49N 9 47E
68 Schwaner Ra., Indonesia 0 35s 112 30E
67 Schwangcheng, China 45 30N 126 20E
45 Schwarzwald (Black Forest), Germany
    48 15N 8 10E
45 Schweinfurt, Germany 50 3N 10 12E
76 Schweizer Reneke, S. Africa
    27 10s 25 20E
45 Schwenningen, Germany 48 4N 8 30E
45 Schwyz, & Cn., Switz. 47 2N 8 39E
40 Sciacca, Italy 37 30N 13 0E
40 Scilla, Italy 38 18N 15 44E
24 Scilly, Isles of, England 49 55N 6 20w
83 Scone, Australia 31 58s 150 57E
31 Scone, Scotland 56 25N 3 24w
100 Scott, Antarctica 78 15s 167 0E
91 Scottsbluff, U.S.A. 41 55N 103 37w
83 Scottsdale, Australia 41 9s 147 30E
36 Scrabby, Ireland 53 53N 7 32w
90 Scranton, U.S.A. 41 25N 75 30w
27 Scremerston, England 55 44N 1 59w
31 Scridain L., Scotland 56 23N 6 5w
27 Scunthorpe, England 53 33N 0 35w
23 Seaford, England 50 46N 0 7E
32 Seaforth L., Scotland 57 53N 6 38w
27 Seaham, England 54 50N 1 20w
24 Seaton, Cumb., England 54 41N 3 32w
24 Seaton, Devon, England 50 42N 3 3w
90 Seattle, U.S.A. 47 45N 122 20w
94 Sebastien Vizcaino B., Mexico
    28 30N 115 0w
51 Sebin Karahisar, Turkey 40 20N 38 21E
44 Seclin, France 50 33N 3 2E
73 Second Cataract of Nile, Sudan
    21 45N 31 12E
84 Secretary I., N.Z. 45 13s 166 58E
64 Secunderabad, India 17 40N 78 35E
91 Sedalia, U.S.A. 38 40N 93 20w
83 Sedan, Australia 34 33s 139 20E
44 Sedan, France 49 40N 5 0E
26 Sedbergh, England 54 18N 2 35w
84 Seddon, N.Z. 41 42s 174 5E
84 Seddonville, N.Z. 41 30s 172 0E
27 Sedgefield, England 54 40N 1 27w
72 Sedihou, Sénégal 12 50N 15 30w
25 Sedom, Israel 31 4N 35 20E
60 Sedov Pk., U.S.S.R. 73 30N 54 10E
76 Seeheim, S.W. Africa 26 48s 17 50E
50 Seg L., U.S.S.R. 63 20N 33 20E
37 Segovia, Spain 40 58N 4 7w
37 Segre, R., Spain 42 10N 1 25E
72 Séguéla, Ivory Coast 8 5N 6 30w
37 Segura, R., Spain 38 8N 0 38w
72 Ségou, Mali 13 28N 6 16w
72 Segou, Mali 13 28N 6 16w
44 Seclin, France 50 33N 3 2E

42 Seine-St Denis, Dépt., Fr. 49 0N 2 30E
76 Sekoma, Botswana 24 35s 23 53E
72 Sekondi-Takoradi, Ghana 4 56N 1 45w
27 Selby, England 53 48N 1 5w
40 Sele, R., Italy 40 31N 15 0E
66 Selenge Mörön, R., China 49 0N 102 0E
72 Sélestat, France 48 18N 7 3E
72 Sélibaby, Mauritania 15 20N 12 15w
73 Selima Oasis, Sudan 22 0N 29 35E
88 Selkirk, Canada 50 8N 96 40w
31 Selkirk, Scotland 55 34N 2 51w
88 Selkirk Ra., Canada 51 0N 117 0w
91 Selma, U.S.A. 32 30N 86 59w
23 Selsey, England 50 44N 0 47w
23 Selsey Bill, England 50 43N 0 48w
75 Selukwe, Rhodesia 19 37s 30 0E
82 Selwyn, Australia 21 37s 140 32E
41 Seman, R., Albania 40 50N 19 50E
68 Semarang, Indonesia 6 55s 110 40E
91 Seminole, U.S.A. 35 10N 96 45w
60 Semipalatinsk, U.S.S.R. 50 30N 80 10E
46 Semmering P., Austria 47 39N 15 50E
44 Semois, R., Belgium 49 48N 5 12E
45 Sempach, Switzerland 47 9N 8 12E
43 Semur, France 47 30N 4 20E
75 Senanga, Zambia 15 59s 23 15E
67 Sendai, Japan 38 15N 141 0E
92 Seneca, L., U.S.A. 42 30N 77 0w
72 Sénégal, Africa 14 45N 15 0w
72 Senegal, R., Mali 13 55N 11 0w
70 Senegambia, Dist., West Africa
    15 0N 14 0w
72 Senekal, O.F.S. 28 20s 27 40E
65 Senge Khambab (Indus), R., Tibet
    32 30N 81 0E
40 Senigallia, Italy 43 43N 13 12E
48 Senja I., Norway 69 25N 17 30E
42 Senlis, France 49 10N 2 53E
98 Sena Madureira, Brazil 9 0s 68 45w
73 Sennar, Sudan 13 42N 33 57E
89 Senneterre, Canada 48 25N 77 15w
43 Sens, France 48 12N 3 18E
41 Senta, Yugoslavia 45 59N 20 1E
37 Séo de Urgel, Spain 42 18N 1 28E
67 Seoul, Korea 37 49N 127 15E
82 Sepik, R., Papua N.G. 4 0s 143 0E
89 Sept Iles, Canada 50 10N 63 30w
90 Sequoia National Park, U.S.A.
    36 20N 118 30w
44 Seraing, Belgium 50 36N 5 33E
65 Serampore, India 22 44N 88 30E
68 Serang, Indonesia 5 55s 106 15E
41 Serbia Fed. Unit, Yugoslavia
    43 20N 21 20E
52 Serdobsk, U.S.S.R. 52 33N 44 8E
68 Seremban, Malaya 2 35N 102 10E
75 Serenje, Zambia 13 2s 30 50E
41 Sereth, R., see Siret, R.
99 Sergipe, st., Brazil 10 40s 37 30w
68 Seria, Malaysia 4 30N 114 25E
41 Serifos, I., Greece 37 11N 24 30E
60 Serny Zavod, U.S.S.R. 39 59N 59 10E
60 Serov, U.S.S.R. 59 45N 60 20E
75 Serowe, Botswana 22 19s 27 1E
98 Serpents Mouth, Ven. 10 0N 61 30w
52 Serpukhov, U.S.S.R. 54 52N 37 40E
44 Serrai, Greece 41 0N 23 30E
43 Serres, France 44 22N 5 42E
75 Serule, Botswana 21 52s 27 32E
75 Sesfontein, S.W. Africa 19 7s 13 39E
37 Sestao, Spain 43 23N 3 5w
43 Sète, France 43 23N 3 40E
72 Sétif, Algeria 36 10N 5 23E
37 Settat, Morocco 33 0N 7 35w
74 Setté Cama, Gabon 2 32s 9 57E
27 Settle, England 54 4N 2 18w
37 Setubal, & B. of, Port. 38 33N 8 53w
88 Seul, L., Canada 50 25N 92 30w
42 Sevan L., U.S.S.R. 40 15N 45 20E
51 Sevastopol, U.S.S.R. 44 37N 33 30E
34 Seven Heads, C., Ireland 51 32N 8 40w
23 Sevenoaks, England 51 16N 0 12E
24 Severn Beach, England 51 34N 2 39w
22 Severn R., England 51 40N 2 35w
22 Severn Stoke, England 52 5N 2 13w
61 Severnaya Zemlya, U.S.S.R.
    79 30N 97 0E
61 Severo-Yeniseisky, U.S.S.R.
    60 25N 93 25E
50 Severodvinsk, U.S.S.R. 64 45N 40 0E
50 Severouralsk, U.S.S.R. 60 10N 59 30E
90 Sevier, R. & L., U.S.A. 39 0N 113 20w
37 Seville, Spain 37 27N 5 58w
88 Seward, Alaska 60 0N 7 35w
5 Seychelle Is., Indian Oc. 4 30s 55 30E
48 Seydisfjordur, Iceland 65 15N 13 52w
83 Seymour, Australia 36 58s 145 10E
43 Sézanne, France 48 40N 3 45E
47 Sfântu Gheorghe, Rum. 45 50N 25 50E
73 Sfax, Tunisia 34 49N 10 42E
44 's Gravenhage, Netherland, see The
    Hague
32 Sgurr Mor, Mt., Scotland 57 42N 5 0w
32 Sgurr na Ciche, Scotland 57 5N 5 29w
32 Sgurr na Lapaich Mt., Scotland
    57 21N 5 14w
74 Shaba, reg., Zaïre 9 50s 26 0E
65 Shaba Gomba, China 32 10N 89 0E
73 Shabani, Rhodesia 20 15s 30 14E
62 Shabicha, Iraq 30 52s 43 45E
100 Shackleton, Antarctica 79 0s 39 0w

60 Shadrinsk, U.S.S.R. 56 15N 64 0E
22 Shaftesbury, England 51 1N 2 12w
64 Shahgarh, India 27 15N 69 50E
63 Shahhat (Cyrene), Libya 32 40N 21 30E
63 Shahr-i-Zabul, Afghanistan 31 0N 61 20E
62 Shahrig, Pakistan 30 12N 67 35E
62 Shahriza, Iran 32 0N 51 57E
72 Shajapur, India 23 20N 76 15E
52 Shakhty, U.S.S.R. 47 40N 40 10E
72 Shaki, Nigeria 8 41N 3 21E
73 Shala, L., Ethiopia 7 30N 38 30E
73 Shallal, El, Egypt 24 0N 33 0E
66 Shamo, Desert, see Gobi Desert
73 Shamo, L., Ethiopia 5 50N 37 40E
74 Shamva, Rhodesia 17 15s 31 40E
65 Shan State, Burma 21 5N 100 0E
34 Shanagolden, Ireland 52 35N 9 6w
72 Shanga, Nigeria 11 1N 4 40E
75 Shangani, R., Rhodesia 18 37s 28 0E
67 Shanghai, China 31 15N 121 35E
66 Shangiao, China 28 20N 116 15E
66 Shangkiu, China 34 35N 116 0E
22 Shanklin, I. of W., Eng. 50 38N 1 12w
84 Shannon, N.Z. 40 35s 175 40E
34 Shannon, R. Ireland 52 36N 9 40w
67 Shannonbridge, Ireland 53 18N 8 1w
61 Shan-si, Prov., China 37 30N 112 0E
61 Shantar I., U.S.S.R. 55 0N 137 30E
66 Shan-tung, Prov., China 36 30N 119 30E
66 Shaohing, China 30 2N 120 30E
66 Shaowu, China 27 25N 117 0E
66 Shaoyang, China 27 15N 111 15E
26 Shap, England 54 31N 2 43w
33 Shapinsay, I. & Sd., Scot. 59 3N 2 51w
63 Sharja, U.A.E. 25 17N 55 18E
63 Sharkh, Oman 21 20N 59 5E
92 Sharon, U.S.A. 41 18N 80 30w
63 Sharon, Plain of, Israel 32 20N 34 55E
63 Sharqiya, Jordan 32 11N 35 15E
66 Sha-si, China 30 25N 112 12E
88 Shaunavon, Canada 49 30N 108 40w
91 Shawinigan, Can. 46 45N 73 0w
91 Shawnee, U.S.A. 35 16N 96 59w
65 Shazia, Tibet, China 33 10N 82 40E
47 Shchara, R., U.S.S.R. 53 20N 25 10E
93 Sheboygan, U.S.A. 43 47N 87 43w
93 Shediac, Canada 46 18N 64 28w
35 Sheefry Hills, Ireland 53 40N 9 40w
34 Sheelin, L., Ireland 53 49N 7 17w
36 Sheep Haven, Ireland 55 12N 7 53w
34 Shefar'am, Israel 32 48N 35 10E
27 Sheffield, England 52 23N 1 28w
66 Shehung, China 30 45N 105 0E
63 Sheikh Miskin, Syria 32 50N 36 10E
63 Shekar Dzong, China 28 45N 87 0E
66 Sheklung, China 23 4N 113 50E
91 Shelburne, Canada 43 49N 65 19w
61 Shelekhov G., U.S.S.R. 59 50N 157 0E
83 Shellharbour, Australia 34 35s 150 50E
91 Shenandoah, U.S.A. 40 48N 95 22w
92 Shenandoah, R., U.S.A. 38 30N 78 40w
72 Shendi, Sudan 16 57N 33 46E
27 Shenfield, England 51 39N 0 21E
66 Shensi, Prov., China 35 0N 109 0E
66 Shentsa, Tibet, China 30 52N 88 30E
67 Shenyang, China 41 50N 124 0E
62 Sheopur Kalan, India 25 40N 76 40E
47 Shepetovka, U.S.S.R. 50 10N 27 0E
83 Shepparton, Australia 36 25s 145 28E
23 Sheppey I., England 51 23N 0 50E
62 Shepshed, England 52 47N 1 18w
72 Shepton Mallet, England 51 11N 2 31w
22 Sherborne, England 50 57N 2 32w
92 Sherborne St. John, Eng. 51 17N 1 7w
72 Sherbro I., Sierra Leone 7 25N 12 40w
93 Sherbrooke, Canada 45 21N 71 57w
27 Sherburn, England 53 47N 1 15w
36 Shercock, Ireland 54 0N 6 54w
23 Shere, England 51 13N 0 28w
22 Sherfield English, Eng. 51 1N 1 35w
90 Sheridan, U.S.A. 44 48N 106 56w
26 Sheringham, England 52 57N 1 14E
94 Sherkin I., Ireland 51 28N 9 25w
91 Sherman, U.S.A. 33 40N 96 40w
64 Sherridon, Canada 55 10N 101 20w
44 s'Hertogenbosch, Neth. 51 42N 5 18E
27 Sherwood Forest, Eng. 53 12N 1 10w
47 Shestakov, U.S.S.R. 68 25N 147 5E
32 Shetland Is., & Reg., Scotland
   60 20N 1 20w
60 Shevchenko, U.S.S.R. 43 25N 51 30E
91 Sheyenne R., U.S.A. 47 30N 98 15w
62 Shiant I., & Sd., Scot. 57 54N 6 20w
62 Shibam, South Yemen 16 0N 48 45E
93 Shickshock Mts., Can. 48 55N 66 30w
22 Shiel, L., Scotland 56 50N 5 30w
22 Shifnal, England 52 39N 2 22w
67 Shiga, Pref., Japan 35 15N 135 50E
72 Shigaib, Sudan 15 5N 23 35E
67 Shigatse, Tibet, China 29 27N 88 55E
66 Shihkiachwang, China 38 0N 114 30E
66 Shihlu, China 19 10N 109 0E
64 Shikarpur, Pakistan 28 3N 68 40E
67 Shikoku, I., Japan 33 30N 133 30E
27 Shildon, England 54 37N 1 39w
61 Shilka, U.S.S.R. 51 48N 116 0E
61 Shillelagh, Ireland 52 45N 6 30w
65 Shillong, India 25 30N 91 55E
65 Shilo, Jordan 32 4N 35 18E
67 Shimada, Japan 34 45N 138 10E
67 Shimane. Pref., Japan 35 0N 132 0E
67 Shimabara, Japan 32 45N 130 25E

67 Shimizu, Japan 35 6N 138 10E
64 Shimoga, India 13 57N 75 32E
67 Shimonoseki, Japan 33 58N 131 0E
64 Shin, L. & R., Scotland 58 5N 4 30w
64 Shindand, Afghan. 33 15N 62 10E
67 Shinjo, Japan 38 50N 140 26E
74 Shinkolobwe, Zaïre 11 10s 26 40E
34 Shinrone, Ireland 53 0N 7 58w
74 Shinyanga, Tanzania 3 38s 33 20E
67 Shio, C., Japan 33 30N 135 45E
67 Shiogama, Japan 38 16N 141 5E
41 Shipka, Bulgaria 42 40N 25 25E
64 Shipki La, India 31 45N 78 40E
26 Shipley, England 53 50N 1 47w
93 Shippigan, Canada 47 44N 64 48w
22 Shipston-on-Stour, Eng. 52 4N 1 39w
63 Shiqma, R., Israel 31 35N 34 35E
62 Shir Kuh, mt., Iran 31 32N 54 10E
75 Shire, R., Malawi 16 30s 35 15E
27 Shirebrook, England 53 13N 1 11w
64 Shiukwan, China 24 58N 113 5E
64 Shivpuri, India 25 30N 77 36E
67 Shizuoka, & Pref., Japan 34 59N 138 30E
41 Shkodër, Albania 42 3N 19 34E
41 Shkumbin, R., Albania 41 0N 19 24E
23 Shoeburyness, England 51 31N 0 48E
64 Sholapur, India 17 40N 76 0E
23 Shoreham-by-Sea, Eng. 50 50N 0 17w
75 Shoshong, Botswana 22 59s 26 41E
91 Shreveport, U.S.A. 32 30N 93 50w
22 Shrewsbury, England 52 42N 2 44w
22 Shropshire, Co., England 52 48N 2 50w
62 Shuqra, South Yemen 13 25N 45 37E
62 Shushtar, Iran 32 0N 48 47E
52 Shuya, U.S.S.R. 56 53N 41 28E
65 Shwebo, Burma 22 36N 95 50E
50 Shyaulyali (Siauliai), U.S.S.R.
   56 0N 23 0E
64 Shyok, & R., Kashmir 34 15N 78 5E
64 Siahan Ra., Pakistan 27 30N 64 30E
64 Siakwan, China 25 45N 100 10E
64 Sialkot, Pakistan 32 36N 74 37E
57 Siam, see Thailand
68 Siam, G. of, S.E. Asia 11 0N 101 0E
66 Sian, China 34 15N 109 0E
66 Siang, R., China 26 45N 112 30E
65 Siang, R., see Dihang, R.
66 Siangfan, China 32 15N 112 2E
66 Siang-tan, China 27 48N 112 45E
50 Siargao I., Philippines 9 50N 126 0E
50 Siauliai (Shyaulyali), U.S.S.R.
   56 0N 23 0E
40 Sibenik, Yugoslavia 43.46N 15 54E
60 Siberia, N. Asia 62 0N 110 0E
68 Siberut, I., Indonesia 1 30s 98 45E
74 Sibiti, Congo (Fr.) 3 38s 13 9E
47 Sibiu, Rumania 45 43N 24 11E
68 Sible Hedingham, Eng. 51 58N 0 37E
60 Sibolga, Indonesia 1 50N 98 45E
68 Sibsagar, India 27 0N 94 42E
68 Sibu, Sarawak, Malaysia 2 25N 111 50E
68 Sibuko Bay, Malaysia 4 10N 118 0E
66 Sichang, China 28 15N 101 45E
40 Sicily, I., Italy 37 40N 14 0E
73 Sidi Barrâni, Egypt 31 35N 26 0E
72 Sidi-Bel Abbes, Algeria 35 12N 0 42w
31 Sidlaw Hills, Scotland 56 30N 3 15w
24 Sidmouth, England 50 41N 3 14w
90 Sidney, U.S.A. 41 18N 103 0w
73 Sidra, G. of, Libya 31 30N 19 0E
44 Sieg, R., Germany 50 48N 7 15E
44 Siegburg, Germany 50 48N 7 12E
44 Siegen, Germany 50 51N 8 5E
40 Siena, Italy 43 20N 11 20E
66 Sienyang, China 34 20N 108 48E
72 Sierra Leone, W. Africa 8 20N 12 0w
90 Sierra Nevada, Mts., U.S.A.
   39 0N 119 0w
41 Sifnos, I., Greece 36 50N 24 40E
47 Sighet, Rumania 47 54N 23 57E
47 Sighisoara, Rumania 46 13N 24 50E
27 Sighty Crag, mt., Eng. 55 8N 2 34w
48 Siglufjordur, Iceland 66 10N 18 58w
47 Sigmaringen, Germany 48 2N 9 13E
44 Signy l'Abbaye, France 49 40N 4 25E
49 Sigtuna, Sweden 59 40N 17 38E
37 Siguenza, Spain 41 0N 2 3w
72 Siguiri, Guinea 11 34N 9 5w
33 Sihanoukville, see Kompong Som
72 Sikasso, Mali 11 25N 5 45w
61 Sikhote Alin Ra., U.S.S.R.
   47 0N 137 0E
62 Si-kiang, R., China 23 3N 110 30E
41 Sikinos, I., Greece 36 40N 25 5E
65 Sikkim, N.E. India 27 30N 88 30E
65 Sil, R., Spain 42 21N 7 0w
65 Silchar, India 24 49N 92 48E
65 Silgarhi Doti, Nepal 29 15N 81 0E
65 Silghat, India 26 40N 93 0E
62 Silifke, Turkey 36 30N 34 0E
65 Siliguri, India 26 45N 88 25E
41 Silistra, Bulgaria 44 6N 27 19E
49 Siljan, L., & mt., Sweden 60 52N 14 50E
49 Silkeborg, Denmark 56 10N 9 32E
27 Silsden, England 53 55N 1 55w
94 Silver City, Panama Canal Zone (Inset)
47 Silver City, U.S.A. 32 50N 108 20w
34 Silvermines, Ireland 52 48N 8 15w
64 Silvrettahorn, mt., Switz. 46 55N 10 10E
50 Simbirsk, see Ulyanovsk
92 Simcoe, Canada 42 52N 80 20w
61 Simenga, U.S.S.R. 62 47N 107 50E

68 Simeulue I., Indonesia 2 45N 96 0E
51 Simferopol, U.S.S.R. 44 55N 34 5E
64 Simikot, Nepal 30 0N 81 45E
64 Simla, India 31 5N 77 17E
48 Simo L. & R., Finland 66 10N 27 0E
27 Simonside, mt., England 55 15N 2 0w
76 Simonstown, C. Prov. 34 15s 18 28E
45 Simplon P. & Tunnel, Switzerland
   46 17N 8 7E
81 Simpson Des., Australia 25 0s 137 0E
61 Simushir, I., U.S.S.R. 47 20N 152 30E
73 Sinai, Pen., Egypt 28 40N 33 40E
94 Sinaloa, Mexico 25 50N 107 55w
72 Sinawan, Libya 31 0N 10 30E
33 Sinclairs B., Scotland 58 30N 3 7w
64 Sind Sagar Doab, Plat., Pakistan
   32 0N 71 30E
73 Sines, Portugal 37 58N 8 53w
62 Singa, Sudan 13 15N 33 59E
71 Singapore, I., Asia 1 0N 104 30E
68 Singaraja, Indonesia 8 0s 115 15E
74 Singen, Germany 47 45N 8 48E
74 Singida, Tanzania 4 50s 34 50E
41 Singitikós, G., Greece 40 5N 24 0E
68 Singleton, Australia 32 33s 151 10E
68 Singora, Thailand, see Songkhla
66 Singtai, China 37 25N 114 45E
66 Sinhailien, China 34 30N 119 10E
66 Sinhsien, China 38 40N 112 15E
66 Sining, China 36 40N 100 45E
73 Sinkat, Sudan 19 0N 37 0E
66 Sinkiang-Uigur, A.R., China
   40 30N 87 0E
66 Sinni, R., Italy 40 5N 16 20E
75 Sinoia, Rhodesia 17 20s 30 2E
62 Sinop, Turkey 42 0N 35 1E
66 Sinsiang, China 35 15N 113 55E
68 Sintang, Indonesia 0 10N 111 35E
37 Sintra, Portugal 38 45N 9 30w
66 Sinuiju, China 40 0N 124 40E
66 Sinyang, China 32 N 114 10E
45 Sion, Switzerland 46 15N 7 23E
36 Sion Mills, Ireland 54 47N 7 29w
91 Sioux City, U.S.A. 42 40N 96 17w
91 Sioux Falls, U.S.A. 43 35N 96 48w
91 Sious Lookout, Canada 50 10N 92 30w
94 Siparia, Trinidad 10 50N 61 30w
83 Sipora, I., Indonesia 2 5s 99 40E
81 Sir Edward Pellew Group, Australia
   15 30s 137 10E
40 Siracusa, Italy 37 7N 15 18E
65 Sirajganj, Bangladesh 23 56N 89 57E
47 Sire, Ethiopia 9 10N 37 5E
47 Siret, R., Rumania 45 40N 27 20E
62 Sirhan, Wadi, Jordan 30 45N 38 30E
64 Sirohi, India 24 46N 72 50E
64 Sironj, India 24 8N 77 0E
63 Siros I., Greece 37 30N 24 55E
64 Sirsa, India 29 4N 75 1E
40 Sisak, Yugoslavia 45 30N 16 20E
68 Sisaket, Thailand 15 10N 104 25E
44 Sissonne, France 49 36N 3 52E
64 Sistan, reg., Afghan. 31 0N 61 30E
43 Sisteron, France 44 10N 5 58E
43 Sitapur, India 27 15N 81 0E
88 Sitka, Alaska 57 6N 135 12w
44 Sittang R., Burma 18 0N 97 0E
44 Sittard, Netherlands 50 59N 5 48E
23 Sittingbourne, England 51 20N 0 43E
51 Sivas, Turkey 39 50N 37 2E
51 Sivrihisar, Turkey 39 35N 31 30E
73 Siwa, Egypt 29 18N 25 38E
65 Siwalik Ra., Nepal 27 0N 84 0E
65 Siwan, India 26 15N 84 20E
34 Sixmilebridge, Ireland 52 45N 8 46w
36 Sixmilecross, N. Ireland 54 34N 7 7w
73 Sixth Cataract, Sudan 16 20N 33 2E
23 Sizewell, England 52 13N 1 25E
93 Sjælland, Denmark 55 30N 11 30E
48 Sjönsta, Norway 67 10N 15 50E
49 Skaga Fjord, Iceland 66 10N 19 30w
49 Skagastölstindane, Mt., Norway
   61 25N 8 0E
48 Skagaströnd, Iceland 65 50N 20 12w
49 Skagen, Denmark 57 45N 10 35E
49 Skagen (The Skaw), Den. 57 48N 10 40E
49 Skagerrak, Scandinavia 57 30N 9 0E
49 Skagway, Alaska 59 22N 135 8w
49 Skara, Sweden 58 25N 13 23E
49 Skaraborg, Co., Sweden 58 45N 14 0E
65 Skardu, India 35 15N 75 40E
33 Skateraw, Scotland 57 1N 2 9w
49 Skeabrae, mt., England 54 38N 3 5w
26 Skegness, England 53 10N 0 20E
48 Skellefte, R., Sweden 65 30N 19 15E
48 Skelleftea, Sweden 64 48N 20 53E
48 Skellefteham, Sweden 64 43N 21 14E
27 Skellingthorpe, England 53 15N 0 35w
27 Skelmersdale, England 53 34N 2 49w
27 Skelton, England 54 33N 0 59w
25 Skerries, Ireland 53 36N 6 7w
25 Skerries, The, Wales 53 26N 4 37w
34 Skibbereen, Ireland 51 34N 9 14w
34 Skiddaw, mt., England 54 38N 3 5w
49 Skien, Norway 59 14N 9 32E
72 Skierniewice, Poland 52 0N 20 0E
72 Skikda (Philippeville), Algeria
   36 55N 6 58E
26 Skipton, England 53 58N 2 2w
41 Skiros, I., Greece 38 54N 24 38E
49 Skive, Denmark 56 33N 9 2E
48 Skjalfandafljót, R., Ice. 65 30N 17 30w
48 Skjalfandi, Fd., Iceland 66 10N 17 30w
49 Skoghall, Sweden 59 23N 13 7E

25 Skomer I., Wales 51 44N 5 18w
41 Skopje, Yugoslavia 42 1N 21 26E
49 Skövde, Sweden 58 15N 13 59E
61 Skovorodino, U.S.S.R. 54 0N 125 0E
49 Skudeneshavn, Norway 59 10N 5 10E
46 Skwierzyna, Poland 52 35N 15 30E
32 Skye, I., Scotland 57 25N 6 20w
36 Slane, Ireland 53 42N 6 32w
35 Slaney, R., Ireland 52 52N 6 45w
47 Slatina, Rumania 44 23N 24 23E
60 Slavgorod, U.S.S.R. 53 20N 79 0E
46 Slavkov (Austerlitz), Czechoslovakia
   49 10N 16 52E
51 Slavyansk, U.S.S.R. 48 50N 37 35E
51 Slea Hd., Ireland 52 7N 10 30w
27 Sleaford, England 53 0N 0 23w
32 Sleat, Sd., Scot. 57 6N 5 55w
32 Sleat, Pt. of, Scotland 57 1N 6 0w
44 Sliedrecht, Netherlands 51 51N 4 45E
40 Sliema, Malta 35 56N 14 18E
36 Slieve Anierin, mt., Ire. 54 5N 7 57w
34 Slieve Aughty, mts., Ire. 53 5N 8 32w
34 Slieve Bernagh, mt., Ire. 52 50N 8 30w
35 Slieve Bloom, mts., Ire. 53 4N 7 40w
36 Slieve Donard, mt., N. Ire. 54 8N 5 53w
34 Slieve Felim, mt., Ireland 52 40N 8 5w
36 Slieve Gamph (Ox. Mts.), Ireland
   54 6N 9 0w
36 Slieve Gullion, mt., N. Ire. 54 6N 6 27w
36 Slieve League, mt., Ire. 54 40N 8 35w
34 Slieve Mish, mt., Ireland 52 13N 9 55w
34 Slieve Miskish, mt., Ire. 51 40N 9 55w
35 Slieve More, mt., Ireland 54 1N 10 4w
36 Slieve Snaght, mt., Ire. 55 0N 8 8w
35 Slievenamon, mt., Ire. 52 25N 7 37w
36 Sligo, & Co., Ireland 54 16N 8 28w
36 Sligo B., Ireland 54 18N 8 40w
49 Slioch, Mt., Scotland 57 40N 5 12w
48 Slite, Sweden 57 41N 18 43E
41 Sliven, Bulgaria 42 41N 26 20E
47 Slonim, U.S.S.R. 53 2N 25 19E
27 Slough, England 51 30N 0 35w
47 Slovakia, Dist., Cz-slov. 48 50N 20 0E
47 Slovakian Ore Mts., Czechoslovakia
   48 30N 19 30E
41 Slovenia, Fed. Unit, Yugoslavia
   46 0N 15 0E
47 Sluch, R., U.S.S.R. 50 48N 27 10E
35 Slyne Hd., Ireland 53 25N 10 11w
34 Smerwick Hr., Ireland 52 13N 10 34w
22 Smethwick, England 52 29N 1 58w
34 Smithborough, Ireland 54 13N 7 8w
76 Smithfield, S. Africa 30 13s 25 37E
92 Smith's Falls, Canada 44 55N 76 0w
83 Smithton, Australia 41 58s 145 2E
83 Smithton & Gladstone, Australia
   31 0s 153 0E
90 Smoky Hill R., U.S.A. 38 55N 100 30w
48 Smöla, I., Norway 63 23N 8 3E
50 Smolensk, U.S.S.R. 54 40N 31 50E
41 Smolikas, mt., Greece 40 5N 20 45E
41 Smolyan, Bulgaria 41 36N 24 38E
51 Smyrna, see Izmir
48 Snaefell, mt., Isle of Man 54 14N 4 26w
48 Snaefell Mt., Iceland 64 47N 15 30w
48 Snaefells Jökull, mt., Ice. 64 47N 23 45w
27 Snainton, England 54 14N 0 33w
32 Snake R., U.S.A. 43 30N 116 50w
44 Sneek, Netherlands 53 2N 5 41E
76 Sneeuwberge Mts., C. Prov., S. Africa
   31 55s 24 30E
46 Snezka, mt., Poland 50 40N 15 55E
51 Snizort, L., Scotland 57 34N 6 30w
48 Snöhetta, mt., Norway 62 10N 9 40E
47 Snowdon, mt., Wales 53 4N 4 10w
88 Snowdrift, Canada 62 J0N 110 0w
83 Snowy Mts., Australia 36 30s 148 20E
83 Snowy R., Australia 37 0s 148 23E
47 Snyatyn, U.S.S.R. 48 30N 25 40E
75 Soalala, Madagascar 16 3s 45 30E
32 Soay I. & Sd., Scotland 57 9N 6 13w
90 Sobral, Brazil 3 46s 40 30w
57 So-ch'e, China 38 15N 77 0E
4 Society Is., Pacific Ocean 17 30s 151 0w
90 Socorro, U.S.A. 34 3N 106 50w
63 Socotra, I., E. Africa 12 37N 54 0E
49 Söderhamn, Sweden 61 20N 17 0E
49 Söderköping, Sweden 58 28N 16 20E
49 Södermanland, Co., Swed. 59 2N 17 20E
49 Södertalje, Sweden 59 12N 17 39E
44 Soest, Netherlands 52 10N 5 19E
41 Sofia, Bulgaria 42 40N 23 30E
50 Sofiiski, U.S.S.R. 52 10N 133 55E
49 Sogndalsfjöra, Norway 61 15N 7 4E
49 Sogne Fjord, Co., Norway
   61 30N 6 30E
49 Sogne Fd., Norway 61 8N 6 0E
73 Sohag, Egypt 26 30N 31 43E
23 Soham, England 52 20N 0 20E
37 Soignies, Belgium 50 35N 4 5E
44 Soissons, France 49 25N 3 19E
47 Sokal, U.S.S.R. 50 30N 24 16E
72 Sokodé, Togo 8 55N 1 12E
72 Sokólka, Poland 53 25N 23 30E
72 Sokolo, Mali 14 50N 6 18w
72 Sokoto, Nigeria 13 3N 5 15E
50 So Iletsk, U.S.S.R. 51 20N 54 50E
22 Solano, Philippines 16 40N 121 15E
22 Solent, The, England 50 45N 1 30w
79 Solfonn, Mt., Norway 60 2N 6 57E
30 Solihull, England 52 26N 1 45w
98 Solimoes, R., Brazil 2 30s 66 30w
44 Solingen, Germany 51 11N 7 5E
49 Sollefttea, Sweden 63 8N 17 5E

81 Solomon Is., Pacific Oc. 7 0s 158 0E
82 Solomon Sea, Papua N.G. 8 0s 153 0E
45 Solothurn, Switzerland 47 14N 7 33E
45 Solothurn, Canton, Switz. 47 19N 7 42E
49 Sölvesborg, Sweden 56 5N 14 35E
50 Solway Firth, Irish Sea 54 50N 3 40w
75 Solwezi, Zambia 12 18s 26 20E
70 Somali Pen., E. Africa 7 0N 47 0E
71 Somali Rep., E. Africa 4 0N 45 0E
94 Sombrerete, Mexico 23 35N 103 35w
23 Somerby, England 52 42N 0 49w
91 Somerset, U.S.A. 37 5N 84 45w
24 Somerset, Co., England 51 5N 3 0w
76 Somerset E., S. Africa 32 42s 25 45E
95 Somerset, & I., Bermuda 32 18N 64 52w
88 Somerset, I., Canada 73 0N 95 0w
76 Somerset W., S. Africa 34 3s 18 50E
23 Somersham, England 52 24N 0 1w
24 Somerton, England 51 4N 2 43w
47 Somes, R., Rumania 47 25N 23 45E
43 Somme, Dépt., France 49 55N 1 53E
43 Somme, R., France 50 15N 1 30E
43 Sommières, France 43 50N 4 0E
41 Somovit, Bulgaria 43 40N 24 45E
49 Sompting, England 50 51N 0 20w
49 Sonderborg, Denmark 54 58N 9 49E
89 Sondre Stromfjord, Greenland
   67 10N 50 10w
45 Sondrio, Italy 46 10N 9 52E
65 Sonepat, India 29 0N 77 0E
65 Sonepur, India 20 55N 83 45E
74 Songea, Tanzania 11 0s 35 45E
68 Songkhla (Singora), Thailand
   7 25N 100 40E
73 Songo, Sudan 10 0N 24 15E
94 Sonora R., Mexico 29 5N 111 0w
94 Sonsonate, Salvador 13 45N 89 50w
45 Sonthofen, Germany 47 31N 10 17E
67 Soochow, China 31 20N 120 40E
46 Sopot, Poland 54 14N 18 17E
48 Sör Trondelag, Co., Nor. 63 0N 9 30E
89 Sorel, Canada 45 57N 73 10w
63 Soreq, R., Israel 31 50N 34 50E
45 Sorgono, Italy 40 0N 9 0E
37 Soria, Spain 41 48N 2 28w
32 Sorisdale, Scotland 56 40N 6 28w
99 Sorocaba, Brazil 23 30s 47 20w
47 Soroki, U.S.S.R. 48 8N 28 12E
74 Soroti, Uganda 2 0N 33 45E
48 Söröy Sound, Norway 70 20N 23 0E
47 Soroya, I., Norway 70 40N 22 30E
47 Sosnowiec, Poland 50 20N 19 30E
47 Soudhas B., Greece 35 25N 24 10E
94 Soufrière, St. Lucia, W.I. 13 45N 61 4w
88 Sound, The, Denmark 56 7N 12 30E
88 Souris, Canada 49 35N 100 30w
90 Souris, R., U.S.A. & Canada
   48 30N 101 30w
73 Sousse, Tunisia 35 51N 10 38E
43 Soustons, France 43 44N 1 19w
76 South Africa, Africa 30 0s 24 0E
84 South Auckland, Bay of Plenty,
   Dist., N.Z. 38 0s 176 0E
80 South Australia, st. 29 40s 135 0E
26 South Barrule, mt., Isle of Man
   54 8N 4 40w
81 South Bend, U.S.A. 41 44N 86 17w
23 South Benfleet, England 51 33N 0 34E
91 South Carolina, st., U.S.A. 34 0N 81 0w
68 South China Sea 10 0N 112 0E
90 South Dakota, st., U.S.A. 45 20N 100 0w
24 South Dorset Downs, England
   50 45N 2 38w
23 South Downs, Ra., Eng. 50 55N 0 30w
23 South Elkington, England 53 22N 0 5w
23 South Foreland, England 51 8N 1 23E
94 South Gamboa, Panama Canal Zone
   (Inset)
100 South Georgia, I., Falkland Is. Dep.
   54 30s 36 0w
25 South Glamorgan, Co., Wales
   51 30N 3 20w
49 South Hayling, England 50 47N 0 56w
74 South Horr, Kenya 2 20N 36 48E
100 South Ice, Antarctica 81 30s 28 0w
84 South Invercargill, N.Z. 46 28s 168 22E
84 South I., New Zealand 44 30s 170 0E
74 South Kirby, England 53 35N 1 25w
23 South Molton, England 51 1N 3 51w
65 South Moscos Is., see Launglon Bok Is.
88 South Nahanni & R., Canada
   61 5N 123 30w
68 South Naturna Is., Indon. 2 50N 108 25E
100 South Orkneys, Is., Falkland Is. Dep.
   60 30s 45 0w
68 South Pagai I., Indonesia 3 0s 100 20E
90 South Platte R., U.S.A. 40 25N 104 0w
33 South Ronaldsay, Scot. 58 47N 2 58w
100 South Sandwich Is., Falkland Is. Dep.
   59 0s 27 0w
88 South Saskatchewan R., Canada
   51 0N 109 0w
100 South Shetlands, Is., Falkland Is. Dep.
   60 30s 60 0w
27 South Shields, England 55 0N 1 27w
32 South Uist I., Scotland 57 15N 7 22w
75 South West Africa, see Namibia
84 South West C., N.Z. 47 32s 167 30E
62 South Yemen, Asia 15 0N 47 0E
27 South Yorkshire, Co., England
   53 30N 1 25w
49 Southampton, England 50 55N 1 24w
89 Southampton I., Canada 64 30N 84 0w
22 Southampton Water, Eng. 50 52N 1 21w
23 Southborough, England 51 8N 0 17E

84 Southbridge, N.Z. 43 45s 172 17E
23 Southend-on-Sea, Eng. 51 33N 0 43E
30 Southend, Scotland 55 18N 5 38w
84 Southern Alps, N.Z. 43 30s 170 30E
80 Southern Cross, Australia 31 9s 119 21E
88 Southern Indian L., Can. 57 15N 99 0w
73 Southern Darfur, prov., Sudan 10 0N 25 0E
73 Southern Kardofan, prov., Sudan 12 0N 30 0E
4 Southern Ocean 60 0s 128 0E
75 Southern Rhodesia, see Rhodesia.
31 Southern Uplands, Scot. 55 30N 4 0w
84 Southland, Dist., N.Z. 44 50s 167 30E
26 Southport, England 53 39N 2 59w
83 Southport, Australia 28 0s 153 30E
23 Southwark, Greater London, England 51 29N 0 5w
27 Southwell, England 53 5N 0 57w
23 Southwick, England 50 50N 0 14w
23 Southwold, England 52 19N 1 42E
49 Sovetsk, U.S.S.R. 55 6N 21 50E
61 Sovetskaya Gavan (Soviet Harbour), U.S.S.R. 48 55N 140 5E
27 Sowerby, England 54 13N 1 19w
44 Spa, Belgium 50 30N 5 53E
37 Spain, Europe 39 50N 3 40w
83 Spalding, Australia 33 27s 138 30E
23 Spalding, England 52 47N 0 9w
46 Spandau, Germany 52 35N 13 7E
90 Spanish Fork, U.S.A. 40 6N 111 40w
72 Spanish Sahara, see Western Sahara
95 Spanish Town, Jamaica, W.I. 18 0N 76 59w
90 Sparks, U.S.A. 39 30N 119 37w
91 Spartanburg, U.S.A. 34 58N 81 57w
41 Sparti, Greece 37 7N 22 18E
40 Spartivento, C., Italy 38 56N 8 57E
40 Spartivento, C., Italy 37 58N 16 7E
67 Spassk-Dalni, U.S.S.R. 44 45N 132 55E
41 Spatha, C., Greece 35 40N 23 50E
33 Spean Bridge, Scotland 56 53N 4 55w
94 Speightstown, Barbados, W.I. 13 15N 59 8w
83 Spencer, C., Australia 35 20s 136 50E
83 Spencer G., Australia 34 0s 137 0E
27 Spennymoor, England 54 43N 1 35w
87 Spenser Mts., N.Z. 42 0s 172 30E
36 Sperrin Mts., N. Ireland 54 50N 7 5w
46 Spessart Mts., Germany 50 10N 9 25E
33 Spey, R., Scotland 57 40N 3 5w
45 Speyer, Germany 49 22N 8 28E
41 Spiddal, Ireland 53 14N 9 19w
40 Spinazzola, Italy 41 0N 16 5E
23 Spithead, England 50 43N 0 56w
100 Spitsbergen (Svalbard), Arctic Ocean 80 0N 20 0E
40 Split, Yugoslavia 43 32N 16 30E
45 Splugen Pass, Switzerland 46 30N 9 20E
90 Spokane, U.S.A. 47 48N 118 25w
40 Spoleto, Italy 42 46N 12 47E
41 Sporades Is., N., Greece 39 20N 24 0E
68 Spratly I., S. China Sea 8 45N 111 30E
46 Spree, R., Germany 51 30N 14 30E
46 Spremberg, Germany 51 33N 14 21E
75 Springbok, S. Africa 29 48s 17 57E
91 Springfield, Ill., U.S.A. 39 23N 89 42w
93 Springfield, Mass., U.S.A. 42 0N 73 0w
91 Springfield, Ohio, U.S.A. 39 42N 84 15w
90 Springfield, Ore., U.S.A. 44 0N 123 0w
93 Springhill, Canada 45 45N 64 0w
76 Springs, Trans., S. Afr. 26 14s 28 21E
82 Springsure, Australia 24 2s 148 0E
90 Springville, Utah, U.S.A. 40 13N 111 35w
27 Sproatley, England 53 46N 0 9w
75 Spungabera, Mozam. 20 28s 32 47E
27 Spurn Hd., England 53 37N 0 8E
88 Squamish, Canada 49 45N 123 10w
40 Squillace, Italy 38 50N 16 26E
61 Sredinny Ra., U.S.S.R. 57 0N 159 0E
61 Sredne Kolymsk, U.S.S.R. 67 20N 153 25E
61 Sredne Tambovskoye, U.S.S.R. 50 50N 137 50E
61 Sredne Vilyusk, U.S.S.R. 63 50N 123 10E
41 Sremska Mitrovica, Yugoslavia 44 59N 19 35E
68 Srepok, R., Khmer Rep. & Vietnam 13 30N 107 0E
61 Sretensk, U.S.S.R. 52 10N 117 50E
65 Sri Lanka, Asia 8 0N 80 45E
64 Srinagar, Kashmir 34 5N 74 55E
40 Srnetica, Yugoslavia 44 25N 16 35E
49 Stade, Germany 53 38N 9 31E
30 Staffa, I., Scotland 56 26N 6 22w
22 Stafford & Co., England 52 40N 2 4w
27 Staindrop, England 54 35N 1 49w
23 Staines, England 51 25N 0 30w
27 Stainforth, England 53 37N 0 59w
26 Stainmore Forest, Eng. 54 29N 2 5w
52 Stalingrad, see Volgograd
52 Stalino, U.S.S.R., see Donetsk
26 Stalybridge, England 53 29N 2 3w
82 Stamford, Australia 21 15s 143 46E
93 Stamford, U.S.A. 41 5N 73 30w
27 Stamford Bridge, Eng. 54 0N 0 54w
75 Standerton, S. Africa 27 0s 29 0E
26 Standish, England 53 35N 2 39w
76 Stanger, S. Africa 29 22s 31 15E
26 Stanhope, England 54 45N 2 0w
41 Stanke Dimitrov, Bulgaria 42 27N 23 9E
83 Stanley, Australia 40 45s 145 20E
27 Stanley, England 54 53N 1 42w

74 Stanleyville, see Kisangani
26 Stanlow, England 53 16N 2 45w
27 Stannington, England 55 7N 1 41w
61 Stanovoy Ra., U.S.S.R. 55 0N 130 0E
83 Stanthorpe, Australia 28 40s 152 0E
88 Stanton, Canada 69 40N 128 40w
27 Stapleford, England 52 56N 1 16w
41 Stara-Zagora, Bulgaria 42 22N 25 41E
46 Stargard, Poland 53 19N 15 1E
52 Staritsa, U.S.S.R. 56 33N 34 59E
47 Starogard, Poland 53 59N 18 30E
47 Staroskonstantinov, U.S.S.R. 49 45N 27 8E
24 Start Bay, England 50 14N 3 35w
24 Start Pt., England 50 14N 3 38w
61 Stary Kheidzhan, U.S.S.R. 60 0N 144 50E
99 Staten I., (I. de los Estados), Argentina 54 50s 64 30w
91 Staunton, U.S.A. 38 11N 79 0w
49 Stavanger, Norway 58 58N 5 32E
27 Staveley, England 53 16N 1 20w
44 Stavelot, Belgium 50 25N 5 56E
44 Staveren, Netherlands 52 53N 5 25E
49 Stavern, Norway 59 0N 10 3E
50 Stavropol, U.S.S.R. 45 5N 42 0E
83 Stawell, Australia 37 5s 142 48E
74 Stefanie, L., see Chew Bahir
46 Steffisburg, Switzerland 46 48N 7 40E
48 Steinkjer, Norway 63 59N 11 40E
76 Stella, South Africa 26 35s 24 45E
93 Stellarton, Canada 45 32N 62 45w
75 Stellenbosch, S. Africa 34 0s 18 55E
40 Stelvio Pass, Italy 46 32N 10 20E
43 Stenay, France 49 30N 5 15E
46 Stendal, Germany 52 38N 11 50E
31 Stenhousemuir, Scotland 56 2s 3 46w
51 Stepnoi, U.S.S.R., see Elista
51 Stepnoi Divnoe, U.S.S.R. 46 0N 43 20E
60 Stepnyak, U.S.S.R. 53 5N 70 55E
76 Sterkstroom, S. Africa 31 32s 26 32E
90 Sterling, U.S.A. 40 38N 103 15w
50 Sterlitamak, U.S.S.R. 53 34N 55 47E
46 Stettin, see Szczecin
88 Stettler, Canada 52 20N 112 45w
91 Steubenville, U.S.A. 40 24N 80 37w
23 Stevenage, England 51 54N 0 11w
91 Stevens Point, U.S.A. 44 40N 89 35w
30 Stevenston, Scotland 55 38N 4 45w
84 Stewart I., N.Z. 47 0s 168 0E
88 Stewart River, Canada 63 0N 139 30w
30 Stewarton, Scotland 55 40N 4 30w
38 Stewartstown, N. Ireland 54 35N 6 40w
46 Steyr, Austria 48 1N 14 21E
76 Steytlerville, S. Africa 33 20s 24 16E
88 Stikine, R., Canada 57 40N 132 0w
91 Stillwater, Minn., U.S.A. 45 2N 92 54w
91 Stillwater, Okla., U.S.A. 36 5N 97 7w
41 Stip, Yugoslavia 41 41N 22 10E
31 Stirling, Scotland 56 7N 3 57w
80 Stirling Ra., Australia 34 27s 118 0E
31 Stobo, Scotland 55 38N 3 18w
49 Stockerau, Austria 48 25N 16 15E
49 Stockholm, & Co., Sweden 59 21N 18 3E
23 Stockport, England 53 25N 2 10w
27 Stocksbridge, England 53 30N 1 36w
27 Stockton on Tees, Eng. 54 34N 1 20w
90 Stockton, U.S.A. 37 58N 121 18w
32 Stoer, Pt., of Scotland 58 15N 5 22w
23 Stoke Mandeville, Eng. 51 46N 0 47w
22 Stoke-on-Trent, Eng. 53 2N 2 12w
27 Stokesley, England 54 27N 1 12w
48 Stokkseyri, Iceland 63 47N 20 52w
41 Stolac, Yugoslavia 43 5N 18 0E
44 Stolberg, Germany 50 47N 6 12E
61 Stolbovoi, I., U.S.S.R. 74 10N 135 30E
61 Stolbovoye, U.S.S.R. 56N 153 50E
23 Stone, England 52 54N 2 9w
33 Stonehaven, Scotland 56 57N 2 12w
22 Stonehouse, England 51 45N 2 18w
31 Stonehouse, Scotland 55 42N 4 0w
88 Stonewall, Canada 50 10N 97 20w
61 Stony Tunguska, R., U.S.S.R. 62 0N 97 0E
48 Storuman, L., Sweden 65 10N 16 30E
48 Stora Lulevatten, Sweden 67 10N 19 30E
48 Stora Sjöffallet, Sweden 67 30N 18 30E
48 Storavan, L., Sweden 66 0N 18 30E
49 Store Bælt, Denmark 55 30N 11 0E
48 Storen, Norway 63 0N 10 20E
48 Storisandur, Dist., Ice. 65 10N 20 0w
89 Storm B., Australia 42 10s 147 22E
32 Stornoway, Scotland 58 12N 6 21w
48 Storolfshvoll, Iceland 63 48N 20 15w
48 Storsjön L., Sweden 63 15N 14 22E
23 Stort, R., England 51 56N 0 11E
49 Storuman, L., Sweden 65 15N 17 0E
22 Stour, R. (Dorset), Eng. 50 52N 2 10w
22 Stour, R. (Essex), Eng. 51 57N 1 0E
23 Stour R. (Suffolk), Eng. 52 5N 0 40E
22 Stourbridge, England 52 28N 2 9w
22 Stourport, England 52 21N 2 17w
22 Stow-on-the-Wold, Eng. 51 55N 1 42w
22 Stowmarket, England 52 11N 0 59E
36 Strabane, N. Ireland 54 49N 7 25w
32 Strachan, Scotland 57 1N 2 31w
30 Strachur, Scotland 56 9N 5 3w
35 Stradbally, Laois, Ire. 53 2N 7 10w
35 Stradbally, Waterford, Ire. 52 7N 7 28w
83 Strahan, Australia 42 8s 145 20E
49 Stralsund, Germany 54 18N 12 58E
76 Strand, South Africa 34 5s 18 45E
36 Strangford, & L., N. Ire. 54 21N 5 43w

36 Stranorlar, Ireland 54 48N 7 47w
30 Stranraer, Scotland 54 54N 5 1w
43 Strasbourg, France 48 35N 7 46E
92 Stratford, Canada 43 20N 81 0w
84 Stratford, New Zealand 39 22s 174 20E
22 Stratford-on-Avon, Eng. 52 11N 1 43w
33 Strath Dearn, Scotland 57 26N 4 10w
31 Strath Earn, Scotland 56 20N 3 50w
33 Strath Halladale, Scot. 58 30N 3 51w
33 Strath Spey, Scotland 57 18N 3 32w
33 Strath Tay, Scotland 56 40N 3 40w
83 Strathalbyn, Australia 35 18s 138 59E
33 Strathaven, Scotland 55 40N 4 3w
33 Strathbogie, Dist., Scot. 57 25N 2 45w
30 Strathclyde, Reg., Scotland 56 0N 5 0w
33 Strathdon, Scotland 57 12N 3 4w
31 Strathmiglo, Scotland 56 16N 3 15w
33 Strathmore, Dist., Scot. 56 40N 3 10w
33 Strathmore R., Scotland 58 25N 4 40w
33 Strathpeffer, Scotland 57 37N 4 30w
24 Stratton, England 50 49N 4 31w
22 Stratton St. Margaret, England 51 35N 1 45w
48 Straumnes, Iceland 66 27N 23 7w
80 Streaky B., Australia 32 37s 134 10E
24 Street, England 51 7N 2 43w
41 Strelka, U.S.S.R. 58 5N 93 5E
40 Stresa, Italy 45 55N 8 30E
27 Stretford, England 53 27N 2 19w
33 Strichen, Scotland 57 35N 2 5w
36 Strokestown, Ireland 53 47N 8 9w
40 Stromboli, I. Italy 38 50N 15 17E
33 Stromeferry, Scotland 57 20N 5 37w
33 Stromness, Scotland 58 59N 3 20w
48 Ströms Vattudal L., Swed. 64 0N 15 30E
49 Strömstad, Sweden 58 59N 11 10E
48 Strömsund, Sweden 63 52N 15 39E
33 Stronsay F. & I., Scot. 59 3N 2 35w
23 Strood, England 51 23N 0 30E
22 Stroud, England 51 45N 2 11w
49 Struer, Denmark 56 30N 8 35E
41 Struma, R., Bulgaria 41 50N 23 14E
25 Strumble Hd., Wales 52 3N 5 4w
41 Strumica, Yugoslavia 41 30N 22 41E
80 Stuart R., Australia 19 30s 127 40E
76 Stutterheim, S. Africa 32 33s 27 28E
45 Stuttgart, Germany 48 49N 9 15E
91 Stuttgart, U.S.A. 34 32N 91 32w
48 Stykkisholmur, Iceland 65 2N 22 45w
47 Styr, R., U.S.S.R. 51 5N 25 40E
47 Styria, Prov., Austria 47 18N 15 0E
62 Suakin, Sudan 19 30N 37 35E
66 Süanhwa, China 40 0N 115 5E
64 Subarnarekha R., India 22 30N 86 45E
41 Subotica, Yugoslavia 46 2N 19 33E
41 Suceava, Rumania 47 32N 26 20E
67 Suchan, U.S.S.R. 43 5N 133 0E
66 Süchow, Kiangsu, China 34 17N 117 15E
24 Suck, R., Ireland 53 25N 8 12w
98 Sucre, Bolivia 19 0s 65 20w
73 Sudan, Africa 13 0N 31 0E
70 Sudan Reg, Africa 11 0N 8 0E
92 Sudbury, Canada 46 35N 81 10w
23 Sudbury, Suffolk, Eng. 52 3N 0 45E
73 Sudd, Reg., Sudan 8 0N 30 0E
46 Sudeten Highlands, Ger. 50 0N 17 20E
37 Sueca, Spain 39 13N 0 20w
73 Suez, Egypt 30 0N 32 5E
73 Suez Canal, Egypt 30 30N 32 15E
73 Suez, G. of, Egypt 29 0N 33 0E
23 Suffolk, Co., England 52 15N 1 0E
35 Sugar Loaf, Gt., mt., Ire. 53 7N 6 10w
83 Sugarloaf Pt., Australia 32 30s 152 30E
35 Suir, R., Ireland 52 18N 7 20w
52 Sukhinichi, U.S.S.R. 54 15N 35 17E
50 Sukhona, R., U.S.S.R. 59 30N 42 0E
74 Sukhumi, U.S.S.R. 43 10N 41 5E
89 Sukkertoppen, Greenland 65 40N 53 0w
64 Sukkur, Pakistan 27 45N 68 56E
63 Sulaiyil, Saudi Arabia 20 30N 45 25E
64 Sulaiman Range, Asia 31 0N 70 10E
62 Sulaimaniya, Iran 35 32N 45 25E
68 Sulawesi, I., Indonesia 2 0s 120 0E
47 Sulina Mouth, Danube, Rumania 45 0N 29 40E
48 Sulitjelma, mt., Norway 67 2N 16 30E
98 Sullana, Peru 5 0s 80 30w
65 Sultanpur, India 26 8N 82 5E
68 Sulu Arch., Philippines 6 0N 121 0E
68 Sulu Sea, Philippines 8 0N 120 0E
73 Suluq (Soluk), Libya 31 44N 20 14E
45 Sulzbach, Germany 49 17N 7 2E
68 Sumatra, I., Indonesia 0 30N 101 0E
68 Sumba I., see Sandalwood I.
68 Sumbawa I., Indonesia 8 30s 118 0E
74 Sumbawanga, Tanzania 8 0s 31 38E
32 Sumburgh Hd., Scotland 59 53N 1 16w
41 Sumen, Bulgaria 43 17N 26 55E
35 Summerhill, Ireland 53 30N 6 44w
93 Summerside, Canada 46 25N 63 50w
46 Sumperk, Czechoslovakia 49 59N 17 0E
91 Sumter, U.S.A. 33 55N 80 17w
52 Sumy, U.S.S.R. 50 58N 34 45E
32 Sunart, Dist., Scotland 56 42N 5 30w
30 Sunart, L., Scotland 56 40N 5 50w
83 Sunbury, Australia 37 48s 144 50E
68 Sunda Sea, Indonesia 6 30s 118 0E
68 Sunda Str., Indonesia 6 0s 105 43E
65 Sundarbans, E. Pak. 22 10N 89 30E
65 Sundargarh, India 22 10N 84 7E

27 Sunderland, England 54 55N 1 23w
23 Sundridge, England 51 15N 0 11E
48 Sundsvall, Sweden 62 21N 17 18E
67 Suo B., Japan 33 56N 131 35E
65 Supaul, India 26 10N 86 35E
91 Superior, Wis., U.S.A. 46 40N 92 1w
92 Superior, L., N. America 47 30N 88 0w
68 Sura, R., U.S.S.R. 55 0N 46 30E
68 Surabaya, Indonesia 7 12s 112 48E
68 Surakarta, Indonesia 7 45s 110 50E
64 Suratgarh, India 29 15N 74 0E
83 Surat, Australia 27 13s 149 1E
64 Surat, India 21 12N 73 5E
68 Surat Thani, Malaya 9 5N 99 25E
60 Surgut, U.S.S.R. 61 27N 73 7E
64 Suri, India 23 55N 87 30E
64 Suriapet, India 17 5N 79 30E
96 Surinam (Netherlands Guiana), S. America 4 0N 56 0w
23 Surrey, Co., England 51 5N 0 20w
73 Surt, Libya 31 10N 16 50E
23 Sursee, Switzerland 47 12N 8 6E
23 Sussex, Canada 45 42N 65 33w
23 Sussex E., Co., England 50 55N 0 16E
23 Sussex W., Co., England 50 54N 0 32w
76 Sutherland, S. Africa 32 21s 20 44E
23 Sutlej, R., India 30 7N 73 30E
23 Sutton, England 51 21N 0 11w
22 Sutton Bridge, England 52 46N 0 12E
22 Sutton Coldfield, England 52 32N 1 47w
27 Sutton-in-Ashfield, Eng. 53 8N 1 15w
67 Suttsu, Japan 42 47N 140 5E
76 Suurberge, C. Prov. 33 8s 25 30E
47 Suwalki, Poland 54 6N 22 53E
63 Suweilih, Jordan 32 2N 35 50E
52 Suzdal, U.S.S.R. 56 27N 40 20E
100 Svalbard (Spitsbergen), Arctic Ocean 78 0N 15 0E
48 Svartisen, mt., Norway 66 55N 13 30E
49 Svealand, Dist., Sweden 59 55N 15 0E
49 Sveg, Sweden 62 2N 14 27E
49 Svendborg, Denmark 55 7N 10 38E
60 Sverdlovsk, U.S.S.R. 56 52N 60 32E
100 Sverdrup I., Arctic Oc. 80 0N 100 0w
50 Svir, R., U.S.S.R. 61 0N 34 0E
41 Svishtov, Bulgaria 43 36N 25 23E
61 Svobodny, U.S.S.R. 51 30N 128 5E
49 Svolvær, Norway 68 20N 14 30E
46 Swabian Jura, mts., Germany, see Schwabische Alb.
22 Swadlincote, England 52 47N 1 34w
23 Swaffham, England 52 38N 0 40E
75 Swakopmund, S.W. Afr. 22 33s 14 35E
83 Swale, R., England 54 13N 1 28w
83 Swan Hill, Australia 35 15s 143 31E
22 Swanage, England 50 36N 1 57w
36 Swanlinbar, Ireland 54 11N 7 42w
83 Swansea, Australia 33 3s 151 35E
25 Swansea, & B., Wales 51 38N 3 57w
76 Swartberge, S. Africa 33 15s 22 0E
66 Swatow, China 23 30N 116 50E
16 Swaziland, S.E. Afr. 26 30s 31 30E
16 Sweden, Europe 63 0N 16 0E
88 Swift Current, Canada 50 20N 107 49w
35 Swilly, L. & R., Ireland 55 14N 7 33w
22 Swindon, England 51 33N 1 47w
46 Swinoujscie, Poland 53 54N 14 16E
27 Swinton, Lancs., Eng. 53 31N 2 21w
27 Swinton, Yorks., Eng. 53 28N 1 20w
45 Switzerland, Europe 46 30N 8 0E
35 Swords, Ireland 53 28N 6 14w
83 Sydney, Australia 33 55s 151 12E
50 Sydpröven, Greenland 60 30N 45 20w
48 Syktyvkar, U.S.S.R. 61 45N 50 40E
48 Sylarna Mt., Sweden 63 2N 12 20E
65 Sylhet, Bangladesh 24 50N 91 52E
49 Sylt, I., Denmark 55 0N 8 19E
31 Symington, Scotland 55 35s 3 36w
23 Symonds Yat, England 51 50N 2 38w
50 Syr Darya, R., U.S.S.R. 44 40N 65 0E
74 Syracuse, see Siracusa
91 Syracuse, U.S.A. 43 0N 76 10w
62 Syria, S.W. Asia 35 0N 38 0E
50 Syrian Des., Si. Arabia 32 0N 40 0E
50 Syzran, U.S.S.R. 53 5N 48 30E
46 Szczecin, Poland 53 25N 14 31E
46 Szczecnek, Poland 53 43N 16 41E
66 Szechwan, Prov., China 30 0N 104 0E
47 Szeged, Hungary 46 17N 20 9E
47 Székesfehérvar, Hungary 47 17N 18 24E
47 Szentes, Hungary 46 39N 20 19E
47 Szeping, China 43 15N 124 15E
47 Szolnok, Hungary 47 15N 20 10E
46 Szombathely, Hungary 47 17N 16 27E

T

66 Ta Liang Shan, mts., China 28 0N 102 20E
76 Table, Mt., S. Africa 34 1s 18 27E
46 Tabor, Czechoslovakia 49 23N 14 29E
74 Tabora, Tanzania 5 2s 32 50E
72 Tabou, Ivory Coast 4 30N 7 20w
63 Tabriz, Iran 38 3N 46 24E
67 Tachima, Japan 37 9N 139 48E
68 Tacloban, Philippines 10 15N 124 55E
98 Tacna, Peru 18 5s 70 20w
90 Tacoma, U.S.A. 47 15N 122 12w
99 Tacuarembo, Uruguay 31 30s 56 0w

98 Tacutu, R., S. America 3 0N 59 40w
27 Tadcaster, England 53 54N 1 18w
72 Tademait, Plat. du, Alg. 28 28N 2 0E
60 Tadzhikistan, Rep., U.S.S.R. 39 0N 72 6E
67 Taegu, Korea 35 48N 129 30E
63 Tafa, Syria 32 44N 36 4E
37 Tafalla, Spain 42 30N 1 42w
52 Taganrog, U.S.S.R. 47 16N 38 55E
68 Taganrog Gulf, U.S.S.R. 46 50N 37 5E
35 Taghmon, Ireland 52 2N 6 43w
88 Tagish, Canada 60 20N 134 0w
37 Tagus (Tajo) R., Spain 40 40N 2 12w
72 Tahan, Mt., Malaya 4 40N 102 50E
66 Tahcheng, China 46 45N 83 10E
4 Tahiti, Pacific Ocean 17 50s 149 40w
90 Tahoe, L., U.S.A. 39 0N 120 0w
62 Tahiri, Iran 27 35N 52 20E
73 Tahta, Egypt 26 44N 31 32E
67 Tai Shan, mts., China 36 0N 118 30E
67 Taichung, Taiwan 24 10N 120 35E
62 Taif, Saudi Arabia 21 0N 41 2E
84 Taihape, New Zealand 39 42s 175 49E
60 Tailakovy, U.S.S.R. 59 20N 74 5E
83 Tailem Bend, Australia 35 12s 139 29E
61 Taima, Saudi Arabia 27 23N 39 20E
61 Taimyr Pen., U.S.S.R. 75 0N 100 0E
33 Tain, Scotland 57 48N 4 3w
67 Tainan, Taiwan 23 0N 120 22E
41 Tainaron (Matapan), C., Greece 36 20N 22 30E
67 Taipei, Taiwan 25 0N 121 38E
67 Taiping, Malaya 4 50N 100 45E
67 Taira, Japan 37 4N 140 58E
67 Taishet, U.S.S.R. 56 0N 98 0E
99 Taitao Pen., Chile 46 0s 75 0w
67 Taitung, China 30 45N 117 40E
67 Taitung, Taiwan 22 55N 121 5E
67 Taiwan (Formosa), China 24N 121 0E
67 Tai-yüan, China 38 2N 112 20E
62 Ta'izz, Yemen 13 43N 44 7E
37 Tajo, R., Spain 40 40N 2 12w
73 Tajura, Libya 32 51N 13 27E
55 Ta-Khingan Shan, China 50 0N 120 0E
55 Ta-Liang Shan, China 28 20N 103 0E
67 Takamatsu, Japan 34 15N 134 0E
67 Takana, Japan 34 0N 135 0E
67 Takaoka, Japan 36 40N 137 4E
84 Takapuna, New Zealand 36 47s 174 47E
67 Takasaki, Japan 36 10N 139 0E
67 Takata, Japan 37 12N 138 12E
74 Takaungu, Kenya 3 35s 39 45E
67 Takefu, Japan 35 57N 136 5E
67 Taketoyo, Japan 34 56N 137 0E
66 Takla-Makan, China 39 45N 85 0E
74 Takla Post, Sudan 5 55N 30 44E
68 Talaud, Is., Indonesia 4 10N 126 50E
37 Talavera, Spain 39 59N 4 46w
68 Talayan, Philippines 6 55N 124 25E
99 Talca, Chile 35 18s 71 45w
99 Talcahuano, Chile 36 35s 73 12w
65 Talcher, India 20 55N 85 3E
60 Taldy Kurgan, U.S.S.R. 45 5N 78 50E
64 Taliguppa, India 14 10N 74 45E
66 Tali, China 25 57N 100 7E
74 Tali Post, Sudan 5 55N 30 44E
68 Taliabu, Indonesia 1 45s 125 0E
32 Talladale, Scotland 57 41N 5 20w
91 Tallahassee, U.S.A. 30 30N 84 10w
83 Tallangatta, Australia 36 8s 147 5E
47 Tallinn, U.S.S.R. 59 29N 24 58E
34 Tallow, Ireland 52 6N 7 59w
62 Talodi, Sudan 10 42N 30 22E
99 Taltal, Chile 25 40s 70 35w
83 Talwood, Australia 28 25s 149 25E
25 Tal-y-Lyn, Wales 52 40N 3 53w
72 Tamale, Ghana 9 30N 0 38w
72 Tamar, R., England 50 45N 4 22w
75 Tamatave, Madagascar 17 50s 49 40E
72 Tambacounda, Senegal 13 50N 13 40w
82 Tambo, Australia 24 54s 146 14E
37 Tamega, R., Portugal 41 15N 8 0w
72 Tamgak Mts., Niger 19 10N 8 35E
64 Tamil Nadu, st., India 11 10N 78 0E
45 Tamins, Switzerland 46 50N 9 22E
72 Tampa, & B., U.S.A. 28 0N 82 20w
49 Tampere, Finland 61 34N 23 38E
94 Tampico, Mexico 22 20N 98 12w
72 Tamsagout, Mali 24 5N 6 35w
83 Tamworth, Australia 31 8s 151 0E
22 Tamworth, England 52 38N 1 41w
48 Tana Fjord, Norway 70 45N 28 20E
73 Tana L., Ethiopia 12 0N 37 20E
74 Tana R., Kenya 1 0s 40 0E
75 Tanami Desert, Australia 20 0s 136 0E
*75 Tananarive, Madagascar 19 0s 47 20E
40 Tanaro, R., Italy 44 47N 8 10E
83 Tanbar, Australia 25 30s 141 58E
74 Tandah, Ethiopia 10 10N 40 0E
99 Tandil, Argentina 37 8s 59 10w
64 Tando Adam, Pak. 25 40N 68 34E
67 Tanega Shima, I., Japan 30 40N 131 0E
72 Tanezrouft, Dist., Algeria 22 30N 2 0E
71 Tanganyika, see Tanzania
74 Tanganyika, L., Cent. Afr. 6 30s 29 40E
66 Tanghla Ra., Mts., China 33 0N 92 0E
72 Tangier, N. Africa 35 50N 5 49w
66 Tangshan, China 39 45N 118 0E
64 Tanjore, see Thanjavur
67 Tanjungpandan, Indon. 2 45s 107 40E
68 Tanjungselor, Indon. 2 50N 116 40E
73 Tanta, Egypt 30 50N 30 54E

* Renamed Antananarivo

83 Tanunda, Australia 34 30s 139 0E
22 Tanworth, England 52 20N 1 50w
71 Tanzania, Africa 6 0s 34 30E
67 Taonan, China 45 29N 122 57E
72 Taourirt, Morocco 34 20N 3 2w
83 Tapa, Mts., China 31 50N 109 0E
98 Tapajos, R., Brazil 6 30s 57 30w
51 Tarabulus, Lebanon, see Tripoli
51 Tarabulus, Libya, see Tripoli
68 Tarakan, Indonesia 3 15N 117 30E
84 Taranaki, Dist., N.Z. 39 0s 174 50E
32 Taransay, I. & Sd., Scot. 57 54N 7 1w
43 Taranto, & G., Italy 40 30N 17 14E
43 Tarare, France 45 52N 4 30E
84 Tararua Ra., N.Z. 40 47s 175 30E
84 Tarascon, France 43 50N 4 40E
72 Tarat, Algeria 26 4N 9 7E
84 Tarawera, N.Z. 39 2s 176 35E
34 Tarbert, Ireland 52 35N 9 22w
30 Tarbert & L.W., Argyll, Scotland 55 58N 5 25w
31 Tarbert, & L., W & E, Harris, Scotland 57 55N 6 50w
42 Tarbes, France 43 13N 0 1E
31 Tarbet, Scotland 56 13N 4 44w
80 Tarcoola, Australia 30 48s 134 52E
83 Taree, Australia 34 48s 152 17E
72 Tarfaya, Morocco 27 55N 12 55w
37 Tarifa, Spain 36 2N 5 37w
62 Tarim, South Yemen 16 15N 49 22E
66 Tarim, China 41 0N 85 0E
66 Tarim Basin, China 40 30N 85 0E
51 Tarkhankut C., U.S.S.R. 45 25N 32 30E
72 Tarkwa, Ghana 5 23N 2 0w
68 Tarlac, Philippines 15 25N 120 35E
26 Tarleton, England 53 41N 2 51w
42 Tarn, Dépt., France 43 50N 2 10E
42 Tarn-et-Garonne, Dépt., France 44 10N 1 10E
47 Tarnow, Poland 50 1N 21 2E
47 Tarnowskie Góry, Poland 50 30N 19 0E
37 Tarragona, Spain 41 7N 1 13E
37 Tarrasa, Spain 41 30N 2 0E
51 Tarsus, Turkey 37 0N 34 50E
47 Tartar's, P. of the, U.S.S.R. 48 20N 24 30E
51 Tartary Str., U.S.S.R. 53 10N 141 30E
50 Tartu, U.S.S.R. 58 22N 26 40E
73 Tasawah, Libya 26 0N 13 30E
39 Taschereau, Canada 48 45N 78 45w
50 Tashkent, U.S.S.R. 41 7N 69 15E
50 Tashkumyr, U.S.S.R. 41 40N 72 20E
70 Tasili Plateau, N. Africa 25 30N 8 0E
68 Tasikmalaja, Indonesia 7 35N 18 30E
84 Tasman B., N.Z. 41 0s 173 30E
84 Tasman Mts., N.Z. 41 0s 172 30E
83 Tasman Pen., Australia 43 0s 147 40E
84 Tasman Sea, Australasia 38 0s 163 0E
83 Tasmania, I., Australia 42 0s 146 30E
47 Tatabanya, Hungary 47 35N 18 30E
60 Tatar, A.S.S.R., U.S.S.R. 55 30N 51 30E
50 Tatarsk, U.S.S.R. 55 30N 76 3E
64 Tatsuno, Japan 35 0N 139 58E
66 Ta-tung, China 40 0N 113 20E
46 Tauern Mts., Austria 47 15N 12 40E
46 Tauern Mts., Austria 47 15N 12 40E
84 Taumarunui, N.Z. 38 55s 175 15E
76 Taung, South Africa 27 32s 24 45E
65 Taunggyi, Burma 20 55N 97 3E
65 Taungup & P., Burma 18 50N 94 20E
24 Taunton, England 51 1N 3 5w
46 Taunus Mts., Germany 50 18N 8 20E
84 Taupo & L., N.Z. 38 47s 175 50E
49 Taurage, U.S.S.R. 55 15N 22 18E
84 Tauranga, New Zealand 37 40s 176 12E
40 Taurianova, Italy 38 22N 16 1E
1 Taurus Mts., Turkey 37 30N 34 30E
60 Tavda, U.S.S.R. 58 7N 65 8E
37 Tavira, Portugal 37 7N 7 40w
24 Tavistock, England 50 34N 4 10w
65 Tavoy, Burma 13 49N 98 22E
31 Taw, R., England 50 57N 3 55w
74 Taweisha, Sudan 12 25N 26 55E
68 Tawitawi, I., Phil. 5 15N 120 0E
36 Tawnyinah, Ireland 53 55N 8 45w
31 Tay, Firth of, Scotland 56 27N 2 45w
31 Tayport, Scotland 56 26N 2 53w
68 Taytay, Philippines 10 40N 119 25E
60 Taz R., U.S.S.R. 65 40N 82 40E
51 Tbilisi, U.S.S.R. 41 45N 44 48E
74 Tchibanga, Gabon 2 45s 11 12E
36 Te Anau, L., N.Z. 45 15s 167 45E
84 Te Awamutu, N.Z. 38 1s 175 20E
84 Te Kuiti, New Zealand 38 20s 175 11E
42 Tébessa, Algeria 35 38N 8 5E
68 Tebingtinggi, Indonesia 3 30s 103 0E
37 Tecuci, Rumania 45 20N 27 25E
31 Tees, R., England 54 39N 1 9w
28 Teesside, England 54 34N 1 16w
35 Tegal, Indonesia 7 0s 108 35E
35 Tegid, L., Wales 52 55N 3 37w
72 Tegina, Nigeria 10 5N 6 11E
80 Tegucigalpa, Honduras 14 20N 87 12w
70 Tehachapi P., U.S.A. 35 5N 119 30w
66 Tehchow, China 37 35N 116 15E
62 Tehran, Iran 35 37N 51 22E
34 Tehtsin, China 28 45N 98 10E
4 Tehuantepec, & G., Mex. 16 40N 95 35w
5 Teifi, R., Wales 52 2N 4 20w
7 Teign, R., England 50 40N 3 40w
7 Teignmouth, England 50 33N 3 31w
7 Tejo (Tagus), R., Port. 39 15N 8 30w

84 Tekapo, L., N.Z. 43 55s 170 30E
41 Tekirdag, Turkey 41 0N 27 25E
63 Tel Aviv-Jaffa, Israel 32 4N 34 45E
94 Tela, Honduras 15 45N 87 25w
68 Telanaipura, Indonesia see Jambi
51 Telavi, U.S.S.R. 42 0N 43 30E
49 Telemark, Co., Norway 59 32N 8 20E
22 Telford, England 52 42N 2 29w
64 Tellicherry, India 11 45N 75 43E
68 Telok Anson, Malaya 3 50N 101 0E
50 Telpos Iz, Mt., U.S.S.R. 64 12N 59 30E
49 Telsiai, U.S.S.R. 56 2N 22 30E
84 Teluk Betung, Indon. 5 30s 105 20E
84 Temuka, N.Z. 44 14s 171 17E
72 Tema, Ghana 5 41N 0 0
4 Temax, Mexico 21 15N 88 50w
76 Tembuland, dist., S. Afr. 31 40s 28 0E
22 Teme, R., England 52 23N 3 7w
60 Temir, U.S.S.R. 49 3N 57 3E
60 Temir Tau, U.S.S.R. 53 15N 87 40E
72 Temiskaming, Canada 46 50N 79 0w
83 Temora, Australia 34 29s 147 33E
91 Temple, U.S.A. 31 3N 97 27w
82 Temple B., Australia 12 15s 143 3E
34 Templemore, Ireland 52 47N 7 49w
36 Tempo, N. Ireland 54 23N 7 27w
99 Temuco, Chile 39 0s 72 0w
65 Tenali, India 16 15N 80 30E
22 Tenbury, England 52 18N 2 36w
72 Tenda, France 44 6N 7 39E
72 Tenerife, I., Canary Is. 28 30N 18 0w
37 Tenes, Algeria 36 36N 0 32w
66 T'eng Ch'ung, China 25 5N 98 25E
66 Tengkow, China 40 0N 106 20E
64 Tenkasi, India 8 45N 77 10E
80 Tennant Creek, Austral. 19 30s 134 15E
43 Tenneins, France 44 22N 0 20E
91 Tennessee, R., U.S.A. 34 45N 87 30w
91 Tennessee, st., U.S.A. 35 40N 86 30w
67 Tenryu, R., Japan 35 30N 137 56E
23 Tenterden, England 51 5N 0 41E
83 Tenterfield, Australia 29 0s 152 0E
98 Teofilo Otoni, Brazil 17 50s 41 30w
94 Tepic, Mexico 21 20N 104 50w
46 Teplice, Czechoslovakia 50 39N 13 50E
72 Téra, Niger 14 0N 0 57E
40 Teramo, Italy 42 39N 13 46E
83 Terang, Australia 38 7s 142 59E
83 Teresina, Brazil 5 2s 42 45w
83 Terewah or Narran, L., Australia 29 52s 147 35E
44 Tergnier, France 49 49N 3 17E
63 Termez, U.S.S.R. 37 25N 67 12E
43 Termini, Italy 37 57N 13 45E
40 Termoli, Italy 42 0N 15 3E
40 Ternate, I., Indonesia 0 45N 127 20E
91 Terre Haute, U.S.A. 39 29N 87 20w
34 Terryglass, Ireland 8 14N 53 3w
37 Terschelling, I., Neth. 53 23N 5 20E
37 Teruel, Spain 40 22N 1 6w
41 Tesanj, Yugoslavia 44 40N 18 0E
88 Teslin, Canada 60 20N 132 45w
72 Tessalit, Mali 20 5N 0 57E
72 Tessaoua, Niger 13 55N 8 18E
22 Test, R., England 51 3N 1 32w
22 Tetbury, England 51 38N 2 9w
75 Tete, Mozambique 16 10s 33 37E
41 Teteven, Bulgaria 42 58N 24 15E
90 Teton, Mts., U.S.A. 43 45N 110 45w
42 Tetovo, Yugoslavia 42 1N 21 2E
22 Tettenhall, England 52 35N 2 7w
42 Tetuan, Morocco 35 32N 5 20w
99 Teuco R., Argentina 24 0s 62 0w
31 Teviot, R., Scotland 55 20N 2 57w
83 Tewantin, Australia 26 27s 153 3E
22 Tewkesbury, England 51 59N 2 8w
91 Texarkana, U.S.A. 33 28N 94 11w
83 Texas, Australia 28 43s 151 3E
90 Texas, st., U.S.A. 31 15N 98 30w
44 Texel, I., Netherlands 53 5N 4 48E
65 Tezpur, India 26 50N 92 40E
76 Thaba Nchu, S. Africa 29 10s 26 57E
76 Thabana Ntlenyana, mt., Lesotho 29 12s 29 22E
63 Thaih, U.A.E. 23 57N 54 0E
57 Thailand (Siam), Asia 16 0N 101 0E
65 Thal, Pakistan 33 30N 70 30E
65 Thala Pass, Burma 28 15N 98 10E
83 Thallon, Australia 28 36s 149 0E
23 Thame, England 51 45N 0 59w
23 Thame, R., England 51 52N 0 47w
84 Thames, N.Z. 37 3s 175 32E
23 Thames, R., England 51 29N 0 40E
64 Thana, India 19 30N 72 58E
23 Thanet, I., England 51 21N 1 20E
64 Thanjavur, India 10 45N 79 17E
43 Thann, France 47 46N 7 5E
64 Thar Des., India 27 30N 72 20E
64 Tharad, India 24 30N 71 30E
65 Tharrawaddy, Burma 17 42N 95 57E
41 Thasos, I., Greece 40 40N 24 40E
43 Thatcham, England 51 24N 1 16w
45 Thawil, Switzerland 47 18N 8 32E
65 Thazi, Burma 21 0N 96 5E
90 The Dalles, U.S.A. 45 35N 121 15w
44 The Hague ('s Gravenhage), Netherlands 52 5N 4 18E
80 The Johnston Lakes, Australia 32 30s 120 40E
88 The Pas, Canada 53 40N 101 20w
24 The Quantocks, England 51 8N 3 10w
49 The Skaw, see Skagen

36 The Skerries Is., N. Ire. 55 14N 6 40w
49 The Sound, Denmark 56 7N 12 30E
24 The Sound, England 50 17N 4 10w
83 The Warburton, R., Austral. 27 50s 138 0E
83 Theodore, Australia 25 0s 150 1E
41 Thermopylae, P., Greece 38 48N 22 45E
41 Thessaloniki, Greece 40 38N 23 0E
41 Thessaly, Dist., Greece 39 30N 22 20E
23 Thetford, England 52 24N 0 45E
93 Thetford Mines, Canada 46 15N 71 5w
76 Theunissen, S. Africa 28 30s 26 40E
43 Thiers, France 45 50N 3 32E
65 Thimphu, Bhutan 27 31N 89 45E
48 Thingvallavatn, Iceland 64 10N 21 5w
43 Thionville, France 49 20N 6 10E
41 Thira, I., Greece 36 24N 25 26E
27 Thirsk, England 54 14N 1 22w
48 Thjorsá R., Iceland 64 20N 19 15w
88 Thompson, R., Canada 51 0N 121 0w
82 Thomson, R., Australia 23 50s 144 0E
74 Thomson's Falls, see Nyahururu
45 Thonon, France 46 20N 6 30E
52 Thorez, U.S.S.R. 48 0N 38 38E
48 Thori, India 27 23N 84 30E
48 Thórisvatn L., Iceland 64 10N 18 7w
48 Thorláksöfn, Iceland 63 50N 21 20w
27 Thornaby-on-Tees, Eng. 54 33N 1 18w
23 Thorndon, England 52 16N 1 8E
27 Thorne, England 53 37N 0 58w
31 Thornhill, Scotland 56 3N 3 13w
26 Thornton-Cleveleys, Eng. 53 50N 3 4w
2 Thorpe, England 52 38N 1 20E
48 Thorshöfn, Iceland 66 12N 15 15w
42 Thouars, France 47 0N 0 10w
41 Thrace, Prov., Greece 41 27N 26 30E
23 Thrapston, England 52 24N 0 32w
84 Three Kings I., N.Z. 34 0s 172 0E
26 Threshfield, England 54 5N 2 2w
80 Throssell Ra., Australia 22 0s 122 0E
44 Thuin, Belgium 50 20N 4 17E
100 Thule, Greenland 76 22N 69 0w
45 Thun, Switzerland 46 46N 7 39E
92 Thunder Bay, Canada 48 20N 89 23w
45 Thunersee, Switzerland 46 42N 7 40E
45 Thur, R., Switzerland 47 37N 8 40E
45 Thurgau, Canton, Switz. 47 38N 9 4E
46 Thuringian Forest, Ger. 50 35N 11 0E
23 Thurlby, England 52 45N 0 21w
34 Thurles, Ireland 52 40N 7 53w
23 Thurrock, England 51 28N 0 20E
81 Thursday, I., Australia 10 35s 142 10E
45 Thusis, Switzerland 46 43N 9 26E
44 Thysville, see Mbanza Ngungu
73 Tibati, Cameroon 6 30N 12 52E
40 Tiber, R., Italy 43 33N 12 10E
63 Tiberias, Israel 32 47N 35 32E
73 Tibesti, Dist., Sahara 20 30N 17 0E
65 Tibet, A.R., China 33 30N 88 0E
63 Tibnin, Lebanon 33 11N 35 24E
94 Tiburon, I., Mexico 29 0N 112 30w
72 Tichit, Mauritania 18 28N 9 30w
37 Ticino, Canton, Switz. 46 20N 8 45E
45 Ticino, R., Italy 45 20N 8 53E
72 Tidjikja, Mauritania 18 25N 11 55w
44 Tiel, Netherlands 51 54N 5 26E
44 Tielt, Belgium 51 0N 3 20E
44 Tienen, Belgium 50 49N 4 57E
55 Tien Shan, mts., Asia 43 40N 86 0E
66 Tienshui, China 34 45N 105 15E
66 Tientsin, China 39 0N 117 5E
66 Tientu, China 18 30N 109 30E
66 Tierra del Fuego Terr., South America 54 0s 68 0w
37 Tietar, R., Spain 40 0N 5 45w
93 Tignish, Canada 46 55N 64 15w
62 Tigris, R., Iraq 32 30N 46 0E
65 Tigyaing, Burma 23 45N 96 10E
94 Tijuana, Mexico 32 30N 117 30w
51 Tikhoretsk, U.S.S.R. 45 55N 40 10E
61 Tiksi, U.S.S.R. 71 50N 129 0E
44 Tilburg, Netherlands 51 34N 5 6E
23 Tilbury, England 51 27N 0 23E
61 Tilichiki, U.S.S.R. 60 50N 166 0E
31 Till, R., England 55 35N 2 0w
72 Tillabéri Niger 14 15N 1 40E
31 Tillicoultry, Scotland 56 9N 3 44w
41 Tilos I., Greece 36 22N 27 21E
83 Tilpa, Australia 30 58s 144 30E
33 Tilt, R., Scotland 56 50N 3 48w
50 Timan Ridge, U.S.S.R. 64 30N 51 30E
84 Timaru, New Zealand 44 20s 171 21E
83 Timboon, Australia 38 32s 143 0E
72 Timbuktu, see Tombouctou
62 Timerein, Sudan 15 57N 36 30E
37 Timimoun, Algeria 29 10N 0 10E
47 Timisoara, Rumania 45 43N 21 8E
89 Timmins, Canada 48 30N 81 0w
41 Timok, R., Yugoslavia 43 30N 22 18E
34 Timoleague, Ireland 51 39N 8 46w
61 Timor, I., Indonesia 9 30s 125 0E
80 Timor Sea, Indian Ocean 14 0s 120 0E
35 Tinahely, Ireland 52 48N 6 28w
72 Tindouf, Algeria 27 30N 8 15w
65 Tindzhe Dzong, China 28 25N 88 10E
67 Ting-hai, China 30 10N 122 12E
67 Tinjoub, Algeria 29 20N 5 40w
48 Tinnoset, Norway 59 42N 9 3E
99 Tinogasta, Argentina 28 0s 67 30w
41 Tinos I., Greece 37 38N 25 0E
24 Tintagel, England 50 40N 4 45w
25 Tintern, Wales 51 42N 2 41w
83 Tintinara, Australia 35 58s 140 1E

65 Tipongpani, India 27 15N 95 50E
34 Tipperary, & Co., Ire. 52 29N 8 8w
22 Tipton, England 52 32N 2 3w
41 Tirane, Albania 41 20N 19 50E
45 Tirano, Italy 46 15N 10 15E
51 Tiraspol, U.S.S.R. 46 50N 29 30E
63 Tirat Karmel, Israel 32 46N 34 58E
51 Tirebolu, Turkey 40 59N 38 50E
30 Tiree I., Scotland 56 30N 6 55w
47 Tirgoviste, Rumania 44 58N 25 30E
47 Tirgu-Jiu, Rumania 45 0N 23 20E
47 Tirgu Mures, Rumania 46 31N 24 38E
64 Tirodi, India 21 35N 79 35E
40 Tirso, R., Italy 40 0N 8 45E
47 Tiruchchirappalli, India 10 52N 78 40E
64 Tirunelveli, India 8 45N 77 45E
64 Tiruvannamalai, India 12 15N 79 10E
88 Tisdale, Canada 52 50N 104 0w
49 Tisted, Denmark 56 58N 8 40E
41 Tisza, R., Hungary 47 50N 21 0E
98 Titicaca, L., Bolivia-Peru 16 0s 69 30w
41 Titograd, Yugoslavia 42 30N 19 19E
41 Titov Veles, Yugoslavia 41 40N 21 49E
41 Titovo Uzice, Y-slav. 43 55N 19 50E
74 Titule, Zaïre 3 5N 25 25E
92 Titusville, U.S.A. 41 38N 79 40w
24 Tiverton, England 50 55N 3 31w
40 Tivoli, Italy 41 58N 12 25E
48 Tjeggelvas, L., Sweden 66 30N 18 0E
94 Tlacotalpan, Mexico 18 50N 95 40w
94 Tlaxcala, Mexico 19 23N 98 10w
94 Tlaxiaco, Mexico 17 36N 97 40w
72 Tlemcen, Algeria 34 55N 1 20w
68 Toba, L., Indonesia 2 30N 98 57E
94 Toba Kakar, Hills, Pak. 31 20N 68 40E
94 Tobago, I., W. Indies 11 17N 60 40w
36 Tobercurry, Ireland 54 3N 8 44w
30 Tobermory, Scotland 56 38N 6 4w
60 Tobol, R., U.S.S.R. 56 0N 66 0E
60 Tobolsk, U.S.S.R. 58 10N 68 30E
82 Tobriand or Kiriwina Is., Papua N.G. 8 35s 151 0E
73 Tobruk, Libya, see Tubruq
98 Tocantins, R., Brazil 3 30s 49 30w
45 Toce, R., Italy 46 13N 8 19E
99 Tocopilla, Chile 22 12s 70 20w
83 Tocumwal, Australia 35 54s 145 56E
26 Todmorden, England 53 42N 2 5w
50 Togliatti, U.S.S.R. 53 37N 49 18E
74 Togo, W. Africa 7 45N 1 0E
47 Tokaj, Hungary 48 7N 21 25E
84 Tokanui, New Zealand 46 51s 169 0E
84 Tokarahi, New Zealand 44 56s 170 39E
51 Tokat, Turkey 40 27N 36 35E
4 Tokelau Is., Pac. Oc. 9 0s 172 0w
67 Tokmak, U.S.S.R. 42 55N 75 45E
67 Tokushima, & Pref., Jap. 34 0N 134 30E
67 Tokuyama, Japan 34 0N 131 50E
67 Tokyo, & Pref. Japan 35 48N 139 45E
37 Toledo, Spain 39 55N 4 0w
72 Toledo, U.S.A. 41 47N 83 30w
72 Tolga, Algeria 34 49N 5 26E
37 Tolima, Mt., Colombia 4 0N 75 0w
37 Tolosa, Spain 43 9N 2 5w
37 Tolo, G., of, Indonesia 2 0s 121 30E
94 Toluca, Mexico 19 25N 99 37w
66 Tolun, China 42 30N 116 30E
47 Tomar, Portugal 39 35N 8 28w
47 Tomaszów, Mazowiecki, Poland 51 30N 20 0E
98 Tombador, Sa. do, mts., Brazil 12 0s 57 10w
72 Tombouctou, Mali 16 50N 3 0w
32 Tomdoun, Scotland 57 3N 5 3w
68 Tomini G., Indonesia 0 0 120 30E
32 Tomintoul, Scotland 57 16N 3 24w
61 Tommot, U.S.S.R. 59 0N 126 30E
41 Tomorrit, Mt., Albania 40 40N 20 30E
60 Tomsk, U.S.S.R. 56 30N 85 5E
94 Tonala, Mexico 16 10N 94 0w
72 Tonale P., Italy 46 18N 10 36E
23 Tonbridge, England 51 11N 0 16E
44 Tone, R., England 51 0N 3 22w
22 Tong, England 52 40N 2 17w
84 Tonga (Friendly) Is., Pacific Ocean 19 50s 175 0w
76 Tongaat, South Africa 29 35s 31 5E
84 Tongatapu I., Pac. Oc. 21 0s 175 20w
44 Tongeren, Belgium 50 37N 5 20E
68 Tongian Is., Indonesia 0 20s 122 30E
84 Tongio, Australia 37 10s 147 35E
64 Tonk, India 26 10N 76 0E
68 Tonkin, G., China 20 0N 109 0E
68 Tonlé Sap, Cambodia 12 30N 105 30E
43 Tonnerre, France 47 52N 3 58E
49 Tönning, Germany 54 19N 8 58E
90 Tonopah, U.S.A. 38 4N 117 13w
48 Tonsberg, Norway 59 15N 10 25E
25 Tonyrefail, Wales 51 35N 3 26w
90 Tooele, U.S.A. 40 32N 112 20w
34 Toomevara, Ireland 52 50N 8 3w
83 Toora, Australia 38 40s 146 20E
76 Toowoomba, Australia 27 30s 151 0E
64 Top, Afghanistan 34 15N 68 35E
50 Top, L., U.S.S.R. 65 30N 32 0E
91 Topeka, U.S.A. 39 0N 95 40w
60 Topki, U.S.S.R. 55 40N 85 40E
94 Topolobampo, Mexico 25 45N 108 48w

24 Tor B., England 50 25N 3 33w
24 Torbay, England 50 28N 3 32w
37 Tordesillas, Spain 41 30N 5 0w
61 Torei, U.S.S.R. 50 45N 104 45E
46 Torgau, Germany 51 35N 12 58E
44 Torhout, Belgium 51 4N 3 7E
40 Torino, see Turin
73 Torit, Sudan 4 29N 32 32E
48 Torne, R., Sweden 67 30N 22 0E
48 Torne, R., Sweden 67 30N 22 0E
47 Tornetäsk, L., Sweden 68 20N 19 25E
48 Tornio, & R., Finland 65 57N 24 12E
99 Toro, Cor del, Chile 29 10s 69 0w
41 Toronaios, G., Greece 40 0N 23 35E
83 Toronto, Australia 32 58s 151 30E
92 Toronto, Canada 43 42N 79 30w
74 Tororo, Uganda 0 43N 34 13E
24 Torquay, England 50 28N 3 32w
37 Tôrre de Moncorvo, Port. 41 12N 7 10w
83 Torrelavega, Spain 43 20N 4 5w
83 Torrens, L., Australia 31 0s 137 40E
82 Torrens Creek, Austral. 20 48s 145 3E
94 Torreon, Mexico 25 30N 103 12w
94 Torres, Mexico 28 40N 110 55w
82 Torres Strait, Australia 10 0s 142 30E
37 Torres Vedras, Portugal 39 3N 9 19w
37 Torrevieja, Spain 37 59N 0 40w
32 Torridon, & L., Scot. 57 33N 5 30w
93 Torrington, U.S.A. 41 50N 73 5w
42 Torteval, Guernsey, Channel Is. 49 26N 2 38w
42 Tortona, Italy 44 55N 8 55E
83 Torrowangee, Australia 31 25s 141 30E
37 Tortosa, Spain 40 48N 0 47E
98 Tortuga I., Venezuela 11 0N 65 30w
47 Torun, Poland 53 2N 18 37E
61 Torzhok, U.S.S.R. 57 10N 34 55E
67 Tosa B., Japan 33 15N 133 30E
24 Totnes, England 50 25N 3 51w
83 Tottenham, Australia 32 10s 147 20E
76 Tottori, & Pref., Japan 35 30N 134 10E
72 Toubkal, Djebel, Morocco 31 15N 7 20w
72 Touggourt, Algeria 33 5N 6 0E
42 Toul, France 48 42N 5 53E
43 Toulon, France 43 9N 5 55E
43 Toulouse, France 43 37N 1 18E
47 Touraine, Dist., France 47 20N 0 40E
43 Tourcoing, France 50 46N 3 3E
44 Tournai, Belgium 50 9N 3 23E
43 Tournus, France 46 35N 4 50E
43 Tours, France 47 24N 0 41E
76 Touws, South Africa 33 32s 20 32E
76 Touwsrivier, S. Africa 33 20s 20 2E
23 Towcester, England 52 8N 1 0w
80 Townshend I., Australia 22 15s 150 38E
82 Townsville, Australia 19 15s 146 47E
25 Towy, R., Wales, see Tywi
25 Towyn, see Tywyn
67 Toyama, B. & Pref., Jap. 36 40N 137 10E
67 Toyohashi, Japan 34 40N 137 28E
51 Trabzon, Turkey 41 0N 39 50E
93 Tracadie, Canada 47 30N 65 0w
43 Trafalgar, C., Spain 36 13N 6 7w
88 Trail, Canada 49 6N 117 58w
41 Trajan's Gate, Bulgaria 42 21N 23 46E
47 Trajan's Wall, Rumania 44 18N 28 20E
34 Tralee, & B., Ireland 52 16N 9 43w
35 Tramore, Ireland 52 9N 7 10w
49 Tranås, Sweden 58 5N 14 58E
68 Trang, Malaya 7 30N 99 40E
83 Trangie, Australia 31 58s 148 2E
41 Trani, Italy 41 17N 16 27E
76 Transkei, S. Africa 32 0s 28 0E
47 Transvaal, Prov., S. Afr. 25 20s 28 30E
47 Transylvania, reg., Rum. 46 18N 24 30E
45 Transylvanian Alps, Rum. 45 35N 24 30E
41 Trapani, Italy 38 1N 12 55E
83 Traralgon, Australia 38 17s 146 35E
37 Tras os Montes E Alto-Douro, Prov., Portugal 41 25N 7 20w
45 Trasimeno, L., Italy 43 8N 12 5E
68 Trat, Cambodia 12 20N 102 30E
83 Traveller's L., Australia 33 14s 142 0E
84 Travers, Mt., N.Z. 42 1s 172 45E
92 Traverse City, U.S.A. 44 50N 85 40w
47 Travnik, Yugoslavia 44 12N 17 38E
40 Trebbia, R., Italy 44 50N 9 30E
47 Trebic, Czechoslovakia 49 15N 15 50E
41 Trebinje, Yugoslavia 42 43N 18 17E
46 Trebon, Czechoslovakia 49 0N 14 50E
25 Tredegar, Wales 51 46N 3 16w
25 Treharris, Wales 51 38N 3 17w
99 Treinta y Tres, Uruguay 33 30s 54 50w
44 Trélon, France 50 5N 4 6E
49 Trelleborg, Sweden 55 21N 13 2E
25 Tremadog, & B., Wales 52 55N 4 8w
37 Tremp, Spain 42 10N 0 50E
27 Trent, R., England 53 33N 0 44w
40 Trentino-Alto-Adige, Reg., Italy 46 5N 11 0E
40 Trento, Italy 46 3N 11 5E
92 Trenton, Canada 44 6N 77 37w
93 Trenton, U.S.A. 40 17N 74 33w
89 Trepassey, Canada 46 34N 53 25w
99 Tres Arroyos, Argentina 38 30s 60 30w
99 Tres Puntas, C., Arg. 47 30s 65 0w
43 Treviglio, Italy 45 30N 9 42E
40 Treviso, Italy 45 41N 12 18E
24 Trevose Hd., England 50 33N 5 3w
42 Trévoux, France 45 57N 4 46E
64 Trichur, India 10 30N 76 15E
83 Trida, Australia 32 58s 144 59E
46 Trier, Germany 49 45N 6 40E
40 Trieste, Italy 45 39N 13 50E
41 Trikkala, Greece 39 35N 21 42E

35 Trim, Ireland 53 35N 6 47W
64 Trincomalee, Sri Lanka 8 40N 81 12E
98 Trinidad, Bolivia 14 30s 65 12W
95 Trinidad, Cuba 21 55N 80 7w
90 Trinidad, U.S.A. 37 5N 104 30w
94 Trinidad, I., W. Indies 10 5N 61 0w
94 Trinidad & Tobago, see Inset
99 Trinidad I., Argentina 39 0s 62 0w
94 Trinité, Martinique, Fr., W.I. 14 42N 60 58w
94 Trinity R., U.S.A. 31 30N 95 3w
73 Trinkitat, Sudan 17 30N 37 50E
51 Tripoli, Lebanon 34 40N 36 0E
73 Tripoli, Libya 32 58N 13 12E
41 Tripolis, Greece 37 29N 22 37E
73 Tripolitania, Libya 30 0N 14 0E
65 Tripura, Prov., India 24 0N 91 40E
5 Tristan da Cunha, Atlantic Ocean 38 0s 12 0w
64 Trivandrum, India 8 40N 76 50E
47 Trnava, Czechoslovakia 48 20N 17 30E
82 Trobriand or Kiriwina Is., Papua 8 40s 152 0E
40 Troglav, Mt., Yugoslavia 43 53N 16 20E
93 Trois Rivières, Canada 46 25N 72 45w
60 Troitsk, U.S.S.R. 54 20N 61 28E
50 Troitskoye, U.S.S.R. 49 43N 136 50E
48 Trolladyngja Mt., Ice. 64 49N 17 29w
49 Trollhättan, Sweden 58 11N 12 15E
75 Trompsburg, S. Africa 30 0s 25 40E
48 Troms, Co., Norway 69 15N 20 0E
48 Tromsö, Norway 69 34N 18 49E
99 Tronador, Mt., Chile 41 30s 71 30w
48 Trondelag, N., Co., Nor. 64 0N 12 0E
48 Trondheim & Fd., Nor. 63 25N 10 23E
51 Troodos, Mt., Cyprus 35 0N 32 45E
54 Troon, Scotland 55 33N 4 38w
31 Trossachs, Scotland 56 13N 4 23w
32 Trotternish, dist., Scot. 57 35N 6 15E
88 Trout L., Canada 60 40N 121 40w
43 Trouville, France 49 20N 0 10E
22 Trowbridge, England 51 20N 2 12w
91 Troy, Ala., U.S.A. 31 45N 85 58w
93 Troy, N.Y., U.S.A. 42 48N 73 37w
41 Troy, Ancient City, Turkey 39 47N 26 18E
43 Troyes, France 48 19N 4 2E
66 Trucial States, see United Arab Emirates
98 Trujillo, Peru 8 7s 78 50w
37 Trujillo, Spain 39 29N 5 53w
95 Trujillo, Venezuela 9 25N 70 20w
83 Trundle, Australia 32 47s 147 40E
93 Truro, Canada 45 21N 63 30w
24 Truro, England 50 15N 5 4w
36 Truskmore, Mt., Ireland 54 22N 8 23w
46 Trutnov, Czechoslovakia 50 37N 15 54E
66 Tsaidam, dist., China 37 30N 95 30E
66 Tsamkong, China 21 15N 110 10E
65 Tsanga, China 30 40N 100 25E
65 Tsangpo, R., China 30 0N 83 0E
75 Tsau, Botswana 20 5s 22 50E
73 Tsefat, Israel 32 57N 35 29E
60 Tselinograd, U.S.S.R. 51 45N 71 5E
76 Tses, S.W. Africa 25 50s 18 10E
75 Tshane, Botswana 24 5s 21 54E
74 Tshikapa, Zaïre 6 17s 21 0E
66 Tsiaotso, China 35 11N 13 10E
75 Tsihombe, Madagascar 25 9s 45 34E
52 Tsimlyansk Res., U.S.S.R. 48 0N 42 30E
66 Tsi-nan, China 36 45N 117 0E
66 Tsinghai, prov., China 36 0N 96 0E
67 Tsingkiang, China 33 45N 119 0E
66 Tsin Ling Shan, mts., China 34 20N 108 0E
66 Tsingshih, China 29 30N 112 0E
66 Tsingsi, China 23 20N 105 20E
67 Tsingtao, China 36 7N 120 25E
67 Tsining, China 35 30N 116 35E
67 Tsitsihar, China 47 20N 124 0E
51 Tskhinvali, U.S.S.R. 42 15N 43 30E
52 Tsna, R., U.S.S.R. 54 30N 41 40E
63 Tstl, Syria 32 50N 35 58E
67 Tsu, Japan 34 38N 136 28E
67 Tsu Shima I., Japan 34 20N 129 15E
67 Tsugaru Str., Japan 41 30N 141 0E
75 Tsumeb, S.W. Africa 19 11s 17 47E
66 Tsunyi, China 27 38N 107 0E
67 Tsuruga, Japan 35 42N 136 4E
67 Tsuruoka, Japan 38 40N 139 52E
67 Tsuyama, Japan 35 7N 134 0E
34 Tuam, Ireland 53 31N 8 50w
4 Tuamoto Arch., Pac. Oc. 17 0s 144 0w
51 Tuapse, U.S.S.R. 44 0N 39 0E
84 Tuatapere, New Zealand 46 5s 167 41E
98 Tubarao, Brazil 28 25s 49 0w
63 Tubas, Jordan 32 20N 35 22E
42 Tübingen, Germany 48 30N 9 0E
73 Tubruq, Libya 32 0N 23 45E
94 Tucacas, Venezuela 10 48N 68 18w
90 Tucson, U.S.A. 32 12N 110 48w
99 Tucumán, Argentina 26 48s 65 30w
90 Tucumcari, U.S.A. 35 12N 103 45w
37 Tudela, Spain 42 4N 1 39w
75 Tudweiliog, Wales 52 54N 4 35w
83 Tuen, Australia 28 33s 145 57E
61 Tugur, U.S.S.R. 53 40N 136 55E
71 Tukrah, Libya 32 30N 20 20E
74 Tukuyu, Tanzania 9 0s 33 40E
66 Tukzar, Afghanistan 35 55N 66 25E
63 Tul Karm, Jordan 32 19N 35 2E
94 Tula, Mexico 23 0N 99 45w
52 Tula, U.S.S.R. 54 18N 37 35E
66 Tulan, China 37 20N 98 20E
90 Tulare, & L., U.S.A. 36 0N 119 40w

98 Tulcan, Ecuador 0 50N 77 50w
47 Tulcea, Rumania 45 10N 28 47E
75 Tulear, Madagascar 23 20N 43 45E
34 Tulla, Ireland 52 52N 8 46w
35 Tullamore, Ireland 53 17N 7 29w
43 Tulle, France 45 17N 1 41E
43 Tullins, France 45 18N 5 30E
34 Tullow, Ireland 52 47N 6 42w
73 Tulmaythah, Libya 32 40N 20 55E
91 Tulsa, U.S.A. 36 5N 96 0w
51 Tulun, China 54 45N 100 20E
98 Tumaco, Colombia 1 40N 78 45w
83 Tumbarumba, Australia 35 54s 148 0E
64 Tumkur, India 13 15N 77 6E
31 Tummel, L. & R., Scot. 56 42N 3 57w
64 Tump, Pakistan 26 3N 62 18E
72 Tumu, Ghana 11 0N 2 0w
83 Tumut, Australia 35 17s 148 9E
23 Tunbridge Wells, Eng. 51 8N 0 17E
83 Tuncurry, Australia 32 5s 152 18E
74 Tunduru, Tanzania 11 10s 37 30E
65 Tung Ting, L., China 29 5N 94 10E
65 Tung Pass, China 29 5N 94 10E
64 Tungabhadra, R., India 15 30N 76 50E
67 Tungaru, Sudan 10 10N 30 50E
67 Tunghing, China 21 45N 107 15E
67 Tunghwa, China 41 40N 126 0E
67 Tungien, China 27 50N 108 30E
66 Tungkwan, China 34 37N 110 0E
67 Tungliao, China 43 30N 122 20E
48 Tungnafells J., mts., Ice. 64 30N 18 20w
65 Tungpu, China 31 40N 98 25E
66 Tungtze, China 28 25N 106 0E
66 Tunhwang, China 40 24s 94 15E
73 Tunis, Tunisia 36 48N 10 13E
73 Tunisia, North Africa 34 0N 9 0E
67 Tunki, China 29 45N 118 15E
48 Tunnsjöen, L., Sweden 64 40N 14 0E
23 Tunstall, England 52 7N 1 28E
91 Tupelo, U.S.A. 34 23N 88 59w
74 Tura, India 25 20N 90 25E
61 Tura, U.S.S.R. 64 20N 99 40E
62 Turaba, Saudi Arabia 28 22N 43 14E
55 Turanain Pl., U.S.S.R. 44 0N 63 0E
47 Turek, Poland 52 0N 18 30E
66 Turfan, China 43 40N 88 55E
66 Turfan Depression, China 42 45N 90 0E
41 Turgovishte, Bulgaria 43 17N 26 38E
51 Turgutlu, Turkey 38 30N 27 40E
67 Turi Rog., U.S.S.R. 45 5N 131 45E
41 Turia, R., Spain 39 45N 1 12w
40 Turin (Torino), Italy 45 2N 7 43E
47 Turka, U.S.S.R. 49 10N 23 0E
74 Turkana, L., Kenya 3 30N 36 0E
60 Turkestan, U.S.S.R. 43 12N 68 10E
51 Turkey, Asia & Eur. 39 0N 33 0E
60 Turkmenistan, S.S.R., U.S.S.R. 39 0N 60 0E
94 Turks Is., W. Indies 21 15N 71 10w
49 Turku, Finland 60 30N 22 19E
49 Turku Pori, Co., Finland 61 15N 22 10E
44 Turnhout, Belgium 51 21N 4 47E
47 Turnu Magurele, Rum. 43 45N 24 50E
47 Turnu Severin, Rum. 44 38N 22 58E
33 Turriff, Scotland 57 33N 2 27w
91 Tuscaloosa, U.S.A. 33 14N 87 31w
40 Tuscany, reg., Italy 43 35N 11 20E
52 Tushino, U.S.S.R. 55 50N 37 26E
22 Tutbury, England 52 52N 1 42w
45 Tuttlingen, Germany 48 0N 8 50E
61 Tuva, A.S.S.R., U.S.S.R. 51 30N 95 0E
11 Tuvalu, Is., Pac. Oc. 7 40s 178 0E
94 Tuxpan, Mexico 20 50N 97 23w
94 Tuxtla, Mexico 16 50N 93 15w
51 Tuz, L., Turkey 38 45N 33 15E
41 Tuzla, Yugoslavia 44 35N 18 20E
31 Tweed, R., Scotland 55 38N 2 20w
27 Tweedmouth, England 55 46N 2 1w
90 Twin Falls, U.S.A. 42 30N 114 35w
83 Twofold B., Australia 37 0s 150 0E
21 Tyldesley, England 53 32N 2 29w
91 Tyler, U.S.A. 32 18N 95 17w
31 Tyndrum, Scotland 56 26N 4 42w
26 Tyne, R., England 54 58N 2 0w
31 Tyne, R., Scotland 55 58N 2 40w
27 Tyne & Wear, Co., Eng. 55 0N 1 35w
27 Tynemouth, England 55 1N 1 28w
63 Tyre, Lebanon 33 17N 35 12E
83 Tyrell, L., Australia 35 23s 142 50E
49 Tyri Fd., Norway 60 40N 10 0E
46 Tyrol, Prov., Austria 46 58N 11 40E
36 Tyrone, Co., N. Ireland 54 40N 7 15w
40 Tyrrhenian Sea, Medit. S. 40 30N 12 0E
48 Tys Fjord, Norway 68 5N 16 30E
25 Tywi, R., Wales 51 50N 3 50w
25 Tywyn, Wales 52 34N 4 5w
76 Tzaneen, South Africa 23 45s 30 5E
66 Tzekung, China 29 30N 104 20E
67 Tzepo, China 36 20N 118 30E
67 Tzuchien, China 27 45N 98 35E

U

63 Uassem, Syria 32 59N 36 2E
74 Ubangi, R., Congo, see Oubangi, R.
61 Ube, Japan 33 55N 131 20E
37 Ubeda Baeza, Spain 38 0N 3 25w
98 Uberaba, Brazil 19 50s 47 50w
98 Uberlandia, Brazil 19 0s 48 20w
98 Ucayali, R., Peru 8 30s 74 20w
61 Uchinya, U.S.S.R. 60 5N 65 15E
61 Uchur, R., U.S.S.R. 58 0N 131 0E
23 Uckfield, England 50 58N 0 6E
64 Udaipur, India 24 48N 73 42E

56 Udaipur Garhi, Nepal 27 0N 86 30E
49 Uddevalla, Sweden 58 23N 11 57E
31 Uddingston, Scotland 55 50N 4 3w
48 Uddjaur, L., Sweden 65 55N 17 50E
72 Udi, Nigeria 6 20N 7 30E
40 Udine, Italy 46 2N 13 18E
64 Udipi, India 13 15N 74 40E
50 Udmurt A.S.S.R., U.S.S.R. 57 0N 52 30E
64 Udon Thani, Thailand 17 45N 102 0E
67 Ueda, Japan 36 27N 138 7E
50 Uelen, U.S.S.R. 66 0N 170 10w
46 Uelzen, Germany 53 0N 10 30E
50 Ufa, U.S.S.R. 54 50N 55 53E
50 Ufa, R., U.S.S.R. 56 0N 57 0E
72 Uganda, E. Africa 2 0N 32 0E
61 Uglegorsk, U.S.S.R. 49 10N 142 5E
61 Ugolyak, U.S.S.R. 64 40N 120 10E
32 Uig, Scotland 58 13N 7 1w
90 Uintah Mts., U.S.A. 40 45N 110 0w
32 Uist, see North Uist, South Uist
75 Uitenhage, S. Africa 33 47s 25 28E
44 Uithuizen, Netherlands 53 24N 6 41E
38 Ujda, Morocco 34 45N 2 0w
74 Ujiji, Tanzania 4 59s 29 43E
67 Ujiyamada, Japan 34 25N 136 50E
67 Ujjain, India 23 10N 75 45E
74 Ujpest, Hungary 47 36N 19 0E
74 Ukerewe I., Tanzania 2 0s 32 0E
65 Ukhrul, India 25 10N 94 20E
50 Ukhta, U.S.S.R. 63 55N 54 0E
73 Ukian, U.S.A. 39 12N 123 10w
51 Ukmerge, U.S.S.R. 55 15N 24 40E
51 Ukraine S.S.R., U.S.S.R. 49 20N 32 0E
61 Ulan-Bator, Mongolia 48 0N 106 59E
61 Ulan Ude, U.S.S.R. 51 50N 107 20E
67 Ulanhot, China 46 10N 121 45E
41 Ulcinj, Yugoslavia 42 0N 19 10E
76 Ulco, South Africa 28 20s 24 15E
36 Uleaborg, see Oulu
83 Ulladulla, Australia 35 22s 150 28E
32 Ullapool, Scotland 57 54N 5 9w
21 Ullswater, L., England 54 35N 2 50w
45 Ulm, Germany 48 27N 9 58E
83 Ulmarra, Australia 29 36s 152 55E
49 Ulricehamn, Sweden 57 50N 13 24E
36 Ulster, U.K. 54 32N 7 0w
60 Ulster Canal, N. Ireland 54 15N 7 0w
60 Ulutau, U.S.S.R. 48 50N 67 5E
32 Ulva, I., Scotland 56 30N 6 12w
26 Ulverston, England 54 13N 3 6w
83 Ulverstone, Australia 41 5s 146 8E
50 Ulyanovsk, U.S.S.R. 54 12N 48 25E
61 Ulyasutay, Mongolia 47 50N 96 40w
51 Uman, U.S.S.R. 48 30N 30 5E
65 Umaria, India 23 35N 80 50E
82 Umarkot, Pakistan 25 12N 69 58E
82 Umboi I., Papua N.G. 5 30s 148 0E
45 Umbrail Pass, Switzerland 46 35N 10 20E
40 Umbria, reg., Italy 43 0N 12 40E
48 Ume, R., Sweden 64 15N 19 30E
48 Umea, Sweden 63 49N 20 20E
76 Umkomaas, S. Africa 30 12s 30 48E
73 Umm Dam, Sudan 13 50N 31 0E
62 Umm Lajj, Saudi Arabia 25 0N 37 23E
63 Umm Qays, Jordan 32 40N 35 40E
73 Umm Ruwaba, Sudan 12 50N 31 10E
75 Umtali, Rhodesia 18 49s 32 40E
76 Umtata, S. Africa 31 40s 28 42E
75 Umzimto, S. Africa 30 15s 30 45E
40 Unac, R., Yugoslavia 44 50N 16 15E
88 Unalaska, Alaska 54 0N 164 30w
98 Uncia, Bolivia 18 30s 66 25w
83 Ungarie, Australia 33 30s 147 10E
89 Ungava B., Canada 59 30N 68 0w
89 Ungava Peninsula, Canada 60 0N 70 0w
88 Unimak I. & Pass, Alaska 54 30N 164 30w
91 Union, U.S.A. 34 43N 81 32w
92 Union City, U.S.A. 36 30N 89 2w
60-61 Union of Soviet Socialist Republics 60 0N 90 0E
76 Uniondale, S. Africa 33 35s 23 19E
92 Uniontown, U.S.A. 39 56N 79 45w
63 United Arab Emirates, Asia 23 0N 54 0E
16 United Kingdom, Europe 55 0N 2 0w
90 United States of America, N. America 39 0N 90 0w
64 Unnao, India 26 45N 80 50E
35 Unshin R., Ireland 54 8N 8 26w
32 Unst, I., Scotland 60 45N 0 50w
45 Unterwalden, Cn., Switz. 46 55N 8 15E
74 Upemba, L., Zaïre 8 30s 26 20E
76 Upington, S. Africa 28 18s 21 12E
84 Upolu I., Samoa (Inset)
46 Upper Austria, prov., Austria 48 15N 15 10E
25 Upper Chapel, Wales 52 3N 3 26w
63 Upper Galilee, Dist., Israel 33 20N 35 20E
90 Upper Hutt, N.Z. 41 8s 175 5E
90 Upper Klamath L., U.S.A. 42 30N 122 0w
36 Upper L., Erne, N. Ire. 54 13N 7 32w
73 Upper Nile, dist., Sudan 10 0N 33 0E
61 Upper Taimyr R., U.S.S.R. 73 40N 96 0E
72 Upper Volta, Africa 12 0N 1 0w
49 Uppsala, & Co., Sweden 59 52N 17 35E
21 Upton, England 53 14N 2 52w
22 Upton-on-Severn, Eng. 52 4N 2 12w
98 Uraba, G. of, Colombia 8 30N 77 0w
50 Ural Mts., U.S.S.R. 59 0N 60 0E
50 Ural, R., U.S.S.R. 49 0N 52 0E
83 Uralla, Australia 30 40s 151 30E
50 Uralsk, U.S.S.R. 51 12N 51 20E
88 Uranium City, Canada 59 40N 108 30w

83 Uranquinty, Australia 35 10s 146 40E
67 Urawa, Japan 36 0N 139 30E
51 Urbino, Italy 43 46N 12 41E
94 Ures, Mexico 29 20N 110 30w
51 Urfa, Turkey 37 15N 39 5E
46 Urfahr, Austria 48 15N 14 20E
50 Urga, see Ulan Bator
60 Urgench, U.S.S.R. 41 40N 60 30E
44 Uri, Canton, Switzerland 46 50N 8 40E
44 Urk, Netherlands 52 40N 5 37E
35 Urlingford, Ireland 52 44N 7 33w
62 Urmia, L., Iran 37 40N 45 30E
26 Urmston, England 53 28N 2 22w
98 Urubamba, R., Peru 13 0s 72 30w
99 Uruguaiana, Brazil 29 45s 57 0w
99 Uruguay, S. Amer. 33 0s 55 0w
99 Uruguay, R., S. America 28 30s 56 0w
66 Urumchi, China 44 0N 88 0E
62 Urup, I., U.S.S.R. 46 0N 150 0E
42 Urville, France 49 40N 1 45w
75 Usakos, S.W. Africa 22 0s 15 31E
42 Usak, Turkey 38 43N 29 28E
99 Uspallata P., Argentina 32 45s 70 0w
42 Uspenski, U.S.S.R. 48 50N 72 55E
43 Ussel, France 45 30N 2 15E
61 Ussuri R., Asia 46 30N 133 30E
61 Ussuriysk, U.S.S.R. 43 40N 131 50E
61 Ust Bolsheretsk, U.S.S.R. 52 40N 156 30E
60 Ust Ishim, U.S.S.R. 57 45N 71 10E
51 Ust Kamchatsk, U.S.S.R. 56 10N 162 0E
60 Ust Kamenogorsk, U.S.S.R. 50 0N 82 20E
61 Ust Kut, U.S.S.R. 56 50N 105 10E
61 Ust Maya, U.S.S.R. 60 30N 134 20E
61 Ust Port, U.S.S.R. 70 0N 84 10E
61 Ust Tungir, U.S.S.R. 55 25N 120 15E
50 Ust Urt, Plat., U.S.S.R. 43 10N 55 0E
50 Ust Usa, U.S.S.R. 66 0N 56 30E
61 Ust-chaun, U.S.S.R. 68 50N 170 30E
46 Usti nad Labem, Cz-slov. 50 40N 14 7E
40 Ustica I., Italy 38 42N 13 14E
51 Ustye, U.S.S.R. 57 40N 94 50E
94 Usumacinta, R., Central America 17 0N 91 0w
90 Utah, st., U.S.A. 39 40N 111 30w
90 Utah, L., U.S.A. 40 20N 111 45w
73 Utete, Tanzania 8 0s 38 50E
91 Utica, U.S.A. 43 0N 75 12w
67 Uto, Japan 32 35N 130 48E
44 Utrecht & Prov., Neth. 52 6N 5 8E
41 Utrera, Spain 37 14N 5 50w
67 Utsonomiya, Japan 36 30N 139 56E
65 Uttar Pradesh, st., India 27 20N 80 30E
64 Uttaradit, Thailand 17 42N 100 1E
26 Uttoxeter, England 52 53N 1 52w
49 Uudenmaa, Co., Finland 60 30N 25 0E
48 Uusikaarlepyy, Finland 63 35N 22 30E
48 Uusikaupunki, Finland 60 50N 21 25E
90 Uvalde, U.S.A. 29 14N 99 45w
50 Uvaly Uplands, U.S.S.R. 60 0N 51 15E
50 Uvat, U.S.S.R. 59 5N 68 50E
74 Uvinza, Tanzania 5 0s 30 27E
74 Uvira, Zaïre 3 19s 29 2E
61 Uvs Nuur, Mongolia 50 15N 92 30E
67 Uwajima, Japan 33 10N 132 30E
98 Uyuni, Salar de, Bolivia 20 0s 68 0w
60 Uzbekistan, S.S.R., U.S.S.R. 38 0N 68 0E
43 Uzerche, France 45 22N 1 30E
43 Uzès, France 44 0N 4 20E
46 Uzhgorod, U.S.S.R. 48 36N 22 18E
46 Uznam, I., Ger.-Poland 54 0N 14 0E

V

76 Vaal, R., S. Africa 26 45s 25 30E
48 Vaasa, & Co., Finland 63 9N 21 30E
46 Vác, Hungary 47 50N 19 10E
64 Vadodara, India 22 22N 73 17E
48 Vadsö, Norway 70 3N 29 50E
44 Vaduz, Liechtenstein 47 9N 9 32E
47 Vah, R., Czechoslovakia 49 10N 18 30E
43 Val-de-Marne, Dépt., Fr. 48 49N 2 30E
42 Val d'Oise, Dépt., France 49 10N 2 10E
88 Val d'Or, Canada 48 7N 77 47w
45 Valais, Canton, Switz. 46 10N 7 30E
52 Valdai Hill, U.S.S.R. 58 0N 33 0E
99 Valdemosa, Spain 38 44N 3 26w
99 Valdés Pen., Argentina 42 30s 64 0w
88 Valdez, Alaska 61 14N 146 10w
99 Valdivia, Chile 40 3s 73 35w
50 Valdosta, U.S.A. 30 5N 83 21w
42 Vale, Channel Is. 49 30N 2 30w
43 Valence, France 44 58N 4 59E
37 Valencia, Prov., & G., Spain 39 28N 0 23w
94 Valencia, Venezuela 10 37N 68 0w
94 Valenciennes, France 50 20N 3 32E
94 Valencia, Venezuela 10 70 30w
49 Valga, U.S.S.R. 57 41N 26 0E
43 Valinco, G. of, France 41 45N 8 30E
94 Valladolid, Mexico 20 30N 88 10w
37 Valladolid, Spain 41 40N 4 45w
37 Vallecas, Spain 40 23N 3 41w

90 Vallejo, U.S.A. 38 12N 122 12w
99 Vallenar, Chile 28 35s 70 45w
40 Valletta, Malta 35 55N 14 29E
90 Valley City, U.S.A. 47 0N 98 0w
93 Valleyfield, Canada 45 10N 74 15w
45 Vallorbe, Switzerland 46 43N 6 20E
37 Valls, Spain 41 15N 1 10E
49 Valmiera, U.S.S.R. 57 30N 25 27E
41 Valona, see Vlone
99 Valparaiso, Chile 33 5s 71 50w
76 Vals, R., South Africa 27 30s 26 45E
43 Valtellina, R., Italy 46 9N 9 50E
95 Valverde, Dom. Rep. 19 30N 71 10w
37 Valverde, Spain 37 30N 6 45w
74 Van, & L., Turkey 38 30N 43 30E
80 Van Diemen G., Austral. 12 0s 132 0E
88 Vancouver, Canada 49 14N 122 50w
90 Vancouver, U.S.A. 45 47N 122 46w
88 Vancouver I., Canada 49 30N 126 0w
76 Vanderbijlpark, S. Africa 26 40s 27 50E
49 Vänern, L., Sweden 58 47N 13 50E
49 Vänersborg, Sweden 58 26N 12 27E
74 Vänga, Kenya 4 33s 39 5E
48 Vännäs, Sweden 63 57N 19 30E
42 Vannes, France 47 42N 2 43w
48 Vannöy I., Norway 70 6N 19 50E
74 Vanrhynsdorp, S. Africa 31 32s 18 46E
49 Vansbro, Sweden 60 36N 14 12E
80 Vansittart B., Australia 13 50s 126 30E
84 Vanua Levu, Pac. Oc. 16 45s 179 20E
42 Var, Dépt., France 43 25N 6 5E
45 Varallo Sesia, Italy 45 50N 8 16E
65 Varanasi (Banaras), India 25 19N 82 57E
41 Varazdin, Yugoslavia 46 19N 16 21E
49 Varberg, Sweden 57 12N 12 19E
41 Vardar, R., Yugoslavia 41 30N 22 20E
47 Varena, U.S.S.R. 54 7N 24 30E
43 Varennes, Allier, France 46 20N 3 28E
43 Varennes, Meuse, France 49 15N 5 0E
40 Varese, Italy 45 49N 8 50E
49 Värmland, Co., Sweden 59 45N 13 0E
41 Varna, Bulgaria 43 10N 28 0E
49 Värnamo, Sweden 57 10N 14 3E
35 Vartry Res., Ireland 53 3N 6 12w
64 Vasht, Iran 28 15N 61 15E
49 Västeras, Sweden 59 37N 16 38E
49 Väster-dal, R., Sweden 60 30N 14 0E
49 Vasterbotten, Sweden 65 0N 17 0E
48 Västernorrland, Co., Sweden 63 0N 17 30E
49 Vastervik, Sweden 57 48N 16 32E
49 Västmanland, Co., Swed. 59 45N 16 20E
40 Vasto, Italy 42 8N 14 50E
32 Vaternish Pt., Scotland 57 36N 6 40w
32 Vatersay, I., Scotland 56 56N 7 32w
48 Vatna Jökull, mts., Ice. 64 30N 16 30w
75 Vatomandry, Madagascar 19 17s 48 55E
47 Vatra-Dornei, Rumania 47 20s 25 30E
49 Vättern, L., Sweden 58 25N 14 30E
45 Vaucluse, Dépt., France 44 0N 5 10E
45 Vaud, Canton, Switzerland 46 33N 6 30E
45 Vaupes, R., S. America 1 15N 71 0w
49 Växjö, Sweden 56 56N 14 48E
98 Veadeiros, Chapada dos, plat., Brazil 15 0s 48 0w
47 Vedea, R., Rumania 44 0N 25 20E
48 Veendam, Netherlands 53 6N 6 52E
48 Vega Fjord, Norway 65 50N 12 0E
48 Vega I., Norway 65 42N 11 50E
44 Veghel, Netherlands 51 37N 5 33E
88 Vegreville, Canada 53 35N 112 10w
37 Vejer, Spain 36 14N 5 59w
49 Vejle, Denmark 55 47N 9 30E
40 Velebit Planina, mts., Yugoslavia 44 40N 15 30E
37 Velez-Malaga, Spain 36 48N 4 5w
37 Velez Rúbio, Spain 37 45N 2 5w
50 Velikaya R., U.S.S.R. 57 0N 28 50E
50 Velikiy Ustyug, U.S.S.R. 60 47N 46 20E
50 Velikiye Luki, U.S.S.R. 56 25N 30 35E
40 Velletri, Italy 41 43N 12 50E
64 Vellore, India 13 0N 79 5E
44 Velzen, Netherlands 52 27N 4 40E
42 Vendée, Dépt., France 46 30N 1 35E
43 Vendôme, France 47 44N 1 0E
40 Veneto, reg., Italy 46 30N 12 0E
40 Venezia, see Venice
96 Venezuela, S. America 8 40N 67 0w
98 Venezuela, G. of, Ven. 11 30N 71 0w
64 Vengurla, India 15 45N 73 35E
40 Venice, & G., Italy 45 27N 12 20E
65 Venkatapuram, India 18 20N 80 30E
44 Venlo, Netherlands 51 37N 6 10E
43 Ventimiglia, Italy 43 51N 7 50E
22 Ventnor, I. of Wight, Eng. 50 36N 1 13w
49 Ventspils, U.S.S.R. 57 29N 21 33E
37 Vera, Spain 37 8N 1 53w
94 Veracruz, Mexico 19 13N 96 18w
64 Veraval, India 21 0N 70 17E
40 Vercelli, Italy 45 19N 8 28E
46 Verden, Germany 52 58N 9 18E
43 Verdon, R., France 43 47N 6 10E
43 Verdun, France 49 12N 5 20E
75 Vereeniging, S. Africa 26 42s 27 52E
42 Vergara, Spain 43·8N 2 23w
61 Verkh, Vilyuisk, U.S.S.R. 63 25N 120 5E
61 Verkhne Kolymsk, U.S.S.R. 65 48N 150 30E
61 Verkhoyansk, U.S.S.R. 67 50N 133 30E
61 Verkhoyansk, Ra., U.S.S.R. 65 0N 132 0E
88 Vermilion, Canada 53 20N 110 40w
91 Vermont, st., U.S.A. 44 0N 72 40w
88 Vernon, Canada 50 15N 119 20w
90 Vernon, U.S.A. 34 12N 99 18w

41 Véroia, Greece 40 35N 22 15E
40 Verona, Italy 45 26N 11 0E
43 Versailles, France 48 48N 2 7E
72 Vert, C., Sénégal 14 45N 17 30w
44 Verviers, Belgium 50 35N 5 52E
24 Veryan & B., England 50 13N 4 56w
52 Veselyy Res., U.S.S.R. 47 0N 41 0E
43 Vesoul, France 47 41N 6 8E
49 Vest-Agder, Co., Norway 58 30N 7 0E
48 Vesteralen, Norway 69 15N 15 45E
48 Vestfold, Co., Norway 59 15N 10 10E
48 Vestmannaeyjär, Iceland 63 27N 20 15w
48 Vestvagöy I., Norway 68 15N 13 50E
40 Vesuvius, Mt., Italy 40 54N 14 28E
49 Veszprem, Hungary 47 8N 17 55E
49 Vetlanda, Sweden 57 30N 15 8E
52 Vetluga R., U.S.S.R. 57 5N 45 55E
45 Vevey, Switzerland 46 28N 6 52E
37 Viana, Portugal 38 20N 8 0w
37 Viana do Castello, Port. 41 40N 8 50w
40 Vicenza, Italy 45 35N 11 37E
37 Vich, Spain 41 56N 2 15E
98 Vichada, R., Colombia 4 30N 70 0w
43 Vichy, France 46 10N 3 28E
91 Vicksburg, U.S.A. 32 12N 90 47w
83 Victor Hr., Australia 35 50s 138 40E
83 Victoria, st., Australia 37 0s 145 0E
72 Victoria, Cameroon 4 0N 9 12E
90 Victoria, Canada 48 28N 123 20w
72 Victoria, Guinea 10 57N 14 50w
84 Victoria, Malta 36 1N 14 18E
68 Victoria, Sabah, Malaysia 5 15N 115 40E
91 Victoria, U.S.A. 28 46N 97 0w
73 Victoria Falls, Rhodesia 17 59s 25 57E
88 Victoria I., Canada 70 30N 109 0w
73 Victoria L., Africa 1 0s 33 0E
100 Victoria Ld., Antarctica 80 0s 160 0E
56 Victoria, Mt., Burma 21 15N 94 5E
58 Victoria Point, Burma 10 0N 98 30E
73 Victoria, R., Australia 15 40s 131 0E
80 Victoria River Downs, Australia
    16 22s 131 8E
76 Victoria W., S. Africa 31 37s 23 5E
53 Victoriaville, Canada 46 0N 72 5w
41 Vidin, Yugoslavia 43 59N 22 52E
29 Viedma, L., Argentina 49 30s 7? 30w
37 Viella, Spain 42 43N 0 47E
46 Vienna (Wien), Austria 48 12N 16 20E
43 Vienne, France 45 32N 4 57E
43 Vienne, R., France 47 10N 0 20E
42 Vienne, Dépt., France 46 23N 0 20E
55 Vientiane, Laos 18 6N 102 30E
95 Vieques, I., Puerto Rico 18 10N 65 30w
45 Vierwaldstattersee (L. of Lucerne),
    Switzerland 47 2N 8 10E
44 Viersen, Germany 51 16N 6 24E
57 Vietnam, Asia 15 0N 108 0E
24 Vieux Fort, St. Lucia, W.I.
    13 45N 60 58w
58 Vigan, Philippines 17 32N 120 20E
37 Vigo, Spain 42 12N 8 42w
55 Vijayawada, India 16 30N 80 39E
41 Vijose, R., Albania 40 40N 20 21E
48 Vikna I., Norway 65 0N 11 0E
70 Vikulovo, U.S.S.R. 56 50N 70 40E
75 Vila Arriaga, Angola 14 35s 13 30E
75 Vila Coutinho, Mozam. 14 34s 34 21E
75 Vila Franca, Portugal 39 0N 8 58w
75 Vila General Machado, Angola
    11 58s 17 22E
76 Vila Luiza, Mozambique 25 40s 32 35E
75 Vila Nova de Seles, Angola 11 35s 14 20E
75 Vila Pereira d'Eça, Angola 16 48s 15 50E
75 Vila Real, Portugal 41 15N 7 50w
75 Vila de Sena, Mozàm. 17 23s 34 40E
74 Vila Verissimo Sarmento, Angola
    8 15s 20 50E
42 Vilaine, R., France 47 50N 1 50w
49 Vilhelmina, Sweden 64 38N 16 50E
51 Viliga, U.S.S.R. 61 20N 156 20E
52 Viljandi, U.S.S.R. 58 23N 25 38E
26 Villa Ahumada, Mex. 30 35N 106 30w
92 Villa Encarnación, Para. 27 20s 56 0w
29 Villa Maria, Argentina 32 20s 63 15w
46 Villach, Austria 46 37N 13 45E
37 Villagarcia, Spain 42 34N 8 46w
26 Villahermosa, Mexico 18 0N 92 55w
37 Villalba, Spain 43 19N 7 43w
37 Villanueva de la Serena, Spain
    39 0N 5 48w
29 Villarreal, Spain 39 50N 0 1w
29 Villarrica, Paraguay 25 45s 56 30w
37 Villarrobledo, Spain 39 20N 2 30w
45 Villars, Switzerland 46 18N 7 6E
37 Villaviciosa, Spain 43 30N 5 30w
43 Ville de Paris, Dépt., France 49 0N 2 15E
43 Villefranche, Alpes-Maritimes, France
    43 43N 7 20E
43 Villefranche, Aveyron, Fr. 44 20N 2 0E
43 Villefranche, Rhône, Fr. 46 0N 4 40E
37 Villena, Spain 38 42N 0 52w
43 Villeneuve, France 44 22N 0 40E
43 Villerupt, France 49 28N 5 55E
43 Villeurbanne, France 45 42N 4 55E
52 Vilnius, U.S.S.R. 54 42N 25 15E
44 Vilvoorde, Belgium 50 56N 4 28E
29 Viluj, U.S.S.R. 63 20N 121 20E
29 Vina del Mar, Chile 33 0s 71 30w
37 Vinaroz, Spain 40 25N 0 30E
91 Vincennes, U.S.A. 38 49N '87 30w
55 Vinh, Vietnam 18 45N 105 49E

68 Vinh Loi, Vietnam 9 29N 105 50E
41 Vinkovci, Yugoslavia 45 20N 18 45E
47 Vinnitsa, U.S.S.R. 49 10N 28 30E
64 Viramgam, India 23 12N 72 3E
42 Virandeville, France 49 35N 1 44w
88 Virden, Canada 49 50N 100 55w
99 Virgenes, C., Argentina 52 15s 68 10w
95 Virgin Is., W. Indies 18 20N 65 0w
36 Virginia, Ireland 53 50N 7 5E
76 Virginia, S. Africa 27 53s 26 45E
91 Virginia, st., U.S.A. 37 15N 79 0w
44 Virton, Belgium 49 35N 5 33E
64 Virudhunagar, India 9 30N 77 55E
40 Vis I., Yugoslavia 43 0N 16 10E
90 Visalia, U.S.A. 36 23N 119 16w
73 Visayan Sea, Philippines 11 30N 123 30E
49 Visby, Sweden 57 41N 18 20E
88 Viscount Melville Sd., Canada
    75 0N 110 0w
44 Visé, Belgium 50 44N 5 42E
41 Visegrad, Yugoslavia 43 47N 19 15E
37 Viseu, Portugal 40 40N 7 53w
65 Vishakhapatnam, India 17 44N 83 16E
76 Vishoek, South Africa (Inset)
    34 8s 18 40E
40 Viso, Mt., Italy 44 45N 7 10E
45 Visp, Switzerland 46 19N 7 54E
47 Vistula, R., see Wisla
50 Vitebsk, U.S.S.R. 55 15N 30 20E
40 Viterbo, Italy 42 26N 12 10E
84 Viti Levu, I., Pac. Oc. 18 0s 178 0E
61 Vitim, & R., U.S.S.R. 59 45N 112 25E
98 Vitoria, Brazil 20 15s 40 15w
37 Vitoria, Spain 42 52N 2 35w
42 Vitré, France 48 10N 1 18w
43 Vitry le Francois, France 48 42N 4 30E
40 Vittoria, Italy 37 0N 14 30E
40 Vittorio Veneto, Italy 45 58N 12 19E
37 Vivero, Spain 43 40N 7 34w
43 Viviers, France 44 26N 4 40E
65 Vizianagaram, India 18 8N 83 24E
44 Vlaardingen, Neth. 51 55N 4 21E
47 Vladimir, U.S.S.R. 56 2N 40 35E
47 Vladimir Volynsky, U.S.S.R.
    50 50N 24 18E
61 Vladivostok, U.S.S.R. 42 58N 131 50E
44 Vlieland, I., Netherlands 53 15N 4 57E
44 Vlissingen, see Flushing
41 Vlöre (Vlöne), Albania 40 30N 19 31E
57 Vogelkop Pen., Indon. 1 25s 133 0E
43 Vogels Berg, mt., Ger. 50 37N 9 30E
43 Voghera, Italy 44 59N 9 1E
75 Vohémar, Madagascar 13 25s 50 0E
75 Vohipeno, Madagascar 22 21s 47 51E
73 Voi, Kenya 3 20s 38 35E
43 Voiron, France 45 21N 5 38E
48 Vojmsjön, L., Sweden 65 0N 16 30E
48 Volda, Norway 62 12N 6 5E
44 Volendam, Netherlands 52 30N 5 4E
50 Volga, R., U.S.S.R. 57 30N 39 0E
52 Volgograd (Stalingrad), U.S.S.R.
    48 42N 44 28E
50 Volkhov, R., U.S.S.R. 59 30N 32 0E
47 Volklingen, Germany 49 15N 6 51E
47 Volkovysk, U.S.S.R. 53 10N 24 30E
76 Volksrust, S. Africa 27 20s 29 58E
61 Volochanka, U.S.S.R. 70 55N 94 10E
61 Volochayevka, U.S.S.R. 48 27N 134 40E
50 Vologda, U.S.S.R. 59 10N 39 57E
41 Vólos, & G., Greece 39 26N 22 57E
50 Volsk, U.S.S.R. 52 5N 47 30E
72 Volta, R., W. Africa 5 40N 0 20E
40 Volterra, Italy 43 23N 10 54E
43 Voltri, Italy 44 26N 8 45E
40 Volturno, R., Italy 41 3N 14 0E
52 Volzhskiy, U.S.S.R. 48 53N 44 55E
44 Voorburg, Netherlands 52 4N 4 18E
48 Vopnafjördur, Iceland 65 45N 14 50w
46 Vorarlberg, Prov., Austria 47 15N 10 0E
50 Vorkuta, U.S.S.R. 67 30N 64 10E
52 Voronezh, U.S.S.R. 51 37N 39 10E
52 Voroshilovgrad, U.S.S.R. 48 35N 39 29E
52 Voroshilovsk, U.S.S.R.,
    see Kommunarsk
42 Vosges, Dépt., France 48 5N 6 25E
43 Vosges, Mts., France 48 20N 7 0E
49 Voss, Norway 60 38N 6 28E
100 Vostok, Antarctica 78 30s 107 0E
100 Vostok I., Antarctica 72 0s 97 0E
50 Votkinsk, U.S.S.R. 57 5N 53 50E
37 Vouga, R., Portugal 40 45N 8 0w
43 Vouziers, France 49 20N 4 44E
42 Voves, France 48 18N 1 35E
51 Voznesensk, U.S.S.R. 47 30N 32 0E
52 Voznesenskaya, U.S.S.R. 55 15N 95 50E
50 Voznesenye, U.S.S.R. 61 6N 35 20E
41 Vranje, Yugoslavia 42 33N 21 55E
41 Vratsa, Bulgaria 43 13N 23 30E
40 Vrbas, R., Yugoslavia 45 0N 17 22E
76 Vrede, S. Africa 27 30s 29 15E
76 Vredendal, South Africa 31 35s 18 25E
76 Vredenburg, S. Africa 32 55s 18 0E
45 Vrin, Switzerland 46 40N 9 6E
41 Vrsac, Yugoslavia 45 8N 21 30E
76 Vryburg, S. Africa 26 48s 24 44E
76 Vryheid, S. Africa 27 50s 30 40E
44 Vught, Netherlands 51 39N 5 17E
40 Vulcano, I., Italy 38 29N 15 0E
52 Vyatka, R., U.S.S.R. 57 30N 49 30E
50 Vyatskiye Polyany, U.S.S.R.
    56 15N 51 30E
52 Vyazma, U.S.S.R. 55 15N 34 20E
50 Vyborg, U.S.S.R. 60 45N 28 40E
50 Vychegda, R., U.S.S.R. 61 30N 48 0E

25 Vyrnwy, L. & R., Wales 52 46N 3 30w
52 Vyshniy Volochek, U.S.S.R.
    57 30N 34 30E
50 Vytegra, U.S.S.R. 61 15N 36 40E

W

72 Wa, Ghana 10 5N 2 27w
44 Waal, R., Netherlands 51 33N 5 40E
44 Waalwijk, Netherlands 51 42N 5 2E
92 Wabash, & R., U.S.A. 40 54N 85 48w
88 Wabiskaw, R., Canada 57 40N 115 30w
90 Waco, U.S.A. 31 50N 97 0w
73 Wad Banda, Sudan 13 3N 27 58E
73 Wad Medani, Sudan 14 23N 33 58E
44 Wadden Zee, Neth. 53 15N 5 0E
23 Waddesdon, England 51 51N 0 51w
88 Waddington, Mt., Can. 51 20N 125 25w
24 Wadebridge, England 50 31N 4 49w
41 Wadenswil, Switzerland 47 13N 8 40E
23 Wadhurst, England 51 4N 0 21E
63 Wadi es Sir, Jordan 31 57N 35 50E
73 Wadi Halfa, Sudan 21 52N 31 22E
25 Waenfawr, Wales 53 7N 4 10w
44 Wageningen, Neth. 51 58N 5 40E
89 Wager Bay, Canada 65 45N 91 0w
89 Wager, B., Canada 65 45N 90 0w
83 Wagga Wagga, Australia 35 10s 147 23E
80 Wagin, Australia 33 19s 117 20E
72 Wagin, Nigeria 12 42N 7 10E
68 Wahai, Indonesia 2 50s 129 35E
84 Waiau, New Zealand 42 54s 173 0E
84 Waihi, New Zealand 37 19s 175 58E
84 Waikaremoana L., N.Z. 38 45s 177 5E
84 Waikato R., N.Z. 37 18s 174 43E
84 Waikerie, Australia 34 1s 140 0E
84 Waikokopu, N.Z. 39 0s 177 58E
84 Waikouaiti, N.Z. 45 38s 170 41E
84 Waimarino, New Zealand 39 7s 175 26E
84 Waimate, New Zealand 44 45s 171 7E
83 Wainganga, R., India 21 30N 80 0E
88 Wainwright, Canada 52 57N 111 0w
84 Waiouru, New Zealand 39 28s 175 36E
84 Waipara, New Zealand 43 3s 172 46E
84 Waipawa, New Zealand 39 54s 176 36E
84 Waipiro, New Zealand 38 2s 178 25E
84 Waipukurau, N.Z. 40 0s 176 31E
84 Wairoa, N.Z. 39 0s 177 30E
84 Waitaki, R., N.Z. 44 52s 171 14E
84 Waitara, New Zealand 39 0s 174 5E
84 Waiuku, New Zealand 37 6s 174 38E
66 Waiyeng, China 23 10N 114 30E
35 Wajima, Japan 37 28N 137 0E
74 Wajir, Kenya 1 57N 40 10E
34 Wakamatsu, Honshu, Japan
    37 30N 139 58E
35 Wakamatsu, Kyushu, Japan
    33 58N 130 50E
67 Wakasa B., Japan 35 50N 135 30E
34 Wakatipu, L., N.Z. 45 0s 168 30E
67 Wakayama & Pref., Jap. 34 10N 135 12E
11 Wake I., Pacific Ocean 19 0N 167 0E
27 Wakefield, England 53 41N 1 30w
84 Wakefield, N.Z. 41 25s 173 7E
67 Wakkanai, Japan 45 25N 141 49E
76 Wakkerstroom, S. Africa 27 30s 30 12E
83 Wakool, & R., Australia 35 30s 144 26E
23 Walberswick, England 52 18N 1 39E
46 Walbrzych, Poland 50 45N 16 18E
83 Walcha, Australia 31 0s 151 38E
44 Walcheren, I., Neth. 51 39N 3 35E
49 Walcz, Poland 53 17N 16 27E
45 Wald, Switzerland 47 19N 8 54E
25 Wales, Gt. Britain 52 30N 3 30w
83 Walgett, Australia 30 15s 147 32E
83 Walhalla, Australia 37 48s 146 30E
90 Walker, L., U.S.A. 38 45s 118 42w
90 Walkerston, Australia 21 14s 149 0E
90 Walla Walla, U.S.A. 46 6N 118 25w
90 Wallace, U.S.A. 47 35N 115 58w
92 Wallaceburg, Canada 42 33N 82 26w
47 Wallachia, reg., Rum. 44 42N 25 20E
83 Wallaroo, Australia 33 56s 138 0E
26 Wallasey, England 53 26N 3 5w
83 Wallerawang, Australia 33 25s 150 0E
22 Wallingford, England 51 36N 1 8w
32 Walls, Scotland 60 13N 1 34w
27 Wallsend, England 54 59N 1 32w
83 Wallsend, Australia 33 0s 151 10E
83 Wallumbilla, Australia 26 30s 149 5E
23 Walmer, England 51 11N 1 24E
76 Walmer, South Africa 34 0s 25 25E
22 Walsall, England 52 35N 1 59w
90 Walsenburg, U.S.A. 37 42N 104 47w
34 Walsoken, England 52 40N 0 11E
27 Waltham, England 53 32N 0 6w
23 Waltham Abbey, England 51 39N 0 0
23 Waltham Forest, Greater London,
    England 51 37N 0 2E
26 Walton-le-Dale, England 53 45N 2 41w
23 Walton-on-the-Naze, Eng. 51 50N 1 18E
75 Walvis Bay, S.W. Africa 22 40s 14 30E
65 Wampo, Tibet, China 31 25N 86 35E
64 Wana, Pakistan 32 25N 69 30E
83 Wanbi, Australia 34 48s 140 30E
23 Wandsworth, Greater London,
    England 51 27N 0 12w
84 Wanganui, New Zealand 39 53s 175 7E
83 Wangaratta, Australia 36 25s 146 23E
66 Wanhsien, China 31 3N 108 30E
75 Wankie, Rhodesia 18 23s 26 25E
95 Wanks, R., Cent. America 15 0N 83 5w
22 Wantage, England 51 35N 1 22w

64 Warangal, India 17 57N 79 36E
83 Waratah, Australia 41 32s 145 48E
83 Warburton, Australia 37 58s 145 57E
84 Ward, New Zealand 41 58s 174 2E
33 Ward Hill, Scotland 58 54N 3 23w
76 Warden, S. Africa 27 50s 29 1E
64 Wardha, India 20 53N 78 36E
22 Wardington, England 52 8N 1 17w
26 Wardle, England 53 39N 2 38w
23 Ware, England 51 49N 0 2w
22 Wareham, England 50 40N 2 8w
83 Warialda, Australia 29 32s 150 30E
27 Warkworth, England 55 22N 1 38w
84 Warkworth, N.Z. 36 28N 174 35E
22 Warley, England 52 29N 2 3w
76 Warmbad, South Africa 24 50s 28 10E
75 Warmbad, S.W. Africa 28 23s 18 40E
49 Warnemünde, Germany 54 10N 12 0E
83 Warragul, Australia 38 7s 146 0E
83 Warrego, R., Australia 29 20s 145 50E
83 Warren, Australia 31 33s 147 58E
92 Warren, Ohio, U.S.A. 41 8N 80 57w
91 Warren, Pa., U.S.A. 41 54N 79 12w
83 Warrenville, Australia 25 40s 147 20E
72 Warri, Nigeria 5 35N 5 57E
80 Warrina, Australia 28 7s 136 0E
26 Warrington, England 53 24N 2 36w
83 Warrnambool, Australia 38 18s 142 29E
47 Warsaw (Warszawa), Pol. 52 16N 21 0E
27 Warsop, England 53 13N 1 9w
47 Warszawa, see Warsaw
47 Warta (Warthe), R., Poland
    51 20N 19 0E
83 Warwick, Australia 28 15s 152 10E
22 Warwick, & Co., Eng. 52 18N 1 35w
90 Wasatch Ra., U.S.A. 39 30N 111 30w
22 Washington, England 54 54N 1 31w
92 Washington, D.C., U.S.A. 38 58N 77 0w
91 Washington, N.C., U.S.A.
    35 32N 76 35w
90 Washington, st., U.S.A. 47 45N 121 0w
64 Washir, Afghanistan 32 15N 63 50E
64 Wassenaar, Netherlands 52 8N 4 24E
43 Wassy, France 48 30N 5 0E
26 Wast Water, L., Eng. 54 26N 3 19w
92 Waswanipi, L., & R., Canada
    49 30N 76 25w
24 Watchet, England 51 1N 3 18w
75 Waterberg, S.W. Africa 20 23s 17 9E
76 Waterberge, mts., South Africa
    24 30s 28 0E
93 Waterbury, U.S.A. 41 32N 73 0w
35 Waterford, & Co., Ire. 52 15N 7 7w
34 Watergrasshill, Ireland 52 1N 8 21w
44 Waterloo, Belgium 50 43N 4 24E
26 Waterloo, England 53 29N 2 59w
72 Waterloo, Sierra Leone 8 26N 13 8w
91 Waterloo, U.S.A. 42 30N 92 16w
32 Waternish, Scotland 57 32N 6 35w
93 Watertown, N.Y., U.S.A. 43 57N 75 50w
91 Watertown, S.D., U.S.A. 44 58N 97 4w
76 Waterval-Boven, S. Africa 25 40s 30 20E
34 Waterville, Ireland 51 49N 10 11w
93 Waterville, U.S.A. 44 30N 69 0w
93 Watervliet, U.S.A. 42 40N 73 40w
23 Watford, England 51 39N 0 23w
95 Watling's I., Bahamas 24 0N 74 35w
23 Watlington, Norfolk, England
    52 40N 0 24E
23 Watlington, Oxford, England
    51 39N 1 1w
88 Watrous, Canada 51 40N 105 30w
74 Watsa, Zaïre 3 0N 29 30E
33 Watten, Scotland 58 29N 3 18w
45 Wattwil, Switzerland 47 20N 9 6E
73 Wau, & R., Sudan 7 50N 28 2E
91 Waukegan, U.S.A. 42 23N 87 51w
92 Wausau, U.S.A. 45 0N 89 35w
80 Wave Hill, Australia 17 32s 130 58E
23 Waveney, R., England 52 22N 1 13E
84 Waverley, N.Z. 39 46s 174 35E
44 Wavre, Belgium 50 43N 4 37E
90 Waxahachie, U.S.A. 32 23N 96 52w
44 Waxweiler, Germany 50 6N 6 22E
90 Waycross, U.S.A. 31 10N 82 25w
64 Wazirabad, Pakistan 32 30N 74 5E
23 Weald, The, England 51 9N 0 20E
26 Wear, R., England 54 48N 1 33w
26 Weaver, R., England 53 20N 2 31w
90 Weatherford, U.S.A. 32 45N 97 47w
91 Webster City, U.S.A. 42 30N 93 48w
57 Weda, Indonesia 1 15N 127 50E
100 Weddell Sea, Antarctica 68 0N 40 0w
83 Wedderburn, Australia 36 28s 143 37E
22 Wednesbury, England 52 33N 2 2w
22 Wednesfield, England 52 36N 2 3w
83 Wee Waa, Australia 30 3s 149 30E
44 Weert, Netherlands 51 16N 5 44E
67 Weifang, China 36 45N 119 0E
66 Weihai, China 37 30N 122 0E
46 Weimar, Germany 50 59N 11 15E
45 Weinheim, Germany 49 37N 8 45E
66 Weining, China 27 0N 103 50E
90 Weiser, U.S.A. 44 15N 117 3w
66 Weisi, China 27 30N 99 30E
62 Wejh, Saudi Arabia 26 15N 36 30E
49 Wejherowo, Poland 54 36N 18 15E
76 Welkom, South Africa 28 0s 26 45E
92 Welland, & Can., Canada 43 0N 79 6w
23 Welland, R., England 52 40N 0 20w
82 Wellesley Is., Australia 16 45s 139 30E
44 Wellin, Belgium 50 5N 5 6E

23 Wellingborough, Eng. 52 19N 0 42w
83 Wellington, Australia 32 30s 148 48E
22 Wellington, Salop., Eng. 52 42N 2 30w
24 Wellington, Som., Eng. 50 58N 3 14w
76 Wellington, South Africa 33 35s 19 0E
91 Wellington, U.S.A. 37 14N 97 26w
84 Wellington, & Dist., N.Z. 41 15s 176 46E
99 Wellington I., Chile 49 30s 75 0w
35 Wellington Bridge, Ire. 52 15 6 45w
24 Wells, England 51 13N 2 38w
80 Wells, L., Australia 27 0s 123 35E
46 Wels, Austria 48 10N 14 0E
25 Welshpool, Wales 52 39N 3 9w
25 Welwyn, England 51 48N 0 13w
22 Wem, England 52 52N 2 44E
90 Wenatchee, U.S.A. 47 25N 120 25w
67 Wenchow, China 27 59N 120 30E
23 Wendover, England 51 45N 0 44w
45 Wengen, Switzerland 46 28N 7 56E
82 Wenlock, R., Australia 12 15s 142 0E
22 Wenlock Edge, England 52 30N 2 46w
27 Wensleydale, England 54 18N 2 10w
23 Wensum, R., England 52 47N 0 55E
83 Wentworth, Australia 34 10s 141 50E
22 Weobley, England 52 9N 2 53w
76 Wepener, South Africa 29 46s 27 1E
46 Werra, R., Germany 51 10N 10 0E
83 Werribee, Australia 38 0s 144 40E
83 Werris Creek, Austral. 31 8s 150 36E
44 Wesel, Germany 51 41N 6 39E
44 Weser, R., Germany 52 30N 9 0E
65 West Bengal, St., India 23 0N 87 0E
47 West Beskids, Mts., Czechoslovakia
    49 30N 19 20E
27 West Bridgford, England 52 56N 1 8w
22 West Bromwich, England 52 31N 1 59w
32 West Burra I., Scotland 60 7N 1 5w
13 West Calder, Scotland 55 52N 3 34w
13 West Dvina R., Europe 55 40N 28 0E
24 West Flanders, Belgium 50 58N 3 0E
91 West Frankfort, U.S.A. 37 49N 88 46w
46 West Germany, Europe 51 0N 9 0E
25 West Glamorgan, Co., Wales
    51 45N 3 55w
23 West Grinstead, Eng. 50 58N 0 18w
30 West Kilbride, Scotland 55 42N 4 51w
26 West Kirby, England 53 23N 3 11w
31 West Linton, Scotland 55 45N 3 24w
31 West Looe, England 50 20N 4 27w
22 West Midlands, Co., England
    52 30N 1 55w
75 West Nicholson, Rhodesia 21 1s 29 20E
64 West Pakistan, Asia 27 0N 67 0w
91 West Palm Beach, U.S.A. 26 40N 80 12w
93 West Pt., C., Canada 49 50N 64 40w
27 West Rasen, England 53 23N 0 24w
44 West Schelde, R., Neth. 51 23N 3 50E
60 West Siberian Plain, U.S.S.R.
    62 0N 76 0E
23 West Sussex, Co., Eng. 50 53N 0 30w
91 West Virginia, st., U.S.A. 39 0N 81 0w
83 West Wyalong, Australia 33 56s 147 10E
27 West Yorkshire, Co., Eng. 53 45N 1 30w
23 Westbourne, England 50 22N 0 56w
83 Westbury, Australia 41 32s 147 0E
22 Westbury, Salop., Eng. 52 41N 2 57w
22 Westbury, Wilts., England 51 15N 2 11w
46 Wester Wald, mts., Ger. 50 40N 8 0E
23 Westerham, England 51 16N 0 5w
80 Western Australia, st., Australia
    25 0s 121 30E
64 Western Ghats, mts., India
    15 0N 74 0E
32 Western Isles, Reg., Scot. 57 45N 7 0w
72 Western Sahara, Africa 25 0N 13 0w
84 Western Samoa, Pacific Ocean (Inset)
61 Western Sayan, U.S.S.R. 52 30N 94 0E
44 Westfriesche Eil anden, Netherlands
    53 30N 5 15E
26 Westhoughton, England 53 34N 2 30w
84 Westland Dist., N.Z. 43 0s 170 0E
35 Westmeath, Co., Ireland 53 30N 7 30w
26 Westmorland, see Cumbria
22 Weston, England 52 50N 2 2w
24 Weston-super-Mare, Eng. 51 21N 2 58w
35 Westport, & B., Ireland 53 48N 9 32w
84 Westport, New Zealand 41 50s 171 52E
33 Westray, I. & Firth, Scot. 59 17N 2 58w
31 Westruther, Scotland 55 45N 2 34w
68 Wetar I., Indonesia 7 50s 126 20E
88 Wetaskiwin, Canada 52 58N 113 20w
27 Wetherby, England 53 57N 1 24w
44 Wetteren, Belgium 51 0N 3 53E
46 Wetzlar, Germany 50 33N 8 30E
82 Wewak, Papua N.G. 3 40s 143 30E
35 Wexford, & Co., Ireland 52 19N 6 28w
35 Wexford Hr., Ireland 52 20N 6 23w
23 Wey, R., England 51 18N 0 30w
27 Weybourne, England 52 58N 1 8E
23 Weybridge, England 51 22N 0 28w
88 Weyburn, Canada 49 40N 104 56w
89 Weymont, Canada 47 50N 73 50w
22 Weymouth, England 50 36N 2 28w
84 Whakatane, New Zealand 37 59s 177 0E
89 Whale R., Canada 55 25N 76 0w
100 Whale, B. of, Antarc. 78 30s 165 0w
26 Whaley Bridge, England 53 20N 1 59w
32 Whalsay I., Scotland 60 19N 0 59w
84 Whangamomona, N.Z. 39 8s 174 44E
84 Whangarei, N.Z. 35 41s 174 20E
26 Wharfedale, England 54 8N 2 0w
90 Wheeler Pk., U.S.A. 39 0N 114 30w
26 Wheldrake, England 53 20N 1 4w
92 Wheeling, U.S.A. 40 0N 80 38w
26 Whiston, England 53 25N 2 45w

* Renamed Bibala
* Renamed Camacupa
* Renamed Ngiva

31 Whitburn, Scot., U.K. 55 52N 3 41W
27 Whitby, England 54 29N 0 38W
24 Whitchurch, Devon, Eng. 50 31N 4 7W
22 Whitchurch, Hants., Eng. 51 15N 1 21W
26 Whitchurch, Salop., Eng. 52 58N 2 41W
25 Whitchurch, Wales 51 32N 3 15W
82 Whitecliffs, N.Z. 43 26s 171 55E
47 White Crisul, R., Rum. 46 18N 22 20E
41 White Drin, R., Y.-slav. 42 30N 20 34E
31 White Esk, R., Scotland 55 15N 3 10W
22 White Horse Vale, Eng. 51 39N 1 35W
84 White I., New Zealand 37 29s 177 14E
47 White Mts., Cz-slov. 49 0N 17 40E
90 White Mts., U.S.A. 37 15N 118 15W
73 White Nile, see Bahr el Abiad
73 White Nile, prov., Sudan 13 0N 32 0E
50 White Russia (Byelorussia), S.S.R., U.S.S.R. 53 50N 30 0E
50 White Sea, Canada 65 30N 37 30E
31 Whiteadder, R., Scotland 55 50N 2 25W
91 Whitefish B., U.S.A. 47 0N 85 0W
34 Whitegate, Ireland 51 49N 8 14W
26 Whitehaven, England 54 33N 3 36W
88 Whitehorse, Canada 60 40N 135 5W
31 Whitekirk, Scotland 56 2N 2 36W
83 Whitemark, Australia 40 4s 148 0E
83 Whitfield, Australia 36 50s 146 23E
30 Whithorn, Scotland 54 44N 4 24W
84 Whitianga, N.Z. 36 50s 175 40E
25 Whitland, Wales 51 49N 4 37W
27 Whitley B., England 55 3N 1 26W
90 Whitney, Mt., U.S.A. 36 45N 118 30W
23 Whitstable, England 51 21N 1 2E
82 Whitsunday I., Australia 20 15s 149 4E
88 Whittier, Alaska 60 5N 540 5W
27 Whittington, Derby, Eng. 53 17N 1 24W
22 Whittington, Salop., Eng. 52 53N 2 59W
23 Whittlesey, England 52 33N 0 7W
27 Whitwell, England 53 16N 1 11W
26 Whitworth, England 53 39N 2 11W
88 Wholdaia L., Canada 60 40N 104 20W
83 Whyalla, Australia 33 0s 137 28E
83 Whyjonta, Australia 29 40s 142 25E
91 Wichita, U.S.A. 37 48N 97 12W
90 Wichita Falls, U.S.A. 33 58N 98 36W
33 Wick, Scotland 58 27N 3 8W
23 Wickford, England 51 37N 0 31E
35 Wicklow, & Co., Ireland 52 58N 6 2W
35 Wicklow Mts., Ireland 53 5N 6 25W
31 Widdrington, England 55 15N 1 35W
24 Widemouth, England 50 45N 4 34W
23 Widnes, England 53 21N 2 46W
47 Wieliczka, Poland 49 59N 20 5E
47 Wielun, Poland 51 12N 18 45E
46 Wien, see Vienna
46 Wiener Neustadt, Austria 47 48N 16 13E
45 Wiesbaden, Germany 50 5N 8 14E
26 Wigan, England 53 33N 2 38W
23 Wight, Isle of, Co., Eng 50 40N 1 20W
22 Wigmore, England 52 19N 2 52W
22 Wigston, England 52 35N 1 6W
26 Wigton, England 54 50N 3 9W
30 Wigtown, Scot. 54 52N 4 27W
30 Wigtown B., Scotland 54 48N 4 17W
45 Wil, Switzerland 47 28N 9 3E
83 Wilcannia, Australia 31 36s 143 20E
47 Wilhelmshaven, Germany 43 34N 8 8E
100 Wilkes, Antarctica 66 0s 111 0E
93 Wilkes Barre, U.S.A. 41 18N 75 48W
100 Wilkes Basin, Antarctica 77 0s 138 0E
88 Wilkie, Canada 52 20N 108 40W
44 Willebroek, Belgium 51 5N 4 20E
95 Willemstadt, Neth., Antilles 12 0N 69 0W
22 Willenhall, England 52 36N 2 3W
23 Willesborough, England 51 8N 0 55E
88 Williams L., Canada 52 0N 122 10W
92 Williamson, U.S.A. 37 38N 82 10W
92 Williamsport, U.S.A. 41 19N 77 7W
83 Williamstown, Australia 37 45s 144 49E
23 Willingdon, England 50 47N 0 16E
27 Willington, England 54 43N 1 41W
45 Willisau, Switzerland 47 7N 8 0E
76 Williston, South Africa 31 20s 20 59E
90 Williston, U.S.A. 48 2N 104 3W
24 Williton, England 51 10N 3 18W
76 Willowmore, S. Africa 33 10s 23 37E
83 Willunga, Australia 35 27s 138 32E
83 Wilmington, Australia 32 30s 138 0E
24 Wilmington, England 50 46N 3 8W
93 Wilmington, Del., U.S.A. 39 47N 75 35W
91 Wilmington, N.C., U.S.A. 34 12N 77 50W
26 Wilmslow, England 53 19N 2 14W
22 Wilnecote, England 52 37N 1 39W
91 Wilson, U.S.A. 35 44N 77 55W
83 Wilson's Promontory, Australia 39 1s 146 29E
22 Wilton, England 51 5N 1 51W
22 Wiltshire, Co., England 51 18N 1 55W
44 Wiltz, Luxembourg 49 58N 5 57E
22 Wiluna, Australia 26 30s 120 4E
22 Wimborne Minster, Eng. 50 48N 1 58W
76 Winburg, S. Africa 28 25s 27 22E
24 Wincanton, England 51 3N 2 25W
23 Winchelsea, England 50 56N 0 42E
22 Winchester, England 51 4N 1 19W
92 Winchester, U.S.A. 38 18N 78 10W
90 Wind River Ra., U.S.A. 43 45N 109 40W
83 Windera, Australia 25 59s 151 37E
26 Windermere & L., Eng. 54 20N 2 57W

75 Windhoek, S.W. Africa 22 37s 17 8E
83 Windsor, Australia 33 40s 150 45E
93 Windsor, Nova Scotia, Canada 45 0N 64 8W
93 Windsor, Ontario, Can. 42 17N 83 0W
23 Windsor, England 51 28N 0 36W
76 Windsorton, S. Africa 28 20s 24 50E
95 Windward Is., W. Indies 13 30N 61 0W
95 Windward Passage, W. Indies 20 0N 73 30W
31 Windygates, Scotland 56 12N 3 1W
91 Winfield, U.S.A. 37 20N 97 15W
83 Wingen, Australia 31 55s 150 55E
83 Wingham, Australia 31 42s 152 3E
23 Wingham, England 51 16N 1 12E
89 Winisk, R., Canada 54 40N 87 0W
72 Winneba, Ghana 5 25N 0 36W
90 Winnemucca, U.S.A. 40 59N 117 45W
88 Winnipeg, Canada 49 55N 97 15W
88 Winnipeg, L., Canada 52 0N 98 0W
88 Winnipegosis, L., Can. 52 30N 99 50W
92 Winona, U.S.A. 44 0N 91 44W
26 Winsford, England 53 12N 2 31W
44 Winschoten, Netherlands 53 10N 7 3E
23 Winslow, England 51 56N 0 53W
90 Winslow, U.S.A. 35 5N 100 45W
92 Winston Salem, U.S.A. 35 8N 80 24W
44 Winterswyk, Neth. 51 58N 6 44E
45 Winterthur, Switzerland 47 30N 8 42E
82 Winton, Australia 22 23s 143 2E
84 Winton, New Zealand 46 10s 168 21E
27 Wirksworth, England 53 6N 1 35W
26 Wirral Pen., England 53 20N 3 5W
23 Wisbech, England 52 39N 0 9E
91 Wisconsin Rapids, U.S.A. 44 26N 89 43W
92 Wisconsin, st., U.S.A. 45 0N 90 0W
47 Wisla (Vistula) R., Pol. 53 0N 18 55E
49 Wismar, Germany 53 54N 11 23E
43 Wissembourg, France 49 0N 7 56E
75 Witbank, South Africa 25 52s 29 8E
23 Witham, England 51 48N 0 38E
27 Witham R., England 53 7N 0 13W
27 Withern, England 53 20N 0 8E
27 Withernsea, England 53 45N 0 1E
23 Witley, England 51 9N 0 39W
22 Witney, England 51 48N 1 29W
46 Wittenberge, Germany 53 0N 11 41E
46 Wittenburg, Germany 51 52N 12 45E
80 Wittenoom, Australia 22 15s 118 20E
44 Wittlich, Germany 49 59N 6 52E
47 Wloclawek, Poland 52 36N 19 5E
47 Wlodawa, Poland 51 30N 23 30E
23 Woburn, England 51 59N 0 36W
23 Woburn Sands, England 52 1N 0 38W
83 Wodonga, Australia 36 3s 146 57E
23 Woking, England 51 18N 0 34W
23 Wokingham, England 51 24N 0 50W
46 Wolhusen, Switzerland 47 4N 8 5E
47 Wolin, I., Poland 53 40N 14 37E
88 Wollaston L., Canada 58 20N 103 20W
88 Wollaston Pen., Canada 69 30N 113 0W
83 Wollongong, Australia 34 25s 151 0E
76 Wolmaransstad, S. Africa 27 20s 26 0E
26 Wolsingham, England 54 44N 1 52W
44 Wolvega, Netherlands 52 53N 6 0E
22 Wolverhampton 52 36N 2 8W
27 Wolverton, England 52 3N 0 47W
27 Wombwell, England 53 32N 1 24W
80 Wondai, Australia 26 12s 151 48E
67 Wonsan, Korea 39 20N 127 25E
82 Wonthaggi, Australia 38 28s 145 38E
23 Woodbridge, England 52 7N 1 20E
83 Woodend, Australia 37 24s 144 33E
34 Woodford, Ireland 53 3N 8 24W
82 Woodlark I., Pac. Oc. 9 0s 152 45E
23 Woodley, England 52 26N 0 54W
83 Woodroffe, Mt., Austral. 26 16s 131 30E
88 Woods, L., Australia 18 0s 133 0E
88 Woods, L., of the, Canada-U.S.A. 49 30N 94 30W
83 Woodside, Australia 38 45s 147 0E
93 Woodstock, N.B., Can. 46 12N 67 45W
93 Woodstock, Ont., Can. 43 7N 80 46W
84 Woodville, New Zealand 40 19s 175 59E
24 Wookey Hole, England 51 14N 2 40W
23 Wool, England 50 41N 2 14W
24 Woolacombe, England 51 11N 4 12W
83 Woolgoolga, Australia 30 7s 153 12E
83 Woombye, Australia 26 40s 152 58E
81 Woomera, Australia 31 5s 136 50E
92 Woonsocket, U.S.A. 42 1N 71 30W
83 Woorooriooka, Australia 27 59s 145 58E
67 Woosung, China 31 20N 121 25E
22 Wootton Bassett, Eng. 51 32N 1 55W
76 Worcester, South Africa 33 40s 19 28E
22 Worcester, Eng. 52 11N 2 13W
91 Worcester, U.S.A. 42 18N 71 45W
22 Worfield, England 52 34N 2 22W
26 Workington, England 54 38N 3 34W
27 Worksop, England 53 19N 1 8W
44 Workum, Netherlands 52 59N 5 27E
44 Wormerveer, Netherlands 52 30N 4 45E
45 Worms, Germany 49 40N 8 20E
23 Wortham, England 52 22N 1 3E
23 Worthing, England 50 48N 0 22W
74 Wota, Ethiopia 7 4N 35 51E
22 Wotton-under-Edge, Eng. 51 38N 2 21W
73 Wour, Chad. 21 20N 15 48E
61 Wrangel I., U.S.S.R. 71 30N 180 0E
88 Wrangell, Alaska 56 30N 132 52W

88 Wrangell Mts., Alaska 61 40N 143 30W
32 Wrath, C., Scotland 58 38N 5 0W
22 Wrekin, Mt., England 52 40N 2 33W
25 Wrexham, Wales 53 4N 3 0W
68 Wright, Philippines 11 45N 125 0E
88 Wrigley, Canada 63 0N 123 30W
46 Wroclaw (Breslau), Poland 51 6N 17 0E
23 Wrotham, England 51 18N 0 20E
22 Wroughton, England 51 32N 1 48W
66 Wu Kiang, R., China 27 30N 107 30E
55 Wu Yis Shan, mts., China 28 0N 118 0E
66 Wuchang, China 30 45N 114 25E
66 Wu-chow, China 23 35N 110 49E
66 Wuhan, China 30 45N 114 15E
66 Wu-hu, China 31 30N 118 20E
64 Wun, India 20 0N 79 0E
65 Wuntho, Burma 24 0N 95 30E
44 Wuppertal, Germany 51 15N 7 15E
45 Würzburg, Germany 49 45N 9 59E
67 Wusih, China 31 30N 120 5E
66 Wuwei, China 38 0N 102 25E
83 Wyandra, Australia 27 15s 145 58E
83 Wycheproof, Australia 36 0s 143 17E
25 Wye, R., Wales 52 15N 3 27W
83 Wymondham, England 52 45N 0 42W
23 Wymondham, England 52 33N 1 8E
76 Wynberg, South Africa 34 0s 18 27E
84 Wyndham, New Zealand 46 20s 168 51E
80 Wyndham, Australia 15 18s 127 58E
25 Wynnstay, Wales 52 36N 3 33W
83 Wynnum, Australia 28 0s 152 58E
83 Wynyard, Australia 41 0s 145 45E
90 Wyoming, St., U.S.A. 43 30N 107 30W
83 Wyong, Australia 33 5s 151 25E
26 Wyre, R., England 53 54N 2 48W
22 Wyre Forest, England 52 23N 2 25W

X

75 Xai-Xai, Mozambique 25 2s 33 34E
41 Xánthi, Greece 41 5N 24 55E
75 Xinavane, Mozambique 25 2s 32 47E
98 Xingu, R., Brazil 6 0s 53 0w

Y

66 Yaan, China 30 10N 101 50E
83 Yaapeet, Australia 35 48s 142 0E
83 Ya'bad, Israel 32 27N 35 10E
74 Yaballo, Ethiopia 4 57N 38 8E
63 Yabis, Wadi, Jordan 32 25N 35 40E
61 Yablonovy Ra., U.S.S.R. 52 0N 114 0E
64 Yadgir, India 16 50N 77 0E
67 Yakiang, China 30 2N 101 10E
90 Yakima, U.S.A. 46 40N 120 35W
72 Yako, Volta 12 58N 2 11W
73 Yakoma, Zaïre 4 0N 22 17E
67 Yakoshih, China 49 30N 120 45E
61 Yakutsk, U.S.S.R. 62 0N 129 0E
61 Yakut, A.S.S.R., U.S.S.R. 66 0N 130 0E
88 Yakutat, Alaska 59 30N 139 40W
82 Yalleroi, Australia 24 3s 145 42E
51 Yallourn, Australia 38 10s 146 18E
51 Yalta, U.S.S.R. 44 28N 34 10E
67 Yalu R., Korea 40 40N 126 20E
67 Yalung, R., China 27 30N 101 45E
67 Yamagata, & Pref., Jap. 38 10N 140 6E
67 Yamaguchi, & Pref., Jap. 34 8N 131 30E
60 Yamal Pen., U.S.S.R. 70 0N 70 0E
67 Yamanashi, Pref., Japan 35 30N 138 30E
52 Yaman Tau, mt., U.S.S.R. 54 0N 59 0E
83 Yamba, N.S.W., Austral. 29 25s 152 15E
73 Yambio, Sudan 4 38N 28 24E
41 Yambol, Bulgaria 42 30N 26 33E
68 Yamdrok Tso L., China 29 0N 90 30E
65 Yamethin, Burma 20 29N 96 18E
83 Yamma Yamma, L., Australia 26 20s 141 25E
64 Yamuna, R. (Jumna), India 27 10N 79 0E
61 Yana R., U.S.S.R. 69 0N 135 0E
83 Yanac, Australia 36 4s 141 12E
65 Yandoon, Burma 17 0N 95 40E
66 Yangchuan, China 38 5N 113 0E
67 Yangtze (Kinsha) R., China 32 30N 98 0E
67 Yang-tze-kiang, R., China 31 45N 121 15E
91 Yankton, U.S.A. 42 58N 97 26W
83 Yanna, Australia 26 55s 146 5E
67 Yao, Chad 12 58N 17 32E
72 Yaoundé, Cameroon 4 0N 11 20E
94 Yaqui, R., Mexico 27 30N 110 0W
83 Yaraka, Australia 24 53s 144 3E
23 Yare, R., England 52 35N 1 28E
64 Yarim, Yemen 14 14N 43 23E
57 Yarkand, China 38 15N 77 0E
64 Yarkhun, R., Pak. 36 30N 72 30E
31 Yarm, England 54 31N 1 20W
93 Yarmouth, Canada 43 50N 66 20W
52 Yaroslavl, U.S.S.R. 57 40N 40 0E
83 Yarram, Australia 38 29s 146 40E
83 Yarraman, Australia 26 50s 151 59E
31 Yarrow, Scotland 55 32N 3 0W
61 Yartsevo, U.S.S.R. 60 20N 90 0E
83 Yass, Australia 34 50s 148 58E
88 Yathkyed L., Canada 62 45N 98 0W
63 Yatta, Jordan 31 28N 35 5E
67 Yawata, Japan 33 54N 130 56E
23 Yaxley, England 52 31N 0 14W
64 Yazdan, Iran 33 30N 60 45E
91 Yazoo City, U.S.A. 32 51N 90 26W

91 Yazoo, R., U.S.A. 32 48N 90 45W
65 Ye-Byu, Burma 14 10N 98 15E
47 Yedintsy, U.S.S.R. 48 5N 27 20E
52 Yegoryevsk, U.S.S.R. 55 23N 39 2E
67 Yehsien, China 37 10N 119 55E
51 Yeysk, U.S.S.R. 46 38N 38 10E
72 Yeji, Ghana 8 11N 0 41W
52 Yelets, U.S.S.R. 52 42N 38 33E
72 Yelimane, Mali 15 4N 10 30W
32 Yell I. & Sd., Scotland 60 35N 1 5W
67 Yellow Sea, China 35 30N 123 0E
88 Yellowhead P., Canada 52 40N 117 45W
88 Yellowknife, & R., Can. 62 14N 114 2W
90 Yellowstone National Park, U.S.A. 44 15N 110 0W
90 Yellowstone R., U.S.A. 46 20N 107 0W
62 Yemen, Arabia 16 0N 44 30E
52 Yenakiyevo, U.S.S.R. 48 20N 38 10E
66 Yenan, China 37 5N 108 55E
62 Yenbo, Saudi Arabia 24 0N 38 20E
60 Yenisei, G. & R., U.S.S.R. 72 20N 80 0E
61 Yeniseysk, U.S.S.R. 58 25N 91 30E
67 Yenki, China 43 10N 129 25E
67 Yenki, China 42 30N 86 0E
24 Yeo, R., England 51 0N 2 48W
64 Yeotmal, India 20 26N 78 4E
24 Yeovil, England 50 57N 2 38W
82 Yeppoon, Australia 23 0s 150 45E
60 Yerbent, U.S.S.R. 39 30N 58 50E
52 Yerevan, U.S.S.R. 40 10N 44 20E
67 Yermakovo, U.S.S.R. 52 35N 126 20E
61 Yerofei Paulovich, U.S.S.R. 54 0N 122 0E
98 Yerupaja, Mt., Peru 10 20s 77 0W
24 Yes Tor, England 50 43N 3 57W
41 Yessei, U.S.S.R. 68 25N 102 0E
42 Yeu, I. d', France 46 43N 2 20W
51 Yevpatoriya, U.S.S.R. 45 15N 33 20E
51 Yevstratovskiy, U.S.S.R. 50 7N 39 44E
62 Yezd, Iran 31 55N 54 22E
67 Yiannitsa, Greece 40 45N 22 22E
66 Yinchwan (Ningsia), China 38 45N 106 5E
66 Yingtan, China 28 20N 116 25E
65 Yinmabin, Burma 22 10N 94 55E
74 Yirol, Sudan 6 30N 30 30E
41 Yithion, Greece 36 40N 22 40E
67 Yiyang, China 28 45N 112 30E
48 Ylitornio, Finland 66 25N 23 45E
48 Yliviska, Finland 64 4N 24 30E
72 Yobe, R., Nigeria 13 0N 12 0E
68 Yogyakarta, Indonesia 7 50s 110 24E
74 Yokadouma, Cameroon 3 35N 14 50E
73 Yoko, Cameroon 5 35N 12 28E
67 Yokohama, Japan 35 25N 139 35E
67 Yokosuka, Japan 35 18N 139 36E
67 Yokote, Japan 39 20N 140 30E
73 Yola, Nigeria 9 10N 12 37E
67 Yonago, Japan 35 30N 133 20E
67 Yonezawa, Japan 37 57N 140 4E
91 Yonkers, U.S.A. 41 0N 73 57W
42 Yonne, Dépt., France 47 50s 3 45E
42 Yonne, R., France 48 0N 3 20E
27 York, England 53 58N 1 5W
82 York, C., Australia 10 50s 142 30E
89 York Factory, Canada 56 4N 92 35W
83 York Sd., Australia 14 57s 125 5E
27 York Wolds, England 54 0N 0 30W
83 Yorke Pen., Australia 34 45s 137 38E
26 Yorkshire, Co., England 54 8N 1 15W
88 Yorkton, Canada 51 17N 102 35W
90 Yosemite National Park, U.S.A. 37 30N 119 30W
50 Yoshkar Ola, U.S.S.R. 56 40N 47 50E
34 Youghal & Bay, Ireland 51 57N 7 51W
83 Young, Australia 34 18s 148 18E
91 Youngstown, U.S.A. 41 20N 80 43W
51 Yozgat, Turkey 39 53N 34 48E
44 Ypres, Belgium 50 50N 2 52E
48 Ystad, Sweden 55 25N 13 49E
25 Ystwyth, R., Wales 52 20N 3 48W
31 Ythan, R., Scotland 57 26N 2 15W
94 Yucatan, Dist., Mexico 19 30N 89 30W
94 Yucatan Str., Mexico 22 0N 86 20W
60 Yudino, U.S.S.R. 55 10N 67 55E
66 Yukiang, R., China 23 20N 109 0E
86 Yukon, R., Alaska 65 0N 154 0W
86 Yukon, Terr. Canada 61 45N 133 30W
66 Yungan, China 26 0N 117 0E
67 Yunkia, China, see Wenchow
66 Yulin, China 18 25N 109 20E
90 Yuma, U.S.A. 32 40N 114 35W
67 Yunnan, Prov., China 25 30N 102 0E
67 Yushan, China 28 46N 119 3E
67 Yushan, Mt., Taiwan 23 30N 121 5E
66 Yushu, China 33 10N 96 10E
67 Yutze, China 37 45N 112 25E
67 Yuzhno Sakhalinsk, U.S.S.R. 46 50N 143 30E

Z

44 Zaandam, Netherlands 52 27N 4 48E

63 Zabdani, Syria 33 44N 36 7E
62 Zabid, Yemen 14 8N 43 15E
94 Zacapa, Guatemala 15 0N 89 35W
94 Zacatecas, Mexico 22 52N 102 15W
94 Zacoalco, Mexico 20 5N 103 33W
40 Zadar, Yugoslavia 44 9N 15 15E
37 Zafra, Spain 38 28N 6 28W
62 Zagazig, Egypt 30 33N 31 12E
52 Zagorsk, U.S.S.R. 56 18N 38 0E
40 Zagreb, Yugoslavia 45 47N 15 58E
51 Zagros Mts., Iran 33 45N 47 0E
64 Zahidan, Iran 29 35N 60 50E
63 Zahlah, Lebanon 33 50N 35 55E
74 Zaïre, Rep. of, Africa 3 0s 23 0E
74 Zaïre, R., Africa 2 0N 22 0E
60 Zaisan, L., U.S.S.R. 48 10N 83 35E
41 Zákinthos, & I., Greece 37 48N 20 57E
47 Zaleshchiki, U.S.S.R. 48 48N 25 45E
75 Zambezi, Zambia 13 38s 23 7E
75 Zambezi, R., Africa 18 50s 36 20E
74-75 Zambia, Africa 15 0s 28 0E
68 Zamboanga, Philippines 6 55N 122 0E
52 Zametchino, U.S.S.R. 53 30N 42 38E
94 Zamora, Mexico 20 0N 102 10W
37 Zamora, Spain 41 30N 5 49W
47 Zamosc, Poland 50 43N 23 18E
74 Zandvoort, Netherlands 52 21N 4 33E
74 Zanzibar I., E. Africa 6 0s 39 17E
72 Zaouiet el-Kahla, Algeria 27 10N 6 40E
99 Zapala, Argentina 39 0s 70 0W
52 Zaporozhye, U.S.S.R. 47 45N 35 10E
52 Zaragoza, Spain 41 38N 0 50W
99 Zárate, Argentina 34 0s 59 0W
72 Zaria, Nigeria 11 0N 7 26E
46 Zary, Poland 51 37N 15 10E
73 Zarzis, Libya 33 30N 14 0E
61 Zashiversk, U.S.S.R. 67 25N 142 40E
64 Zaskar Mts., Kashmir & India 33 0N 77 20E

76 Zastron, South Africa 30 10s 27 3E
47 Zawiercie, Poland 50 30N 19 30E
47 Zdunska Wola, Poland 51 38N 19 0E
44 Zeebrugge, Belgium 51 19N 3 12E
44 Zeeland, Prov., Neth. 51 30N 3 50E
76 Zeerust, South Africa 25 33s 26 14E
62 Zeila, Somali Rep. 11 0N 43 30E
44 Zeist, Netherlands 52 5N 5 15E
47 Zelenogradsk, U.S.S.R. 54 53N 20 29E
73 Zemio, Central Africa 5 3N 25 11E
41 Zemun, Yugoslavia 44 51N 20 25E
47 Zenjan, Iran 36 39N 48 30E
46 Zerbst, Germany 51 59N 12 8E
45 Zermatt, Switzerland 46 1N 7 44E
45 Zerriess, Switzerland 46 43N 10 6E
29 Zetland Co., see Shetland
47 Zeya, & R., U.S.S.R. 54 10N 127 20E
51 Zeytin, Turkey 37 53N 36 53E
37 Zezere, R., Portugal 40 10N 7 40W
47 Zhabinka, U.S.S.R. 52 17N 24 3E
52 Zhdanov, U.S.S.R. 47 2N 37 36E
50 Zhitomir, U.S.S.R. 50 20N 28 42E
52 Zhlobin, U.S.S.R. 53 0N 30 0E
47 Zhmerinka, U.S.S.R. 49 2N 28 10E
61 Zhupanovo, U.S.S.R. 53 50N 159 35E
47 Zielona Gora, Poland 51 57N 15 31E
44 Zierikzee, Netherlands 51 40N 3 55E
72 Ziguei, Chad 14 43N 15 48E
72 Ziguinchor, Sénégal 12 25N 16 20W
63 Zikhron Yaagov, Israel 32 35N 34 57E
62 Zilfi, Saudi Arabia 26 30N 45 22E
47 Zilina, Czechoslovakia 49 15N 18 50E
73 Zillah, Libya 28 39N 17 50E
66 Zilling Tso, L., China 31 45N 89 0E
66 Zima, U.S.S.R. 54 0N 102 5E
72 Zinder, Niger 13 45N 9 3E
62 Zira, Iran 28 12N 51 29E
41 Zlatograd, Bulgaria 41 20N 25 0E
52 Zlatoust, U.S.S.R. 55 5N 59 25E
73 Zillah, Libya 28 39N 17 50E
46 Znojmo, Czechoslovakia 48 50N 16 2E
45 Zofingen, Switzerland 47 18N 7 57E
75 Zomba, Malawi 15 23s 35 19E
73 Zongo, Zaïre 4 10N 18 50E
51 Zonguldak, Turkey 41 30N 32 0E
73 Zouar, Chad 20 28N 16 32E
72 Zouérabe, Mauritania 22 35N 12 30W
41 Zrenjanin, Yugoslavia 45 23N 20 26E
45 Zug, & Cn., Switzerland 47 11N 8 31E
45 Zugersee, L., Switzerland 47 10N 8 35E
44 Zuid Holland, Neth. 51 50N 4 30E
75 Zumbo, Mozambique 15 30s 30 24E
72 Zungeru, Nigeria 9 57N 6 45E
45 Zürich, & Canton, Switz. 47 22N 8 32E
45 Zürichsee, (L. of Zürich), Switzerland 47 15N 8 38E
40 Zurrieq, Malta 35 52N 14 26E
44 Zutphen, Netherlands 52 18N 6 12E
73 Zuwarah, Libya 32 58N 12 1E
60 Zverinogolovskoye, U.S.S.R. 54 30N 62 30E
60 Zverovo, U.S.S.R. 71 40N 83 20E
47 Zvolen, Czechoslovakia 48 33N 19 10E
47 Zwettl, Austria 48 49N 15 9E
46 Zwickau, Germany 50 42N 12 25E
45 Zweibrücken, Germany 49 14N 7 22E
45 Zweisimmen, Switzerland 46 32N 7 24E
44 Zwolle, Netherlands 52 22N 6 7E
47 Zyrardow, Poland 52 0N 20 30E
60 Zyryanovsk, U.S.S.R. 49 20N 85 12E

PRINTED IN GREAT BRITAIN BY VARNICOAT LTD., PERSHORE, WORCS.

A satellite view of an area on the Nepal-Chinese border. On the higher mountains, snow has melted first from the warmer southward-facing slopes. *(Photo NASA)*